ICE!

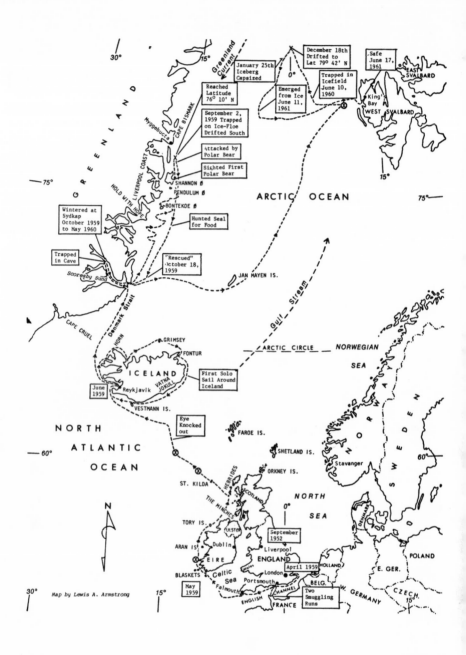

Map by Lewis A. Armstrong

ICE!

by Tristan Jones

A
TRISTAN JONES

CLASSIC

Sailors Bookshelf Publishing
Hillside, New Jersey

Also by Tristan Jones:

The Incredible Voyage
Saga of a Wayward Sailor *
Adrift
Dutch Treat (Novel)
Aka (Novel)
A Steady Trade—A Boyhood at Sea
Heart of Oak
One Hand for Yourself—One for the Ship
Outward Leg
The Improbable Voyage
Somewheres East of Suez

  * Available from Sailors Bookshelf

ISBN 0-943869-01-3

Grateful acknowledgment is made to Dodd, Mead &
Company for permission to quote from "My Husky
Team" by Robert Service which appeared in *More
Collected Verse of Robert Service*

Contents

Acknowledgments

For help, support and encouragement in making the voyage to the Arctic, thanks to the many good people of whom lack of space prevents mention. Some are dead, many are old, many may think they are forgotten; they are not. In this book they live. They, too, *made* the voyage. This saga is theirs.

For help, support, and encouragement in writing this book, thanks to:

Dimitra Nikolai, who typed it, as she does anything, courageously;

Frank Braynard, New York (of the Manhattan South Street Seaport and organizer of the Tall Ships events), for his hospitality to my boat *Sea Dart* during the spring and summer of 1977;

Russell Gurnee, New Jersey, past president of the Explorers Club, and his wife, Jeanne Gurnee, chairman of the Society of Women Geographers (U.S.A.), who were the first to recognize my message;

Professor H. Barraclough Fell, of Harvard University, author of *America B.C.*, who, interpreting ancient inscriptions in North America, has cast a bright light on old legends of Celtic trans-Atlantic voyages.

TRISTAN JONES
Hope Bay
British Antarctic Territories
New Year's Day, 1978

Author's Postscript to the Sailors Bookshelf Edition

Recently, a famous Broadway stage producer asked me to write a stage-script based on the experiences I wrote about in this book.

I did not do it; not only was I busily engaged in the present voyage of "Outward Leg," but also because I feel that the matter of loneliness is too personal, too *internal*, to be shared except through some means like a book, or perhaps a record, where the recipient is solitary.

Loneliness—or, to look on its bright side—solitude, *cannot be shared*. That is it's paradoxical genius. That is why we should determine to *make the most of every moment when we are alone.*

Nothing has changed. The ice is yet as threatening. We are yet, as we shall always be, only secure *within ourselves.*

As Sam Johnson put it so well: *"If you are solitary be not idle; if you are idle, be not solitary."*

Tristan Jones
Onboard *Outward Leg*, at Phucket, Thailand
June 1st, 1987

PART I

Vidi
(I saw)

Oh, they say there's a troopship just leaving Bombay,
Bound for old Blighty's shores,
Heavily laden with time-expired men,
Bound for the land they adore,
There's many a soldier just finishing his time,
There's many a twirp signin' on,
You'll get no promotion this side of the ocean,
So cheer up my lads, bless 'em all!
Bless 'em all, bless 'em all,
The long and the short and the tall,
Bless all the sergeants and W.O. Ones,
Bless all the corporals and their bleedin' sons,
'Cos we're sayin' goodbye to them all,
As back to their billets they crawl,
They'll get no promotion, this side of the ocean,
So cheer up my lads, bless 'em all!

**Song of the British Army in India
(origin in 1920s).**

1

August 1952

In Aden Military Hospital everything was hot, dry, and sandy: the walls, the floors, the nurses, the sheets, even me. After six weeks of lying painfully on my stomach with a badly bruised spine, I had taken the first hobbling steps over to the shady veranda and had gazed with pained eyes across the dun-colored town to the arid escarpment of the Crater. Ships lay at anchor beyond the shimmering docks, waiting like mother-hens for the long, black, sinister-looking barges to be bustled alongside by tiny, tooting tugs.

The British army doctor's verdict had been quite definite—no more heavy work; certainly no more seagoing. I would be lucky ever to be able to walk properly again. Ever again, at twenty-eight years of age! Just arrived in full manhood and condemned to idle ashore for the rest of my life—never again to feel the lift of a ship's hull under my feet as she departed her haven and danced to the sea's welcome swell; never again to meet the first flying fish glittering in the midforenoon sunlight as the vessel drew the waiting tropics to her heaving forefoot; never again to sense the magic anticipation of a new, strange shore rising over the horizon ahead, or to hear the icebergs calving from their mother mountains in the low, long, bittersweet dawn of the Arctic; never again to know the utter comfort of a mug of cocoa more softly, gratefully sipped from a great china mug than any wine from any chalice, as the iced hull slipped through the hazy, freezing fog of the Denmark Strait.

I leaned on the balcony rail, mid-Victorian Gothic iron, beaten into shape by men in faraway England, an England pregnant with the power of Empire, a hundred years before, when my grandfather was a boy apprentice on a Black-ball line trooper to India; half a century and more before my father deserted sail in Capetown to join the Australian Horse and chase Christian de Wet and his Boer commandos across the Kalahari desert of South Africa.

Gazing across the shimmering midday heat to the great Crater of Aden, past the miles of mud hovels to the glistening hotels and stark minarets in the distance, I felt, for the first and only time in my life, self-pity. I grabbed the hand-rail tightly and looked down to the dusty courtyard below. It was crowded with the usual complement of beggars and local patients' families, some with cooking pots steaming over small fires, some just patiently waiting in the shade for the next call of the muezzin to prayer. It was a good fifty-foot drop. More than enough. It would be so easy. A painful heave over the rail when none of the eagle-eyed matrons of the Queen Alexandra's Royal Nursing Corps were around; two seconds' rush through space and it would all be over.

"Good morning, Jones. Still alive I see!"

"Good morning, Matron. Yes, but only just."

She smiled at me, her blue green Scottish eyes the color of the heather of Tiree itself.

"Och, come now," she rejoined, "a braw laddie like you talking like that; just imagine it! You've far to go yet. Let's see now, you're Welsh, are you not? And talking like that—just think of all the folk that you'll meet when you get home."

"What, Matron, in Greenwich Hospital for Naval Pensioners?"

"If you go on talking like that, then that's where you'll probably end up. But I think not, Mister Jones. If I've got you reckoned up, well, you'll be back on your feet in no time at all." She smiled again. "And mark wnat I've said, for all my family were well noted for the second sight. Now, my lad, no more fashin' yoursel'. Off you go for your meal—and this afternoon you can pack your kit."

"Matron?"

"Aye, pack your kit; you're off to England on this night's flight. I'll have a nurse around at five o'clock to help you. And mind, laddie, no flirting now, or I'll have you on Captain's Report."

"Aye, aye, Matron!"

At dusk the Royal Air Force Transport plane took off. I remember only a few details of the flight—that the plane crew was efficient, friendly, and kind; that we landed somewhere in Tripoli and again in Rome; and that the fields of England were startling in their greenness as we swooped down onto a base in Wiltshire. And that my mind was made up. No matter how much pain and suffering it would cost me, I would go back to sea. Somehow, only God knew how, I would find the strength and the means.

As we flew out of Aden into the lightened sky to the west, across the southern end of the Red Sea, I glimpsed for no more than a few seconds the Strait of the Bab el Mandeb, its rough white water far below looking like snow flakes in the dark sea of the narrow, rock-strewn channel. The Bab el Mandeb—the *Gate of Tears*! Despite the pain from twisting my head, I stared down at it. The Gate of Tears . . . the Sea of Sinbad . . . I *would* go back, even if it killed me. Nothing could keep me from the wide waters of the world!

I *would* see the flying fish and the dolphins, the porpoise and the whales; I *would* see the trade wind clouds and the albatross; I *would* hear the call of the calving ice and the hymn of the wind over Tierra del Fuego and trace the weft of green Sargasso weed as it drifts from Bermuda to the Azores. I *would* creep into the womblike fiords of Greenland and whistle on the wind to the coral reefs of the Arafura Sea and hear the wailing muezzın-call of the Comoros!

"Good luck," whispered the air force nurse as I was wheeled down the ramp onto the ground of England.

"It's not luck we need, love."

"No? What is it?" She leaned closer; her femaleness even in her starched uniform disturbed me. Uncomfortable, with a cracked pelvis.

"Bastardy, sweetheart. Bastardy, and a good pint of ale."

"Well, the Royal Navy's got plenty of that," she laughed.

The ambulance wafted smoothly through the English lanes and roads for a couple of hours, finally coming to a halt before the venerable hospital of Haslar, where men had been treated after all of England's past fifty or so wars. After two months in the care of the British army and air force, I was once again in the stern arms of My Lords Commissioners of the Admiralty. There would be no kidding and joshing here. *Fear God, Honor the Queen! Up Spirits! Pipe Down!* Everything to order, like an orchestration of clockwork precision. And yet, as with the Royal Navy rope, there was a "rogue's strand" running right through the middle of it all. A saving grace of toleration and humor which made, but only just, life bearable in the "Andrew" (the British sailor's name for the Royal Navy).

Gradually the days of English summer passed by, the trees in sweet blossom, warm worn brick, cottagelike walls, grey flagstones washed by the feet of thousands of broken men from the Nile, Copenhagen, Trafalgar, the African Coast slave-chasers, the Crimean War, Tel el Kebir, Jutland and the convoys, Gallipoli, the Falklands, North Cape and the convoys, the Mediterranean, the Pacific, the North Sea, and the Channel.

"Must have been a hard lot in the days of sail, eh, mate?" I commented to the sick berth "tiffy," an Irish lad who ran our ward.

"Yeah, and sure the bloody seas was rougher, too, auld son."

I laughed. He was right. They'd gone back to sea from here in the old days, with God only knows what limbs and other spare bits missing. They'd gone back to sea to sail the great, swiftly lumbering wooden walls of England, and by the living Jesus, so would I. And if I couldn't go in their navy, then I would go in my bloody own! The die was cast. I hobbled around, but faster now, with rising ambition and the star of *Cymru*—Wales—the brightest star that ever the sea shone under, racing in my blood, and the song of Madoc and Morgan in my mind, willing my body to repair itself all the faster.

But how? And then I remembered all the sailing lore I'd learned from my old master, Tansy Lee, and I thought of all the surplus war boats and materials lying rotting in Her Majesty's Dockyards, and I suddenly saw it all clearly. I sat down on the nearest bed and grinned: *I knew how*. I would shortly be discharged with a pension of ten dollars a week, and a paying-off gratuity of fifteen hundred dollars. I would somehow get hold of one of those craft and put all the knowledge and care I had left into her. I would lay hands on good galvanized wire and canvas, rope and fittings. I would cherish and put all I had into her. God would do the rest, and the Devil, who had done his bloody best to nobble me, could go and get stuffed. Once I was back at sea, nothing, *nothing* in the whole world, could touch me!

Sure it would take time, maybe years. It would also take a lot of patience, courage, and determination. I wasn't at all certain about the time, the patience, or the courage, but by Jesus, I knew I had the fourth attribute. The fifth—luck— was in God's hands, but I couldn't expect him to do much without a great deal of help from me.

I hit one fist into the other: I'd do it! The game was afoot!

I don't want to join the army,
I don't want to go to war,
I'd rather sit around Piccadilly Underground,
Living off the earnings of a high-paid lady.
I don't want to join the army,
I don't want me bollocks shot away,
I'd rather be in London, lovely dear old London,
Fuckin' all me bleedin' life away!

First World War British Army song. This was
not an antiwar song, it was the soldier's
sardonic comment on the shirkers and
profiteers at home.

2

Free!

The first place I made for after my discharge from the Royal
Naval Hospital at Haslar was the Sussex Bar, right in the
center of Portsmouth. This was the great gathering place of
all the time-serving men. If there was anyone around who
knew anything about what small craft were available, anyone in the Service, that is, this would be the place to find
him. My new issue civilian suit, cheap and ill-fitting, felt
strange, and after carrying my sea bag from the bus stop,
my back was paining me.

The first two pints went down like a balloon in a spring
Channel breeze. I looked around. Kiwi grinned back at me.
I'd seen him last three years before, in New York.

"Hi, Tris. What're you doin' here, mate?"

"Wotcher, Kiwi. Just got my discharge. Having a quick
look round."

"Heard you got clobbered. Singapore, wasn't it?"

"Aden, bloody hell hole."

"What were you doing there?"

"Official Secrets Act, old chum." I tried to look con-
spiratorial.

Kiwi, so called because he had been born in New Zea-
land, grinned. "Come on, Tris, what the bloody 'ell you
been up to?"

"Catching butterflies."

"Yeah, well, what are you goin' to do now?"

9

"Looking for a job. Something to do with small boats, if I can."

Kiwi poured another pint of foaming ale down his lithe body, then turned to me. His gold stripes and anchor gleamed under the bright pub lights. "Why don't you stick around for a week, Tris?" he said. "I've got my discharge coming on Monday next. Look, I've been watching the papers for likely jobs, and for us blokes, me an able seaman, you a stoker, there ain't much around. But I see the White Star Line are taking on crew up in Liverpool for the South America run."

"What's the money like?"

"Pretty fair, fifty quid a month and all found."

"Blimey, that's not bad, is it? How long does a round trip take?"

"Well, Tris, it's September now. Supposin' we took off on the west coast of South America run, we could be back for Christmas, and you'd have another two hundred quid up your sleeve, if you took it easy. Better than hanging around here, spending money."

"Yes, Kiwi, but it's big ships again. And anyway, I don't know if they'll take me in my condition, buggered up like this. It's as much as I can do to carry that bloomin' sea bag."

"Well, listen, old son," he said, putting his hand on my shoulder, "give it a try anyway. Why don't you go up to London and stay at the Union Jack Club? It's only a week, and you've nothing to lose."

"O.K., Kiwi, I'll tell you what I'll do. I'll have one more pint of ale, then I'll catch the train up to the Smoke and book in at the Union Jack Club. It's only five bob a night and the beer's cheap and there's stacks of crumpet round Waterloo Station."

"Right, Tris, do that and I'll see you next Monday. We can have a night in the Smoke, a few pints of wallop, look up the birds round the Dilly, then take off early for Liverpool. We can be at the shipping offices by nine o'clock on Tuesday."

"O.K., Kiwi, but I'm not promising anything with the White Star, I've got my mind on something else."

"What?"

"My own boat. A sailboat."

"You must be joking, Tris. A bloody yachtsman? You? Christ, that costs a fortune."

"Not the way I'm going to do it."

"Well, anyway, Tris, hang on until Monday. See you then. By the way, mate, watch them birds up round Waterloo. Things have changed a bit since you was last up there; they're all bleeding rotten now. You've only got to look at 'em and you're away up the sick bay with a dose of clap that'd kill King Kong. The Yanks ain't there to clean 'em up, now."

"Right, thanks for the tip, Kiwi. See you next Monday!"

At Portsmouth Station I bought a couple of boating magazines to read on the journey up to London. As the train trundled through the autumn countryside, I glanced at the scenery only now and again, for my eyes were on the Craft for Sale advertisements. It was clear that any kind of production boat was well beyond my means.

None of the naval surplus craft were suitable, for they were all powered vessels which would require money for fuel and regular engine overhauls. Besides, they didn't have the range for what I wanted. From the very first I aimed at ocean passages. I would settle for nothing less than a five-thousand-mile range.

The scene in London was morbid. World War II had been over for years and the scars still showed, not only in the buildings, but on the faces of the people. They had taken a hammering, and the only bright thing in the air was the coronation of the new queen in June. This and the end of rationing of food and fuel, which they had suffered for the past twelve years. London was at the nadir of her fortunes, and though I have seen her several times since at times when things were supposed to be bleaker than ever, I have never seen the Londoners looking more grim than they did in the winter of 1952. That was the middle classes, of course, not the ordinary working man. He'd always had the rough end of the stick, and now he was as witty and cheerful as ever and would still stand a hearty sailor a pint in the pub, if he had a couple of shillings in his pocket.

At that time the Union Jack Club was run on the lines laid down by Florence Nightingale for the operation of British army field hospitals during the Crimean War. It was cheap, the bar was always crowded, the dining room spotless, the meals sustaining (in a very British way—boiled cabbage and steamed bacon, with rubbery fried eggs that could have decorated the walls of the Museum of Modern Art). The waitresses were dressed in a sort of pre-World War I outfit which Queen Victoria herself would have approved, and they slaved along with lowered glances, on low heels, under the eye of a female superintendent whose stern demeanor would have made the American bald eagle look like a bloody parakeet. The decor of the place was a cross between the foyer of a public bathhouse and the gentlemen's waiting room at the Winter Palace in St. Petersburg. I always thought, when entering the Union Jack Club with its mock Gothic ornamental pillars and decorative tiles *à la* Aubrey Beardsley, that if ever there had been a British Communist revolution led by sailors of the fleet, the first resolution of the Soldiers', Sailors', and Workers' Party of the London Soviet would have rung out from behind the potted plants of the Union Jack Club.

But British beer is too good to foment revolution, so we had to make do with concerts on a vintage piano and strings by equally vintage ladies (vintage vinegar). They all, with the exception of the violinist (who appeared to be still chained to the railings with the suffragettes), looked at us as if we had only just returned from chastising the dreadful Mr. Kruger and relieving Mafeking. The tunes they played as we sank our beer gave added strength to this impression—selections from *Bohemian Girl* and *The Witch of the Wood*. I could always tell the Welshmen in the audience;

they would stare at this trio of Saxon dragons as if they thought it would have been better to let the bloody Germans take over after all. Even Wagner would be more *musical*.

The Scotsmen were mainly recognizable by the glazed look in their eyes as they dreamed of bagpipes, haggis, and the Khyber Pass; the Irishmen, by their look of transfixion as they worshiped the three Mother Machrees on stage; the Englishmen, by the way they totally ignored the whole proceedings and played billiards as if all four other phenomena in the hall did not, could not, and never would exist.

The place was run like a prison, with the exception of the smell of urine and the porridge. The guardians of Law, Order, and Discipline carried out the letter of the *Queen's Rules and Admiralty Instructions*, making sure that while drunkenness and cleanliness went hand in hand, the least sign of affection between two of the returned heroes was clamped down on with the utmost severity. The slightest sign of liberation of any variety was pounced upon with the same horror as a cockroach caught in the kitchen. The hall porters, who looked like veterans of the Ashanti War; the kitchen staff, who appeared still to be resisting the Siege of Cawnpore; the library attendant, whose walrus mustache made him look like the bastard son of Lord Kitchener; the night-desk clerk, an ex-Indian army sergeant major, who, rumor had it, was actually Martin Bormann in disguise; plus the Holy of Holies, the Commanding Officer—all, *all*, would have descended on the offending demon like a ton of bricks. We lived in the shadow of a ghostly gibbet.

But it was somewhere for us, the Legion of the Lost Ones, to sleep and eat, so that's exactly what I did, spending the rest of the day in the friendly pubs around Kensington, or going down to Greenwich to see if I could find a boat.

On Monday Kiwi arrived, half-sozzled, wearing the most God-awful grey suit. It looked like the one Trevor Howard wore in Noel Coward's film *Brief Encounter*. But the face above it had had no brief encounter; it had had a bloody long one. And so had mine, so we went to Piccadilly, got drunk, performed a ten-shilling "short time" with the same straggly whore, then went off on the night train to Liverpool.

Back in those days, train journeys in England took much longer than they now do. The rail system was only just beginning to overcome the traumatic effect of six years of war and the nationalization which followed. From London to Liverpool, a distance of around two hundred miles, took eight hours. Since we were traveling second class on Admiralty warrants, our compartment was unheated, except by the fifty or so unwashed bodies crowded inside.

By dawn we were passing through the English northern midlands, the Black Country, as it is called. A hellish blight of smoke, soot, and grime in the green fields of England. Our legacy from a revolution which not only shook the world, but remade it. Among the great grey slag heaps, across swamps of stagnant brown water, long, dreary black rows of steelworkers' cottages oozed away over the exhausted hills into the sulphurous fog beyond. Above, in the molten steel sky of Staffordshire, towered black cumulus clouds.

Kiwi looked out of the window as the train pulled into Stoke-on-Trent. "Christ, they've got some smashing-looking women here," he murmured, eyeing the lasses on their way to the mills—those "dark, satanic mills" Blake raged against.

"Kiwi, you horny twit, is that all you can think of?" I said. "All this stinking bloody smoke around, all this hopelessness, all these people with their wasted lives, exhausted from fighting a bloody war for this? Look at them—they lost one generation on the Somme in 1916, and now they've lost half another in this last bloody lot. And look what they've got to show for it—a four-roomed house you couldn't swing a cat in for two quid a week, twelve quid for forty hours in one of those grimy supershithouses, and a few pints of beer on Saturday. No bloody wonder they vote Labour. And all you've got to say, you ignorant colonial bastard, is how pretty the women are. Of course they're bloody pretty; what else have they got?"

"Arr, you bloody Welsh are all the same, always stirring up political shit." He passed me a cigarette.

"Too bloody right, and wouldn't you? This is our country. Look what's been done to it!"

"Well, if you don't like it, what are you going to do about it?"

"Bloodywell fight to change it."

"Not a chance in hell, Tris."

"My way, there might just be!"

"What are you, the Lone Ranger?"

"No, and I ain't Oliver Twist either. And neither are a lot of those people out there."

"Labour'll ruin the country, bloody welfare state, nationalizing everything, chucking away the colonies——"

"Listen, mate, me and millions, not bloody thousands, *millions* like me never got one measly thing out of those goddamn factories, or private enterprise mines and railways, or the bleedin' Empire, but bloody starvation, misery, and flamin' war! To hell with the Empire! Give me Wales and England and Scotland for us, so we can own our own lands and make them once again what they should be!"

"Bolshevik Welsh bastard."

The train pulled into Crewe. A tall, red-faced military police monster eyed us, recognizing our Service issue suits and hating the thought we were out of his power. As we passed him Kiwi looked straight into his storm-trooper eyes.

"Thank Christ we've got a bloody navy!" he growled.

The monster, in puttees and kicking boots, glared at us.

"Go and fuck yourself," I said to his great beefy face. He staggered back in shock, then drew himself up to his full height and shouted down the platform to a policeman just emerging from the lavatory, "Constable, arrest those men!"

"On what charge, sergeant?" The bobby's voice was calm and low.

"Obscene language and insulting Her Majesty's uniform," replied the dragoon.

The constable, a fair-looking chap of around thirty, turned to us. "Is the charge correct, you two?" He looked at me.

"I never used no obscene language, mate. All I did was tell him to go and fuck himself."

"What about you?" said the copper, just barely able to stop himself from grinning.

"Well, officer," said Kiwi, "all I can say is, if that's Her Majesty's bloody uniform, I pity the bloke she's married to, 'cos he'll have a bloody hard time in bed! If that's her uniform she must be built like a brick shithouse!"

The policeman nodded at the stationmaster's office. "I think you two had better come along with me." He turned to the red-capped beetle-crusher. "I'll take these two along and question them. I'll see you for any evidence later, sergeant."

"Right," said the sergeant, huffing and glaring at us. He snapped his beady, piglike eyes around the platform, searching for other victims among the hundred or so uniformed men alighting from the train. The bobby walked along with us for twenty yards or so, then said in a low tone, "Andrew, eh?"

"Yeah."

"What depot?"

"Chatham."

"Chatty Chats. I was Portsmouth meself, destroyers, came out in '46."

"You did the right thing, mate," said I.

"Yes, I sometimes wonder, though. Now look, you two, sod off as soon as we turn the corner."

"How are we going to get to Liverpool?" I asked the grinning rozzer.

"Buggered if I know. Take the bus. I'm letting you go because that MP back there is a right bastard and I can't stand him. But if I see you again, it won't be Liverpool for you two, it'll be bloody Chester Prison."

"O.K., wings, thanks a lot. We'll have a pint for you when we get to the 'Pool."

"Right, Jack, right, mate, now piss off—"

"Christ, we got out of that one," I said.

"Only one snag, Tris—the bloody sea bags!"

"Oh, Jesus!"

Kiwi grinned. "Ah, well, it was good while it lasted. Right, there's a bus over there. Liverpool, here we come!"

We clambered onboard with all we had in the world on our backs. As we settled into our seats, Kiwi murmured, "Well, Tristan, me old mate, there's one thing."

"What's that?"

"It's either ship out or the bleeding Salvation Army."

"Don't talk to me about bloody armies!"

"Right, not if they've got bastards like that one back there in 'em.

The bus rolled off. "How d'ye feel now, Kiwi?" I said.

"I'm dying for a bloody pint, mate!"

I grinned; we were free at last. And my back didn't hurt anymore.

Now, gather round you sailor boys
And listen to my plea,
For when you've heard my tale you'll pity me,
I was a goddamn fool in the port of Liverpool
The first time that I came home from sea.

I was paid off with my share
Off a ship from God knows where,
Five pound ten a month was all my pay,
With a whisky and a gin I was very soon taken in,
By a little girl whose name was Maggie May.

How well do I remember when I first met Maggie May,
She was cruising up and down in Canning Place,
Her figure was divine, like a frigate of the Line,
And me bein' a sailor I gave chase.

Next morning I awoke, bleary-eyed and stony broke,
No shoes, no pants, no waistcoat could I find,
When I asked her where they were
She replied, "My dear young sir,
They're down in Paddy's market, number nine."

To the market I did go, no clothes there could I find,
So the bobbies came and took poor Mag away,
The judge then guilty found her,
For robbin' a homeward bounder,
An' little Maggie's down in Botany Bay!

Chorus: Oh Maggie, Maggie May, they have taken her away,
And never more round Lime Street will she roam,
She robbed so many sailors and captains of the whalers,
Now poor old Maggie never will come home!

Liverpool merchant seaman's song, origi-
nally nineteenth century.
A "pulley-hauley" shanty, sung when the
longboat falls were heaved in.

3

Entertaining the Ladies

Comparing London to Liverpool is like comparing Monte Carlo to Pittsburgh, Pennsylvania. Not that I'm for one or opposed to the other. It's just that one is for the eyes and nose, while the other is for the ears and the heart.

Liverpool is like a small New York, only much, much kinder. The biting wit of the people on the street is the same, with its dislike of pomposity and bullshit, and so is the attitude to government, except that, as far as I can see, corruption is better hidden in Liverpool. The friendliness, too, is a bit less offhanded than in New York. New Yorkers are better at hiding their personal feelings toward a stranger than are Liverpudlians, but not as good at masking their public feelings.

London reflects the outer Britain, the country which the prating pedlars of propaganda would have us believe is the United Kingdom. It is the city of Covent Garden Theatre and the Ballet Rambert and red-coated, black-busbied Guardsmen standing at the gates of "Buck House." The city of the military mustache and the bowler hat, the umbrella and the briefcase, Hampstead Heath and pale blue gentility.

Liverpool, on the other hand, is the real center of industrial Britain, where the heartstrings of England, Ireland, Scotland, and Wales all join together. If London is the capital of the Normans, then Liverpool is the capital of the

19

Celt and the Saxon. If the umbrella is the symbol of London, then that of Liverpool is the wheelbarrow. London has its nose in the air, Liverpool has its in a pint of beer.

Kiwi and I pulled in on the train. The terminal, down by the docks, under the shadow of the great brick-pile Liver Buildings, was abustle with seamen from all over the world, shoppers coming in from the country and from over the River Mersey, Irish and Welsh coming in from the west, Scots heading through from the north.

"Tris," said Kiwi, as we headed for the nearest pub, "do you think the Liver bird will shit today?" He looked up at the two carved stone birds perched atop the twin towers of the huge Dock Authority building. The legend in Liverpool is that every time a virgin passes, one of the birds shits.

"If the Irish boats come in, I wouldn't be at all surprised."

"Never had your end away in Ireland, then?"

"Yeah, but her wig fell off."

"How come?"

"She was too busy telling her rosary beads to hold it on."

We entered the pub. There was none of your London nonsense here, no red-plushed seats and cut-glass chandeliers, nor carpets. Just a plain wooden bar, two dartboards, and sawdust on the floor.

"What'll we do, Kiwi?" I asked, after the third pint.

"We'll have to hang about until tomorrow. The shipping office is closed in the afternoons, the recruiting side anyway. They don't want to take chances of getting a load of pissy-assed seamen in there when the pubs shut at three. The best thing we can do is get a night's lodging. We shouldn't go to the Seamen's Institute, though."

"Why not?"

"Jesus, it makes Portsmouth Barracks look like the Strand Palace Hotel."

"Where do we go, then?"

"We wait till the pubs shuts at three, then hop over to the Mersey Ferry. The bar on the boat is open all day, so we ride over and back a few times, have a couple of pints, then at opening time, nip ashore on the other side, find a good pub, and ask around."

"Sounds good to me. Game of darts?"

"Right, you're on."

And so it was, and by the time we did alight from the Mersey Ferry, we were three sheets in the wind, about ten pints each under our belts. It was a bit shaky, playing darts on the ferry. Every time a tug or a big steamer passed by, the boat would roll, and then we would demonstrate true skill, aiming for double-twenty at the top of each lurch and winding up with a treble six or even a bull's-eye.

As we landed on the Wallasey side, I said to Kiwi, "You know, my old man brought the first roller-skating rink ever landed in Britain, back in 1924. He brought it from Australia in his ship."

"What happened?"

"He did pretty well for a year or so, then the slump came and he went bust. No one could afford the three-pence-a-go any more."

"Where was that, Tris?"

"New Brighton, just along the road a few miles. Why don't we go there? It's a sort of seaside holiday resort."

"Won't be much there now. Season's over."

"Not in New Brighton. There's always a good crowd in the pubs, and plenty of crumpet at the New Brighton Palace Dance Hall. That's where my old man had the rink."

"O.K., you're on," he said, and we headed for the green double-decker bus.

By the time we'd had a few in the local pubs, it was time to find lodgings. I signaled to the landlord, a small, rotund, friendly fellow.

"Know anywhere we can doss for a few days, guv?"

"Seamen?" he asked, sizing us up.

"Sort of; R.N.——" The navy was very popular in Liverpool.

"Oh, right, Jack. Yeah, there's a place just around the corner, nice and clean, good meals. Tell Aggie I sent you."

"Ta, guv, see you later."

"You'd better hurry. Closing time at ten-thirty."

Aggie turned out to be an aged treasure, spotlessly pina-
fored, rosy cheeked, eyes asparkle. Before we knew it we
were signed up and settled in. "If you hurry, I can get you
in for the last sitting at supper, love," she said. We spruced
ourselves up as best the beer under our belts would allow,
turned our jerseys around to show the clean side, and
headed for the dining hall. Once there, we were in for a
surprise. The place was crammed with old ladies, none of
them looking a day under eighty. It was an old folks' home!
There were about twelve of them, all sitting around the
open fireplace, some knitting, some chatting in low, sweet
voices. As Kiwi and I scoffed down the tucker, well cooked
and plentiful, for which we were paying twelve shillings a
day (one dollar, at today's rate), a couple of the old ladies
eyed us, smiling.

"D'you play the piano, Tris?" Kiwi said to me. "You're a
Welshman. All Welshmen play the piano."

"Well, of course I learned. I was never very good at it and
that's years ago. Couldn't get much practice in bloody
destroyers, now could I?"

He turned and pointed his spoon. "Well, there's one over
there."

"O.K.," I said, standing up and walking over toward the
wall. "Do you ladies mind if I have a go at the piano?"

They all smiled sweetly. One, more lively than the rest,
said, "Oh, no, by all means do, we shall be delighted.
Ladies, I've had a word with Agnes and she tells me that
these two young men have just retired from our brave
navy."

The old dears sighed and twittered.

"But you must first introduce yourselves, and as we've
no one to do it for us, I'll introduce myself—Mrs. Rosina
Steele, widow of dear Captain Steele." Then she went on to
introduce all the rest, whose names, though not their faces,

escape me now, twenty-five years later.

The piano turned out to be a pianola, a sort of phony piano into which you insert a roll of paper, with holes punched, like a computer program. When you pump with your feet, the air from the bellows inside the machine blows through the holes and makes a sound resembling music. At the side of the pianola was a large basket crammed with paper rolls. I grabbed the nearest one, inserted it into the roller-holder, and started playing. As the notes came flowing out, Kiwi's face was a picture of startled desperation. It was "Selections from *Bohemian Girl*"—the same music we had escaped from in the Union Jack Club, back in London. Awful, terrible, sentimental, sloppy tripe.

Kiwi, standing at my shoulder, whispered, "Jesus H. Christ!" The little old ladies were sitting entranced, listening to the music of their youth, when they had been beautiful in a different way, listening to the music they had danced to with their sailor lovers just back from the sea. The dreams in their faces were tangible. Even a rough bastard like me didn't have the heart to stop, so I pedaled away while the paper-music slowly rolled itself out and the clock ticked away inexorably over the potted plants, towards pub-closing time. When the tune finally came to a grinding, wheezy halt, the clock stood at five minutes before pub-closing.

I jumped up and shut the lid. The ladies clapped and sighed. Kiwi edged for the door. "Thank you so much, Mr. Jones," said Mrs. Steele, grasping my hand. "You have made such a welcome change to our evening. We are so grateful indeed to you. Now may we offer you some tea and cake before you go to bed?"

"Highly honored, ma'am," I replied, "but we have to make a very urgent telephone call to London."

"Oh, really? It must be naval business, I'm sure."

"Yes, ma'am, an extremely urgent *intelligence* call."

"Something to do with those dreadful Russians, I

shouldn't wonder," said Mrs. Steele, addressing the company in general. All the ladies put on suitable expressions of alarm.

"No, ma'am, not this time." I leaned closer to her ear and whispered, "Albanians."

"Oh, dear, how very exciting. Well, off you go and do your duty, dear Mr. Jones, and don't forget, I want a word with you tomorrow."

"Thank you, ma'am, and good night, ladies."

"Good night, God bless you," they all echoed, as the aspidistra plants in the hall quivered at our hasty passing.

As I followed Kiwi through the cut-glass-windowed door, I distinctly heard Mrs. Steele say to the others, "Our dear, brave navy—they never sleep, you know!"

Outside, haring round the corner to the pub with just two minutes to go to closing time, Kiwi turned to me and murmured "Bloody *Bohemian Girl*, fucking Albanians—where in Christ's name do you get it from, Tris?"

"From the circumstances, Kiwi—two pints, best bitter, please!"

"Sorry, sir," said the blowsy barmaid, "we've just rung Time Gentlemen Please."

"Holy Shit!" whispered Kiwi.

"Well, Kiwi, you got the women and song, what more do you want?"

"Ahh, let's turn in," he said. "We've to be at the Seaman's Pool tomorrow, early!"

Sadly we turned our steps towards the door of the old ladies' home.

Oh, the sun is on the harbor wall,
We must away to sea;
It's not the leavin' of Liverpool that grieves me,
But me darlin' when I think of thee.

So fare thee well, my own true love,
When I return united we shall be;
It's not the leavin' of Liverpool that grieves me,
But me darlin' when I think of thee.

Old capstan shanty, eighteenth century,
early nineteenth—it also survives, changed
somewhat, as an American folk song.

4

Faith, Hope, and—Luck!

The scene in the Merchant Marine recruiting office next day was something like a proletarian United Nations meeting. There were about five hundred men all jammed into the assembly room, with its green paint peeling up to shoulder level, as if it had been blistered by the colorful appearance of all the men who had passed through in the last fifty years. There were Lascars from the West Coast of India who walked as if they were climbing a ship's ladder, small, black men, with violinists' faces and long (for those years) hair. There were blue black, lithe, and handsome Somalis from the desert coast of Northeast Africa, standing like painted ibis birds on the fringes of the floor. Arabs from the Yemen, good seamen, nothing like the people I had encountered in their poor, dry land. Laughing Chinese from Hong Kong and Macao, cooks and stewards to a man, who could make a living out of what even a Liverpool stoker would throw away. There were big, hefty, black tribesmen from the Gold Coast and Nigeria, their tribal scars cut on their cheeks in neat, curious patterns; small, fat, worried-looking Maltese, talking their strange mixture of Italian, Arab, and English; hungry-eyed Cypriots; big, jolly mulattoes from the West Indies; and seamen from the underdeveloped countries of the West—Irish, Scots, Welsh, and Norwegians, and a combination of all of these, the "Scousers," as the Liverpool sailors are called around the sea world. They all accepted the presence of the others with mutual respect and good humor. No prison-yard or dole-office scowls here. These were seamen. They had only one enemy—the sea.

As we went into the assembly room, we were handed cards with numbers and had to wait until our number was called before going into the signing-on office and passing the medical examination for tuberculosis and VD, plus sundry other ailments to which merchant seamen are prone, not the least being, in the case of non-Moslems, drunkenness.

After about an hour's wait Kiwi went in. Moments later he was back out again. "O.K., Tris, I'm in," he said.

The signing-on official sat at a desk, a burly, jovial man in the blue uniform of the Harbor Authority.

"Name?" he asked. I told him.

"Discharge papers?" I handed them over. He looked through them, scanning each line, grunting with approval. Coming to the third page, he looked up and said, "Mmm, looks alright. Can you be onboard tomorrow afternoon?"

"Sure, tomorrow morning if you like."

"Right." He turned the last page, then sighed and looked up at me again.

"Sorry about this, chum. We can't take you on. You've a medical discharge from the navy. Look, it says 'Discharged Physically Unfit for Sea-Duties.'"

"But I'm almost recovered now. I've even started running in the mornings."

"Sorry, my friend, it's impossible."

"Look, I'll even sign on as galley hand or steward."

"I know it's hard on you, old son, but we can't take the risk. The insurers wouldn't wear it, and we can't have uninsured crew onboard—it's against Seamen's Union regulations. Sorry, mate, there just isn't a damned thing I can do about it. During the war it was different—then we'd take anyone we could get—but now——"

"O.K., well, thanks anyway. Don't worry, I expect I can find a berth ashore somewhere." I tried to grin.

"I hope you do," he said, standing up. "And jolly good luck."

"Thanks." I left his office feeling as if the world had caved in. As I walked out Kiwi offered me a cigarette. "How'd it go, mate?"

"I've had it, Kiwi; they won't take naval DW's [Discharged Woundeds]."

"Oh, f'chrissake."

"Never you mind, mate, you carry on. I'll find something, don't fear. Anyway, I've still more of a hankering for small craft than those bloody lumbering tin factories."

"Let's go and get a pint." He looked at his watch. "Ten minutes to opening time."

And so we went and sank another five gallons of Tetley's finest ale in the pub and another on the ferryboat back across the Mersey. I found myself wondering if this was to be my last sea trip, but as I looked out of the ferry windows on the fifth trip across and saw beyond the river mouth the Irish Sea stretching away into the distance, I knew it wasn't going to be, not by a long chalk.

When we finally arrived back in the Old Ladies' Rest Home, we both had quite a load on, but nevertheless managed to sink a good meal and give the ladies a rendering of selections from *The Pirates of Penzance*.

After the performance, Mrs. Steele came over to me.

"Well done, Mr. Jones, but you have been naughty because I did ask you to come and see me today for a chat. But never mind, talk with me tomorrow. My son is coming over from Holland to visit me, and you must join us for tea. Your friend will be gone to his ship by then, and I don't want you sitting here alone amongst all the ladies."

"Thank you, Mrs. Steele. I'll be delighted to."

Off we went, first round to the pub for a last pair of pints, then up to bed.

In the morning we slept late, then, after lunch, Kiwi took off to buy some seagoing gear over in Scotland Road, near the docks, and I bought him a last pint around the corner before he left.

"Cheers, Tris. I know you'll make out. You always did. But if you find it hard going, hang on here and I'll fix you up when I get back."

"Oh, sod off, Kiwi—I'd rather dig bloody graves."

"Right, old son, well, so long, see you again!" (And I did see him again, seventeen years later. It was in Bermuda; he was chief bosun's mate, still with the White Star Line, and I was the skipper of *Barbara*, bound on a forty-thousand-mile voyage.)

But this was all in the future, and at the time he left me in New Brighton, I thought I'd still be there when his ship returned.

At teatime, spruced up in a new shirt and navy tie, I joined Mrs. Steele and her son in the dining room for tea.

"Mr. Jones, may I present my son, Duncan? Duncan, Mr. Tristan Jones."

It was to be the first of many, many fateful meetings with people, in all kinds of circumstances all over the face of the world. Meetings which at first did not seem to signify anything, but which, in retrospect, the presence of some guiding hand, call it God or what you will, was startlingly clear.

"Pleased to meet you, Duncan. Work round here?"

"No, actually." His tone was educated, clipped and precise, just like his mother's. "Actually, I work in Holland. I'm over there on an exchange of information on the steel building of small craft. You see I work for Cammel Lairds, the shipbuilders over here in Birkenhead. The Jerries pinched all the Dutch timber, and you know they've lost, or are rapidly losing, the Dutch East Indies——"

"Yes, new country. What do they call it . . . Indonesia?"

"That's right. Well, the Dutch have taken to building small craft—work boats, harbor ferries in steel; even yachts."

"Yachts?" I was all ears.

"Yes, and they're getting quite good at it, too. Once you get down below on most of them, you'd never dream they were built of steel, all paneled out with Nigerian mahogany. Their galleys are a wonder, too."

"Where do they sell them, in Holland?"

"A lot, yes, but many go abroad, to the West Indies and the States and quite a few to South America." He puffed at his pipe.

I was getting more and more curious. Small craft! "And how do they get them out to South America?"

"Some are shipped out, but others are sailed out. You see the Rio businessman looks upon it as a great status symbol if he has a yacht which has crossed the Atlantic."

"How big are these yachts?"

"Oh, anything up to eighty feet long."

"Sail or power?"

"Both, but of course the ones which cross over under their own steam, so to speak, those are all sail."

"Really—and who takes them over?"

"Delivery crews. They join the yacht in Holland, sail her over, then either fly back or bring back another yacht, say from the States or the West Indies. The only snag is finding crews. The big cargo ships pay much better, and of course the usual sailing yachtsman simply hasn't the time to go off on a trip that long."

"Mr. Steele, if I come over to Holland, will you help me get in touch with these yacht builders?"

"Why, d'you want to buy one?" he smiled.

"No, I want to sail one, or two, or three."

I then went on to tell him my story about how I had studied navigation in the navy on my off-watch periods, and seamanship; about how I had been involved in Medfoba, which was the original name given to what is now the Outward Bound organization, formed to get young, big-ship seamen interested in sailing small craft just for the fun of it; and about how I was hoping to buy my own craft one day and make my own voyages. Both he and Mrs. Steele listened intently. When I finished, Mrs. Steele spoke up. "Now, Duncan, you must help this man. You know your father went to sea in sailing ships from 1875 on, until those dreadful Germans started their silly war. Before he died he told me, dear old thing, that the Age of Sail is not dead. And we need this man, and others like him, others who may follow him, to bring back sail and sailors to Liverpool and all those other ports that your dear father took me to so long ago."

"Yes, I will, by Jove, of course I will. When you come over, look me up in Leiden and I will make sure my Dutch friends fix you up. Here's my address; I'll be there in two weeks' time. Do you need anything for fares? You can pay me back when you're working."

"No, thank you very much, I can manage fine. Yes, by gum, I'll see you as soon as I get over there, which will be right after you are!"

"Now, my dear Mr. Jones, look, your tea is cold. Let me pour you some more, then perhaps you'd like to play Duncan and me a little tune on the pianola?" Mrs. Steele gently touched my arm.

"Certainly, ma'am." *A little tune?* I'd have played them the bloody *Hallelujah Chorus* and the *1812 Overture* together, the way I was feeling!

And that is how I made my first real contact with the yachting world, with the builders and the sailors. That is how I was able to learn a mine of knowledge about sailing craft and the way to run them, during eight transatlantic voyages, a complete circumnavigation of South America and a circumnavigation of the world.

By 1958 I had saved enough money, together with my still untouched naval discharge money and pension over the five years, to look for a vessel suitable for carrying out a voyage I had long had in mind. To take a sailing-boat nearer to the North Pole than anyone else had ever done! Even to try to cross right over the Arctic Ocean!

Now I had sufficient money to find and fit out a hull, plus the experience to do the fitting out properly, and the determination to tackle the voyage. And this I would have to do completely alone.

Mrs. Steele died while I was at sea, in October 1954.

To the memory of her and of her husband, and to her son, this book is dedicated, for it shows how I managed to live long enough to see their dream start to come true.

Now you take the paint brush
And I'll take the paint pot;
And we'll paint the Ship's Side together;
When Jimmy comes along, we will sing our little song;
Thank Christ we didn't join forever!

Royal Navy traditional song,
"Jimmy" is slang
for a first lieutenant.

5

Master and Mate: 1958

In August 1958, I left the yacht *Slot van Kappel* in Lisbon, after a hard and fast passage of almost two years around the world. The two co-owners were set on a leisurely cruise up along the Spanish and French coasts before returning to England and selling the boat. I had no time to waste, because on passing Antigua I had had an extrasensory message, as well as a dream, that my old skipper, Tansy Lee, was fast sinking. It was not surprising, as he had been born in 1860. He had been steadily at sea since 1872, under sail the whole time, except for a spell during World War II when he'd gone to sea in an armed trawler at the age of eighty, as he said, "to 'ave anovver go at them bloody 'Uns."

I had joined him in 1938, at the age of fourteen, in his old boomie sailing ketch *Second Apprentice*, knocking around the North Sea and the English Channel in coastal and Continental trade—coal to Cherbourg, fodder to Ramsgate, scrap iron to Germany, ballast to Hull. Rates were low, pay was a pittance, hours were long and arduous, but the food and the ways of sail were abundant, tasty, and well digested. Tansy was the skipper; I was his crew.

Tansy himself had gone to sea first at the age of twelve, with his father in "the Trade," as cross-channel smuggling was then known. But when he reached the ripe age of fifteen, his family "caught religion," and so Tansy was put into the Royal Navy. That would have been around 1875.

His first ship was a revenue cutter patrolling the rough Channel, flushing out Tansy's recent colleagues in all weathers. His tales were fascinating. They had worn tarred straw hats and cutlasses; once a week the crew had assembled to witness floggings. Indeed, some of the men that Tansy sailed with in the Revenue Service had themselves served their apprenticeships with men who had fought with Admiral Nelson at the Battle of Trafalgar in 1805. Tansy had gone on to sail with the navy all over the world: in the Ashanti Wars, in the antislave service on the east coast of Africa, and in the Boer War. During World War I, he was recalled into the Royal Navy for service on Q-boats, old sailing vessels fitted with six-inch guns hidden in the hold. After surfacing, a German sub would order the Q-boat crew to abandon ship. The crew would fake a panic over the side, then, when the gunner had the U-boat's range weighed off, down would fall the bulwarks, bang would go the guns, and glug-glug would go Jerry.

After his discharge from the navy, Tansy took over the family boat, an eighty-five-foot boomie ketch. When his brothers passed away, he continued to ply cargo while sail faded away and died in ignominy the world over. By 1938 there were only a dozen sailing vessels at work around the British Isles. The art was kept alive by a few elderly hardnuts like Tansy Lee and Bob Roberts, who persisted in the Trade until the late 1960s.

I had always been conscious that I was a direct link between the past centuries of sail-in-trade and the future, when sail will come into its own again. I can't wait for the oil wells to run dry, for the last gob of black, sticky muck to come oozing out of some remote well. Then the glory of sail will return. It may be unrecognizable, compared to the clouds of canvas which used to scud the seas, but sail it will be, computerized or not. Again we will use the winds of God and bend them to man's will. Again the needs of sail will dictate a grace and beauty to the hulls which has not been seen in ship design for almost a century, and we shall look back on the ugly slabs of hacked power which now so arrogantly force the seas and thank the Lord himself that the last one is headed for the breaker's yard. Merchant seamen will eye their vessels with love and pride, as they once did, instead of thinking of them as mobile factories. I hope I live long enough to see that day.

But on the train down from London to Sandwich, back in 1958, I had little inkling of all this. All I knew was that I must make my voyage. Sail it would be because it never occurred to me to do it any other way. The Arctic it would be because most of my heroes had left their marks there: Davis, Hudson, Cook, Bering, Shannon, Amundsen, Norden, Peary, Nansen . . . Nansen! *Nansen* and the *Fram*! I would try to do as well as the *Fram*. I would never be able to do as well as Nansen, because with my education I would never be able to write about it, or to get the flavor of adventure, pure and simple, through anyone else's skull, through their bloodstream and bones, into the fibers of their being, as Nansen had done. I would never be able to learn, as he had done, that true humanity, true charity, can only come to a man through real effort and endeavor against the impossible.

Physically by this time, at the age of thirty-four, I was in excellent condition after six years under sail in all conditions of weather and welfare. Mentally, I was shaping up. I was extremely pragmatic, almost to the point of short-sightedness; very curious about every and all things, though not yet very observant about people and their nature, as I would become later. If I had great faults, they were that I thought I knew more than I did and that I didn't suffer fools gladly. I was still impetuous in most things, where later I would find that one should be choosy about what one is impetuous about. I was, to use the sailor's phrase, "full of piss and vinegar."

As the train chugged through the apple orchards of Kent, my mind was intent on finding a suitable vessel. If possible, she would be somewhere near one of the Royal Dockyards.

There, through the grapevine of ex-sailors, I would be able to get hold of good cheap gear. I had now fourteen hundred pounds (three thousand dollars) saved up. That should be enough to find a craft, furbish her for a five-year cruise, and victual me without too much strain.

I took the one and only taxi in town to Tansy's cottage, about a two-mile hike in the glorious English autumn—apples on the trees and sweet wildflowers by the lane's edges—through a countryside so rich that even the cows looked as if they owned the land they grazed upon. The ancient taxi wheezed out of the neat, tidy, spoon-fed Borough of Sandwich, once one of the ancient Cinque Ports of medieval times, but now stranded some miles inland through centuries of silt deposits. Through villages and hamlets as old as man's delight in the taste of a pint of ale, through the weft and warp of England, the taxi trundled. Past gnarled oak trees forged by the forceful Channel breezes as they blew eternally eastward from the Celtic Sea, bringing their lilting chant to the green-topped cliffs and gently rolling downs; past the swinging rings of creaking inn-signs, worn away through untold lives—the Iron Duke, the Royal Oak, the Sailor's Return . . . .

Tansy's cottage was like Tansy. It managed to glower and grin at the same time. Low, with a steep thatched-straw roof and whitewashed walls, the bedroom curtains drawn at the shady orchard end, it looked, as he so often did, as if it were blind yet all-seeing. The weatherworn brick path from the green wicker gate was so eggshell delicate it seemed it would crack under the weight of a sailor's sea bag. An empty swing dangled expectantly. The old wooden door had a rope's-end served into a back-splice, with a Turk's-head knotted into it so shipshape you would think it had grown that way. That was the knocker. So I knocked.

Tansy's niece, Daisy, opened the door, but not in the cheerful way she had done on my previous visits. Her rosy smile was a sorrowful frown. She grabbed my arm.

"'Lo, Daisy, what's up?"

"Oh, Tristan, he's gone——" She burst into tears. I put my arm around her shoulder.

"Come on, love, where's Bogey?" This was her husband.

"Out fishing, but he'll be in any moment." She sniffed, then said with a gallant attempt at a smile, "But come in, Tris, I'll make a pot of tea. And there's some cake if you'd like. You must be famished."

"Thanks, Daisy. Yes, I am a bit, but let me do it for you."

"No, don't be silly, I'm all right." She walked into the kitchen, just beyond the tiny, cluttered living room, with its flowery wallpaper, shiny piano, and best-china-bedecked dresser in the corner. A stern photograph of King Edward VII glared down imperiously from one side of the chimney, while Queen Alexandra did her royal best not to look frightened from the other. A coronation mug, where Tansy had kept shillings for the gas meter, stood at one end of the mantel shelf, with a Peek Frean's biscuit tin, where he kept his half-crowns for his daily outing down to the pub, in the middle. At the far end was a small china statue of a little lad eating a bunch of grapes, only his arm and the grapes had been knocked off years ago.

As Daisy tinkered with the tea tray in the kitchen, I studied the pictures on the walls. Tansy's dad, looking like the wrath of Jehovah in the center of a group of lifeboatmen, stood next to the Ramsgate rescue craft. They all looked stolidly intrepid, except for one, a rather small, mustachioed chap in the front row, to starboard, who looked half-crocked. The caption said, "Ramsgate Lifeboat Crew 1872—ready, aye, ready."

On another wall was a picture of Tansy as an able seaman on the West Coast of Africa during the Ashanti wars. Tansy and his mate wore pith helmets and white neckerchiefs, like the Foreign Legion used to, bandoliers across their shoulders, Lee-Enfield 303 rifles, with cutlasses slung from their belts. The Ashanti tribesmen in the picture looked fierce.

Just as Daisy trotted in with the tea, there was a rustling under the table. Tansy's old Labrador dog, Nelson, looked at me through his one good eye. He hopped over on three legs and nuzzled my leg. By now he was at least twelve years old and wise in the ways of the world. His tail wagged, but it looked like the black feathers on a funeral horse. I patted him. Nelson sighed.

"When did he go, Daisy?"

"Last week. We put him away three days ago."

"Where?"

"The Baptist Chapel. He couldn't stand parsons. He wanted to be buried behind the Royal Oak pub, but you know how folks are, so we settled for the Baptists. I mean, they're not the same, are they?"

"No, I suppose not. A bit more easygoing, like, I'd say, Dais."

"Anyway, all his old chums came for the funeral. You should have seen it, Tristan. Some of the old boys could hardly walk. At least not until they got the darts out in the pub. Tansy had left twenty pounds for beer money. Well, they got through that within an hour of opening time. Old Shiner Wright, the landlord, reckoned it was the best day's business he'd done in years."

"Bully for him. Was there free booze?"

"Yes, three free pints all around. The old boys, by the time they'd got that lot down, as well as the twenty quid's worth, couldn't think what it was all about. I swear some of them thought it was Coronation Day."

"Tansy would have loved that, Daisy. Right up his street."

Daisy poured another cup of tea and cut another slice of Dundee cake.

"What will you and Bogey do now, Dais? Will you keep this place running, or what?"

"I don't know yet. There's an editor fellow down from London wants to buy it."

"What's he like?"

"Funny little cove, effeminate-like. Bogey says he sits down when he goes for a pee." She giggled.

"Ah, well, lass, that's the way it goes!"

"Yes, and Tansy said he wanted you to have Nelson."

"Nelson? What am I going to do with him? Look, girl, I'm going to be knocking around looking for a boat, and then I want to do some serious cruising. Hell, it's going to be hard enough for me, without some lame old mutt traipsing around after me."

Nelson knew we were talking about him. He looked at me with an eye so pitiful it would have melted the heart of Attila the Hun.

"Can't you take him?" I asked her.

"We've already got two, and with the baby on the way. . . ." Nelson stood looking at her, his tail brushing my foot.

"Oh, Jesus Christ, Daisy. Well, all right then, but I can't see me taking a bloomin' cripple to sea. One's bad enough, but with two——" I fondled Nelson's head and he fairly jumped for joy, putting his one front paw on my lap.

"Now cut that out, yer black bugger, behave yourself!" He dropped to the floor, all ears, wet nose, and attention.

Just then Bogey came in, bobble cap, ginger hair, eyes like the summer sky, seaboots and sweater, and a great sack of flounder under his arm. We sat by the fire yarning and drinking tea, eyeing the grandfather clock for pub-opening time. Just before dusk, off we went to the Royal Oak, Daisy, Bogey, Nelson, and me, to talk of times with Tansy at an ancient wooden table in the garden, while the sweet, quiet English evening folded itself into a parcel of dreams, leaving light caught in the leaves of trees and streaming with cheery sounds through the backdoor of the Royal Oak. And though we laughed at tales of Tansy, we silently wept in our hearts for the passing of a good man.

My father was the keeper of the Eddystone Light
And he loved a mermaid one fine night,
The result of the union were offspring three,
A dolphin and a porpoise and the other was me!
Oh, Ho! *the wind blows free,*
Oh, for a life on the rolling *sea!*

From a traditional English Channel song.

6

God Helps Those What Helps Themselves!

I stayed with Daisy and Bogey Knight for the next two days, Monday and Tuesday. Bogey, like most Channel fishermen, did not go out on Mondays and Fridays because of old superstitions. He and I sat around in his living room in the morning until opening time, then, with Daisy's blessing, for she was pleased to have Bogey's great frame out of the way while she prepared lunch, we adjourned to the Royal Oak. Two pints of ale and a game of darts, then back to the cottage for cold cuts from Sunday's dinner, with applesauce, for it had been pork this week, all washed down with a great jeroboam of "scrumpy," as rough cider is called in those parts.

Old Tansy had never installed running water. As we ate I could see beyond the kitchen door, with its rusty horseshoe. There was a whitewashed wall streaming with sunlight, and on it the shadow cast by Tansy's well-water-bucket yoke, and there were deep grooves worn by the bucket chains as he, and his father before him, and *his* father before *him*, had restowed the yoke. There was a small window above the stone sink, and I could see the tips of mint leaves growing outside, nourished by the sink drain, which emptied straight into the garden soil.

"What will you do now, Tristan, old son?" said Bogey.

"I'm looking for a boat. I want to have a shot at making a different cruise."

"Not much round here, all fishin' boats. No sail left, except for a few old yachts, an' like I was sayin', most of them are survivors from Dunkirk." He warmed his undershirt by the open fire.

"I thought I'd have a look around Sheerness, Bogey. There's this advertisement for an ex-R.N.L.I. [Royal National Lifeboat Institution] hull up there, and I think I'll go and see if I can do anything with her. The price is reasonable enough—four hundred quid [a thousand dollars in those days]—and it'll leave me with a tidy sum to fit her out, if she's any good."

"When was she built?"

"It says 1908."

"Should be good then. Is she one of those beach-launched boats?"

"I think she must be, Bogey. It says thirty-four feet. Must be a Watson design."

"Should make a good conversion, 'cos in those days they were building hulls like bloody cathedrals with the finest wood ever brought into U.K."

"It's not a cathedral I want, Bogey, just the flamin' parsonage'll do."

And so it was that next day Nelson, my sea bag, and I caught the early morning train to Tunbridge and Sheerness, with me wearily wondering how much wandering I was in for before I found a boat. Nelson got stroppy with every male dog coming in sight and handsomely gallant with every bitch, making all the old ladies on their way to Tunbridge market nervous and sharp. As soon as the compartment was clear, I gave him a belt over the ear. "Pipe down, you randy old bastard."

By late afternoon we were in Sheerness, for distances in England are only great in time and memories, not in miles. Shortly, we were at the back of a boatyard looking at a hull, all thirty-four abandoned feet of her. I often wondered afterwards if we looked at her or if she looked at us. She seemed an even sorrier sight than Nelson with his one eye and three legs or me after three days of knocking back the bevvys with Bogey. The dirty grey paint on her sides was peeling off, and she was covered by an even dirtier tarpaulin, tattered and oily, which had been played upon by every wind in southeast England for the past decade. Grabbing a ladder, I propped it against the boat's side and lifted the rotting canvas cover. Inside the bottom of the boat was a two-foot-deep pool of black, stagnant rainwater, with a botanical display around the edges that would do justice to Kew Gardens. Minnows jumped, frogs croaked, and a rat rustled into safer hiding.

I hopped inside the hull. Out with the knife; quick poke around into the double-diagonal planking underwater. Vicious shove into half a dozen frames. "Mahogany . . . oak . . . mmm."

I sloshed my way aft, poking and prodding. Back out, I shinned down the ladder and checked the garboard and the deadwood aft. All sound. I stood back to study her. She had the classic lines of a lifeboat, with a whaleback cuddy fore and aft. Her original short stubby masts and oarlocks were still in her. She was narrow in the beam, only seven feet, but she was built like a tank. Her keel was as straight as a die, and under the filthy paint her West African mahogany was as good as a Steinway grand piano—a good inch and a half thick!

Her rounded hull was fitted with two long but shallow galvanized-steel bilge keels. She would need ballasting internally and even then she would not be able to carry much sail. But in the strong Arctic winds she wouldn't need much sail. The watertight bulkheads fore and aft were still sound, and there was room for a good twelve-foot cabin amidships and eight feet to spare for the cockpit—nice and roomy.

Nelson emerged from sniffing the keel. I looked at him. "Nelson, old son, I think we've got ourselves a boat." He looked at me, then at the boat, moving his tail as if to say,

"Well, I hope to Christ you know what you're doing."

Then the owner arrived, a worker at the Royal Dockyard, which was, at that time, in the process of closing down. After introducing himself, he said, "Make a good fishin' boat. She'll take any amount of power in that hull."

"Yeah, but all I want is a boat for messing around in. Like on weekends, you know, trips up the Thames and all that, take the bird out for a jaunt. I like the hull, but the price is a bit steep for me."

"Well, seeing as how it looks like she'll go to a good home, how about 350 nikker?"

"Three hundred?"

"I'll tell you what, you being ex-R.N. and all, I'll let her go for 325."

"Right, you're on." I shook the slight little man's hand and the deal was concluded.

Next day I went into Chatham and bought a surplus Army tent, pumped out and cleaned the inside of the boat, set up the tent inside the hull, and there we were, in residence. Paying rent revolts the Celtic soul.

The five months of hard work which followed, from blooming August until snowy January, lie outside of the realm of this tale. If you are a boatman, you will know what effort was expended, what problems were solved, what limits of exasperation were reached, what resigned patience was nurtured, what poking around in heaps of scrap to find good but cheap materials, what marvels of expediency were arrived at, and how many tears were almost shed when nothing at all seemed to be going right.

Finally the day came when *Cresswell* (her original Lifeboat Institute name) started to take shape, to become a vessel instead of a hulk. I sat patiently in a snowbound shed cutting sheets of quarter-inch pure lead, recently "salvaged" off a blitzed London church, into "kentledge," as we call the shaped ballast cut to fit very closely between the frames of the hull in the bilge of the boat. I studied every surplus war material leaflet which came my way, and soon I had installed my engine. This was a twin-cylinder, horizontally-opposed diesel engine which had formerly been mounted on a trailer. The trailer had been towed around London behind a truck, and served as an auxiliary fire pump during the great German aerial bombardments. With the pump end detached and a shaft and propeller buttoned on, it worked admirably, with its ten horsepower, to shift *Cresswell* along at five knots or so. And it used only half a pint of fuel an hour! I started it by ramming lubricating oil down into two brass cups which fed the oil into the cylinders. Then I swung like hell on the handle, there was a loud explosion of noise and fumes, and off she went. I stopped the thing by simply shutting off the fuel. There was no throttle or astern gear.

The deck and doghouse I built also out of West African mahogany, which was expensive, but I wanted to carry the scantlings of the boat (i.e., the material specifications) right through the additions. Between the mahogany strakes I laid oiled canvas, just as it was in the hull, and over the deck and doghouse roof I laid and painted canvas so fine that even after I played water on deck for hours not one drop got through. I laid out the entire compartment, with access from above through a close-fitting hatch with hasps like you'd find in the Bank of England.

The amount of good, solid, hefty material which I collected on my nightly forays in a borrowed dinghy under muffled oars to the abandoned Royal Dockyard on the other side of the river and the muted conversations on the misty jetties and foggy foreshores, keeping a wary eye out for H.M. Dockyard Police, plus the number of pints stood for in the Admiral Jellicoe pub would be a wonder to anyone except those who have fitted out a long-distance cruiser with such meager resources as I had. I had no qualms of conscience about it, for I thought My Lords Commissioners of the Admiralty owed me something a bit more than a measly ten dollars per week.

The sails, the standing rigging, the running rigging, the diesel fuel tank (of finest copper), the zinc water tanks, the fuel piping, the stove, the one good sleeping berth in the cabin, the steering cables, the huge hand bilge pump, and the great brass fog siren, all came out of Her Majesty's custody and into mine, and so into the furbishing of the gallant ketch *Cresswell*. With the aid of half a dozen boat-loving cronies employed in the Dockyard, we fitted her out as good as Captain Watts (the *gentleman's* boat outfitter) could have done for two thousand guineas and more. Practically everything except the engine, that is. We'd have had one of those, too, for there were a dozen old fleet tenders lying rotting and woebegone at their moorings, but their engines were all too big. So we made do with the London Fire Brigade pump engine. The engine trade name was Vixen, and if ever a collection of nuts and bolts had a will of its own, that one did. But once running she'd run forever, and I got hold of some insulation out of H.M. Dockyard in which I sheathed the engine compartment. What with that and the rigid-resilient mountings (which I got out of the old Dockyard printing shop), she was at least smooth and steady, once the initial purgatory of starting her had been suffered.

I had concentrated first on the cabin, so that Nelson, the sea bag, and I would have somewhere reasonably warm and dry to live during the coming winter months. By mid-October, we were cozily battened against the weather and the curiosity of the local constabulary.

By Christmas (which we celebrated by making the church roof sheet-lead deal with some of "the boys" in the Elephant and Castle district of London), the masts—beautiful, hollow British Columbia pine—the rigging—courtesy of Sheerness dockyard and a week of fog—and the engine were all in place. By the end of January I had hand sewn a total of fourteen hundred square feet of heavy canvas sails, as well as received delivery of eight hundred square feet of heavy Dacron sails from Jeckells', up in East Anglia. By the time the ice had cleared out of the River Medway at the end of February, she was ready for launching, with one of the most lovingly applied paint jobs seen in the Thames Estuary since Queen Victoria was a lass. The outside of the hull was white gloss, picked out with French blue on the rubbing strake and Admiralty varnish (*fourteen* coats) on the "brightwork." Down below, all was Royal Navy grey, for one of our nocturnal outings had rewarded us with a great thirty-gallon drum of the stuff. It wasn't very chic-looking, but then, neither were Nelson nor I, and it served its purpose. Anyway, it was the light grey used in warships on tropical stations, so it would remind us of starry, balmy nights in the West Indies and the South Pacific during the long, dark, cold, Arctic nights to come.

Down below, I had a bit of brasswork—two gun tampons, the great bronze badges which they used to wedge into the muzzles of a destroyer's guns when they were not in use. A brass fiddle rail ran around the table and there were brass portholes set into the doghouse sides. Then there were pictures of Shackleton, Nansen, and Scott, all cut out of old "London Illustrated News" magazines, and one of the queen at the forward end of the cabin.

The coke-and-wood-burning stove was an admirable little contraption I had located in the old captain of police's office in the dockyard. As my need was much greater than his possible successor's, I borrowed the stove on a permanent basis.

In March 1959 I was ready to get in the navigational gear. The sextant I already had, an old Dutch model from the 1880s which had a micrometer reading so fine and brass-polish-worn that no one but I could read it. The chronometer I bought in a Petticoat Lane flea market for seven shillings (about a dollar). It was a fine London job from around 1860, brass, set on all-round gimbals, in a beautifully made walnut case with a green baize cushion inside. It was accurate to less than a second a day. A taffrail log, for telling the distance run, snaffled from Her Majesty's stores, cost three pints of ale.

I scoured the secondhand bookshops of London for read-

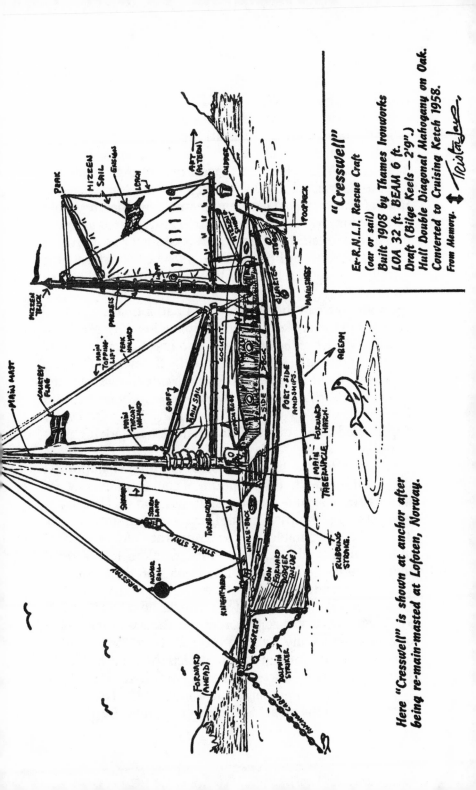

"Cresswell"

Ex-R.N.L.I. Rescue Craft
(oar or sail)
Built 1908 by Thames Ironworks
LOA 32 ft. BEAM 6 ft.
Draft (Bilge Keels – 2'9".)
Hull Double Diagonal Mahogany on Oak.
Converted to Cruising Ketch 1958.
From Memory.

Here "Cresswell" is shown at anchor after being re-main-masted at Lofoten, Norway.

MIZZEN TRUCK
MIZZEN
PEAK
MIZZEN SAIL
ENSIGN
LORRI
AFT (ASTERN)
RUDDER
FOREDECK
MAIN TOPPING LIFT
PEAK HALYARD
PREBIES
BACKSTAYS
QUARTER STERN
WANDERERS
ABEAM
MAIN MAST
COURTESY FLAG
GAFF
MAIN THROAT HALYARD
MAIN SAIL
COCKPIT
COACHROOF
SIDE DECK
PORT SIDE
AMIDSHIPS
MAIN FORWARD HATCH
SHROUDS
STERN LAMP
THROAT
WHALE-BACK
FORWARD
RUBBING STRAKE
STAYSAIL STAY
FORESTAY
BOW (FORWARD BULWARK)
KNIGHT-HEAD
CATSPREY
BOWSPRIT
DOLPHIN STRIKER
FORWARD (AHEAD)
ANCHOR CABLE
ANCHOR BALL

ing material. Some of the bargains I found were a complete works of Shakespeare, Gibbon's *Decline and Fall of the Roman Empire*, a full set of Mark Twain's works, Marx's *Das Kapital*, plus definitive editions of Kipling, Byron, Wordsworth, and Keats, together with the works of W. B. Yeats and Wilde. I also managed to scrounge several of Joseph Conrad's books—*The Nigger of the Narcissus*, *The Heart of Darkness*, *Lord Jim*—and many of the Maigret books by Simenon, which I think much of. I also secured a copy of one of the greatest sailing fiction books ever written, *The Riddle of the Sands* by Erskine Childers, who was later shot as a traitor by the Irish Free State troops during the Irish Troubles.

I found later in the voyage that I had a treasure indeed onboard in the books by Alain Gerbault *In Search of the Sun* and *The Voyage of the Firecrest*. I also had Cervantes's *Don Quixote* and several scruffy volumes by Balzac and Dumas.

These, together with my *Reed's Nautical Almanac*, the *Admiralty Pilot for the Arctic Ocean East of Greenland*, and Charles Darwin's *Voyage of H.M.S. Beagle*, were to be my appreciated companions during many long, dark nights to come.

So much for the modern works. Even more important than all these, with the exception, of course, of the navigational volumes, were the English translations of *De mensure orbis terrae* by the Irish monk Dicuil, written around A.D. 825, and the Venerable Bede's accounts of Celtic settlement in Iceland up to the century before the Norsemen arrived there, *De Ratione Temporum*. I had notes on the account of the voyage made by the Greek geographer Pytheas of Massalia from Britain to Iceland (or Thule, as he called it) in 330 B.C. There was also a collection of translations of the works of Strabo and Pliny, written around the birth of Christ, which gave accounts of sailing directions from Britain to Thule. There were also scraps of written Celtic lore of the voyages of Saint Brendan to the islands of the North, and translations of the great Icelandic sagas. Snorri Sturluson's

Prose Edda and a history of Iceland entitled *Islendingabók* by Ari the Learned; also, the *Sturlunga saga* and the *Fornaldar-sögur*, the Sagas of the Old Times, Icelandic translations of the Celtic and Romance legends of Tristan and Yseult, or Erec and Blanchfleur, together with the classic *Islendingasögur*, the Saga of the Icelanders. These tales, woven of fact and fantasy, of calamitous cowardice and cold courage, are living proof of the leavening influence of the Celt on the savage Viking soul, for in no other Scandinavian culture was such a standard of heroic prose and poetry reached. Nowhere else did the blood gush from the word so wetly and redly, nor the sun rise in such paeans of splendor; nowhere else was man so human, nor yet so godly, except in the old (much older than the Sagas) legends of the Gaels.

By the end of March I had spent approximately $2,700.00 on lead, charts, engine, navigational tables, tools, and other items which, for one reason or the other (usually the other), were impossible to obtain from Royal Navy stores. Also on food and beer and a brand-new bowsprit.

By the time I had laid in my two years' supply of canned food and other bits and piece of necessary gear, such as sleeping bag and warm clothing, I had about a hundred dollars left. With this I launched *Cresswell*, stood a pint of beer all round at the Admiral Jellicoe, bought a compass, a small radio receiver, and a bundle of mutton cloths from the local butcher to serve as extra blankets and insulation for the cabin, and I was off, in foggy weather, flat calm sea, down the Medway, out of the Dickens-haunted Thames Estuary, and into the North Sea. Destination Whitstable.

As *Cresswell* lifted her thirty-six feet to the first sea swells, I was elated. Nelson stood up forward in the bows, sniffing the wind, standing as steady as a rock on his three legs, content that there was a full bag of bones for him in the engine compartment and that he was at sea again.

In the afternoon the fog lifted. The low green hills of north Kent and, beyond them, the North Foreland's chalky white cliffs, rose out of the murky North Sea waters. Soon

Whitstable was in view and I had completed my first solo voyage in my own craft. It was only a matter of thirty-five miles or so, and there was no wind, but the old Fire Brigade pump worked as good as a homing Trojan, and there was plenty of daylight to spare as I guided *Cresswell* into the open roadstead, to anchor in front of the town of Whitstable on that faraway April evening.

It was good that we called at Whitstable, for here I found out more of the history of *Cresswell* than I ever imagined I would. In Sheerness, where I had fitted out in the shadow of the dockyard walls, she was something of a mystery, of uncertain age and lineage. But as soon as she stepped her forefoot into the salty North Sea swell, I knew by the very movement of her hull that here was a vessel which had known men and the sea. She was no shy virgin.

If you wake at midnight, and hear a horse's feet,
Don't go drawing back the blind, or looking in the street,
Them that asks no questions isn't told a lie.
Watch the wall, my darling, while the Gentlemen go by!
  Five and twenty ponies
  Trotting through the dark——
  Brandy for the Parson,
  'Baccy for the Clerk;
  Laces for a Lady, letters for a spy,
And watch the wall, my darling, while the Gentlemen go by!

If you do as you've been told, 'likely there's a chance,
You'll be give a dainty doll, all the way from France,
With a cap of Valenciennes, and a velvet hood——
A present from the Gentlemen, along o' being good!
  Five and twenty ponies
  Trotting through the dark——
  Brandy for the Parson,
  'Baccy for the Clerk,
Them that asks no questions isn't told a lie——
Watch the wall, my darling, while the Gentlemen go by!

Rudyard Kipling, "A Smuggler's Song."

7

Watch the Wall, My Darling!

Two good things about not having much money: your pockets don't get holes in them and you meet a lot of interesting people whom otherwise you might miss.

The boatman who ferried me ashore in Whitstable was obviously not one of the Brethren, though he was a cheerful enough chap, well fed, rotund under his blue jersey, with sparkling grey blue Saxon eyes over a smoothly shaven jaw. But he didn't have the lean and hungry look, and his oar strokes were a mite too gentle for me to confide in him what was on my mind.

"You come far?" he asked me, as we headed for the town jetty.

"Only from Sheerness. I motored all the way; no wind."

"That's usual this time of year. Where're you bound?"

"Oh, just knocking around. You know, Ramsgate, maybe Broadstairs. Depends on the weather." I tried to sound uncaring.

"Yeah, I s'pose so." He'd got the message alright, and charged me a shilling, twice the going rate. "Well, it'll help him buy a new peaked cap," I thought, as I handed him one-thousandth of all my worldly wealth.

I headed for the shops, to buy some safety pins and envelopes and exchange surreptitious niceties with the lasses behind the counters. Then, as it was but half past four and still thirty minutes to go before pub-opening time,

I sipped a slow cup of tea and chewed a sticky bun, surrounded by most of the genteel, elderly ladies of the resort. I was waited on by a chirpy little London cockney girl who managed to look sedate and ladylike in front of the dowagers and at the same time wiggle her hips every time she squeezed past my table.

It was raining when I eventually made my way to the Standard after fixing a date with the waitress for ten o'clock. Business picked up and soon the public bar was filled with fishermen and longshoremen. After a while one of the crowd, a cheerful-looking, lanky, red-haired fellow, dressed like most of the others in jersey and bobble-cap, approached me.

"Saw you come in with the old *Mary Eleanor*."

"Not me, mate, that's the boat *Cresswell*, ex-R.N.L.I.," I replied.

"Not on your nellie. I know that boat. By the way, my name's Bill Travers, ex-Australian navy. I took my pension over here."

"Tristan Jones, ex-R.N." I finished off my pint. He bought another.

"Like I was saying," Bill went on, "I had to look twice at that hull, but no mistake. You've done a bloody good job of the conversion, but she's still the *Mary E*. I knew her, in fact I sailed in her, once or twice, about ten years ago. She belonged to a bloke called Rattler Morgan. He used to be in and out of Ramsgate running stuff over to France. He got her from the joker who took her over to Dunkirk in 1940 for the evacuation."

"What? I never knew she was in that lot."

"Yes, and that bloody patch on the starboard bow is where a Jerry plane put a forty-millimeter shell right through her and killed four Tommies and a Frenchman." He swigged his beer again. "How long have you had her, mate?"

"Oh, a few months. Found her derelict in Sheerness."

"I'm not surprised, 'cos Rattler drew five years in the nick when they eventually caught up with him. They reckoned he'd moonlighted more flamin' booze into Froggyland than Johnnie Walker had sent legally."

I pushed over another three bob for two more pints.

"Where you bound, mate?" He was studying me closely.

I eyed him. "Well, speaking sort of general-like, I'm heading down Channel. What I'd like to do, if I can, is get over to Ireland for the summer. I heard living is much cheaper over there."

"On the blink, then?"

"Oh, I've got a few bob, but I wouldn't mind a few more."

"Yeah? Well, I might be able to put you onto something."

The conversation drifted into the usual realms of boats and people, the age-old exercise of sailor-strangers meeting in a bar, finding out if they have friends in common and if one knows any of the vessels the other knows, then a joke or two, a game of darts, hints on what pubs are good—the same scuttlebutt the world over.

Towards the end of our seventh pint, Bill leaned over close to my ear.

"If you're stuck, Tris, I can put you in with a setup which is genuine, and you'll earn more than a few bob in just a couple of runs over the other side."

"What are they running?"

"Scotch."

"What's in it?"

Bill lowered his voice. "Two hundred quid a time. A hundred on sailing and a hundred when the stuff's landed."

"Where?"

"I can get you to the blokes at this end, but I can't tell you about the other end. They'll put you right on that score when you sail."

"What's in it for you?"

"I sail with you. I get a hundred nikker for the trip."

"Where's *your* boat?" I was wary.

"Piled her up off Portland back in November. No insurance."

"How do I know you're O.K.?"

"Ask him." Bill nodded towards the landlord of the Standard.

I had already spoken to the landlord, who had known old Tansy Lee when he used to frequent the pub, and I'd weighed him off as a straight-shooter. He had probably taken his share of the "bent" booze.

"Right," I said. "Hang on a minute and I'll have a word with him. If he okays it, Bill, you're on."

A few minutes later I got the landlord to one side and he confirmed that he had known Aussie Bill for some years, that he always paid his due, and that he was trusted by all and sundry in the town. I returned to Bill. "Right, cobber, you're on. When do we sail?"

"When can you be ready?"

"Where are we bound?"

"The Nab."

"The Nab? Well, let's see, that's about . . . 140 miles. If we get an easterly, say thirty-six hours; a westerly, say three days. How soon can your mates meet me there?"

"I'll ring 'em up to confirm, but off the bat I'd say yes in three days. It'll be ideal. Not much moon."

"O.K., you talk to them and if it's O.K., we'll sail tomorrow at dawn and be off the Nab for sure in three nights from now."

"Good on you, blue. Have another pint. Then I'll get on the blower and find out the score."

"Right. Hey, Bill, you married?"

"You must be jokin'!"

"Got a bird?"

"Yeah, all over the place." He grimaced. "Why?"

"Well, I've got a date with this tart in the caff down the road and I can nip down and see if she can bring one of her mates, if you like. They both look like goers."

"Sounds fair enough. What time?"

"See you back here at ten. How're you fixed?"

"Not too good, but I can buy a couple of gin and bitter lemons."

"That'll do."

He disappeared into the saloon bar where the telephone was located, at the posh end of the pub. At ten o'clock I reappeared with my girl and her friend. Being *gentlemen* that night, we took them into the saloon bar with its black leather sofa-seats and soft, pink lights, where the bank and bookmakers' clerks sat with their wives brushed and combed and not five bob between the lot of them. We soon had the lasses titteringly teased over Booth's Dry Gin so that by the time "Gentlemen Please" was called they would have willingly sailed with us for the Nab. Instead we hauled them around to the fairground and whooshed and whizzed our way into their eyes and thighs to the tune of the organola.

Merry with beer and gin, we made our satiated way back to the girls' rooming house. At twelve, as the clouds broke, the battle-ax who shepherded their morals locked tight the door as they wafted their way to wherever girls go when a door is locked. Bill and I wended stumbling weary steps through the winklestalls of Whitstable in the wet-streaming, windstormy night.

The old ferryboat man, the same one who had taken me ashore that afternoon, nine pints and two orgasms ago, said not a word. He took one look at Aussie Bill, then a fleeting glance at me. As we came alongside *Cresswell*, old Nelson wagged his tail, all the while staring at Bill through his eye.

"I know that bugger," said Bill, reaching up and patting him. "That's ol' Tansy Lee's dog!"

"Did you know Tansy, mate?"

"Know him? Course I did. I've had more pints with Tansy than you've had hot breakfasts!"

"Blimey, I used to sail with him. He was my first skipper!"

"Yeah? Where is he now then?"

"He kicked the bucket last August."

"Aboard?"

"No, he was ashore, sort of semiretired the month before."

"Christ, he wouldn't have liked that, Tris."

"Too bloody right, but he had a good send-off. They had practically every old salt on the coast at the wake."

"I'll bet that was a sight for sore eyes."

"So they say, Bill. Want a nightcap? There's some Black Label here."

"Good on you, mate, splash it out. We'll bloody soon replace that!"

And so, for an hour into the windy night, as the boat rocked away on the tide's changing, tales of Tansy were exchanged, while Nelson made a fuss of Bill, whom, of course, he remembered from five years back.

Bright as the bottom of a soldier's sock, we were up at dawn, with the anchor weighed and the mainsail filling to a good easterly. The wind and rogue's luck were with us, and we bowled down the Channel, after clawing our way around the North Foreland.

It was a magnificent, swift sail, that first run down the English Channel, and *Cresswell* made the Light on Selsey Bill in just forty-eight hours out of Whitstable. As we had a day to spare, I stood off about six miles and we whiled away the hours hove to, fishing. We caught two bream.

On the morning after, that is the day of the night of our rendezvous with "the Brethren," the wind swung around to the west, so we slowly started beating in to Spithead, the channel between the Isle of Wight and England. By dusk we had the old Nab Tower (an artificial island with a great round fortress, built during the Napoleonic Wars to guard the naval port of Portsmouth from French intrusions) in sight, and by ten in the evening we were hove to in the lee of the fort, showing two dim lights from the forestay.

At eleven we heard the noise of an engine close by, and

soon we were tied up alongside a motor fishing vessel, around eighty feet in length, with her engine softly keeping us head to sea in position while the soft-spoken Hebridean Scottish crew quietly and quickly transferred 150 cases of whisky onboard. These they distributed into *Cresswell* with an eye to her trim. They were obviously good seamen, but we knew no more about them, for they spoke only of the job. Their skipper, a chubby man of around sixty, with an Oxford accent and a peaked cap, shook my hand as the last cases were loaded and pressed an envelope into my pocket. "There's half there. Your destination is written down. Don't open it until you're half-way across the Channel. Head due south until you know the destination. You'll get the other half when the cases are ashore. Good luck!" The lines were cast off, and as we hoisted the mainsail, the fishing craft became a dark shadow, disappearing towards the east. *Cresswell*, with the extra weight of the booze, was well down in the water.

"Let's get away from here fast, Tris. She's probably got another rendezvous and won't want us around."

"Right. Hoist the jib and mizzen. We've got a good run out to Selsey Bill, then a smashing broad reach due south. Where d'you think the destination is?" I fingered the envelope, itching to open it.

"I don't know for sure, but if it's where I think it is, you've got no worries. I've been there a hundred times."

By two in the morning we had dropped Selsey Bill light astern and were leaping over the short Channel seas with every sail drawing. We showed no lights, and when there was no shipping around, it was an eerie feeling. The night was pitch black overcast, and *Cresswell* became a ghost ship on a sea of spirits.

By dawn I reckoned by the log we were half-way over the Channel, and I opened the envelope eagerly.

"What is it, Tris, Omonville?"

"Yeah, Omonville, how did you know?"

"I didn't, but the Major knows me, and I thought that's

where he'd send us. He knows I know that bay like the back of my hand."

"Good. How much water?"

"No problem, you can drive her straight onto the beach under mizzen and jib. It's soft sand. Chuck out the stern anchor as you go in. We'll be there at half tide up. In half an hour she'll be afloat again and we can kedge out."

"Pity we've no chart."

"Don't worry; I've got one in my head. I was there only a month ago last time. It's a cinch."

I thought, "By God, it has better be a cinch, or no voyage for me!" More like five years in a bloody French jail!

That evening we sighted the fishing boats off Cherbourg, and as dusk fell handed the sails and motored in among the fleet. The idea was that if a radar sight of us had been gained by the French customs or navy, they would think we were a fishing boat. We waited hove to, in the middle of about a hundred fishing craft, all with nets out, until around midnight, then slowly made our way out of the western end of the fleet. Anyone who has not done it cannot imagine the difficulties of such navigation; there is always the risk of getting the nets or lines wrapped around the propeller. Not only is this risky, as the propeller shaft might be bent by the nylon lines piling up as the propeller revolves, forcing the shaft out from the hull, but it also meant being seen and reported by the French fishermen. The only way out of that predicament would have been to ditch all the booze before the fast French police launches arrived on the scene. But we were lucky and careful, and so emerged unscathed, though the night was very dark and a fresh breeze, around twenty-five knots, was blowing from the west.

By two in the morning we were off the bay of Omonville. Down main, and, guided by Bill, who certainly did know the waters, for the entry was tricky, I eased her in, no lights, and as quiet as a wary witch. I soon spied the dull, silver beach right ahead, and when I judged we were fifty yards off, softly lowered the kedge anchor and slowly sailed the boat under mizzen and jib right onto the beach. She touched with a slight judder, then slid up over the silky sand and came to a halt. The moment she bumped, a car's headlamp blazed right in front of us for half a second, and we were soon boarded by six men led by another whom Bill knew. The cases were offloaded in less than ten minutes, while not one word was spoken except a few muttered exchanges between Bill and their chief. As the cases were offloaded, the boat was lightened and her stern lifted out of the sand, then her bow. Ten minutes after the Frenchmen had disappeared back into their wagon, we were hauling *Cresswell* out again to the kedge anchor. With the westerly wind blowing offshore, on the eastern side of the Cotentin peninsula, we were soon out in deep water with the main, mizzen, stays'l and jib pulling like dray horses, headed back for the French fishing fleet. As we came up to the outer craft of the immense fleet, we handed all sail, started the engine, and again chugged our way slowly through them. Then, after an hour of this, we broke through the northerly line of nets and were away, with all sail and the engine pushing, the wind fair for England.

"Good job!" said Bill, handing me an envelope with my other half of the earnings inside. *Cresswell* seemed to be quite at home, Nelson normal. They'd both done all this before.

"Yeah, two hundred quid will see me O.K. for two years."

"Fancy another run?"

"Not really, Bill. Too risky."

"We can ask for another destination."

"Where?"

"I know a good 'un, don't worry."

"When?"

"Before the moon grows."

"Next week?"

"If you like." He grinned. "Head for Weymouth, north-

northeast by north; drop me off there and I'll fix it up."

"Right. You're on, but mind you, Bill, this is the last one."

I then explained to him what my true intentions were, and after a first grimace of astonishment, he saw that I was serious.

"O.K., Tris, just this one. That'll at least give me enough to put down a deposit on my own boat. Once I've got that, I'll be right."

And that's how, when I set sail from Falmouth for Ireland, I had onboard two years' supply of canned and dried food, a new rubber dinghy, three years' supply of boat's stores, and three hundred pounds sterling.

After all these years, I do not regret having done this. It helped keep some otherwise impoverished Hebridean island going for a few more months; it brought the delights of good Scotch whisky to many a benighted Frenchman; it helped Aussie Bill (whose name I have changed because he is now a prominent figure in the worldwide charter boat scene) recoup his loss and find his feet; and it taught me that *Cresswell* was an extraordinary vessel.

After a few days in Falmouth, I got out the charts for the south and west of Ireland. Saint Brendan's land! Falmouth parish church bells rang as *Cresswell* cleared for Erin. "Oh God, our help in ages past. . . ." In the offing, Nelson sniffed the Atlantic breezes for traces of Chihuahuas away across the ocean in Mexico, from whence blew the wind. I sang my own song, for we were free with all the world before us.

PART II

Veni
(I came)

*Foolish men overlook and disregard their present blessings,
because their thoughts are always intent on the future, but the
wise keep the past clearly in mind through memory. To foolish
people the present, which allows us but the briefest instant to
touch it and then slips from our grasp, does not seem to be ours
or to belong to us at all. . . . With most people, a stupid and
ungrateful forgetfulness has possession of them, and wipes from
their minds every past accomplishment . . . breaking the* unity
of life, *which comes from the* weaving of the past into the
present. *For by separating yesterday from today, as if it were
something different, and tomorrow, likewise, as if it were not
the same as today, it soon makes what is now happening into
what has never taken place, by not recalling it. . . . So those who
do not keep or store in memory things that are past, but let them
float away, actually leave themselves vacant and empty daily,
while they cling to tomorrow, as if what happened last year or
day before yesterday or even yesterday mattered nothing to
them, or had not happened to them at all.*

This habit, then, is one interference with peace of mind.
(Emphasis added)

Plutarch, "On Peace of Mind," *Essays*.

Oh some they came from Boston
And some came from New York,
Some came from the County Down
And some from the County Cork,
Some they came from Kerry
And some came from Kildare;
But the boys who bate the Black 'n Tans
Were the boys from the County Clare!"

Irish Republican Song. The Black and Tans were British-recruited auxiliaries, a bad lot. The words' order changes according to the locale. I have arranged it for Corghain. Sung to the tune of "Wearing of the Green."

8

The Irish Islands

From Falmouth, my sail plan was to cross the St. George's Channel, as the English call the Celtic Sea, and make for a landfall in southwest Eire. The most likely haven to make for was Bantry Bay, about 250 miles' straight sailing. In this long, wide bay, on its northern shore, was the port of Castletown. But if the weather held good, I would hold on course for Knights Town, in the lee of Valentia Island, at the southern end of Dingle Bay. The first landfall, in both cases, would be the Fastnet Rock, a lonely pinnacle, surmounted by a lighthouse, twenty miles south of the southern shore of County Cork. I would be heading west-northwest-by-northwest, and as the prevailing winds which sweep into the British Isles are southwesterly, it meant I would be on a close reach, that is, with the wind coming from about sixty degrees off the bow. This was important, because *Cresswell* was an old-fashioned gaff-rigged ketch, and unlike the modern Marconi-rigged ocean-goers, she could not sail very efficiently with the wind anywhere ahead of fifty degrees off the bow.

Bear in mind also that these were the days before the self-steering wind-vane gear, as now shipped aboard ocean-cruising boats, was developed to its present efficiency. In *Cresswell* it was all hand-steering with the wind anywhere abaft (behind) the beam (right angles to the boat), except when she was closehauled or on a close reach

67

(that is, sailing with the wind ahead of the beam). Then, the sails could be trimmed and she would sail herself for long periods, holding the course with only minor adjustments to the helm. So in those conditions I always tried to shape a course where the wind would be slightly ahead of a direction at right angles to the boat's intended course.

If that sounds complicated in practice, imagine what a job it was to work out the courses. It was for this reason, among others, that my course for Iceland was laid out to pass outside the western periphery of the British Isles. To have gone directly up the east coast of England and Scotland would have been a thousand miles shorter, but in the North Sea the winds are both strong in force and fickle in direction. On the Celtic fringe they are strong, but mostly steady in direction. For this reason, the old sailing directions of Pliny had given this route. For this reason, too, the isolated Christian missions, the last remaining refuges of the light of Western civilization, had been able to communicate with each other during the centuries of savage destruction, blood, and ignorance which in Europe we call the Dark Ages. Now, replete with 184 twelve-ounce cans of corned beef, 100 pounds of porridge, 500 pounds of rice, 300-weight of potatoes, 200-weight of flour, 5 pounds of yeast, 50 pounds of tea, and 70 of sugar, 240 pounds of peanuts, 20 pounds of lemon powder, besides new fish-trolling gear, I was ready to take off.

In Plymouth, on a swift trip up by train from Falmouth, I had been able to obtain all the charts I would need of the Irish and Scottish Islands, the Faroes, Iceland, Eastern Greenland, Jan Mayen Island, and Svalbard. This had cost a tidy sum, but it was essential to have them.

On 7 May I worked *Cresswell* out of Falmouth, having cleared with the customs for Eire, and worked my way out against the wind, until, early on the morning of the eighth, my thirty-fifth birthday, I dropped the light of Lizard Head, Cornwall, astern. This was the last sight I would have of England for more than four years. As I made a kettle of tea I glanced out of the hatchway at the lightening dawn in the east over the ray of the Lizard Light. I threw Nelson a bone. "Well, old son, that's that. Ireland, here we come!"

The passage over the Celtic Sea took three days, because of a slight shift of the wind to due west on the second day. The weather was fair, with not much cloud or rain, so I was able to get good sights, which put Fastnet right on the starboard bow early in the false dawn. Beyond it I could see, as the sun rose slowly in the east behind me, the faraway, seemingly low hills and mountains of Ireland, rising, first black, then lightening to grey, purple, blue, and finally green, Irish green, emerald green indeed. The sea itself was blue green, topped with fresh frisking white horses, driven by the Gulf Stream wind, charging along to the rim of Ireland and beyond, to the roaring coasts of Cornwall and the singing shores of Wales.

On the port bow there was nothing between *Cresswell*, Nelson, and me but salt water all the way to Battery Point in New York. It sometimes happens, presumably due to abnormal activity of sunspots (as the gigantic hydrogen explosions spearing out millions of miles from the surface of the sun are called), that there is freak radio reception, and local radio broadcasts are bounced back to earth thousands of miles from the transmitter. On the night before my sight of the Skelligs, the holy sanctuaries of the Christian monks in the sixth century, ten miles or so off the coast of Kerry, I hove the boat to (that is, dropped the headsails and stopped her) while I made supper. The pressure cooker was steaming away merrily, with the spuds, corned beef, and Oxo gravy bubbling away inside, and I was fiddling with the dial of my small transistor radio receiver trying to find the shipping forecast from Niton radio station in the Isle of Wight. Suddenly I heard a conversation, loud and clear, between a *New York taxi driver* and his radio control office. There was no doubt about it, because he was heading for La Guardia Airport! The reception lasted quite clearly for several minutes, then static took over and I was back with Saint

Brendan in the sixth century, sailing in the moonless dark, off one of the oldest coasts in the world.

On the morning of the third day out, I sighted the two conical peaks of the Skelligs, the remains of two mountains lost to the ocean in some dim and distant past. I worked my way into the lee of the larger islet, which rises two hundred feet sheer out of the sea, and as the landing stage hove into clear view, let go the sheets, dropped the anchor over the bow, and looked around. There was no one in sight. I lowered the sails and waited a few minutes to make sure the anchor was biting properly, for the seabed around the islands is littered with rocks; then, admonishing Nelson to keep a good lookout, I went below to snatch some sleep. This having been my first solo voyage of any length in *Cresswell*, I had not slept much in three days, no more than ten minutes or so every few hours. I was crossing a heavily used shipping lane, and I did not yet know all of my craft's idiosyncrasies when she sailed herself; so, until I was sure of her steadiness, I was forced to keep watch on her. The weather was fine and springlike, with the wind blowing gently from behind the island and flat calm water in the roadstead.

It must have been mid-forenoon when I was awakened by Nelson barking and growling at the hatchway. "Pipe down, you son of a bitch," I growled in return, but he persisted and so I turned out of my bunk, donned my jersey, and made for the companionway.

"Halloo, there, halloo the boat riding there at anchor this fine day!"

I poked my head up over the hatch and gazed towards the shore. There, standing on the tiny landing stage, was a man in a peaked cap wearing pajamas and carpet slippers, holding a bicycle.

"Hello!" I shouted. He was about fifty yards away, but voices carry well over water, even against the breeze.

"Where are you hailing from in that fine, upstanding boat of yours?"

"England. Falmouth, England!" I shouted back.

"Arr, ye poor fellow, the shame of it! Come ashore and have a drink!"

"I'll be right with you!"

I had been towing my brand-new Avon rubber dinghy, and in three shakes of a gnat's ass I had the oars onboard and was paddling away for the jetty. The man in pajamas caught the painterline as I came alongside and tied it to a ring set in the stone.

"*Céad Míle Fáilte*," he said softly in Erse. "A thousand welcomes."

"*Ddwy Da*," replied I in Welsh. "A good day to you."

"Is it Saxon you are?"

"Welsh."

"Corrigan's the name." He spoke now in English. "I'm the keeper here, and sure it's not a soul I've seen for the three weeks past of my life. Is there no one with you?" He was a large, hefty man, about fifty, with Viking blue eyes.

"Just the dog."

"Bejasus, he earns a fine keep for himself. He'd guard a tinker."

"He's been at sea most of his life. He's used to it and knows what to do." I climbed onto the jetty and took his proffered hand.

"Did you ever see the like of such? Now, it's up the brew we'll be climbin' an' you can tell me of the news. Are there wars still burning down the world?" His eyes saddened.

"Nothing big."

"There's the pity of it. A fine thing, wars. Sure they bring good pensions to half the widows of Ireland!"

"Have you no radio?" I asked him as we puffed our way up the finely paved but narrow concrete path to the lighthouse perched a hundred feet above the sea.

"Sure, Flaherty's thinkin' of installin' one but it's me against it, what with all the strange things comin' out of the blue sky and the gulls screamin' their heads off in pain at all the human misery, what with all the riots and strikes and wars goin' on."

"I thought you said wars were a fine thing?"

"Sure, and so they are, as long as the birds do be left in peace."

"That's a thought," I said. Arguing with a Gaelic Celt is always an exercise in convoluted geometry fit to make the Sermon on the Mount sound like the concept of relativity.

Once in the lighthouse cottage, low, lime-washed walls and slated roof, with kettle singing on the peat-burning, black-polished stove and mugs of tea to hand (for the Western Irish and Scots are tremendous tea drinkers), I addressed myself to Corghain, as Corrigan was known in his native tongue.

"How is this island called Skellig Michael? Who was Michael?"

"Begab, it's terrible pagans you must be in the wild land of Wales, if you don't know that the chief of all the angels and everythin' so high it would touch the foot of Almighty God"—he crossed himself swiftly—"is Michael himself with his flamin' sword and terrible eyes."

I crossed over to the open door, the one on the side away from the wind, and looked down onto the sea, a hundred feet below. *Cresswell* was sitting down there in the green water over the black shadows of rock patches, like a toy boat. I saw Nelson, a mere dot, padding his way round and round the deck. In the near distance, a mile or so away, rested the perfect cone of Little Skellig, grey and blue, with the green grey Atlantic breakers heaving mightily against its symmetric shore.

At eye level and above me, in the blue sky tempered by fat cumulus clouds spawned by the Azores High a thousand miles to the southwest, wheeled hundreds of fulmar petrels, surely, with the albatross, the most beautifully moving creatures in the whole natural world. With the faintest movement of their wings, they glided onto the ocean airstreams and soared up, up, a thousand feet or more to hover like a song of joy and love. Then their wings sagged and down they went, right down to the neck bristles of the Atlantic seas heaving far below. It was a sight of holy wonder.

"What are the round huts up there on the cliff face?" I asked Corghain. They were shaped like beehives.

"The cells that the monks lived in in the old times. Sure, when all hell was loose upon the world it's to here they came, and wasn't King Olaf of Norway himself christened here on this very island?"

"When was that?"

"Long, long ago, before the English came,"—he spoke as if it were yesterday that Gilbert, Raleigh and Cromwell had brought bloody murder to Erin—"when the wild Norsemen changed their ways and became themselves a blessin' to God."

We climbed on up the steep narrow path cut into the face of the sheer cliff and came at last to two pinnacles on the peak, steep, needlelike crags, one with a hole about three feet diameter passing straight through it horizontally. Corghain told me to pass myself through the hole and lean over the crevice between them to kiss the rock on the other side. "It'll leave you never short of a word in your head," said he.

Once my head passed through the hole I found myself looking straight down a *two-hundred-foot drop*, to where great Atlantic rollers crashed into a split cutting almost right through the island. The sight was enough to make me dizzy, but I persevered and leaned right over the four-foot gap, seemingly hanging between heaven and earth, and brushed the hard, cold rock on the other side with my lips. As I wriggled back to Corghain and safety, he said, "Sure, and it's the storyteller you are now even though it was myself that was thinkin' you were before you stepped your foot on this shore!" I was sweating, for I'd been swinging out there in space supported only to the thighs, with Corghain sitting on my feet.

Shaken, I trod down the hill with Corghain still telling me

tales, for he was a man of the long memory.

"Do you get a lot of fog around here?" I asked him.

"Aye, we do, and in the winter it's a fog so thick you could poke your finger in it and leave a hole. Sure and all, before the German war, Flaherty, whose younger brother's in America and who has great, grand ideas that would turn a hare into a fine racehorse, installed the new electric fog signal house."

"Look." He pointed down, far below, to a small concrete hut perched over the great tumbled rocks of the shore where the ocean breakers broke in white spume under the soughing wind. "Look, you see, that's the place. In the old days we'd go down there in a fog, feelin' our way with nothin' but suspended vapor before our eyes and little else but faith in the Lord behind them, and set off the maroons [explosive fog signals—like big fireworks] by hand. Three hundred of the wild explosive cartridges we have in there. Well, Flaherty, whose older brother is no less than an inspector on the trams of Dublin City itself, said that this was too slow and dangerous, so he brought this little spalpeen of a fellow with his suit and tie, lookin' like he dug money out of the sands of Kerry, and his gossoon to carry all the wires and paraphernalia, batteries and such like. Sure you would have thought it was Thomas Edison himself come for a holiday! Then they set up the wires down the holy cliff of Archangel Michael, so we could set off the maroons one at a time from the cottage. Flaherty to me he said that this would preserve our lives until the Second Comin', with no more perilous scramblin' down the cliff, or risk of blowin' ourselves directly into the presence of the good Lord himself."

"That was a good idea."

"Sure, and it was, and would you not expect it to be, Flaherty's brother bein' in Boston and all and the Dublin tramways behind him?" He puffed on his short pipe as the cottage came into view below us. "But they got a sort shirk-it, they called it."

"A what?"

"A sort shirk-it."

"And what happened?"

"Well, I put my finger to the pressin' thing on the box and Holy Mother of God," he crossed himself, "if the whole three hundred maroons didn't blow up all at the same time with an explosion so mighty it almost lifted the island right out of the sea!" His eyebrows shot up above his sparkling blue eyes.

"What did the Dublin men do then, Corghain?"

"Ten Hail Marys, two mugs of tea, and off to the mainland they went. Flaherty brought over another three hundred maroons, which we still set off in God's way without fancy wires and boxes. But never a sight I had again of the spalpeen, nor his gossoon, and that was all of twenty years' past."

We sat for a while in the whitewashed living room of his cottage, with the box-bed set in the wall by the fireplace and the picture of Patrick Pearse, the poet who gave labor to Irish independence, gazing with the look of crucified Christ from the wall and a calendar from Boston over the door.

"And where is it you go from here, Tristan?"

"I'm thinking of Waterville Spunkane, in Ballinskelligs Bay, for I must see the police and enter Ireland legally."

"Ahh, they'll not miss a paper or two from a good man like yourself. Look, why don't you head for the Blaskets. I've good friends there, and Tom Keanan's king of it all. He'll look after you as I look after the light."

"Well, Corghain, the weather looks promising enough, and it's only fifty miles, so that's what I'll do. We'll write down the names of your friends, and it's them I'll see when I fetch the Blaskets."

Corghain walked down the hill with me to the jetty, still puffing on his pipe. "A fine craft you have there, and God go with you and calm the waters" were his last words as I pulled away from the jetty. Nelson was pleased to see me safe back onboard. We would sail that evening after tea and make a night passage to the Blasket Islands, the next parish to America!

They have considerable knowledge of the stars, and their motions, and the dimensions of the earth, and the Universe around. Also of science in general, and of the powers and spheres of influence of the immortal gods. These subjects they debate, and also teach to their young students.

Julius Caesar, *De bello Gallico* VI. 14—
"Description of the Celtic Druids."

9

The Old Times

The radio weather forecast from Niton was good, and in the western approaches to the British Isles this is more the exception than the rule. "Sea areas Shannon, Fastnet, Land's End, winds moderate to fresh, increasing to gale force in twenty-four hours." It was time to strike while the iron was cold—the cruel cold blasts of Atlantic iron, which in the waters of that world are enough to daunt Finn McCool himself. Like a long, steady procession of Inquisition torture-masters, the sweeping black clouds of the low-pressure, anticyclonic gales roll in from the southwest, winter and summer, to breed a race of seamen and to sound a bass dirge to the rising descant of Celtic song, and draw a curtain of blinding energy and mighty force across the drift of Gaelic dreams.

Hauling a sixty-pound anchor with its arresting chain is always a chore, but soon it was lashed down on the foredeck, the jewel green moss of Saint Michael's seabed clinging to it. Up jib, up staysail, and away, waving to Corghain as he slowly clambered the track to his eyrie and the portrait of Patrick Pearse, with the fulmar petrels hovering on the bellied edges of the clouds high above. On the fishing line I had left hanging over the stern was a fine shiny pollock, about eight pounds, which, before you could say "Holy Mother of God," was in the pressure cooker and sizzling away on the stove for supper. I grabbed the wheel and headed out to the offing, to pass well clear of the Dursey Islands and the Bull Rock, where many a fine mariner over the centuries has taken leave of this world, for this is the weather-edge of Europe, the receiving end of all the Atlantic furies. It was not for nothing that Shannon Airport was built on the western end of Ireland. The tail winds of the Atlantic all push home here.

The night descended with stars steady and bright peeping through the scudding black clouds and a half-moon rising astern. As I was off a lee shore, I stayed on deck to fondle the kicking wheel and listen to the wind softly wailing in the shrouds, and to glimpse, now and then, lonely calling lights, signals of innocent intent, low on the distant black shore of Ireland. And I recalled what I had learned of the Old Times, before history had been trimmed to suit the ambitions of Rome and her heirs.

Around three thousand years ago and more a people had lived in the west of Europe, the people who built the accurate Stonehenge solstice computer. Dark, with prominent noses, lithe, intelligent, worshiping the life force itself. Their descendants, clearly recognizable from other strains around them, still endure in the wild places on the edge of the continent—the mountain fastnesses of Northern Scotland, Wales, the Irish Islands, parts of Cornwall and Brittany. These people were called, in Ireland, the Goidels, or Gaels; in Britain, the Brythonics.

About twenty-five hundred years ago, into their midst came a great wave of wandering fair-haired, blue-eyed nomads from northern Persia and Afghanistan—the Gaulish-Celts. When the Gaulish-Celts reached what is now Rumania, they split off into three main branches. One turned southeast down through Turkey and the Middle East, to mix with the Semites and become the Phoenicians. Others pushed on into North Africa to leave behind a racial strain known as Berbers, before crossing north over the Strait of Gibraltar into Spain (Iberia) to form the blood base of the nations of Portugal, Aragon, and Castile. Some of these Celto-Iberians, about 800 B.C., under one of the first known ocean navigators, Mabo, pushed on across the western ocean to the West Indies and America, there to establish Punic colonies and become the ancestors (at least by language) of the Pima Indians of New Mexico. The second stream of Gaulish-Celts turned directly south into the Greek peninsula and founded the great civilization of which the modern western world is the inheritor. The third stream pushed on due west across the plains and mountains of Europe, leaving behind pockets in Austria and Switzerland, to become the Gauls of France. From France other Gaulish-Celts passed on into the British Isles and, mixing with the Brythonic Goidel tribes, became the Cymru of Wales and Picts and Scots of Northern Ireland and Scotland. The Goidel Celts pushed out of England and Wales became the Erse of Ireland.

With Gaulish-Celtic intelligence overlaid onto the dreaming imagination of the Goidel-Brythonics of Western Europe, a great culture with widespread communications was developed, a loose confederation of states, in the ancient Greek style, with high priests, called *vates*, in charge of religion, kings, princes, and druids in secular command. To imagine that when Julius Caesar invaded Gaul he was fighting blue-painted savages is foolish. He in fact managed to overcome, and only by the skin of his teeth, a highly organized alliance of more-or-less democratic states peopled by a race in a state of civilization not far short of Rome itself, with a system of communications by land and sea, as good as, if not superior to, that of the Mediterranean folk. The Celts were sailing as far afield as present-day Morocco in the south, Germany in the east, America in the west, and the then much warmer Iceland in the north.

When an invading army subdues a country, the majority of the inhabitants of that country remain as they were before the conquest. So with Britain during the so-called Roman times. Ninety-five percent of the population were Brito-Celt during the Roman occupation; ninety percent after the Norman Conquest; and probably eighty percent now, even after all the successive inroads by continentals and Scandinavians. But in four areas the population always was, and still is, ninety-nine percent Celtic—North Wales, the Irish Islands, the remote fastnesses of the Scottish Highlands, and Brittany.

As early as 330 B.C., Pytheas of Massalia (now Marseille) sailed westward through the Mediterranean to the great Phoenician port of Gades (the modern Cádiz). There he transferred to a Gaelic curragh, a great ocean-worthy vessel over a hundred feet long, built of hides stretched over a wooden frame, even more sea-fit than the oar-and-sail-propelled galleys of the eastern Mediterranean. From Gades the ocean venturers of the western edge of the world sailed northwards, calling at the Celtic port of Vigo and the island of Oléron, on the west coast of Gaul, near the present-day port of La Rochelle. In those far-off days, before the might of Rome was hurled across the Rubicon, Oléron was a center of a maritime activity as important as Venice and Genoa were to become fifteen hundred years later, after the tide of barbaric ignorance had at last subsided in Europe.

Here, at Oléron, the first internationally respected laws of the sea were drawn up between maritime merchants from as far afield as the Baltic, Iceland, Morocco, the northeast coast of America, and Phoenician Lebanon. Through Oléron passed southward-bound around the Gibraltar Strait, or overland across Gaul to the Mediterranean Phoenician port of Massalia, wool, tin and gold, ambergris and walrus tusks and sweet-scented pine needles from the far-flung lands of the Northern and Western Celtic people in Iceland and America. From as far north as the Faroes and Scotland came the wools and ambergris, also from the Baltic; while from Cornwall, Ireland, and Wales, as well as England, came hundreds of cargo vessels every year in the spring and summer, bearing gold, tin, and woad dyes, much prized in Lebanon and Persia. In the great long

warehouses of Oléron and Gades, these goods were exchanged for the fine woven silks, the aromatic scents, the
wine and spices from the Mediterranean and the East, by
Greek and Phoenician sailors, some of whom, calloused
and wise in the ways of the sea, had ranged as far afield to
the east as Arabia, Ceylon, Mozambique, and Borneo, and
who told fantastic tales of sandy deserts, coal black people,
and yellow men with slanted eyes living in unimaginable
splendor, and of a land of gold and silver far to the east of
Borneo. The Celts, in their turn, told of a country way to the
north where hot water spewed out of the ground and
islands were born out of the sea, only to die again in clouds
of steam. They told stories of Lugh, the god of light, born on
the island of Tory, off the kingdom of Terganaill (Donegal),
who made far-ranging journeys into Europe with his
mighty spear which he could hurl fifteen miles, who was
the grandson of Balor, king of the Formorians, and who
founded the cities of London (Londinium), Leyden
(Lugudunum) in modern-day Holland, and Lyons, far
away in eastern Gaul. They told tales of Dedaanan, the king
of the Firbolgs, and his enemy, the magical man with three
legs called Manaanan who ranged as far as the Isle of Man
and Etrusca in Italy, where his sign, the triskelion (three
legs), is still in use, and who, long, long before, with his
great army, "rode the white horses" across the sea from
Man to Ireland to defeat the Firbolgs at the battle of Moy-
tura. And to this day, when the Atlantic winds sough
across the blue green waters of the ocean, sailing men speak
of the driven seas as "white horses."

It was with these storytelling sailors that Pytheas set off
northward on his voyage to Thule, the end of the world,
calling first at the busy Eirean port where now stands the
city of Limerick. They sailed north through the Faroes, six
days' hard sailing, ever to the north, until they sighted the
spouting volcanoes and devil-torn rocks of Thule—Iceland.
There they picked up a cargo of ambergris and walrus
tusks, gathered by Celts temporarily settled in that lonely

outpost of the world, and then returned south again. It is perfectly obvious from Pytheas's account that this was no voyage of exploration, but a merchant-venture along an old established trade route.

In the night watches, as the curragh ploughed north, the Gaelic sailors from the Irish Islands and the rocky coast of Wales told Pytheas tales of *Iarghal*, "the land beyond the sunset" (later known in low Latin, even to the Irish and Welsh fighting to stay outside the Roman Empire, as Hy-Brasil), the enchanted land westward across the ocean, the Land of the Dead, to which the spirits of the Gaels sailed across the watery wastes of the Atlantic. Tales were told by men who had actually seen this land; who, after many weeks of hard voyaging, had sighted the land in the west far, far away; who had landed and seen the *Iarghaltes*, "the Sundowners," *red men of the redland,* and who had stayed with them and traded with them for tusks and furs. They had made their way back across the ocean to Erin and to Cymru (Wales), and, as old men, told the tales over the tribal fires of peat on the cold winter nights when the sea was too wild for the curraghs to sail. And so Pytheas learned of the Celtic colonies of North America, the land of *Iarghal*, that is, if he did not already know about them.

So the stories passed back to Phoenicia, where, along with all other knowledge of distant parts of the world, they were locked away until Phoenician power shifted, a millenium and a half later, to Venice and Genoa. In tattered scraps, these stories were handed down among families anciently rooted in Lebanon, like that of Christopher Columbus. (Columbus found an Irish sailor, living in Galway, who had seen the "redland" far to the west. This Irish-Gael sailed west with Columbus in the Santa Maria, and I have seen the stone slab on which his memory is kept in the church of Saint Nicholas in Galway town. He had seen the "red men" in the land of the sunset, *Iarghal*, in 1478!)

When Caesar entered Gaul with his army to seize the land now known as France and to cross the Channel to tackle the heart-islands of the Celts, the old sea passages were still maintained, for the Mediterranean sailors of Rome were no match for the Atlantic-hardened mariners of the West. Caesar's invasion force sailing for Britain in early 55 B.C., in fact, encountered a British fleet of 220 seagoing vessels in the Channel. A sudden calm in the wind enabled the Roman galleys, commanded by Brutus, with slaves at the oars, to drive alongside the great curraghs and board them with overwhelming hordes of foot soldiers. A far cry from the usual story of the "civilized" Romans landing unchallenged on an island populated by primitive, blue-painted savages! What better camouflage is there for a night attack than blue woad dye?

Rome's power extended as far as the eye could see from the land, and as far as the foothills of the mountains of Wales and Scotland. There, on the high ocean seas and the remote broken rises, the tide of the Roman Empire beat itself for 450 years, but made few inroads. The Celtic sea trade, from Iceland and Germany, though drastically diminished, continued. With Rome astride the ocean road to Cádiz, the American trade died, delaying, for good or ill, the arrival of Christianity on that continent for fifteen hundred years. The far-flung, lonely Celtic outposts of *Iarghal* were cut off from Europe, their folk to mix with the Amerindian *Iarghaltes*, and to become part of the Algonquin tribes. From then on, legends record only isolated voyages across the Atlantic, such as the Irish Saint Brendan's in the sixth century and the Welsh Prince Madoc in the twelfth century.

About 290 years after the birth of Christ, the Roman governor of England, Carausius, sent a mighty fleet to sail completely around the British Isles, and then to Iceland, carrying a legion to raid Gaelic settlements in that remote land, as well as the coasts of the wild Picts in Northern Scotland and the Erse of Ireland. The only relics ever found of this expedition, apart from the written accounts, are two Roman coins recovered from the seabed at Bragoarvellir and one at Hvalnes, both sites on the southeast coast of Iceland.

As is well known, when an invading army subdues a country, the effect on the culture and racial composition of the people is mainly felt only among the high and mighty. The common people, the vast majority, are not changed one whit. This is especially so among the seafaring folk of the conquered country. They are brought up on local sea lore and traditions. Once the conqueror is onboard their craft, in their sea, he is present on the sufferance of the native, unless the conqueror is himself a seaman from a hard-weather land. This the Romans were not. The sailors of Carausius's fleet must have been Celts. Their sailing masters knew very well the coasts and the passages as far as the shores of Iceland.

As the military power of Rome waned in Western Europe during the violent incursions of the Goths and the Teutons, so the assault of the Roman Christian church on the militarily unconquered Celtic lands of Wales and Ireland increased. Finally, Saint Patrick, a Welsh Christian, entered Ireland and captured the romantic Irish soul.

With the coming of the Saxons, Angles, and Jutes into England in the fifth century from the fog-bound marshes of North Germany, the Celts were again cut off from land communication with the Mediterranean, the center of world power. But the old sea trade went on and still the curraghs ploughed the deep seas, finding their way by the sun, moon, and stars, while back at home, in Wales, Ireland, and Scotland, the Teutons were resisted. But when the Goths reached Cádiz, the sea roads to Rome were cut, and Christian Ireland and Wales were separated from the main body of their new religious and cultural sources in the Mediterranean. But sea travel still continued between Brittany, Ireland, Wales, and Iceland.

In those days, the northern latitudes were a good deal warmer than they are now. It is estimated up to five degrees Fahrenheit on the average. Certainly, from all accounts, the ocean weather was kinder, and no tales of icefloes or bergs are found in the old Celtic stories and very few in the Norse sagas, even of Greenland and Labrador.

While a wary "detente" had been reached between the Celt and the Saxon during the seventh century, far away across the North Sea, in Norway, the gradual immigration of people across the mountains from Sweden, together with a tremendous increase in the birthrate, had caused the peaceful farmers in the *vikke,* as the remote, tiny homesteads at the inner ends of the deep fiords were called, to turn to fishing the sea for food, and then to raiding each other's miserable plots. In the course of this warring, a type of craft was developed, the *karfi,* which made full use of the excellent timber readily available and of the bitter experiences gained over the years from the rough seas of that country. The *karfi* was a vessel about forty feet long, double-ended, with excellent coastal characteristics. It could deal with the steep heavy seas in rough weather, it could sail fast in the calm waters behind the long coastal island leads, and it could be beached easily for a raid or upon returning home with loot.

From the *karfi,* the next step forward was the *hafskip*, or, as it was more commonly known, the *knarr*. This was the much longer, wider, oceangoing "longship." It was, in contrast to the Celtic curragh, like comparing a Maserati to a Model T. It was fast, and it was big enough to carry thirty men with all their battle gear and provisions; it was shallow and could be sailed up rivers deep into enemy territory. The average knarr was eighty feet long, nineteen feet beam (providing excellent stability), and about four-and-a-half feet draft amidships. From the bottom of the keel to the top of the gunwale, the hull was about seven feet high.

Tents were erected when the knarr hove-to at night. The Vikings (as the vikke farmers were known) had no rudders or compass; steering was by a large sweep oar over the starboard (steer-board) quarter, and navigation was by the stars and sun for latitude. The longitude was mainly guessed at. From Norway, it was "sail into the setting sun for five days, then turn left for Britain and Europe, right for Iceland." It was as crude as that. Though we hear of all the successful Viking voyages, we have no idea how many were lost in the ocean. The number must have been great. With the bad weather in their area, I would hazard a guess of probably thirty percent losses.

Once the Norsemen had the knarr, they let loose upon all of northern Europe, and indeed as far round the continent as the shores of Morocco, a sea invasion of burning, looting, murder, and rapine unique in mankind's long history of warfare. In the process, they cut the Celtic sea roads and invaded most of the Gaelic lands. They ravaged England, France, Scotland, and Ireland. Only in three places were they successfully resisted—North Wales, Brittany, and a few of the Irish and Scottish Islands. These became small isolated centers of the old Celtic culture, overlaid with remnants of Greek and Roman civilization and ancient knowledge—a light kept flickering fitfully, but faithfully, by the Christian monks and anchorites hidden away in almost inaccessible fastnesses and islands, from the volcanic desert of the Vatnajökull of Iceland in the north, to the rocky, steep inlets of Brittany, protected by the terrible tides of that shore. For the darkest three hundred years in Western man's history, the tiny lamps flickered; some extinguished only to be lit again on yet another storm-tossed rock, like Tory, Iona, and Barra; some to die forever. During three dark centuries these selfless, faithful Celts held the sum total of Western man's culture in their hands.

As *Cresswell* heaved and sloughed her way through the kindly night, with St. Finan's Bay and Puffin Island under the lee, I thought of these tales of the sea empire of the Gaels. Here I was passing through one of the crossroads of the ancient world, a world of light and magic and beauty, a world of delightful dreams as well as terrifying nightmares, on the track of a race of people, *my people*, who worshiped the life force not only in living things such as the oak tree and the elder, the ash and the thorn, but in the rocks of the world and the sigh of the wind and the thunderous crashes of the mighty ocean on the shores of their homes. And I thought of the curtain of lies cast upon the world in the cause of goodness by the Christian missionaries, who drummed into the ears of the magical folk for centuries the incessant untruth that nothing before the Son of God was good. That all before Jesus was sin and ignorance and savagery, that all was evil, that the living spirit of the wind and the oceans, of the waving heather on the soul-hills was evil. How the memory of the Celtic ways, of their stories and art, full of love and terror, was cast into the first doorway of hell so that men's minds could be chained to the cross. And how the resulting cleavage of the Celtic mind is still, to this very day, shown in rivers of terror and violence in the back streets of bloody Belfast.

Ever since the Norman conquest of England, and especially after the loss of the Plantagenet domains in France, the aim of the English Power has been to dominate Europe, and especially Northwest Europe. The method has at all times been to secure a position from which the balance of power could be held, making sure that no one country on the continent became powerful enough, militarily or economically, to dominate any two other European countries.

With the shift of economic power from the Mediterranean shores to Northwest Europe after the great sea explorations of the fifteenth and sixteenth centuries, the geographical situation of Britain dictated an enormous increase in her political power, for she sits fair and square across the sea routes of the most powerful nations of the continent, and at that time, of the world. From the north of Scotland you can gaze out to sea, north and eastward, and know that you are looking at Iceland and Norway. Move south and in turn you look towards Denmark, Germany, Holland, Belgium, France, and Spain. Over very short lines of communication, the English could reach out and throttle the ocean throats of all these countries.

There was, however, only one Achilles' heel—Ireland. *Whoever controls the west coast of Ireland controls the sea approaches to Northwest Europe.* Cromwell knew this full well; he was the originator of modern sea power. The Spanish, the Dutch, the French, the Italians, the Germans also knew it, and for centuries their aim was to foment revolt among the Irish Catholics to keep England looking over her shoulder and thus divert her attention.

Nowadays the world runs on oil. Oil is moved in supertankers which are deep-draught vessels. The seas around Northwest Europe are shallow. The supertankers cannot enter the narrow seas. Western Ireland has fine, extensive, natural, deep-water ports. In the next decade or two, a great percentage of European industry will be drinking oil coming through the Irish gullet. Whoever controls Ireland will, to a large extent, control North-European industry; thus the shipment of arms to the IRA and the Protestant extremists of Ulster from *Libya*, of all places!

But to the English, God is an Englishman, and so he revealed to them the extensive oil deposits under the North Sea. And once again the Irish threat is neutralized, while Irishmen kill and maim each other for foreign causes of which they know nothing and care less. Pawns in a power game. The Celt can see and touch the stars, but when he looks at his feet he is lost unless he tries to understand himself.

As the light on Bray Head, Valentia Island, dropped down over the horizon over *Cresswell*'s bucking starboard quarter, and as the shimmer of the loom of Great Blasket light shivered under the stars ahead, I recalled the stories of long ago. Now I was sailing one of the oldest trade routes in the world, where every rock, every blade of grass, every tiny islet had its own legend of wonder, delight, bloody death, heroic blunders, and magic. The magic of the youth of the world! The magic of innocence, as it was before the veil was ripped asunder and the blanket of sin was flung over the worship of life!

On the eighteenth day of December,
In nineteen-twenty-two,
The Tans in their big Crossley tender
Outside of the town of Macroom,
But the boys of the village were waiting,
With hand grenades primed on the spot,
And the Irish Republican Army—
Put paid to the whole fuckin' lot!

Irish song (I suspect, because of the last line,
it originates in Dublin or Liverpool—I never
heard an Irishman, outside Dublin and
Belfast, use so-called obscenity in Ireland).

10

The Next Parish to America

The sight around me, as the dawn shone over Dingle Bay, was astonishingly beautiful. Away to the east, across silver-shining water (though fairly rough, for the Irish Atlantic is not Long Island Sound, and every view is well earned the hard way), rose a line of piled mountains, Macgillycuddy's Reeks, lifting black, shattered elbows into the heartbroken sky. The shores were misty with Gaelic modesty and the Reeks seemed to be borne in the air by some mighty unknown force.

To the north lay my destination, the Blasket Islands, sprawling low out into the ocean in gallant defiance of all the laws of gravity. There is an optical illusion here which makes the horizon seem to run downhill to the west. It looked as if the Blaskets were trying to escape from Erin. The island furthest to the west, Inishtooskert, was uninhabited. It lay slinking on the surface of the sea, blue green below its grey, scaly skin, with the sun shining on it betimes as the clouds passed over on their way to take rain to England. On the inshore side of Inishtooskert lay the main island of the Blaskets, Slievedonagh; and behind it, seeming to claw the ocean like the talons of a great eagle, the headland of Sybil Head and the Three Sisters, which are as far as Ireland flings herself after the setting sun.

As I had no detailed chart of the islands, and as navigation among the reefs and rocks is tricky, I clambered forward on the heaving deck and handed the jib and staysail. This was always hazardous in *Cresswell*, because her bow had a whaleback deck, rounded, to shudder off the heavy seas breaking over her. Consequently, the actual treadway of the foredeck was tiny in area, no more than a triangle of about six square feet. But I had rigged good, hefty guard-rails all around the boat, and while on the bow they were only a foot or so above the gunwale to allow the headsails to pass over them when the boat was beating to windward, if I kept low, on my knees, I could manage well enough. Not being able to swim since my spine was damaged in Aden, I had always to be careful on any boat in motion. I could, and still can, float all right, but I cannot manage the kicking motion of swimming; and if I fell over the side, the chances were that the boat would, with her sails balanced to govern her course, carry on away from me.

With the headsails dropped down on deck and lashed to the hand rails, *Cresswell* rode head to wind and sea under her mainsail and mizzen, and even in those lively eight-foot waves off Dingle Bay she was steady enough for me to make a breakfast of fried corned beef and eggs. This is a very simple, easy meal, and Nelson loved it. Some of the pollock from the night before was left, and so as there would not be much time for lunch (there never is when you enter a haven in mid-forenoon), we scoffed that as well, and I washed the lot down with a pint mug of hot tea.

After breakfast I swilled down the decks and squared up all the gear above and below. I am very reluctant to enter any port with an untidy-looking craft. It's impolite to on-lookers, if there are any, and if there are not, it's still unseamanlike. Besides, while carrying out these cleaning chores, there's time to think about the passage in, and whether all the gear is in place.

After I had a good swill and scrub around the decks and a sweep-out below (it's surprising how scruffy a boat be-comes, especially if she's coastal-passage-making, with the company landing ashore often), I drank another mug of tea, smoked a cigarette, and thought for half an hour. I could plainly see the roadstead between Slievedonagh and Inishtooskert, where, in 1588, one of the largest ships of the Spanish Armada, *Nuestra Señora del Rosario*, "Our Lady of the Rosary," a great lumbering galleon of one thousand tons, with the bastard son of King Philip of Spain on board, went to anchor in the calm water of Blasket Sound. During the night a great storm rose out of the southwest, leaving the galleon completely open to the weather. Her anchors dragged in that terrible sea, and she beat herself to death on the fierce fangs of the Three Sisters. King Philip's bastard son is buried in the graveyard at Vicarstown. The intention, when the Armada sailed in pomp and glory from Cádiz, was that he would become the king of Spain's viceroy in Northern England. Instead he got six feet by three of Irish sod in the rocks of Kerry.

A lot of people wonder why it was that so many of the ships of the Spanish Armada were wrecked on the West Coast of Ireland. If we look at maps of Ireland for the period, the reason is soon obvious. On all of the maps at the time of the Armada, the West Coast is shown as a straight line running north to south, with just one inlet, the great bay of Galway, whereas in reality it is a very jagged coastline, a continuous series of rocky headlands flung out far to the west of the general trend of the coast. The Spanish fleet sighted Ireland, and from the first northern headland they came to, sailed due south, straight into the rocks. The survivors of the Armada in Ireland were very few indeed. The word was out that they must be slaughtered to a man, and slaughtered they were, not only by the English but by the Irish too. Great was the amount of loot taken from the ships of His Most Catholic Majesty. Eight years before the Armada sailed, two Spanish ships had sailed for Smerwick Harbor in County Kerry, to foster revolt among the Irish. Well informed by the Irish, the English lord deputy for Ireland, Lord Grey, along with his friend and ally, Sir Walter Raleigh, intercepted the ships, took six hundred

Spanish and Italian prisoners, and on the heights of Sybil Head, had them all massacred and cast from the dizzy cliffs into the raging seas a thousand feet below. Meanwhile, back in the courts of the Estoril and Hampton Court Palace, the spinets tinkled and bejeweled feet twinkled.

There is the impression that very dark-featured folk from the West of Ireland, Wales, and Scotland are the descendants of survivors of the Armada. I very much doubt it. They are much more likely remnants of the old pre-Celtic folk who inhabited the lands five thousand years ago. Their general characteristics are wiriness, occasional frenetic energy, imagination to the extremes, and they are mostly long-headed with prominent noses. This type is very common in the Irish Islands, Cornwall, Wales, and some of the Hebrides. Others may be descendants of Iberian merchants who established themselves on the coast of Ireland in the sixteenth and seventeenth centuries, but this would be in the large towns and ports of the mainland, certainly not on the islands or in Wales.

All the while I was thinking of these things, I was also thanking the gods for the easy and safe passage across the Celtic Sea, which had brought me beyond the ken of the French Customs. They'd have a job to catch me now. *Cresswell* had a good run to the nor'rard ahead of her, southwesterly winds on the port quarter, and after I departed the Blaskets she made good time. That was important, for I wanted to be off Iceland early in the summer in order to sight as much as I could before the winter set in with its raging gales.

By mid-forenoon, carefully looking out for rocks and shoals, I had worked my way inside the Blasket Sound until I was within sight of the harbor of Slievedonagh. There, as I didn't know the depths, and there were no large craft lying inside the tiny creek, I hove to again. The wind was freshening, girding its loins for the gale due that night, so I started the engine and handed all sail. Very shortly, a small curragh came alongside, with two men in it. The boat was of tarred canvas stretched over bent wood frames. She was about fifteen feet long and had a cuddy fore and aft. She looked very seaworthy indeed, and the men in her knew how to handle their oars, though they had hardly any blades. They rowed out to *Cresswell* at a good speed with the curragh slicing the waters, yet the blades seemed to glide gently and slowly. One of the men was large-boned, but not heavy, while the other was slight and very dark, almost like an East Indian or a gypsy.

"*Céad Míle Fáilte*," they both said in low, gentle tones.

"A very good day to you," I replied. Nelson was fascinated. They had fish in the curragh.

"A fine craft ye have there. Is it Belfast ye're from?" asked the larger man.

"The boat's from London, but I'm from Wales."

"Then you have the Erse?"

"Something like it."

"Keanan Blinder's the name, and this is my second cousin Keanan Black."

"Tristan Jones, and it's Mr. Keanan the Postman I'm looking for."

"Well, that's very convenient, for it's him you're looking at," he laughed.

I said, hopping below, "I've a message from Corghain on Skellig Michael." I got the postcard up from the bookshelf.

"Is it still alive he is, the auld blatherer?" said Keanan the Postman.

"He is, and still setting off the maroons one by one."

They roared with laughter.

"Come aboard," I said. "I've a touch of the hard stuff here."

"Is it English territory you're on?"

"Aye."

"Then I'll not put me foot onboard. No offense to you, for it's a fine man you are as we both can very well see, but I was arrested in Liverpool one fine day in the darkness of the Troubles, and when they let me go and I was onboard that mighty ferrycraft to Dublin, I swore by the merciful Mother of God that it's never again I'd set foot nor shoulder onto anything English as long as I live. But sure, there would be no harm in sliding a drop down here as I sit in my boat now, would there, and we'll drink to your fine and timely arrival, for it will be blowing the trousers off the devil himself in very short order." Keanan looked up at the black clouds moving across the water-heavy sky, racing for the Reeks in the east.

"That's for sure, and we do be better to enter the harbor straight," said Keanan Black. He was a quiet man, with weathered eyes and hard hands.

"Then we'll wait until you're safely alongside before your health is tokened," said Keanan the Postman. "Come now, we'll guide you in. What draft is it you have?"

"Two feet and a half," I replied.

"Oh, bejasus, that's no more than a cup in a spilt saucer."

"How's the entrance?"

"Like a dog's hind leg, but sure to a fine sailor like yourself it's no more than the daisies in the mouth of a bull."

"Lead on, Mr. Keanan."

And so the welcome to the Blaskets was made, and in ten minutes *Cresswell* was cozily secured in one of the tiniest harbors in Europe, if not the world.

The two Keanans, after a dram or two to the health of Corghain on Skellig Michael and the catching of the fine pollock the night before, then escorted me to the post office, which was Keanan Blinder's cottage. This was an old cottage with a thatched roof. Unlike the ones in Wales, the rush thatch rested on the inner edge of the stone walls, so that all around, where the eaves would have been, there was a platform, the top of the wall, which a man could walk around to repair the roof after the wild Atlantic storms had done their worst. On many of the cottages this ledge around the thatch was planted with flowers—a very refreshing sight to see after a week of nothing but the green seas, the fulmar petrels, Nelson, and Corghain's pajamas.

The cottage was one story, and the main part consisted of one large living room, into which the fireplace projected about four feet. This again was unusual, and Keanan said it was to make the room warmer. To one side of the massive chimney was a box-bed on a stone shelf. As in most of the cottages I saw on the Irish Islands, there were two doors, one on either side of the living room. The door facing away from the wind was always left open in the daytime. The walls were whitened with lime-wash, and the only decorations were a picture of Christ holding in one hand his bleeding heart, a photo of Patrick Pearse taken long before he was shot by the British army after the 1916 Easter Rebellion, and a calendar from Nestlé's Milk Company in Philadelphia, U.S.A.!

I remarked on the calendar, and Keanan told me that everyone on the Blaskets had relatives in the United States, mostly around New York and Boston, and that, in fact, about three-quarters of the income of the fifteen hundred or so islanders was in the form of remittances from these exiles. The emigration from this part of Eire was still going on in dribs and drabs, but until World War II it had been massive. In 1959, expatriation was mainly to England, where the men were hired by the big construction contractors. Some went on contract as far afield as Nigeria and Australia, building dams and electricity-generating stations. This had been going on for years, and it was always a shock to meet some old man speaking Gaelic, dressed in the simple way of the islanders, with his short, stubby pipe, once-a-week shave, and the sparkling, expressive eyes and gentle voice, and to hear him speak of the time he was building Sydney harbor bridge or the Mersey Tunnel. Their sojourns in faraway distant lands did not seem to affect them one iota, except that they could converse on any subject under the sun.

I remember sitting on a garden wall, looking across to the West, as the sun set over Inishtooskert, listening to one ancient man of about eighty tell me of his days with the British army in India (he had served two years on the Khyber Pass), and how he had been recruited into the Australian police while he was still in India, and how a group of Irishmen and Scots had sailed from Calcutta for Sydney with twenty camels intended for use in the Australian desert! I can hear him now, intoning the tale with every embellishment that a Gaelic Celt can muster, yet with tiny details remembered from sixty years before. He even recalled the colors of the loincloths of the ghilly-ghilly men on the Suez Canal bum-boats and how, as a lad in Liverpool, he and the other Irish recruits had spat on the king's shilling. The sergeant major had lost his temper at them, thinking it was an insult, until an officer ("Sure, a fine, tall, jewel of a gentleman he was, for had he not a hundred acres in West Meath itself with keepers and partridges running around like fishwives on a Friday?") informed the sergeant major that the Irish Islanders seal a bargain by spitting on a coin, which signifies that the promise will be kept regardless of the financial result.

That night the gale blew, and with it came sheets of rain and lightning. As Keanan Blinder walked back through the rain with me, I could see the vague ghosts of people walking around their cottages. Keanan explained that when there is lightning and thunder, they sprinkle holy water on the ground around the walls.

I stayed in Slievedonagh harbor the next day, for the Atlantic furies were loose and screaming vengeance for the bastard son of the king of Spain. After the morning chores, when the sky had cleared up a touch, I went, at Keanan's invitation, to lunch with him. It was a fine nutritious meal of fish and potatoes, goat's butter and porter ale. I asked him about a small flower which was growing wild all over the village. It seemed vaguely familiar.

"Sure, there was a fine fellow over here before the German War (the last one, for we call the first one the English War), and he came over here all the way from London. We had a few flowers growing here, but he said he would send us some better seeds. One fine day after he'd gone (and wouldn't all the days be fine after that, for he was a devil of a man for knowing everything), he sent us six packets of seeds. Well, when the little flowers showed themselves they were growing wild, for we'd thrown the seeds away. London Pride, they're called."

"How was life in the old days, Keanan?"

"Not much harder than now, Tristan, but of course we'd no radios to hear the fine experts of Dublin sorting out all the cares of the world. I remember when I saw my first radio and this Dublin man turned on the music. Keanan Buffer—a fine woman she was, such a command of the tongue!—when she heard that, she says to the Dublin man, 'Holy Mary Mother of God, did you ever see the like? Blinder, get the paper and pen out, sure we've to write to America and tell our brother of this miracle!' "

"When was that?"

"Let me see . . . the shark washed ashore the same year as King Edward condemned himself to eternal damnation by casting off himself the crown of England and marrying a divorced woman and leaving us nothing to fight but thin air. That was . . ."

"1936," I prompted.

" 'Tis right you are, then it was 1935."

"But radio was invented in 1910."

"Sure it was and all, and who invented it?"

"Marconi, and he was an Italian."

"Right, and was he not a good Catholic son of the Holy Church herself?"

"What have you heard about television?"

"Ach, we'll never have it here. Father O'Rafferty says it's the work of a Scotch Calvinist. What's his name?"

"John Logie Baird."

"Right you are, indeed. 'Tis the work of the devil himself!"

As I walked back to *Cresswell* that evening, I noticed the

crosses stuck in the thatch. Saint Bridget's crosses, they are called. I would not see them again until I reached Taquila, on Lake Titicaca, high up in the Andes. There are many surprising similarities between the Andes Quechua Indian and the islanders of Ireland. This is but one of them. Another one is the clothes they wear, even the brightly colored woven belts and the long stockings, and the leather sandals.

When I took my leave of Keanan the following morning, as he stood on the jetty, I asked him how I was to get the boat and myself officially entered into Ireland.

"Aah, sure, a fine man like yourself, what would we be wanting to do that for? You're here, are you not? We'll let God do the entering of you, and the devil take the office spalpeens in Dublin City."

"Well, fare you well, Mr. Keanan, and thank you for everything. One day I will be back this way."

"Sure, with a double-ended boat like that you might be back sooner than you think, for it's a holy wonder to me you know which way you are going, forward or backward. But God save you and keep the seas kind. Is it to England you are bound now?"

"Scotland."

"Good whisky they have, in the Catholic parts, anyway." His eyes twinkled with humor.

Cresswell edged her way out of the tiny creek, with most of the folk on the island standing on the mole head to see me off. I could hear the women saying, "Holy Mary, Joseph, and Jesus, what kind of a mother can the great man that he is have, who'd send him to sea alone like that and such a ruin of a dog? Do ye never catch pneumonia?" they called out thinly in the keening wind.

"He does not, he catches eight-pound pollock," retorted Keanan.

" 'Tis a fine craft he has there."

"Aye, bigger than the curraghs of Aran, and him a fine man, to be sure, but no bigger than Keanan Darcy's boy

who's short in the head." As I left them out of earshot, I
stored in my memory the sights and the sounds of the
island next to New York, an island where there is not one
tree and where fat people are greatly admired. As it was in
the ancient tribes of Israel, where waxing fat women were
worshiped for their beauty, so it is still in the Blaskets,
where life has always been too hard and strenuous for
anyone to put on too much weight. But if I ever did get
beyond my normal 150 pounds and sought a mate, it's to
the Blaskets I would go, for the people are handsome, with
a grace and carriage which would do justice to a ballet
dancer.

Cresswell was soon floundering away in the rough seas
left by the recent storm. There was not much wind, and I
wished to preserve my ten gallons of diesel fuel. The distance from the Blaskets to the Aran Islands is about one
hundred miles between ports, and it took two days to
cover. But on the second day the wind piped up and
Cresswell danced again, while I sang the Eriskay love-lilt in
the starboard shrouds as the green waters flashed by, and
Nelson gnawed a fresh sheep bone.

Wales England wed; so I was bred. 'Twas merry London gave me breath.

I dreamt of love, and fame: I strove. But Ireland taught me love was best:

And Irish eyes, and London cries, and streams of Wales may tell the rest.

What more than these I ask'd of Life I am content to have from Death.

Ernest Rhys, "An Autobiography."

11

On the Track of Columcille

The morning of the second day out of the Blasket Islands, the wind shifted round from southwest to the west. *Cresswell* had been running directly before it for a glorious twenty-four hours; now she was on a broad reach. That means that the wind was blowing from a direction at right angles to the boat, which is the fastest point of sailing, especially in a gaff-rigged ketch, for all the sails get their fair share and more of the wind, and all pull together.

The wind increased to around thirty-five knots by mid-forenoon, and it was plain, although there had been no warning on the radio, that we were in for a spot of lively weather. I dowsed the jib at eleven and the mizzen at noon. The sky was still fairly clear, and from a noon sextant sight between the scurrying clouds, forerunners of a high wind, I obtained a latitude which put me about twenty miles due west of the mouth of the River Shannon.

If I had had charts for the Shannon entrance, I would have worn in there for safe haven, to wait out the gale; but as I had not, I decided to weather out the blow. Duly I stood the boat out to the west, to put as much sea room as possible between *Cresswell* and the broken-toothed coast of Ireland. By mid-afternoon I had made a further ten miles out into the ocean offing, and the wind had increased to gale force. The main was reefed down four hands, and I settled down to hand steer her due north for the night. This course would keep me well clear of coastal hazards. During the morning I had made a large pot of burgoo—layers of porridge and corned beef, porridge and bacon, porridge and anything else to hand, each layer laced with a dram of whisky. All that night it blew, and by midnight, after crawling around on the heaving deck with seas crashing right over, I had the sails down to mizzen and storm jib only. This kept the boat moving through the water, but not fast. Now she was only rearing, bucking, and dropping fifteen feet, instead of twenty, every four seconds, while the strain on the wire rigging and the masts was minimized. Of course, any double-diagonal–built vessel, after working in heavy seas like that for hours on end, will start to take water through the garboard (where the hull joins the keel), and *Cresswell* was no exception. This meant that I had to pump her out once an hour or so, to keep the water inside the boat as low as possible. Pumping out was heavy work, and I soon found myself wishing I could change places with Nelson, who, as usual in rough weather, was comfortably wedged in between the bulkhead and the table forward in the fairly dry cabin.

The night was thunderous and black, with slashing rain cutting visibility down to a few yards. No lights, no moon, no stars, nothing but the roaring wind and the flailing ocean raging fiercely in the wan light of the small kerosene lamp hanging in the mizzen shrouds. By two in the morning I'd had enough of fighting the kicking wheel, so I struggled forward onto the foredeck and dropped the storm-sail—an endeavor something like trying to subdue a berserk mountain bear in the dark while riding on a giant fairground switchback with someone throwing three tons of icy cold water at you every five seconds.

As soon as the spitfire jib was down and lashed, the boat came head-up to wind and sea, weather-cocked with her reefed mizzen, and there we were, in comparative peace and security. I lashed an extra line around the rubber dinghy, which was stowed upside down atop the cabin roof,

then went below. The contrast between the noise outside
the boat, with every wet, wintry spirit in the Atlantic
screaming in the rigging, and down below was amazing.
Even though the cabin was heaving up and down like an
elevator gone wild, it was a haven of comfort. I managed
precariously to make tea, half filled the pint mug, leaves
and all, then dropped into wary, one-eyed slumber. Nelson
crawled topside to keep watch.

The sky at dawn would have brought tears to the eyes of a
bloody undertaker. Greys and blacks low on the western
horizon, while slashed across the east was a blood-gutter
streak of flaming red across the length of Ireland. It was
enough to make Columcille, the holy Saint Columba, throw
away his crozier. But I knew I was near enough to the Aran
Islands to try to get into their lee before all hell and damnation was let loose on the world from the watery west.
Clouds like the eyebrows of John L. Lewis himself. I decided to make a course west of the outermost of the Aran
Islands, though I was strongly tempted to run for the
nearest shelter, which was the passage between Inisheer
Island and the coast of Clare. But I knew that if I did that, I
would have the devil's own job to beat to windward, westward, again, to reach the port of Kilronan, on the main
island of Inishmore.

By mid-afternoon, in terrific seas, I had worn around the
westernmost of the Aran rocks, and was running free,
under mizzen and working jib, at a great rate. As I reached
the shelter of Inishmore Island, I looked to the north. The
seas were moving mountains. I rounded up in the bay of
Kilronan about six o'clock, dowsed sail, and motored up to
the jetty. *Cresswell* was in good order; nothing had broken
or been washed away. Everything had held tight and seamanlike. When I tied the mooring lines, for there was no
one around in the lashing rain, I stood back and looked at
her. There was an indefinable *something* about her, something I'd not noticed before, an air, an ambiance. I stood
there and stared at her. How many gales and storms had

she tackled from 1908 onwards? How many hard, strong, hefty men had shoved her out into seas raging beyond belief to rescue the helpless? How much strong emotion had been broadcast in her hull over the years in innumerable dramas of courage and bravery, patience and perseverance; how many sacrifices had been made on her heaving deck? She looked absolutely content; and then I realized with a shock, as I stood there, wet through under my oilskins in the pouring rain out of the black sky of Inishmore, that the old girl had enjoyed herself! She had reveled in it. The bloody old bitch was a storm-finder who'd sulk like a child in calm, balmy weather and refuse to hardly move; but, by God, when it blew she loved it.

I hit the side of the companionway as I climbed down the ladder. Nelson wagged his tail in anticipation of supper. "Old son," I said, "the old girl is as happy as a pig in shit out there. She's a cow in breezes or light winds, but, Jesus, she'll wear out the hammers of hell in a blow."

I fried up some of the already prepared burgoo, while Nelson wagged his tail even faster, sniffing the aroma of the sizzling bacon, well laced with Johnnie Walker. "I bloody well knew it, mate," I murmured, as I patted him, "I sensed it. She's got a mind of her own most of the time, but, by Christ, when the odds get heavy, she's with us all the way." Nelson hopped up topsides to piss over the side, which he always did before meals. Must have learned that from Tansy.

When the rain cleared, the first locals arrived on the jetty. They were mostly men, a crowd of about a dozen or so, all dark, with the long heads and prominent noses of the pre-Celts, all speaking Gaelic. The older men were wearing homemade tweed jackets and pants with slits up the legs about to the knee, so they could roll the pants up when they pushed their curraghs out. They also wore "pampooties," as they called the leather sandals worn rough side out and laced with cord.

The brightly colored woven wool belts they wore were

made in startling colors. These they called "criss," and years later I saw very similar belts among the Quechua of the high Andes, the fishermen of Lake Titicaca.

Among the crowd were two or three small boys, wearing a kind of skirt, something like that worn by the Evzone soldiers of the palace guard in Greece, or like a plain Scottish kilt, only not pleated. When I remarked on this later, I was told that "the little people" always had a fancy to steal boy-children, though they never bothered with the girls. So until they were nine years old, the boys were dressed in skirts to disguise them and to keep the leprechauns from stealing them.

Contrary to what the Freudians might think, the custom seemed to have absolutely no effect on the sex habits of the males of Aran. Still, they stay unmarried and continent until well on in life, the late thirties or early forties, and apart from husbands and wives joined in holy wedlock by the church, the sexes were separated rigidly from the cradle to (literally) the grave. On some of the islands, husbands and wives are buried in plots apart.

The skirted lads grow up to be fine, hefty fishermen, though the losses through heavy weather and fog have always been grievous. The islanders, as do all true sailormen, dread fog much more than storms. Over the centuries they have lost many of their menfolk by exposure in the open curraghs in thick fog, lasting for a week or more.

Two things struck me about the Aranmen: the difference in their faces and features compared to those of the mainland Irish, and the almost clinical cleanliness of their cottages. Here again, as in the Blaskets, many islanders live in exile in England and America. They spoke with familiarity of Manhattan and Fifth Avenue, yet knew nothing of Dublin.

All the fields in the Aran Islands are hand built—a painstaking task undertaken by men and women alike. When the Aranmen speak English, they call the fields "gardens." The soil is built up with sand and seaweed set down in alternate layers, all carried up from the beaches in baskets by asses, along the small, rocky lanes which in Ireland are known as "boreens." The islanders, besides being among the most devout people I ever came across anywhere, and besides being extraordinarily good boatmen, are also expert horse-riders. There was only one wheeled cart on the island, and that was used to carry the porter ale up to the pub from the jetty. All other transport was by a kind of sled about eight feet long, with runners of iron made from metal salvaged from the wrecks of that savage shore. The only other place I ever saw this was in Funchal, in the Madeira Islands, where they have been used ever since the first settlers arrived there in the thirteenth century. I have since often wondered, when I've sat drinking Bual wine on the main square of Funchal, if an Aranman had been among the Portuguese who found the Atlantic Islands, and if he thought that he had indeed arrived at Saint Brendan's "Isles of the Blest." There must be a connection. As far as I know, sleds are not used in mainland Portugal, or at least I have never seen any.

The cottages on Aran are interesting. Like those on the Blaskets, they have no eaves, but the fireplaces in Aran do not stick out into the room; they are flush with the wall. Alongside the fireplace there is a little alcove where the broody hens are put. As there is no real soil on the island and peat brought from the mainland runs out often, the main fuel used was cow dung, which, as it had been dried, did not have a very offensive smell.

Some of the cottages are extended when the family grows, but the fishermen told me that they never add on to a dwelling towards the west, "for he that builds towards the west is stronger than God." In quite a few cases I noticed that additions had been made to the little homes by actually cutting into solid rock to the east of the houses, rather than to the west.

I stayed with the Aran Islanders for two days, listening to their tales of fishing. They were frightened of the basking sharks, which grow to about thirty feet in length and which, they said, sometimes chased their curraghs. They had every reason to be scared of these monsters, because, although, like the whale, the basking shark is not a man-eater, feeding only on small plankton and tiny organisms of the ocean, it could easily upset one of the twenty-foot-long, canvas-covered curraghs.

At a gathering on the night before I sailed for Inishbofin, two of the older men and a couple of the younger ones performed what they called the "salmon-leap." They lay face up on the stone floor, with their arms held close to their sides and their feet close together, then, with a mighty lurch of the shoulders they threw themselves up into a standing position without using their hands in any way. An extraordinary performance. I have never seen this anywhere else, before or since. They seemed to do it better with a couple of porter ales under their belts, and there was much merriment, especially from the girls and women, on their side of the room.

The eternal separation of the sexes does not include division of labor. In all the Irish Islands the only clear-cut male job was fishing, and the only definite female tasks were washing, cooking, and wool spinning, at which the older women seemed to be engaged from waking to sleeping. This, again, was similar to the custom of some of the Andes Indians. Every other task—spreading the sand and seaweed, carrying great balks of driftwood miles from the beach, digging potatoes, even repairing the wind-torn thatch of the roofs—seemed to be shared alike by both sexes. Again, as with mountain Indians of South America, the females seemed to have much the heavier load of work. It was not unusual to see the women of a family hard at it in the fields while the men sat drinking porter and telling stories. The famous poteen, an illegal and highly dangerous brew distilled from potatoes, is not made on the inhabited islands, nor, I was told, on any of the outlying islands. It is made on uninhabited islets close inshore and in the inland regions or desolate bogs and fastnesses of the rocky mountains. (Later, on the voyage north to Tory Island, passing close to the shores of Connaught beyond Achill Head, I did indeed sight several times the brown smoke of the poteen-men on islets close inshore.)

"Sure, now, in the old days before the Republic," said one of the Aranmen, "the Royal Irish Constabulary, they were fine men, with particular principles, and if it was a still they sighted with the smoke rising to heaven, why, they'd stand back for a pipe or two of good, strong tobacco, to give the poteen-men time to pack up and be off. But these Civic Guards of De Valera, why the fellows are so enthusiastic for the Republic they'd be down on you like a falling haystack, with no time at all for you to know they were there. Great men they are for lawful enthusiasm, but terrible men for patience. Aye, in the R.I.C., they were true Irishmen, and if they could help it, never brought the injustice of English laws onto our heads." All the other older men agreed with him.

The next sail, from the Aran Islands, was to Inishbofin, eighty miles north, the westernmost part of county Galway. I left Inishmore to the farewells of the fisher-folk, late in the afternoon, for the weather was kindly. By the following dawn I was off Slyne Head, with the quartzite Twelve Pins of Connemara gleaming away under the morning sun beyond the misty, blue grey hills of Connemara. The ocean was still bumpy, but the wind was fresh enough to drive *Cresswell* through the cross-seas without too much discomfort.

I was safe in the lee of Inishbofin by two in the afternoon, watching the lobsterboats being offloaded onto a French coaster. This is the main source of all the lobster and crayfish eaten in Paris, and they were sending out six or seven thousand lobsters weekly. The operation was run by a couple of Frenchmen who lived on the mainland. Each lobster had the sinews in its claw cut to prevent it from fighting with, and possibly damaging, the other lobsters.

They are kept alive all the way to Paris, and even after, until they are ready for the customer's table. What a contrast, the tiny island of Inishbofin, on the wild, stormy, rain-lashed shores of Connemara, under weeping grey skies, with the Champs-Elysées!

I went ashore in the afternoon to stretch my legs and, entering the pub for a pint of porter, met several of the local men. (No woman would be caught dead in a hotel bar in most parts of Ireland.) They were, as is usual among those folk, most courteous and accommodating to strangers, and especially to sailor-strangers.

One old chap told me how the island got its name— "White Cow." He said that long, long, ago, even before the days of Lugh, the god of light, two Fomorgian sailormen were wrecked on the island. Sitting on the beach, they were approached by an old woman driving a white cow. When they tried to milk the cow, the old woman struck the cow and the men with her stick, and they all turned into white rocks. "And, sure, they are still there, the big white rock and the two smaller ones, for all to see and to bear witness of the truth of this tale." To this day, no Inishbofin boatman will carry a white stone in his vessel. He will even pick out white pebbles from the loose stone ballast he might take on as cargo from the mainland.

There's more to it than the old man's tale, though. The symbol of the dead in Celtic times and before, to the ancient Britons, was the white stone. In some parts of North Wales you will see people cross themselves when passing a white milestone on the road. In Spain, too.

In 1959 there were about eight hundred people on the island, and a friendlier lot I've never met. When I explained that I was going for a walk across the island, three of the younger fishermen came along, and we spent the time naming all the birds we came across in English, Erse, and Welsh, laughing all the while under the lightening sky, with cumulus rearing up thousands of feet as the wind dropped. I never saw a place with such a variety of birds—wheatears, starlings, larks, wrens, stonechats, ravens, choughs, house sparrows, looking exhausted, as if they'd just arrived on a windward beat all the way from Trafalgar Square; swallows, wood pigeons, crows, herons, oyster-catchers, ringed plovers, curlews, terns, black-headed and herring gulls by the hundreds, and guillemots and the lovely fulmar petrels by the thousands. Down on the lee side of the island, the cormorants were busy at work fishing, while on the beach lay a hundred seals or more. The place was a living zoo.

On the way back to the pub, along a rocky boreen, the fishermen, who to a man are great storytellers, told me of the Spanish pirate Bosco, who built the castle in the harbor and stretched a great chain across its entrance to prevent enemies taking him by surprise. A cruel despot indeed. He used to fling his prisoners, men and women alike, over the high cliffs to their deaths below on the rocks. And they told me of Grace O'Malley, the great woman pirate *Grannuille*, who was queen of all the islands in the days of Good Queen Bess, and how she levied toll on all ships that sailed the Western Irish waters, French, Spanish, and English alike. Queen Elizabeth offered to make her a countess. But *Grannuille* sent a letter to Her Majesty declining the invitation, because, she wrote, she held herself inferior to no woman, and especially an *Englishwoman*! When she did eventually visit London, it was with such pomp and show of power that even the court of the Virgin Queen was astonished.

I spent one night in Inishbofin, refreshed by the walk across the island, the stories, and the porter ale. For the night I was invited to moor *Cresswell* alongside the French coaster, to avoid the worry of the anchor dragging; but after an hour or two of listening to the scrunching and screaming of thousands of lobsters and crayfish crawling over piles of mussels, scratching, with their sinewless claws, against the iron sides of her hold, I moved out again to quiet anchorage.

From Inishbofin to Tory Island, off the coast of Donegal,

is about 180 miles, and I covered this in four days of fine
weather, dry, and with a good breeze from the southwest.
For one whole day I was completely becalmed and sat it out
in the ocean swell, fishing, but catching nothing. I spent
two days in the shelter of the high cliffs of that desolate, yet
interesting, island, with its tall tors, or rock pillars (whence
the name). This was the home, in the legendary days, of the
one-eyed god Balor, the grandfather of Lugh, the god of
light, who killed the fierce old god of darkness with his
sword of lightning, and after whom London and the cities
of Leyden and Lyons, faraway in central Europe, are
named. Saint Columba, who founded the great Christian
refuge in Iona in 563, also lived here. The first Irish follower
of Saint Columba was named Dhugan, and his descendants, the Doogans, are still there.

Because Saint Columba, or Columcille as he was
called, banished rats from Tory Island when he landed
there in 555, no rat can ever live there, and even the ones
that survive shipwreck die only minutes after crawling up
the beach or over the rocks. The elder Dhugan is always the
guardian of the clay which is the specific, holy and anointed
by Columcille himself, against rats. Under no circumstances, not if he was offered a million pounds for a
spoonful, will he sell it. He will only give it, and the recipient must be worthy of the gift. I was honored indeed
when Dhugan gave me a great handful of this magic clay to
take onboard.

I'd had a rat onboard *Cresswell* ever since mooring
alongside in Falmouth, and it was misery to hear the thing
scratching away where neither Nelson nor I could get at
him. I had tried everything—traps, poison, even smoking
him out. Five minutes after Columcille's clay was placed
onboard, in a paper bag on the lower galley shelves, he was
out on deck and Nelson had him in his teeth. Don't ask me
how or why, I can only tell that it was so.

Close by the landing jetty of Tory there is a Christian
cross, but unlike any other in Ireland it is in the shape of a *T*.

This is very ancient and most strange, for the only other place I ever saw it was in Ethiopia, where it is in common use by the Coptic church. It is the cross of Saint Anthony, who is held in great esteem in the Abyssinian church. Could it be that the same Saint Anthony who took Christianity into East Africa in the second century was also here in Tory Island? By what route could he have come except with Celtic mariners from Marseille or Cádiz?

One of the fishermen I talked to showed me his curragh, which was different from those in the islands further south, because the canvas was fastened to the gunwale after being stretched over the oak frame. In the Blaskets and in the Aran Islands the tarred canvas is fastened to the actual frames themselves.

Again, the number of birds in the sky above the island was limitless, as were the seals in the surrounding waters. In the evening, I retired to the old fisherman's house, for there is no pub on the island, and, over tea, listened to the tales of the Viking raids and how the monks used to hand-ring the bells in the tops of the ancient round-towers so that the islanders could take refuge from the bloody swords of the Northern sea-savages. Again, he spoke as if it had all happened last week.

This was the last of the Irish Islands, and from here I would plough into the plunging, plundering green seas of the Minches, the North West Approaches, 140 miles to the northward, to the Hebrides, over one of the roughest stretches of water in all the seas of the world!

From the lone shieling on the misty island,
Mountains divide us, and a waste of seas,
Yet still the blood is strong, the heart is Highland,
And we, in dreams, behold the Hebrides.

"The Canadian Boat Song,"
Anonymous - c. 1845.

12

Behold, the Hebrides!

I took my leave of Dhugan the Elder, of Tory Island, on the last day in May. The weather forecast was about normal for the next part of the world in that time of the year. "Winds southwesterly, force five, sea areas Shannon, Rockall, Hebrides." As I was anxious to reach Iceland before midsummer, so that I would have at least two months of reasonable weather before the equinoctial gales of September set in, I pushed off without delay, northward direct to the southernmost islands of the Outer Hebrides, and the first port in the group, Castlebay, on the island of Barra.

As the anchor came aboard, I reflected that I had passed right along the coast of Ireland, from south to north, calling at five havens, without having officially entered the country, without having to show one piece of paper. Now I was leaving Irish waters with no official clearance and nothing to show for my sojourn but memories of good people, fascinating storytellers, kindness and courtesy, humor and hospitality, a bottle of poteen and a pound or two of Dhugan's rat specific.

I took on a few gallons of sweet streamwater from Tory Island and some diesel fuel from a fishing boat resting in the bay. Then, after a lunch of lobscouse, I hoisted sail and was away on the wind.

Lobscouse is a very old method of cooking several meals at once in one pot. Thinly sliced potatoes go on the bottom, in a layer about two inches thick, then sliced carrots or turnips or other roots, followed by cut cabbage (and on Tory Island, dandelion leaves) and sliced onions, a one-inch layer, then on top of it all, fish cut into small chunks, just the flesh. Water is added until it just covers the food, a cube or two of beef bouillon (these days), and the lot is brought to a boil, then left simmering for a couple of hours, until the fish falls to pieces and mixes with the rest. A pressure cooker three-quarters full of this lobscouse provides about four meals. All you have to do is dish it out of the pan after it's warmed up. When the pot got low, I used to make a curry paste and add that to liven it up. It's good and sustaining, and very little trouble. It can be concocted before sailing, while the boat is steady at anchor. This obviates having to mess around too much at preparing food while the boat is lurching around in heavy seas such as are the case usually in the North West Approaches of Britain. Then, when sea legs are found, which usually takes a couple of days, another two-day stock can be prepared. In *Cresswell* I used to place the pot, after the food was cooked, in a "haybox," that is, a box packed with hay for insulation. This kept the pot hot for up to twenty-four hours, thus saving precious kerosene.

Lobscouse was once the staple food on the ocean-sailing ships out of Liverpool to America and the Far East. Liverpool sailors were nicknamed "scousers" for that reason.

The run from Tory Island was a rough 220 miles, with hard winds, which meant shortening sail. I rigged the "dodgers" (canvas cloths) around the cockpit, which was not self-draining. With the frequent rain showers, I spent the whole three days of the passage in oilskins. I had black oilskins, because yellow is supposed to be unlucky in a boat, at least in those waters, and I would take no chances, even though I am not particularly superstitious.

There are many superstitions among fishermen and sailing men. Such as never mentioning the word "rabbit" onboard and not sailing if you see one of these animals on the way to the boat. Never having a priest onboard and always referring to them as "the men in black." Never sailing out with a menstruating woman onboard. Never sailing on a Friday the thirteenth, or any Friday if it was avoidable. Never whistling onboard a sailing craft (it was supposed to anger the wind, but I suspect that it was just that it got on other crewmen's nerves; it was once a flogging offense in the Royal Navy, but that was because signals were passed between plotters at the Spithead mutiny of 1792 and at the Nore by that means). Again, it is very unlucky indeed to coil a rope "widdershins," or counterclockwise, or to stir a cooking pot in that fashion, for it is against the direction in which the sun travels. In ancient days, if a man found his wife stirring the pot "widdershins," he had the right to kill her, for it was thought she was putting a curse on his voyage.

As the light of Tory Island fell into the sea astern at dusk, Nelson and I could see the lights of many steamers out on the north horizon. The North West Approaches to Britain is one of the busiest shipping areas in the world, with trade coming from around the globe to Glasgow and Liverpool. This meant that I had to stay topsides all night, despite having the sails neatly balanced so the boat steered herself. Having a good stock of batteries for the radio, I indulged in the luxury of listening to music until the transmitters closed down around midnight. Then I switched to the trawler band and listened to conversations from as far away as south Iceland and the Norwegian Sea.

During the first night out from Tory Island, an overeager cod hooked himself on one of the two lines I had streamed astern. I made some batter and fried him up for a midnight special, which was a comfort from the rain and wind while bouncing and bashing over the seas.

The next day, early in the first light, I hove to and slept for an hour, then plodded on and at mid-forenoon sighted, far away on the starboard bow, low and misty, the rocks of Skerryvore and, beyond them, like Afghans in ambush, the turbans of the grey hilltops of Tiree, the island from where the matron at the Aden hospital hailed. Tiree and its neighboring island of Coll have the highest sunshine average in the British Isles, and I remembered the matron's eyes. I wondered if she was at home and was tempted to haul over to the isles to see, but June was upon us and the north was waiting, so I held course steady for Barra. I picked up the light of Bernerey, the southernmost of the Outer Hebrides, at dusk, and by midnight I was quietly hove-to in the Barra Passage, awaiting the dawn to show the way into Castletown. Again I was forced to stay topsides all night, for there were many ships and fishing craft in the passage. The wind had dropped to a breeze, and the sky was clear and starlit. I rigged up the bright Tilly oil lamp, hung it over the side, and tried my luck for a fish, but they were too crafty, and in the dawn the deck bucket was forlornly empty. At seven in the morning Nelson took over the watch and I turned in for two hours, until the light improved for entering the port. By eleven there we were, safe and secure, anchored in a lovely bay with a wide, white, sandy beach.

The harbor master was soon out in his launch, uniform and all.

"Where're you from?"

"Falmouth." I didn't tell him about Ireland.

"That's a lang run, laddie."

"Aye."

"Weel, mon, ye're lucky." A big man, he was standing in his blue motor launch, grabbing my gunwale with his great hamfists.

"Why's that?"

"There's a weddin' on, and it's you that's invited."

"What time?"

"As soon as ye're ready, the hard stuff's already oot."

"Where?"

"At the church up yonder." He pointed up the hill to the

grey tower. He didn't say "kirk," for this was a Catholic island.

"I've no suit."

"Och, lad, dinna fash ye'sel. Come as ye are. This is no' London."

So it wasn't, as I soon found out, with the fiddles playing and the lads and lasses dancing reels and jigs and even some modern dances. Whisky there was by the crate and beer by the hogshead. I had put two anchors down, and for the first time since leaving England, I took Nelson ashore with me. (He was getting randy and the island had a fair chorus of bitches yapping at him from the beach). In short, we had a whale of a time; so much so that it took me a week to find out who got married! I slept in a different cottage every night, and it was like home away from home, only better.

There was still no electricity on Barra in 1959. The population (around twelve hundred) gained their living fishing or crofting, working a small plot of land with potatoes and sheep for wool. They lived in what they call "black houses," oblong thatched cottages about fifty feet long and twelve feet wide, the narrow gable end facing the prevailing wind, like a boat at anchor. The cottages were built of stones, not hewn, but picked from the rocky ground and packed with moss. The walls were surprisingly thick, four to six feet, and the insides were lime washed, just as they had been on the Irish Islands. The insides of the black houses consisted of one long living room where everything was done. If the family grew, an addition was built on, but not, as in Eire, only to the east.

Crime is virtually unknown on the islands, and often the innkeeper left the bar while the customers paid their money into the till!

From the heights overlooking the dazzling white beaches, probably the prettiest beaches in the United Kingdom, I gazed down bewitched at the patches of purple and green where large rafts of seaweed had washed up, and the brown streaks where the peat streams ran their meandering way to the sea. Overhead, gulls and petrels screamed welcomes to the fishing craft entering the bay.

The island airfield, which in fact was the main beach, could only be used at low tide. It is the only one I've ever seen where the flight schedules were dictated by the state of the moon. A lady was in charge, who was thought to be the only female airport manager in Europe, if not the world.

The Outer Hebrides had been described by Pytheas 330 years before the birth of Christ. Agricola's fleet had called there in the first century A.D.; Ptolemy had shown them on his map of the world, drawn in the second century A.D. (the same map which had shown Peru). On it he gives the island of Skye the name of *Scitis Insular* and modern-day Lewis, the biggest of all the Hebrides, is called *Dumma*. But, before Ptolemy, Pliny had listed thirty islands in the Hebrides. In fact, he misnamed them, for their Celtic name was *Hebudes*, but to the ancient Gaels they were *Tir Nan Og*, "The Land of the Ever Young."

Columcille arrived in the Hebrides in A.D. 563 and by the time of his death, in 597, not only the islands, but the whole of Scotland was under Christian tutelage.

The centuries of peace lasted until around A.D. 800, when the dreaming islands were rudely awakened by the arrival of the Vikings, who drove their knirrer-longships south from the Faroes and the Orkneys. The latter they called the "Nordereys," while the Hebrides became the "Sudereys." Thus the oldest rocks in Europe became part of the kingdom of Norway for three hundred years until Scotland, under King Alexander III, defeated the Vikings in 1263. The Norse people of the islands were slowly absorbed into Scottish culture, yet kept their own identity.

The Celts always held on in the southern islands. The difference between the Norse-descended folk of the northern islands and the Gaels of the south was further widened during the religious reformation of the sixteenth century.

The dark, gloomy spirit of Calvinism appealed to the Norse blood, while in the south the Gael was faithful, as always, to the teachings of Rome, Saint Patrick, and above all, Saint Columcille. For five hundred years after the Scots defeated the Vikings, sporadic warfare flamed among the Lords of the Isles—the McLeods, the McLeans, the McNeils, the MacPhees, until the strength of the clans was broken, finally, at Culloden. The Lords of the Isles became lords of empty lands, as the clansmen flew in droves, like wild geese before a storm, to America and Canada. The lonely islands dreamed on, sad, bereft, and beautiful.

Time was pressing. There were only two months left of reasonable sailing weather. I sat down in the cabin with the charts and worked out a route. I had intended to pass up through the Outer Hebrides, in their lee, out of the way of the great Atlantic rollers, then sail north for the Faroes on the way to Iceland—the old "steppingstone" way of the ancient traders. But I had wasted a week in merrymaking. I traced the track to Iceland on the chart. I would sail direct. But first, there was a tiny dot on the chart, well to the west of the Hebrides, sixty miles out, all alone and remote in the deep Atlantic—St. Kilda—where I wanted to call and look around.

In 1942 I was in a destroyer which picked up two Norwegian seamen from St. Kilda. They had been torpedoed and, after surviving a lifeboat trip of two weeks, had washed ashore on the remote islands. There they had survived on birds' eggs for some weeks before being rescued. I recalled, vaguely, seeing the abandoned village from the decks of the warship. But we had not been allowed to go ashore because the skipper was anxious to get in and out fast in case of a U-boat attack.

Now I was in my own ship. Now there were no U-boats. Now I could see for myself. I cleared Barra for Reykjavík, Iceland, hauled up the anchor, hoisted the main, mizzen, and jib, and was off with a good forecast and a stiff breeze, through the Barra Sound, between that island and the lovely islet of Eriskay, flung like a green garment over the blue waters. Eriskay, where in 1745 Prince Charles Edward Stuart, "Bonnie Prince Charlie," landed from France with Gallic gold to rally the clans and cry rebellion against the House of Hanover. A rebellion that was later smashed on the bloody field of Culloden. Ever since the bagpipes have mourned the defeat of the clans.

Eriskay, where in 1941 the S.S. *Politician*, badly damaged by German torpedoes, drifted ashore carrying twenty thousand cases of whisky. *Uisque-bach Gu-leor*! Whisky galore! As soon as she touched the rocks, the news spread faster through the islands than the fiery crosses lit for the 1745 rebellion! In three days there was not one case of booze left onboard the pounding *Politician*.

Eriskay, where the musical poem of the Gaelic love-lilt was born! I settled down to a close reach for two days and nights in search of the three small dots of St. Kilda in the immense, eternal, infinite, heaving ocean.

To sail to St. Kilda was rough. With the seas piling up on the continental shelf after their passage across the Atlantic, it could not be otherwise, especially as *Cresswell* was sailing on a course only fifty degrees off the wind. But I had rested well in Barra and was fit as a fiddle. The days of empty sea and the nights under starlit skies, with the west wind moaning low in the shrouds and around the hounds-bands, passed by. The daytime summer skies were clear enough to give me good sextant sights, and on the third morning out I spied the mighty capsized cliff of Boreray, the most remote part of the British Isles, dead ahead. I hove to, had breakfast and an hour's sleep, then worked into Village Bay, where there had once been a settlement.

As *Cresswell* sailed up to the root of the bay, I lowered the mainsail. The gaff hoist slipped out of my hand, and the heavy, twelve-foot-long spar clattered down on deck with a sharp crack. At this a million, a *million*, birds lifted up from the cliffs, which rise over fourteen hundred feet straight from the ocean, and darkened the noon sky. There were so many birds, sea birds of all kinds, that they turned day into night, and there was such a noise with their screaming that I can still hear it now. I had never seen anything like it before, nor have I since. It was so violent, that rise of life from the white cliffs of Dun and Boreray, that I was genuinely frightened in case they should attack the boat. Even Nelson cowered under the cabin table.

I dropped the hook and looked around. The granite cliffs were snow white with bird-shit. There was a tremendous feeling of sadness about the place, intensified by the wheeling and screaming of the birds. It was a sadness so real that I could reach out and touch it. Overhead, the sky was dark with rainclouds, which swept low over the lonely peaks of grey Hirta, the main island. The heavens themselves seemed to be weeping as the first raindrops pattered on deck. Then, as the birds descended to their nesting ledges, all was quiet again, except for the soughing of the wind as it swept down the valley and over the ruined cottages of the village which had once, only a short time ago, known the cry of mothers and the laughter of children. Despite my fatigue I stayed on deck for an hour, taking in this melancholy scene; then, with a shudder, I stepped below into the warm and cozy cabin, gave Nelson a shove with my foot so he would go topsides, and turned in to sleep until the rain ceased. I fell into darkness trying to sort out the pad of Nelson's paws on deck from the patter of the great, dolloping raindrops.

When I woke it was around two in the afternoon and the rain had stopped. After a quick meal of lobscouse, I made ready to go ashore. I took some rope, an ax, and my knife. And Nelson. From the deck, I had seen some sheep climbing the steep cliff faces, looking like goats.

I looked around the old village. Here, people had lived from the Iron Age on, right up until 1930. In ancient times they were the most isolated people in the Western world. Their life was very tough indeed. They could not fish from boats because there was no wood for boat building, so they

fished from the rocks, where the great Atlantic seas rushed
and gushed at these lonely specks of land under the grey
skies. Their main food was birds' eggs and bird-meat. They
made their clothes out of bird-skins and feathers. Then
sheep, which they plucked, not sheared, were introduced,
and for a while life improved.

Through all these centuries there were only three families
on the islands. The only visitors, from the mid-eighteen-
hundreds on, were stray trawlers coming to rest and the
twice-annual boat from the mainland. In 1912 influenza
arrived on the island and killed off many. These folks were
converted Calvinists. What the effects of that stern, gloomy
philosophy, together with the results of hundreds of years
of inbreeding were on these simple people, I can hardly
imagine. The sum result was that in 1930, the British government, under strong public pressure, decided to
evacuate the island.

All 36 of the surviving islanders (the population in 1850
had been 110) were taken to Ardtornish, in Argyll. And
what do you think the British government did to these
people who had never before seen a tree? They set them to
work for the Royal Forestry Commission! Of course, they
were totally unfit for this kind of labor, and eventually they
all drifted off to disappear in the slums of Glasgow. *Sic
transit miseria!*

I searched through the old cottages. All the thatched
roofs had blown away. Inside there was only tough grass
growing. But the spirit-presences were so strong they were
almost physical. I looked into the manse, the old preacher's
house, the biggest house in the village, with its tin roof
clattering away in the wind, and found old *Encyclopedia
Brittanicas* from 1840. The dining table had collapsed, and
the glassless windows swung in the breeze. There was an
air of complete and utter hopelessness about the place—as
the French say, *"une tristesse absolue."* I could not understand why this should affect me so. I had visited many
ruined places—the Coliseum, the scattered ruins of South

Turkey, and old, abandoned castles in Spain. Far from feeling sad, I had been curious, then interested, and even proud that men could leave such works behind them. As I knocked a timid sheep over the head with my ax and roasted it over a fire of wood chopped from one of the manse shelves, I thought and thought about it. Then it dawned on me. The reason I felt so sad here, in this tearful, remote place, was because there were relics and ruins of people of *our time* and of *our age*. This is what the world would be like if a nuclear holocaust came about.

I looked around me. *People who had lived here were still alive*. They had lived here, and played here, and cried here, and sung here, *during my lifetime*. Now it was all gone. Finished. Dead. Here, there was no proud achievement. Here man had been defeated, despite a long, hard, bitter struggle. There was the sadness, the sense of ineffable gloom. The presences around me were in the depths of misery.

I looked around the tumbled stones of the three churches, dedicated to Christ, to Brendan the Voyager, and to Columcille, then made my way back to the boat. Nelson was pleased to get back onboard. He had not liked the village one bit.

As I took off into the ocean dusk (I didn't fancy a night there), I wondered to myself how Iron Age people had reached these remote rocks. When the pro-English General Campbell arrived, chasing Bonnie Prince Charlie after the defeat of the 1745 Scottish rebellion, how was it that the islanders had never even heard that a war had been fought? Why were there so many bird beaks on the floors of the cottages? The last conundrum I figured out on the passage to Iceland. The poor souls had used the bird beaks in the place of wooden pegs, to fix the rush thatch to the roofs!

But still, there was something fascinating about the place, named after a saint who is not even on the Christian calendar, something mysterious and yet at the same time hopeful. After all, what else can we do but admire the plain courage of all the folk who had wrenched an existence out of those barren rocks for so many centuries?

St. Kilda is now (1977) a British government wildlife reserve, and there is a rocket-tracking station on the main island of Hirta. I am told there are even more birds there now!

Now give me a nail and a hammer,
And a picture to hang on the wall,
Give me a pair of stepladders,
In case that I should fall,
Give me a couple of waiters,
And a dozen bottles of ale,
And I'll bet you I'll hang up that picture,
If somebody drives in the nail!

One of Tansy Lee's drinking songs.

13

Background to the Sagas

As is shown in the old legends of the Gaels, and also in the accounts of the Greek Pytheas and the Roman Pliny, the Celts of Ireland and Wales made the long voyages to Iceland and back with surprising regularity, many centuries before Christ. But there was no permanent Celtic settlement there until the 750s, when a hundred or so monks and anchorites, womanless, tiring of incessant Saxon and Norse raids on their coastal eyries, gathered up their parchments, bell, crosses, and tools, and, mustering among them hardy curragh sailors, sailed north to find a safe refuge on the wild, semibarren, volcanic islands of Papey and Papos. The monks knew well the old Gaelic legends. Had not the holy Saint Brendan sailed these waters and had he not told of fiery mountains being spewed out of the sea from the depths of hell and of a blasphemous sailor lost into the red-hot molten rock?

The monks had read of Cormac ua Liathain, who long before had sought his desert in the seas of the wild north. There Cormac had meditated for twenty years to drive the wailing banshees from his Gaelic soul and find his peace in the contemplation of infinite forgiveness.

From the monasteries of Aran, Anglesey, Bangor, Clonfert, and Clonmacnoise, the holy men set sail in their curraghs. Northward they pounded to Iona, off the coast of Strathclyde, there to listen to the clear words of *De Ratione*

Temporum and *Librus Regium Questionum*, the works of the Venerable Bede, written far away in Wearmouth and Jarrow, giving them directions garnished from many voyages to the Faroes and Iceland during the past centuries.

With twenty to thirty men in each curragh, the saintly fleet bowled and rolled over the stormy waters, the wind bellying out the Celtic crosses on the flaxen sails. They called at the already established Christian outposts on the lonely Faroe Islands, then pressed on north, to Thule, the last land in the world. They took with them sheep and ponies, corn and beer, oats and flax, and iron tools to carve refuge from the rocks. The men of the fleet sailed on, singing hymns as the stone deadman-anchors were raised, the sails hoisted, and the hide hulls slid away from the Faroes to take the cross of God to the country they thought nearest to hell.

For a hundred and twenty years the Gaelic colony of holy men clung to the steaming rocks of Lon and Sieda. For more than a century the holy fathers, the *papar*, dug into the desolate sands of Skeidara and the earth ledges of the tiny islands of Papey and Papos. They had regular communication with the mother monasteries of Britain and Ireland, with young men arriving to replace the older men dying in hard labor and prayer.

In 860 the first Norseman, Naddod the Viking, blown off course on a voyage from his lonely vikke in Norway to the Orkneys, sighted Thule. But having also sighted an island of fire "risen from the sea," Naddod, wary of meeting the devils of hell, or more of his own breed, turned south and did not land. Upon his return to Norway, tales of his adventure fell upon the ears of a landless Swede, a Norseman, to be sure, but no Viking, loitering around the wooden eating-hall of Harald Fairhair, king of Norway. In short order, Gardar Svarvasson, though penniless, rousted allies from among the idle sea-rovers of Norway and set sail to discover this mysterious land. Rumors of the Christian expeditions of long ago had filtered back to the vikkes, to the lonely Norwegian fiords, over the years. Perhaps there there were rich pickings to be had for the slash of a bloody sword?

The feelings of the Gaelic holy men as they stood on the forlorn shores of the Vatnajoküll, with the black clouds bursting over the Vestmannaeyjar Island out to the southwest, as they stared, horrified, at the blood-red-striped sail of Svarvasson, with his scowling dragon's head bow-stem, charging in from the east, can only be imagined. But Gardar Svarvasson was, first and foremost, an explorer; indeed, he was one of the first of the ancient sea-rovers of whom the record is at all clear.

Following the custom of the Norse, he called a council of war, and, with his twenty-two Vikings, argued the alternatives. They were seeking land for their families; this was not land, this was a desert of hard rock, fit only for Christian lunatics. They would sail on, to the west, and seek good grazing soil for sheep and cattle. They would leave the meager pickings of the Vatnajoküll, this smoking land, to unlucky latecomers.

Up went the striped squaresail, over the shield-bedecked gunwale the long oar sweeps were thrown, and the dragon's head bit into the wind again. Past the long, black, melancholy shores of the Landeyjaer, past the storm-tossed, inhospitable peninsula of Reykjanes and the rocks of the Skagi they pressed with all muscle and flaxen sail, until before them opened up the wide, heart-lifting expanse of the Faxaflói, with the waters shining in the afternoon's pale sun. There they gazed, stupefied, beyond the mountain-rimmed gulf of green, white-spumed waters, at the stupendous cone of Snaefellsjökull rearing up, like the curse of Thor himself, into the cloud-swept skies of Thule.

But they found the pastures cold and windswept between the knurled claws of the Snaefell, and so pressed on north past the snarling mass of Ondverdarness, and finally entered Breidafiord, the broad fiord, where they wondered at the thousand skerries and swift currents, stronger than any they had ever seen. They stared at the seal-covered rocks and skulking reefs, and the seven ax-clefts struck by the gods into the Isharjardajub, a mighty rock heap thrown, defeated, into the sea by the snow-shouldered mount-mass of victorious, arrogant Glama! Gardar and his men plied their iron-banded arms to the sweeps, gliding the knarr into the Kalelen deep-fiord, where the icefalls of the Drangajoküll tumble into the sea like panicked sheep leaping from the mother herd.

Still Gardar was not satisfied, and after a rest of several days, onward to the north they went, with no sign of man, only the birds in their massed thousands as they swooped over the striped sail, only the seals and the walruses as they moaned low in the pale light of the falling sun. On they went, with the North Horn, the Hornbarg, under a stormy lee, to Húnaflói, the great expanse of fish-ridden water with the low land around flatter and richly grassed, green valleys driving inland between the tumbling, stark, rock mountains. Warmer and drier, too, they were, for they were now protected from the southwest fist of the wind. Gardar's men peered beyond the green of the valleys and the soft blues and greys of the mountains. They could see, behind the bluff peaks, the steely, silver-gleaming glint of ice on the high falls.

Gardar now determined to winter on this coast, before returning to Norway with news of his magnificent find. The longship headed east along the coast. He missed the best wintering haven, Eyjafiord, having been blown past it in a night storm, but, just to the east of the mighty upthrust of Skjálfandi, "the Trembler," he entered a long, south-running fiord, where he and his crew built a house. They named the place Húsavík. House-Bay. No Celtic kindness yet in names.

There, at the darkening of winter, for the winds now blew from the north hard into the fiord, Gardar left one of his viking crew, with a thrall and a bondwoman named Nattfari. Gardar sailed on east in the spring, headed for

Norway. A few months later Nattfari gave birth to a son—
the first child known to have been born in Iceland. This is
recorded in the Norse *Landnamabok*, a history of Iceland.

Gardar Svarvasson, never a man to hide his light under a
bushel, named the land *Gardarholm*. The millenium of
peace in Thule was over.

While Gardar was on his way home to Norway, Floki the
Fisherman, a mystic by nature, sailed for Thule from
Stavanger, Norway, with a small crew, a cage of ravens,
and various small animals for sacrifices. Floki was continually making sacrifices to the gods and invoking their assistance in the smallest things (which is probably the reason
for his small crew). He landed in Breidafiord and wintered
there. Floki was no farmer, though he did take some live-
stock. Whether he did this for breeding or for sacrifices is not
clear from the sagas. What is sure is that the fishing that
winter was bad, which is not surprising, considering how
the winter gales storm into Breidafiord. Floki longed for the
spring. When April came, it was still snowing, still cold, so
he left in anger, ranting and raving at the weather, the
gods, and the land, which he called in his spite, Iceland.
Floki returned to Norway and gave his late winter home as
bad a reputation as Columbus gave San Salvador, that
barren stretch of sand, a good one. But one of Floki's crew,
named Thorolf, who had made a very courageous passage
over the wild Flaxaflói in his parted tow-boat, swore to all in
Norway that the new land was so rich that butter dripped
from every blade of grass, and forever after he was known
as Thorolf Butter.

The following year Ingolf Arnarson and his brother Leif,
having killed the two sons of the Earl Atli of Gaular, in
South Norway, had, according to the Norse law, to pay
blood-money. Being penniless, they called together their
thralls and cousins, fitted out a longship, and sailed for
Iceland.

The first year Ingolf and Leif spied out the land, as Gardar had done before. The second year they made another

expedition with settlers, but Leif, in his longship, sailed first for Ireland, where he raided for slaves. Twelve of these, warriors all, he captured and carried to Oraefa, where many fine farms now thrive, nestled between the rocky outcrops of the jökull. The Irish warriors eventually killed Leif and stole away with Leif's women and boat. They sailed to an island off the south coast. There they held out for many months against Leif's berserk avengers, but in the end, defeated, they threw themselves off the high cliffs into the sea, from whence comes the island's name, Vestmannaeyjar—"Irishman's Island."

From 865 on, the Norse immigration into Iceland was regular and steady. With them, the Vikings brought many captives from the Gaelic lands of Ireland, Wales, and Scotland. The anchorites of Papos, Papey, and the Vatnajökull had now retreated into the fastness of Kirkjubaejar, a site so holy that even the Norsemen were afraid to visit it.

Between 890 and 920 events took place which greatly increased the Norse immigration to Iceland. A Viking army, plundering the west of Europe, was battered into defeat by the Gaelic Bretons of Northwest France. The survivors of this army fled, some east, to join their kinsmen in Normandy, some north, to join Hastern and the Great Horde, who were invading Saxon England. Here, with the continuous harrying of King Alfred and his Celtic allies, they were again hammered into defeat, and the Viking array, split into ragged tatters, was thrown back from the Saxon-English shore.

In 902, King Cearbhuil, the monarch of Leinster in Ireland, defeated a Norse army and in 1014 the great Brian Boru finally threw the Viking plunderers out of Baile Atha Cliath (Dublin) and into the sea. The Norse survivors of this debacle sailed for North Wales, the very heartland of the Celts, where they were promptly decimated and flung back in bloody disarray to sulk in their sea-lair of Man. But here the Vikings found no respite, not even in their own flaunting grounds, the North Sea, the Irish Sea, and the English

Channel, for now the Celt had regained his sea legs and the Saxon had found his. With the aid of lessons well learned from the Norsemen, they time and again attacked and defeated the dragon-head ships of the Vikings, forcing them ever northward. These seaborne hammers, struck bloodily year after year from the British Isles, turned the Norsemen's bows towards Iceland, where they arrived in increasing numbers, along with their families and Celtic captives. Gradually, over the next two centuries, the two bloodstrains mixed. The *Landnamabok*, the old book of families and their settlements, drawn up around the year 1000, shows four hundred families living in Iceland, and one-seventh of the names in the book are unmistakably Celtic.

Despite the rockiness of the country, there is almost no stone in Iceland suitable for building or carving. There were hardly any trees, the woodcarving of which would give vent to artistic expression. The only way that the Icelanders could express themselves on a higher level than tilling the soil, fighting, or fishing was through words—spoken and written. The Celtic leavening on this race of hard warriors, farmers, and fishermen gave breath to the greatest flowering of literature the world had seen until the Catholic Renaissance. There is no other viable explanation of how the works, for example, of Geoffrey of Monmouth, and the great Welsh legends came to be translated into Icelandic Norse. So far as is known, there was nothing similar in Norway, which, word-wise, was practically dormant until Ibsen, nine hundred years later.

There were three sources of Celtic influence in Iceland. First, the surviving anchorites of the old Christian settlement, who came into contact with the early Norse settlers. Second, intermarriage between Celts and Norsemen (Helgi the Skinny, prince of Norway, was born in the fourth century of a Norse nobleman and an Irish princess, and one of the foremost chieftains of Iceland, Olav Peacock, was born of Hoskuld Dallakollsson, descendant of Aud the

Deep-minded, and Mael Curcaigh—Melkorka, in Norse—daughter of the great King Murcataigh of Ireland). Third, there were the hundreds of Celtic thralls and bond-women (not exactly slaves, more like indentured servants). These thralls were, as often as not, sturdy warriors captured in battle and held until ransom was paid (which it seldom was, for there was rarely anything to pay it with). Some of the Icelandic thralls had been great and powerful men of influence in the Gaelic countries, men such as those Celts mentioned in the sagas, like Njal, Kormak, and Kjartan. As a result, there are place names of Celtic origin all over Iceland.

But the conversion to Christianity of the wild Vikings proved, in the first centuries of Icelandic settlement, beyond even the vocal charms of the Irish and the Welsh. Soon the whole island was worshiping gods more fitted to its terrible aspect, more amenable to its inhospitable climate, more understanding of its awful wrath. The old gods of the Northmen soon displaced the Son of Man even in the Celtic blood, and Niörd, Tyr, Balder, and Odin were among those worshiped. However, Thor of the mighty hammer and the fertility god Frey, with his great phallus always stiff and erect, were the most feared and respected.

The attempts of the crown of Norway to establish sway over Iceland failed, having been resisted with all the craft, guile, and violence of the Icelandic Norsemen and Celts. Soon a system of self-government was developed. This was the Althing, the parliament, which the Icelanders claim was the first democratic parliament ever established. This is untrue; the Althing was not representative of the people, but only of the more prosperous landowners. It derived its origin from the Law of the Gulathing of southwest Norway, which had as much to do with democracy as the Senate of ancient Rome. The Althing was, in fact, an institute for the maintenance of a wealthy, powerful, and avaricious establishment of land barons.

In any case, it had been preceded as a representative

body by over one thousand years. The Eisteddfodd of Wales was a meeting place where every man could speak and no man could be held in jeopardy for anything said during the sessions.

During the twelfth and thirteenth centuries Iceland prospered as a fount of literature. But the Norse spirit was shortsighted and lazy, always seeking the easy, if violent, way out of a dilemma when it came to day-to-day living. The few trees that grew on the island were cut down, and no attempt was made to keep the cattle alive during the cold winters; instead they were killed wholesale and the car- casses buried in the snow (though this in itself helped the literary effort, calfskin vellum being used for writing the sagas). No attempt was made to develop the right kind of clothing for the climate, nor to resow pasture land.

And so, around the fourteenth century a plague caused the population to stagnate, then slowly decline. Gradually Iceland withdrew again, back behind its curtain of mist and fog, until very recent times, when it became first a staging point of ship convoys during two world wars, and later an important airways crossroads on the great-circle routes from Europe to the Western Hemisphere.

But about seven hundred parchments of sagas and pre- cious translations survived the centuries of isolation. Seven hundred, or about one tenth of the total written. A treasury of lively, human stories, full of Gaelic dreaming, of deep, abstract, oblique meaning in the simplest descriptions. And full also of Norse vigor and humor; the humanness of the characters shines strong and bright across the dark span of the lonely years between us and them.

As I took my departure from the heartbroken islands of St. Kilda, I thought of this long-ago time, and with a slight wind barely moving the vessel over the swells from the west, I settled down to watch the moon set beyond the stupendous cliffs of strange Boreray.

A whole island tipped over on its side. Cliffs fifteen hundred feet high, ghostly white under the moon, with millions of skuas and guillemots clinging to the ledges, so many that the black granite rock looked like some spirit-land rearing straight up into the clouds from the black, night-gleaming, heaving, ocean sea.

Soon the ghost-rocks had dropped astern. We were alone in the night at the edge of the world, with only the rustle of the wind on the stays and the slop-slop of the bows. The boat plunged on into the night, black silver with the moon's west-sinking, until the first flickering spider's touch of pale dawn light, low on the eastern horizon. Before I hove to, to sleep an hour, I searched below the dawn. There, a mere smudge of deeper color in all the other greys, was St. Kilda—the Islands of the Dead. I stared for a minute or so, then, hungry and sleepy, clambered below. It was my last glimpse of Britain for over three years.

PART III

Vici
(I Conquered)

For my purpose holds
To sail beyond the sunset, and the baths
Of all the western stars, until I die.
It may be that the gulfs will wash us down:
It may be we shall touch the Happy Isles,
And see the great Achilles, whom we knew.

Alfred, Lord Tennyson
"Ulysses"

In the country of the blind, the one-eyed man is king.

Old Spanish saying.

14

A Rough Passage

With the wind in the southwest, the passage from St. Kilda to Iceland, for the first two days, was on a broad reach, the fastest and the easiest sailing. Frequently sighting the fountain-spouts of whales, the great blue whale and the sperm whale, in patches of bright sunlight as the dark shadows of wheeling clouds slid over the rough face of the ocean waters, *Cresswell* danced and streamed to the northwest. Often, we were accompanied by porpoises, shooting over to the boat's side at tremendous speed, jumping high into the air off the tops of the seas. They would convoy us, sometimes for hours at a stretch, sometimes flashing away with a squirm of their powerful tails, sometimes drifting alongside, flickering their bodies every now and again, seeming to make no effort, yet keeping up with us at a good five knots.

Down below, I would know when the porpoises were arriving, for their conversations, their whistling screams of joy, were plainly transmitted through a mile of water and through the hull.

Nelson's attitude to the porpoises was exactly the same as it would have been had they been children. He balanced himself against the knighthead, on the bow, and jumped around, watching their every playful move, yapping as they performed their rolls. He jumped with excitement when the mothers playfully rammed and nudged the youngsters against the bow of the boat.

On the third day out there was a radio forecast from the BBC: "Sea areas Rockall, Malin, Iceland, winds increasing to gale force, storm imminent." I was not surprised. Already, the night before, I had picked up a transmission from a trawler to a weathership keeping gallant and sacrificial watch out in the vast deeps of the ocean indicating that the weather was deteriorating seriously. Sure enough, towards dusk, at about latitude sixty north, longitude fourteen west, the sky in the west was coal black torn cumulus, while overhead stretched ragged strips of cirrocumulus, the "mackerel's tails." Away to the east, in a deep purple sky, the moon rose blood red. I hoisted my way up forward onto the heaving foredeck and handed the staysail. Then, after bringing the boat's head up into the wind, I lowered the gaff head and peak and tied two reefs in the main.

Half an hour after all was battened down, the weather slammed down on us, and soon we were in a sea of frenzy. *Cresswell* was still able to steer herself roughly north by northwest, so I lashed the wheel and let her go at that. All that night I was occupied in pumping out the hull, for despite the dodgers, a lot of sea was coming onboard, and I was often knee-deep in icy cold water in the cockpit.

Cresswell's cockpit, unlike those of most modern ocean-going sailing craft, was not self-draining, and no matter how much precaution I took against seas coming onboard, the cockpit, in rough weather, would always take a great amount of water in a surprisingly short time. This was because the boat was a shallow draft hull with almost flat bilges; unlike the modern deep-keel craft, there was almost no room for water taken onboard to stow itself. A ton of water coming in meant about six inches slopping around right through the boat. So it was pump, hard and often. But I had a good old Royal National Lifeboat Institution pump, a great brass monster, which could jerk out half a gallon at a stroke, and the water was soon got rid of. It was heavy work, though, and coldly wet. I was out in the cockpit,

almost smothered under two jerseys, two pairs of fear-
naught trousers, seaboot stockings, seaboots up to my
thighs, apron-type oilskin trousers, an oilskin coat, a
sou'wester, and a towel around my neck, lashed to the
binnacle with a heavy line tied with a bowline. But still the
cold spray continually found its way inside my clothing,
and I spent the whole storm, all three days in it, pumping
out the hull, tending the sheets, adjusting the wheel, grabbing a bite to eat when the chance arose, which was not
often, thoroughly wet and miserable.

With the boat's sails reefed down and the seas growing as
the wind drove them from the west, progress was much
slower. When she was reefed down, *Cresswell* never made
more than 2½ knots, which is about the speed of a man
walking at a moderate pace. And most of that was sideways, because she made a lot of leeway, not having a big,
deep, outside keel.

These defects in her windward ability I had accepted. I
intended to get into the ice, and with a deep keel that would
have been almost impossible, as the keel would be crushed
between the ice floes; but with a rounded hull and no
outside keel the possibility was that she would be lifted
upwards by the ice pressure, as you squeeze an apple pip
out from between forefinger and thumb.

The action in a small vessel in a storm is a wonder to
behold. Every separate part of the hull and rigging works its
own way, tremendous forces pulling and pushing every
three seconds or so. The strains imparted onto the masts
and the running-rigging are stupendous, and unless you
are absolutely familiar with every little bit and piece of the
craft, unless you know the strength of each block, each
wire, each halyard, you spend the time waiting for something to give. And when something gives on a sailing craft
in heavy weather, with everything tensioned like a violin
string, something else is going to go with it, and something
else with *that*, and so on, ad infinitum. This anticipation of
something giving way is probably the most worrisome

thing of all and is probably the main reason for exhaustion. More so, even, than lack of sleep or hard physical effort. That, and the lack of food due to the inability to cook it. I reckon that many craft have been lost because of exhaustion, both mental, caused by worry, and physical, caused by neglecting to eat properly.

The answer, of course, is always to sail in the best order you possibly can, with all the hull and rigging, sails and gear well maintained, and always to have food available which can be eaten without cooking. Even bars of chocolate or corned beef. Food undeniably tastes better warm and is more comforting; but when it comes to refueling the body, all that really matters is to get the protein inside you.

The storm south of Iceland lasted for three days and nights. Wet, cold, and weary, I watched the skies clearing in the west, grabbed a handful of burgoo, dolloped some out for Nelson, then turned in, with the boat handling herself in a diminishing wind, still under reefed sails.

When I woke it was close to noon, so I hove the boat to and snatched a sextant sight of the sun. We had moved only seventy miles in three days, on a course almost due north! But as the wind dropped to a moderately stiff breeze of about twenty knots, it backed around to the south. I prepared to shake out the reefs and get her once more on a broad reach, this time heading west-north-west, so as to keep plenty of sea room between me and the south coast of Iceland, which, at this time, was about three hundred miles to the north.

I climbed up to the foot of the main mast and let go of the peak halyard; then, holding that under one foot, I prepared to let go of the throat halyard. Suddenly there was a loud crack aloft. I jerked my head up to see what was happening—then everything went black.

The first thing I saw when I tried to open my eyes was blood all over the side-deck and the doghouse side. My head was throbbing and every movement increased the pain. Then I realized, with a shock, that I could only see *through one eye!* The other was blackly blank, and blood was dripping down my oilskins. For the first and only time in my life at sea I was violently sick. Nelson, covered in blood and spew, was still holding onto the bottom of my pants leg, and I could see where his teeth had bitten in so hard that the tough oilskin material was chewed away. He had saved my life by stopping me from sliding over the side.

Slowly, sitting there on the pitching deck with the green seas still breaking in great waves over and against the sides of the boat as she rocked and rolled and pitched and tossed, I came to, grabbing at the handrail, and looked around me.

Through my good eye I saw that the throat-block grommet, the heavy wire cable-strap slung around the mast above and resting on the hounds-bands (heavy blocks of hard timber bolted through the mast), had snapped as I had eased the throat halyard to raise the mainsail. The continual wear and tear, the everlasting rubbing and chafing had worn through the seizing around the throat-block strop and had finally worn away several strands of the wire, making it so weak that it gave way. The peak halyard block, also held on the same strop until then, had exploded loose, and the twelve-foot-long spar, with its heavy iron headband on the outer extremity, had crashed down and walloped me right over my right eye. I gingerly touched my forehead and eye socket. My eye was out on my cheek! There was a great round thing sitting just below the eyebrow!

Horrified, I took hold of it and, opening my eyelid with the other hand, shoved it back in. The salt of my hands stung my eye socket. For the first time in years I wanted to cry. Nelson was still hanging on to my trouser leg, whining, looking up at me pitifully with *his* one eye.

Slowly I made my way down to the cabin, where there was a small mirror set into the doghouse side. What I saw was a bloody mess. My right eyebrow was split wide open, with an half-inch bloody gap, now beginning to coagulate, while the eyelids were swelling. I forced the lids open and saw that the eye was blood red. I tried to move it and to my immense relief it moved; through the damaged eye I could see a glimmer of daylight. I hadn't lost the sight!

The first-aid gear was kept up forward, with the sail repair kit, and I made my way along the pitching cabin, grabbing the table as I struggled forward, and snatched up both kits, the first aid in its metal box, the sail kit in its blue bag. Back in the companionway, I fumbled around for a match to light the stove and heat up some water. In this I boiled the smallest needle I had onboard and the smallest fishing line, a nylon wisp of baitline, used for catching sprats. Then, with my seaman's knife, always kept razor sharp, I opened the wound up, squeezed the two sides together and put three great big stitches right across it, and tied a round turn and two half-hitches in the end of the nylon line. In the process I was sick three times, until my stomach could cough up no more.

Still covered in blood and regurgitated burgoo, I sat down and, shaking, made cocoa while Nelson stretched out on the opposite berth and looked at me as if to say, "You silly bugger, what did you do that for?"

After turning out the stove, with the boat still wallowing violently, I turned in to steady myself. I rose an hour later, head still throbbing, and spent the rest of the afternoon cleaning up the blood and spewed food.

Next morning, I hauled myself up the mainmast carefully, by the topping lift, seized the strop around the mast (a hard, cold, windy job), secured the blocks, slid down again to the deck, hoisted the mainsail; and we were off again. All in all, this took ten hours in a sloppy, jerking sea, with waves as high as eight feet, suspended atop a wildly waving mast, blind in one eye.

The weather for the remainder of the voyage to Reykjavík was fairly steady, winds of around twenty to twenty-five knots, and on the tenth day out of St. Kilda, I sighted through my one good eye, Reykjanesta, the southwest corner of Iceland, through a misty haze of low clouds

sweeping across the Skagi. I left plenty of sea room between *Cresswell* and the long, rocky, dangerous shore of the
Reykjanes peninsula, then hove to for the night, ready to
sail into port the following day. It was only thirty-five miles
away, on the southeast side of the Faxaflói, so there was no
hurry. There was no point in entering at night. In this
moderate weather the bay would be alive with fishing craft.

I bandaged my head up; fortunately, my eye no longer
hurt very much. Apart from bloodstains on deck and a few
dents and scratches where the gaff boom had clattered
down, the boat was in good order. However, there was sea
water in the fuel tank, so the engine was out of commission.
I did not feel like siphoning out the tank, a messy job, even
in port, and a nauseating job at sea, as I would wind up
swallowing about a pint of diesel oil. I left that job until
arrival, as the weather forecasts indicated a good breeze on
the morrow, which would blow me right into harbor.

The sun rose at around four in the morning; I hoisted sail
after breakfast and made my way into the wide Faxaflói,
past the port of Keflavík, busy with fishing craft, and so into
the harbor of Reykjavík.

With the yellow-jack pratique flag flying from the mainmast, I waited for the customs to come onboard.

"Hello, Englishman!"

"Good afternoon."

"Where you come from?"

"Scotland, Barra."

"Good trip?"

"Fair."

"What happen your head?" The customs man, a jolly-
looking fellow around fifty-five, with a red face, pointed at
my blood-soaked bandages.

"Oh, I always dress like this."

He laughed. "What happen?"

I told him.

"You go up the hospital; free for seamen. See Dr.
Jorgensson; he put you right. Then you come to my house,

we have some schnapps, yes?" He punched my shoulder playfully.

"Right, mate, you're on!" I would have grinned, but cracking my face hurt too much.

At the seamen's hospital, Dr. Jorgensson said I had made as good a job of the eye repair as he could have done. But I think he was merely trying to cheer me up. It left a wide scar, which reminds me, to this day, to always keep an eye on the blocks.

"Now take it easy here, rest for a week," he said. "And mind you, no strong drink."

"Right you are, sir."

I made my way up to the house of Alpi, the customs officer, where supper, cooked by his beautiful, merry, Rubenesque wife, was waiting, with a portion for Nelson. Then Alpi and I got stinking drunk and finished up flaked out over the floor of the living room in the warm, wooden house on the side of the hill overlooking the bay where Floki had sailed with his sacrificial ravens so long ago.

The schnapps did more for my eye than anything else I could think of, and in a few days I could see as well out of it as before, except perhaps when I looked aloft at the rigging strops. Then I could see a hundred times better.

By now, in mid-June, the days were much longer, and sunset was not until about ten-thirty at night, so I determined to make sail again from Reykjavík, now that my eye was good, and head for Greenland, where I would make the first attempt to reach latitude eighty north. It was already too late to try for Svalbard, unless I was going to winter there. It would be better to sally up the Greenland coast this year, and, if conditions there were too hard for wintering, try to get back to Iceland. Here, I could winter on the north coast and prepare the boat for the voyage into the deep Arctic early in the spring of 1960. The idea was to get to the edge of the pack ice as early in the summer as possible, so as to be able to shoot the sun right through the twenty-four-hour day, and then, with a northerly running current shifting the ice and the boat, to try to drift north over the winter, as far north as possible—I hoped to beat Nansen's record of eighty-four north—then emerge from the ice in the spring of '61.

I would need the boat in good order and a minimum of two years' food and stores. Iceland was the place to get ready to tackle the Arctic!

I'm a sailor lad in a fishin' boat,
Learnin' all about seafarin',
An' me education, scraps of navigation,
As we hunt the bonny shoals of herrin'.

Old fisherman's song about the Icelandic
grounds. It originates in Yarmouth, England.

15

Around Iceland Single-Handed

One evening while we were sitting in Alpi's living room eating liverwurst and jam sandwiches, Mrs. Alpi asked me, "What will you do now, Tristan?"

"Well, love, my eye's a lot better, but it's still a bit early to head up for the Scoresby Sund in Greenland. There'll be far too much pack ice and bergs yet to make the Sund safely. What I would like to do, while I'm waiting around, is have a go at sailing right around the island."

"What island?" she asked.

"Iceland," I replied.

Alpi perked up. "Alone?" he asked, over the sound of Grieg from the record player.

"I'll take Nelson, of course, he's very handy. Keeps a good watch when I heave to, and he's great in a fog."

"My God, but don't you know the distance involved? It's over one thousand miles straight sailing. If you get contrary winds, it will be more like two thousand."

"Yes, but the Maury wind charts indicate a pretty regular shift of wind around the end of June, and I can get to the North East Cape, off Thistilfiord, easily with this southwest breeze. Then I'd wait for a wind shift from southwest to the north, slide around the eastern shore, and be on a nice flat sea south of the island all the way back here."

I was trying my best to make it sound like a weekend cruise around Catalina Island.

"But supposing the wind doesn't shift to north; you might be waiting there for a month and miss the short Greenland summer, or at least one precious month of it, and it only lasts until the end of August." He unfolded a chart of the Iceland coast.

"Well," I said, pointing my finger at the island of Grímsey, sitting all alone in the Arctic Ocean about thirty miles off the north coast, "I will wait here. If the wind doesn't shift by the end of June, then I will head direct northwest for Scoresby Sund from Grímsey!"

Alpi frowned. "Hmm, and what about permits to visit Greenland? You know the Danish government is very particular about who visits their colony, and it sometimes takes weeks to get all the permits approved in Copenhagen."

"Bugger the Danish government!" I said, remembering Keanan the Postman. "Anyway, if I clear Reykjavík for Jan Mayen Island and the wind happens to take me into Scoresby Sund, what can they do about it? If they get snotty, I'll plead *force majeure* and then they can't refuse my entry, and in those latitudes they can't very well chuck me out of the port until the weather and I are ready for sailing, can they?"

"You bloddy crazy Valisaman. Don't tell anyone I heard that!"

"Handsome is as handsome does, Alpi."

"Well, have another sandwich, anyway." He passed the tray.

The next two days I spent preparing the boat for a fast sail around Iceland, as well as the estimated year in the Arctic. That's where I would be heading if the winds did not shift to schedule. I took in an extra twenty gallons of diesel oil, ten gallons of kerosene, extra cold weather lubricating oil and antifreeze, and a full set of arctic clothing. Alpi introduced me to one of his friends who had returned the previous year from working with a Swiss geophysical expedition in Greenland. Jokki had a complete set of Eskimo clothing, mostly made of caribou skin.

The suit all together—boots, socks, undervest, under-pants, gloves, trousers, and jacket—weighed only about ten pounds! Only the socks were not caribou skin. These were of blanket material, or duffle. The undergarments were of caribou fawn skin, softer, warmer, more pleasant to the skin than the finest silk or man-made fiber. The boots were of bleached young sealskin. Jokki also threw in a sleeping bag, the real arctic kind, with a short-fiber sheepskin lining. "And mind you sleep naked in this," he warned, "otherwise, if your sweat freezes you might get frostbite."

I got the whole rig for just twenty pounds (fifty dollars then), a real bargain.

With a good forecast of steady southwesterlies, I motored out of Reykjavík. I had cleared the engine fuel lines of sea water, so that my engine was working well, and I had checked and rechecked all the rigging, running and stand-ing.

The first hop, of about 120 miles, was to the deep inlet of Arnarfiord, up in the northwest peninsula, and we had a steady, but rough, passage across the wide mouths of the Faxaflói and the Breidafiord. The coast was very busy, with a continual coming and going of fishing craft large and small, so there was no sleep for me on this passage. By the time I entered the Arnarfiord, I was, as I always am after a few days in harbor, weary. I sailed right into the far end of the fiord, along the blue water, with great high stony mountains reaching up either side of the fiord, to where the icefalls of the mighty massif of Glama reach down to the sea.

I guided *Cresswell* in a little further towards the shore at the end of the fiord and dropped the hook. The first thing that struck me, in the clear air of the sub-Arctic, was the clarity of vision. The snow-clad peak of the Glama was all of ten miles away, yet it seemed to be only a mile. The second thing was the range of hearing, especially on the water. A voice speaking in normal tones two miles away, on a calm day, could be heard quite distinctly.

The next morning, early, there was such a palaver and blowing of sirens as the fishing boats took off out to sea that I could not help but be at my breakfast and have the anchor up and the sails hoisted before even the early rising Icelanders were out milking the cows in the green meadows of grassland rising between the Glama's rough, clenched knuckles.

As *Cresswell* sailed north, past the twin guardians of the Isafiord, the grey glowering heads of the Stigahlid and the Grunahlid, the wind increased, and with it, the clouds. Low, dirty, black, and menacing. But the weather held below gale force that night, until I had rounded the Horncap, the northernmost point of Iceland, and was sailing over comparatively calm waters, with a good stiff wind, southeast, to make the Húnaflói before dark on the morrow.

There are two islands called Grímsey off Iceland, one way out in the Arctic Ocean, and the other sitting just inside the Húnaflói, which is a very extensive inlet biting deep into the north coast of Iceland. With the help of the tide, I beat steadily all day until I could slide *Cresswell* in very cozily 'twixt the island and the mainland. There I rested, for there was not a living soul around, only birds and a few seals lying around on the pinkish rocks of the shore. To the northwest, as I let go the anchor in clear, clean water, shone the ice cone of the Drangajökull, all of thirty miles away; yet with the evening sun shining on the snows almost horizontally, it seemed as if I could reach out and touch it with my hand. My fishing line yielded a great fat halibut that night, but I found it very oily, and the only part I could eat with relish was the fins. It was a pity, because he was a giant, about forty pounds. I boiled up the head for Nelson, and he loved it.

At sunset, around ten-thirty in the evening, the sky turned a mottled green, a soft, pale green, tinged with brilliant orange over the far-off peaks of the Eiríksjökull far to the south. In the rushes and driftwood washed up on the stony beach, eider and harlequin ducks rustled their wings, while from the Arctic Ocean a low, cold sea-ice fog slowly crept in with the night breeze. This sea-ice fog was so low, yet so dense, that, standing in *Cresswell*'s cockpit, with my head in clear, fresh air, looking down I could not see my waist. It was like being afloat in a blanket of cloud. Above, the stars shone much bigger, much brighter than they appear in any shoreside southerly latitude (with the outstanding exception of Lake Titicaca, I was to find out much later). The Great Bear was almost directly overhead, pointing its tail at Polaris, a massive mammal leading a chubby cub over the deep, dark blue velvet of the polar night sky. Polaris was only about twenty degrees north of the vertical. I was about forty miles from the Arctic Circle. The ice floes I saw were far out on the northern horizon, low and gleaming on the grey green sea, but with the wind in the southwest, they were being held back from the shore, or at least their southerly progress was being impeded.

I sighted the seaward Grímsey Island on the evening of the fifth day out of Reykjavík, and I was feeling both pleased and lucky as it hove into view through a low-lying mist. I had had good winds, none over thirty knots and all fair, coming from abaft the beam, pushing *Cresswell*, heavily loaded, at a good rate through the seas.

Coming into the lee of the stark, barren island, I was not happy with the anchoring prospects. The swell all round the island would not make for a comfortable anchor, so, after a short sleep in the forenoon, I weighed anchor and headed for Thistilfiord, on the northeast corner of Iceland.

The sailing was splendid, and, making good time through the night, I decided to press on to the southern side of the Fontur peninsula, where we would be protected not only from the southwest, but also from the north. The following day, after beating hard to windward all afternoon and most of the evening, we at last went to anchor in the lee of high land at the root of the fiord.

I waited there for four days, in a flat calm, until the wind started to ease down from the north. The change of wind was right on time, just like clockwork, and I decided to sail immediately, even though it was night. The four days at anchor were spent resting and tending the gear, repairing a split No. 1 jib and listening to the cries of thousands of skuas and guillemots nesting on the cliffs, watching, again in delight, the magic wonder of the fulmar petrel's flight. The way out of the fiord was, as I had verified on the way in, clear of any obstacles, and I wanted to make a good fast run south, down the east coast of Iceland before the seas worked up from the north. Once past the Vestra Horn, the Western Horn, I would again be in the lee of the land, with the wind coming offshore and relatively calm seas. Temperatures dropped sharply with the coming of the north wind, and I wrapped up well. Now we were off again, bowling along, with the wind dead astern, sailing fast in the offing of the great bay of Vopnafiord; then, as dawn filled out the sky with light, past Seydisfiord.

That evening the great rocky plateau of the Vatnajökull, the ancient refuge of the Celtic Christians from the savage, overbearing Vikings, hove into sight, and I determined to make the next day for anchorage under Oraefajökull, where their original settlement had been fifteen hundred years before.

I had charts for the narrow entrance to the Skeidarafiord, so made my way in without too much bother and anchored behind the island, which almost blocks the river fiord from the sea. I arrived there about four in the afternoon and went ashore, taking Nelson with me, for he had seen rabbits on the shore, and despite his missing leg, the hunter instinct of the Labrador was strong in his blood. I spent the daylight hours of the evening climbing over the rocky ground, looking for traces of the Gaels, but found none except what might have been a flint ax-head. There were a number of piles of stones which, standing alone on grassy slopes, could have been the remains of huts or storage sheds, but there was nothing obvious to my untrained eye. Disappointed, I returned onboard and, after a meal of burgoo and bacon, turned in. It was a warm evening; Iceland in the summer, especially in the southeast, can be as climatically mild as England.

Early the next day, I slid out of the Skeidarafiord and, with the wind still blowing from the north, laid a course for the islands of Vestmannaeyjar, about a hundred miles to the west. The scenery on this sail was magnificent. The seas were quiet compared to what they usually are when the wind blows the long rollers of the Gulf Stream straight up against the wild shores, but now it was ideal sailing, with a good wind and an almost flat sea. To the north, to landward, the tremendous heights of the inland volcanic plateau stood out clearly in the sunlight against the dark clouds interspersed with patches of blue sky. In the northwest the great, volcanic, snow-covered cone of Hekla rose into the sky from a heaving rock plain.

During the night, we passed through a fleet of fishing craft, and I was wide awake the whole time. There must have been a thousand out there, fishing the south coast, taking advantage of the ideal conditions. Their engines thudded, their lights twinkled all around, and often, as I passed about two miles away to avoid their nets, I heard them talking and singing as they tended the nets. On one occasion, I even heard the clashing of cooking pans on the galley stove as supper was served. It is always a worry, navigating under sail through a fishing fleet. The answer, of course, is always to make sure that your navigating lights can be clearly seen, yet are not in a position where they dazzle the helmsman. Also, have an efficient radar reflector.

In the late morning the Vestmann Islands came into view, their high cliffs sparkling in the sun, the green seas heaving around the bases of the cliffs. Green for the Irishmen who, long, long ago, escaped from their cruel lord, Leif Arnarson, and, finally starved into defeat by

Leif's avengers, threw themselves over the high cliffs onto the rocks below, rather than surrender to the berserk Norse savages.

Here I anchored again and in the lee, or calm, side of the islands, with a great swell heaving the boat, spent a fitful night. I caught a cod and fried his liver. Nelson had the head, as dogs evidently do not need vitamin C to the same extent as humans. Anyway, he got enough out of the great staring eyes, which to him were a tasty morsel.

I left the Vestmann Islands the following day—it was too uncomfortable an anchorage to consider staying there any longer, and, besides, the month was passing and the north was calling. By evening of the next day, I had passed my earlier track from St. Kilda, and on the night of 30 June, 1959, the first recorded single-handed circumnavigation of Iceland was completed. It had taken twenty days, with eight nights at anchor.

As I beat against the northeast wind into Faxaflói and Reykjavík, I reflected on how fortunate I had been that the wind-shift had come so propitiously at the northeast cape. I was tired and determined to rest for two days before making off to Greenland and the north.

Alpi was on the jetty to meet me. His house overlooked the harbor, and he had recognized the old-fashioned gaff rig of *Cresswell*.

"I knew you did it" were his first words, as we shook hands. "My friend Jokki sighted your boat off the Hornafiord on Thursday, from his ship heading for Copenhagen, and he sent a radio message."

"Christ Almighty, Alpi, the bloody sea's getting like Piccadilly Circus these days. Can't go nowhere without someone breathing down your bloody neck and sending bloomin' telegrams——"

"Not where you're going," he said, mysteriously.

We headed for his house to scoff smorgasbord and quaff schnapps.

"I won't enter you in this time," said Alpi. "You've already got clearance for Jan Mayen. We'll let it stand at that."

"Thank God for that, Alpi. All I need now is a heap of forms to fill in."

"You like writing forms, eh, Tristan?" he grinned.

"Yeah, like a hole in the head!"

She's a tiddly ship, through the ice floes
   she slips,
She's sailing by night and by day,
And when she's in motion, she's the pride of
   the ocean,
You can't see her fanny for spray.
Side, side, Cresswell's ship's side,
Nelson looks on it with pride.
He'd have a blue fit if he saw any shit
On the side of the Cresswell's ship's side!

The Arctic Ocean song, 1959–61.

16

Mysterious, Misnamed, and Misunderstood Greenland

Aeons ago, when all the continents of the world were joined together, before they started to drift apart at the stately rate of two inches per hundred years or so, the miniature continent of Greenland was directly under what was then the equator. Thousands of millions of years before, when the earth was only one-fifth of its present age, the first rocks of Greenland had spewed forth out of the molten core of the world, forming a nucleus around which the five other vast continents, Europe, Asia, Africa-Australia-Antarctica, India, and America huddled, like young cubs feeding off their mother.

This one-time hub of the world's continents, now known as Greenland, eventually was covered by an immense blanket of tropical vegetation inhabited by nightmare monsters like the dinosaur and brontosaurus. That this was so is indicated by the unimaginably vast deposits of coal lying under the two-mile-thick layer of ice. The release of the pent-up power of the ice and coal of Greenland could provide the whole earth with energy for untold generations.

Gradually the miniature continent drifted away, towards what is now the Arctic. By some process which is not yet understood, the nature of the sun changed, and for many centuries the phenomena known as sunspots were very active, shooting great streamers of hydrogen hundreds of thousands of miles into space. This caused a cooling of the earth, especially at the poles. The great Ice Age was upon the earth, and Greenland was covered with a thick, thick blanket of ice. The mother continent of the world was frozen and remained so, entirely, for many thousands of years. It is still thawing out, slowly.

Once the sun, a variable star like all the others, again calmed down, the Arctic regions began to warm up. Eventually the island of Manhattan, which during the depths of the great Ice Age, with a vast amount of the world's sea water frozen into great sheets of ice, had been forty miles inland, had a harbor once more.

Around three thousand years ago one of the periodical warm-ups of the world was in full swing, and the Arctic regions were basking under a climate much milder than is now the case. This happy state of affairs continued until the early sixteenth century, when what we know as the Little Ice Age, which lasted about two centuries, began. Until a few thousand years ago Greenland was a land completely empty of humans. Birds and fishes had arrived thousands of years before, with the first warming. Then the animals—the musk ox, the polar bear, the Arctic fox—had entered the country over the eighteen-mile-wide strait which separates western Greenland from the Canadian islands. After many, many centuries, the Eskimos, a hardy race of people who had learned over untold generations of suffering to come to terms with the cruelest climate on earth, crossed the Smith Sound from Ellesmere Island to Etah, and slowly spread down to the south of Greenland, then up the east coast. When the first wandering Norse sea rover found the shores of Greenland, the Eskimos had just reached the southern tip.

The history of the Norse settlement of Greenland was, after a very promising start, a story of unmitigated disaster.

Contrary to the history I was taught in school, Eric the

Red was *not* the first Norseman to sight Greenland. This dubious honor belongs to a landless, penniless itinerant who first arrived in Iceland about A.D. 919. Too late to grab a piece of real estate for himself, he called together his companions, checked the hull and rigging of his knarr, embarked sheep and pigs for food, and sailed further west. His name was Gunnbjorn, and he returned to Iceland in 920 with tales of the great shore seven hundred miles towards the sunset, which he called *Gunnbjornarker*. This was a very human thing to do, just as it had been for Gardar to call Iceland *Gardarholm*, as it would be later for Columbus to name Colombia, Amerigo Vespucci to name America, Abel Tasman to name Tasmania, and for Cecil Rhodes to call a great chunk of Africa Rhodesia. This is nothing more than graffiti on the grand scale.

Eric the Red, who had the fortune to be "in with the media," which in those days consisted of the saga-singers, was born near Stavanger, Norway. He, too, arrived too late for the great Icelandic land-grab, and, having heard the tales of Gunnbjorn's much earlier voyage, sailed west.

On the shores of Greenland, which he reached in 981, he found willow, birch, and juniper, and short stubby grass in the valleys between the rocky morains. The summer was warm and kind. He returned to Iceland and spent the next four years mustering up twenty-five ships and five hundred settlers. With these, in 985, he established three colonies: one on the west coast of Greenland, which lasted three hundred and sixty years; one on the east coast, which survived a little longer; and one at the southern tip. The last trace of the Norse colonies of Greenland was found, 555 years later, by a German Hanseatic merchant, Jon Greenlander, of Hamburg. He sailed his ship into a fiord near Cape Farewell in 1540. There on the beach he found a man, one lone man, lying face down, dead. The corpse was small and thin, yet dressed in European-style clothes. In his hand he clutched a wooden harpoon with an iron tip.

This was the last descendant of the Viking Norsemen of

Greenland. The last of a race of strong, tall, robust people who had scourged all the known seas of the western world. This stunted dwarf, holding a primitive iron weapon, was the last of the Iron Age men. They had existed only a thousand years.

The Norse colonies died out for two reasons. First, around the early 1500s, the Little Ice Age began, which would last for two centuries; and second, unlike the Eskimo, the Viking refused to come to terms with the change in nature. He insisted on wearing European-style clothes. The skin of a caribou or a musk ox was beneath the notice of the proud Norsemen. Yet it would have saved them. They had encountered the Eskimos, whom they named *Skraelings* (screamers), many times over the centuries, and bloody battles had been fought. They would have done better to have learned how to dress from the Eskimos, who have survived ten thousand years.

During the centuries of Norse occupation of the coasts of Greenland, or at any rate small sections of them, trade into and out of the country by any ships but those of the Danish-Norwegian federation was strictly forbidden by edict from the court of Copenhagen. This, of course, led to the arrival of the Bristol ships, and in short order there was a flourishing trade in walrus tusks, caribou skins, bearskins, sealskins, whale blubber, and bone. Then, in the late 1500s, with the disappearance of the Norse colonists, the trade in slaves began. It is on record that in most years during the late 1500s anything up to one hundred Bristol ships were on the coast, many of them dealing in Eskimo slaves. Where these slaves were taken is a mystery, but I suspect they were used for seal hunting in the Arctic.

Arctic exploration in modern times began with the search by European mariners for the northeast passage to China, in the mid-1400s. Then, with the "discovery" of North America, the focus of exploration was changed to probing for the northwest passage to China. Voyages in pursuit of this elusive goal went on for the next four and a half centuries. Many, such as the Hudson voyage and the Franklin expedition, resulted in tragedy. In the latter, 129 men, in two ships, the *Erebus* and the *Terror*, stuck in the ice and ran out of food. Not knowing how to get to the food which was swimming under them, they starved to death, with the survivors eating the bodies of their comrades, then gradually starving again until there were more deaths, and so on, until finally the last man expired after eighteen months on a sparse diet of human flesh. This was in 1846. A gory story of brave, steady men driven to desperation. The mental state of the last man, huddled in the ragged tatters of a makeshift tent against the bitterly cruel blasts of the Arctic blizzards, knowing he was all alone in the black, everlasting night, contemplating his home and family and the dead comrades he had eaten, is beyond human imagination.

The summer in Greenland is short, only three months' duration. The shore ice and pack ice take all spring and one month of summer to thaw. Then leads, or passages, open up between the shore ice, heaped and immobile, piled up to 180 miles out from the shore line, and the pack ice. The moving pack ice floes are anything up to three miles long and six feet thick. By the end of July these leads may be a few miles wide. Between the ice floes the sea is calm, and in a favorable wind the sailing is magnificent.

The difficulty is finding the right leads, because many of them are dead ends, which get progressively narrower and finally, after many miles, wind up in a field of solid ice. The main risk is being caught in the passage between the shore ice, which is fixed and solid, and the pack ice, which might be moving at a great rate, carried south on the southerly running Greenland current. If the pack ice forces a small craft against the shore ice, she will be ground to bits in a matter of minutes.

But in nature every situation has not only disadvantages, but advantages, too. In the arctic summer it is broad daylight for most of the clock around; and in the twilight, which lasts for only an hour before the sun again rises, the sky is usually so clear that with the starlight alone it is possible to see many miles and even read a newspaper.

The shore ice, frozen across the mouths of the fiords in the cold winter, begins to break up in early June, and by mid-July there are clear entrances and long leads between the pack ice. It was for this reason that I delayed sailing for Greenland until July 2.

As I took my farewell of Alpi and his wife, together with some of their friends, they said to me, "Now don't forget, *if* you get to Ella, look up Mr. De Limos. He is a very good man and will help you."

"I'll be sure to do that *when* I reach Ella. So long, Alpi, don't take any wooden kronor!"

I sailed out of Reykjavík in the early morning, the last town of any size bigger than half-a-dozen huts that I would see for another twenty-two months.

Cresswell was soon out of the fishing fleet, heading across the Denmark Strait, which is probably, after the Mozambique Channel of Africa, the widest strait in the world, about eight hundred miles. The first five days were lively, with a northeaster blowing over my starboard quarter, but then the wind died and for two days I was becalmed. By this time maverick ice floes had become a common sight, and, sitting there fishing, waiting for a wind, I would sometimes have to start the engine to move out of the way of a floe. They were moving very slowly, about half a knot, to the south. On the second day, becalmed, I motored over close to one of them. The sides of the floe were not protruding underwater, so I tied the boat up to two spikes which I drove into the ice. With the boat safely secured, I took Nelson for a walk in the sunshine. It was warm enough to wear only a shirt, with the sleeves rolled up, shorts, and my British army boots. I felt rather like a Lancashire collier on the beach at Blackpool.

The seas were calm, almost Mediterranean blue, and looking over the sides of the floe, down into the green depths of the Arctic Ocean water, I saw thousands of shrimp floating around. There was no other sign of life. After an hour's stretch, I untied the boat, withdrew the spikes, and set off again, clear of the floe. Once well away from it, I set to making a shrimp net from a plastic mosquito net and some box-wire lashed onto the end of the harpoon handle.

"Well, old mate," I said to Nelson, "one thing's for sure—if it's like this all the way, first of all we won't starve for fresh food, and secondly we won't get very far to the north!"

By this time I was at latitude sixty-nine. I remember it quite well, because that evening I caught a halibut, a big one. He weighed on my hand scales exactly sixty-nine pounds. Again, he was much too oily to eat, so I boiled up his fins, which I ate for supper, while Nelson had his head. I tried giving him the head raw, because I wanted to see if I could persuade him to eat uncooked fish and thus save on cooking oil, but he turned his nose up at it. Then I cut off the best bits of the halibut flesh and pickled it in lemon juice made from pure lemon crystals. After a week of marinating, the halibut had given off a lot of oil, and the tang of the lemon detracted from the greasy feel of the meat.

After three days of calm, dodging the ice floes, which were passing more frequently, the wind piped up again, this time from the southwest, and soon we were off, under all working sail, in a calm sea, with a good breeze.

On July 9 I was sailing due west along a wide gap between two great fleets of pack ice. They were moving south, which meant that my actual course was to the southeast. I was concerned about this, because to the south of Scoresby Sund, my destination, there is no possible haven for a couple of hundred miles. Nothing except the high-cliffed, barren, inhospitable coast of King Christian IX Land, with the well-named Cape Cruel jutting out into the shore ice.

But on the eleventh a lead to the north opened up and I changed course, with the gentle breeze astern of *Cresswell*. There was a mist on the western horizon, hiding the land, which otherwise I would have seen, even from fifty miles off. Although I knew my position from the sun sights, which, despite the lack of a clear horizon because of the pack ice floes, were reasonably accurate, I did not realize that I was actually sailing up the so-called shore lead—that is, the gap between the fixed shore ice and the moving pack ice. But, luckily, there was a very wide shore lead, and so I had no problem, apart from fatigue and eyestrain, in reaching Cape Brewster on the fourteenth of July. There, the wind dropped, and I spent almost a whole day motoring between gleaming, gigantic icebergs passing through the mouth of Scoresby Sund on their way out to sea from the ever moving glaciers.

The colors were fabulous. All around us the mountains and glaciers reared up to the blue sky—greys, greens, and silvers of every shade. The Sund itself was sparkling blue, as we always imagine the Mediterranean to be and as it so rarely is. Proceeding majestically through all this were great white, gold, pink and green, yellow and pale blue mountains of floating ice, some of them a mile or more in length and up to a thousand feet high!

Soon, under the gossamer, spider-web, cirrus sky that presages the aurora borealis and a high wind, I sighted, away to the north, the wireless aerials of the radio station at Scoresby Sund hamlet, a little collection of wooden buildings, neat and tidy in the Danish fashion. By supper time I was at anchor, awaiting the arrival of the powers-that-be.

"Good evening, where have you come from?" He was a slender, yet big-boned man dressed in a lumber jacket and khaki trousers with sealskin water-boots. His florid face had the broken blue veins of a European who has spent many years in a cold climate, an appearance very similar to the symptoms, in more southerly latitudes, of alcoholism.

"Hello, pleased to meet you. I've come from Reykjavík."

"Have you permits to navigate in Greenland?"

"Well, no. I cleared for Jan Mayen, but as I was becalmed

and lost my way, I decided it would be best to head in here!"

"O.K., it's a good story. I'll believe it. But don't stay here too long, in case one of the inspectors arrives from Denmark, or there'll be hell to pay. As soon as you're ready, make out again for Jan Mayen, yes?"

"Yes."

"Meanwhile, welcome to Greenland!"

"*Mange tak!*" I mustered up one of my few Danish phrases.

"Hey, that's good, come for supper later on! But don't bring your dog ashore."

"Don't tell me you have quarantine regulations here?" I said.

"It's not that. All the dogs here have tapeworm, and he'll soon catch it from them."

"Thanks for the tip. I'll be over in an hour, as soon as I've squared everything away. No shore leave for you, old son," I said to Nelson.

That night I ate with the wireless crew, who had been on this tour of duty for almost two years and still had another year to go before returning to Denmark. One of them, who was to be married upon his return home, said that he loved the land so much he intended to return with his wife and settle down.

I spent two days in Scoresby Sund cleaning out the bilges, decarbonizing the engine cylinder heads, checking the rigging and sails, and storing onboard fifty pounds of charcoal fuel for the small solid-fuel heating stove. In the late afternoons I went climbing over the rocky hillsides among the brilliantly colored, lichen-mossed rocks, along the shores littered with great boulders brought down by the ancient icefalls, watching the musk ox, with its straggly black hair, like a horse's mane, the large bearded seals and the smaller hair seals basking on the flat rocks at the water's edge of the deepest fiord in the world—Scoresby Sund,

4,600 feet deep, with vertical walls of rock around it rising straight up to heights of 6,500 feet. Beyond the sheer cliffs on the high plateau, the great snowy mass of Petermanns Peak reared its head 10,000 feet above the fiord! A giant's playground. Over to the west, the Stauning Alps rose 9,000 feet, and this seemed low, for the icecap around the base of the mountains is 6,000 feet deep!

This part of the Arctic, on the east coast of Greenland, is unique in that it has short, intensive summers, when the temperatures rise up to nine degrees centigrade. For this reason, among others, the tremendous, seemingly limitless glaciers of the country are among the most productive in the world, calving off many thousands of huge bergs all year round, but especially in the warm summer. And for this reason, also, the waters off east Greenland are among the most dangerous to shipping of all the Arctic seas.

At the head of the northwest fiord of the Sund is one of the fastest moving ice-masses on earth—which calves off anything up to fifty bergs a day in the warmest days of summer. And these can be over a mile in length! What a source of energy if only it could be harnessed!

As I climbed over driftwood washed up on the shore after floating on the currents all the way from Siberia, I reflected that the first strikes, the first probes north, into the East Greenland ice by sailing craft had been made by a British expedition from Liverpool, in the year 1824. They had reached Shannon Island, named after one of their leaders. I intended to penetrate the ice fields further north, if possible to latitude eighty-four north, which is the furthest that the great Norwegian Nansen reached in the *Fram* sixty-six years earlier. The odds were against this, but if I didn't outdo Nansen, at least I'd beat the Liverpool expedition! Scoresby Sund is on latitude seventy-two north. There were only thirteen degrees between me and the furthest north under sail! Only 780 miles! By ocean sailing standards, a mere eight days' sailing!

Out of the night that covers me,
Black as the pit from pole to pole,
I thank whatever gods may be
For my unconquerable soul.

In the fell clutch of circumstance
I have not winced nor cried aloud.
Under the bludgeonings of chance
My head is bloody, but unbow'd.

Beyond this place of wrath and tears
Looms but the Horror of the shade,
And yet the menace of the years
Finds and shall find me unafraid.

It matters not how strait the gate,
How charged with punishments the scroll,
I am the master of my fate;
I am the captain of my soul.

William Ernest Henley, "Invictus."

17

Tooth and Nail, Head-On!

My aim, upon departing from Scoresby Sund, was to sail north as hard and fast as possible through the ice fields, along the shore lead, between the shore ice and the pack ice. My destination was Kap Bismarck, on the coast of Queen Louise Land, approximately 380 miles north, on latitude seventy-six degrees, forty-five minutes north. If I made a swift, easy passage, I should arrive within two weeks. If, on the other hand, the passage was slow because of ice obstacles and hazards, and I arrived late in the northern summer, I would winter near the Danmarks Havn wireless station, in a small bay which might or might not be ice free. Then, when the ice broke up the following summer, I would press on north up the coast of Germania Land and attempt to buck the current and the ice to a point north of latitude eighty-four, the furthest north ever reached to date by a sailing ship.

If the passage was fast, I would call briefly at Kap Bismarck, then press on further north while the ice was still fairly loose, hoping to reach the magic eighty-four-degree point that same autumn. Then, the ice would seize the boat and, on the current, carry *Cresswell* south again over the winter, back to civilization. If the drift back south was slow, I still had a good chance of weathering it out, for there was two years' supply of food onboard, and plenty of seals around.

The yearly inspector's ship was expected to arrive any day, and as I was eager to beat the coming winter in late September, I sailed out of Scoresby Sund anchorage with few regrets, apart from losing the fine company of the Danish radiomen and meteorologists, who had been hospitable and informative.

I motored out of the Sund through the loosening pack ice, dodging mountainous icebergs floating out into the Arctic Ocean. Once clear of the shore ice, which extended about forty miles, I found a wide-open lead to the north, though well dotted with isolated ice floes of all sizes. I was headed for the radio station at Myggbukta, on the coast of Hold with Hope peninsula, about 160 miles north. After three days and nights of hard sailing, in a flat sea, with the south wind dead astern, I was off the island ($\emptyset$) of Bontekoe, where I moored onto an ice floe which had found its way around to the southern side of the island and gone aground. Here I slept fitfully for one "night." I was concerned in case another floe should come around the island and trap *Cresswell* against the one she was already moored to. After a few hours' sleep I decided to stay at Bontekoe $\emptyset$ for one more day, carrying out the necessary chores which had been neglected during the three-day passage north, when I had been on the wheel practically the whole time.

After the work was done, I took a good look around, though I did not leave the boat. I could have climbed over the piled up ice on the southern shore, but I was wary of possible accidents and also of the boat's breaking loose from the floe, if the wind shifted. During the day, it was warm enough to wear my normal sailing clothes—jersey, sheepskin jacket, long cotton underpants, and blue jeans, with long stockings and sea boots. But at night it turned cold, and I was glad to be in the sleeping bag for the short "dark" hours.

I watched the broken-up bits of the great pack ice field as they floated by the island—long ice fields, several miles across, which took hours to pass; "ice cakes" only as big as a motor car; chunks and the slushy "brash," melting on the sides of the larger floes and sinking into the ocean. On many of the floes and fields, there were seals, sometimes in small groups, sometimes alone, and I watched them through the binoculars as they woke from their brief naps and popped their heads up for a startled look about for marauding bears.

Over to the west, as soon as the sky clouded over, a strange phenomenon appeared. A perfectly recognizable map of the terrain below was reflected on the white bases of the clouds. It tallied up quite well with the information I had on the charts. Water of the fiords and leads showed up black on the surface of the clouds, while the ice and snow was a mottled grey color, and the vegetation, lichen on the rocks ashore, reflected a yellow or brown. It was as if someone was holding a huge mirror in the sky. This is what the Danes called the "ice-blink." "Very useful," I said to Nelson. Now I knew how to find a good water lead in cloudy weather.

By this time I had taken to wearing snow goggles, because the summer sunlight, which strikes a glare through the dry, clean air, made the ice of the floes shimmer with blinding light. After suffering a headache, I soon realized that snow blindness is in fact the result of eyestrain caused by the constant, instinctive seeking of shadows which, because of the angle of the sun's rays, are almost nonexistent. Man's greatest aid to judging distance, in normal conditions, is the effect of light and shadow. If the shadow effect is changed, as it is, for example, in moonlight, or under fluorescent lighting, then our eyes search continually for the normal references, straining themselves to gauge distance. The effect of the reflection of light from the ice is also a cause of blindness, but a minor one compared to trying to find normal seeing distance in abnormal conditions.

The thought of the continual procession of bergs and ice fields across the top of the world, for thousands of square miles, was, at first, somewhat terrifying. I was relieved that there was no one else with me. Eventually I realized that the so-called Arctic hysteria, the feeling of panic which exploring parties have reported, is, in fact, only a form of mass hysteria transmitted from one nervous member of a group to the others. Being alone, I stood a much better chance of avoiding this affliction. I decided to consider only the immediate environment, and to hell with the rest of the Arctic. That could look after itself.

When I left the ice-floe off Bontekoe ∅ and headed north for the radio station at Myggbukta, it was obvious that I stood no chance at all of getting to the shore. The ice was one solid frozen mass of heaped-up, stranded floes and bergs, with ledges and needlepoints jumbled up higgledy-piggledy into the sky as far as the eye could see. The nearest I could approach the shore of Gausshalv Island, where the radio station was located, was about thirty miles, and I dared not chance walking over the shore ice for that distance. I decided to carry on north.

Here I had to turn my course east, out into the ocean, towards the moving continent of pack ice floating down from the North Pole, looking like an army on the move—horsemen and gun carriages, coaches and long lines of foot soldiers marching across the rim of the world.

After heading east for forty miles offshore, I eventually found the edge of the fixed mass of shore ice and, picking my course carefully, headed again north. There was little wind on this passage, and progress was painfully slow. I did not use the engine, as I wished to conserve fuel for emergencies, in case I was trapped in thin ice. The wind was so weak that it took me almost ten days to cover the eighty miles to latitude seventy-four, away out over the ice piled up on the Home Foreland. I was still in an area where the British Liverpool expedition of 1824 had left marks, right up the coast, in the names of headlands and islands.

At latitude seventy-four progress was almost halted altogether, for the pack ice was much closer to the shore ice, and the shore lead, so-called (though it was anything up to two hundred miles out to sea), was very indistinct. Many times I headed up one lead only to find myself in the middle of a solid field of ice many times bigger than a New York City block. Then I would have to turn the boat around and motor out against the southerly breeze, running with the current to escape the mass of ice closing around the boat.

It was now the first week in August, and there was already a noticeable change in daytime temperatures. After two more weeks of struggling to find my way through this maze of icy jigsaw puzzles, the wind changed to the north and the temperature fell below freezing. I donned my fawnskin underwear, a shirt and an extra jersey, the Eskimo-made caribou-skin jerkin and trousers, and the sealskin boots.

Until the eighth of August there had been light twenty-four hours a day. After that the sun was down below the horizon for rapidly increasing periods of time, so that by the end of August, daylight and darkness each took half of every twenty-four hours, as they do below the equator. As the skies were mostly clear of cloud, I was still getting quite accurate sun sights. However, I had difficulty in finding my course through the ice, for there was rarely any ice-blink, which would have indicated water passages.

I reached Pendulum Island, at latitude seventy-four, forty-five north, on August 18, and, to my delight, found clear water running north, ahead. There were still many, many ice floes around, and after a brief rest (tied up against a floe in fairly open water), I pushed on, ever north, using the engine, as there was rarely room to beat against the wind. Progress was slow, as the engine was only ten horse-power and *Cresswell* was heavy with stores. Hammering against the strong north wind and current, I could not make more than two knots over the ground, and most of that to east or west, dodging the floes and bergs, which were becoming disturbingly frequent, especially at the end of the easterly legs.

When I reached the edge of the shore ice, off Kap Philip Broke, the southeastern cape of Shannon Island, at latitude seventy-five north, I saw my first polar bear. They are difficult to spot except when they are fairly close, say about three hundred yards. The dirty yellow color of their fur blends in perfectly with ice which is more than one season old, but I happened to be scanning the inshore side of the ice, as best I could, with the binoculars, when suddenly a slight movement in one hummock of piled-up floe caught my eye.

It is difficult to gauge distance in clear air over ice, but I reckoned he was about two hundred yards from the boat, walking on all fours. From fore to aft he was all of ten feet long, and he looked as if he weighed a ton. By this time, with the wind coming south off the ice, Nelson had picked up his scent and went rigid, sniffing the air, the classic pose of the hunting Labrador. When he sighted the bear with his one eye, he jumped and disappeared down below.

I had been warned about bears out on the ice by the Danes in Scoresby Sund. They had told me that a polar bear ashore was, like the grizzly bear out of the woods, a timid beast, who would avoid any encounter with an enemy. But once out on the floes, he was king of all he surveyed. He had only seals and wolves (possibly) to deal with, and he became a hungry, arrogant, violent, very dangerous wild beast, whose weight alone was enough to knock the life out of the strongest man. I put *Cresswell* on a broad reach, out to the east, adjusted the sails, for there was a perfectly clear stretch of water ahead on that course, then went below to make hot chocolate and warm myself.

"Thank God there's water between us and him," I said to Nelson, who was cowering under the cabin table. He bumped his tail in the floorboards. But I was disturbed by the thought that if I did not fetch Kap Bismarck and got stuck in the southward drifting ice pack, one of these brutes, or maybe even more than one, might get wind of us and attack.

By August 30 I was on latitude seventy-five degrees fifty minutes north—only sixty miles south of Kap Bismarck and safety. But try as I would to find a clear passage, it was almost impossible. Stretched right across the northern horizon was a solid barrier of piled up shore ice, rising in hummocks up to three hundred feet above the ocean level, along with a moving mass of pack ice and bergs, some of the latter up to nine hundred feet high and three miles from bow to stern.

Choosing one seemingly promising narrow lead running slightly west of north, hardly wider than three times the beam of *Cresswell*, I pressed on. By now the tops of the ice floes were well above deck level of my boat. I was, therefore, most of the time protected from the wind to about a third of the way up the mast. The engine was pushing the boat at four knots over the ground, going flat out, while the ice floes, moving on the current, were traveling at around a knot and a half. Our combined speed, therefore, was around six and a half knots—eight land miles per hour. All day, all night, for two days, I stayed at the wheel continuously, without a break, wending my way through these never-ending walls of gleaming ice as high as a garden wall, sometimes in a narrow passage hardly wide enough for the boat, sometimes in wide stretches.

I was still cold, even though I had thrown two blankets over my Arctic clothing and rigged up a windshield of canvas, forward of the wheel, to keep off the boat's own wind, created by her speed. The rigging was frosting up. This was a great worry. Every time I reached a stretch of wide lead or clear water, I had to lash the wheel, leave the boat at the mercy of the current, climb the masts, and knock off the ice with a small ax.

Doing this became a nightmare of cold and superhuman effort, short of sleep as I was. High up the mast the north wind blew intensely cold, frosting up all my clothes, with my breath forming an inch-thick layer of solid ice over the thick scarf tied up around my head between the goggles and the collar of my jerkin.

Not to have knocked the ice off the rigging would have been to commit suicide. It formed so quickly in the wind that within three hours it could create such a weight high up on the craft that it would overcome the weight of the ballast in the keel and capsize her. *Cresswell* would sink immediately. If I did not drown right away, I would freeze to death. If I managed to clamber onto the floe, I would both freeze and starve to death anyway in a long, protracted agony over a couple of days. Getting rid of the ice was a matter of staying alive.

By the morning of September 1, I was almost falling asleep on my feet. I had reached latitude seventy-six degrees ten minutes north. Bismarck station was a mere thirty miles away. Perhaps there was just enough clear water ahead to make it to Bismarck and sleep in safety. Perhaps around this next cape of ice, perhaps around the corner of that berg, the ice would clear just enough to get me thirty miles. Thirty miles in an ocean-crossing sailing yacht was a mere six hours' normal sailing; in a motor car, half an hour on a good road. Thirty miles—the difference between safety for the duration of the bitterly cold winter, and extreme discomfort, danger, and possibly even death, a cold, lonely death, in the ice. I pressed on, more by willpower now, for my physical strength was ebbing with lack of sleep. I was about three hundred miles nearer the Pole than the northernmost tip of Alaska.

Suddenly, my fate was decided for me, though I did not realize it at the time. The lead I had followed for the past day of cold torture ended up in a perfect wall of ice. I turned a corner, and there I was, like being in a harbor. By this time my fuel stock was so low, and the engine so cold, that getting out of this impasse under power was out of the question. I decided to take a chance. I tied the boat by a bowline only from the end of the cul-de-sac and went to sleep. I slept four hours, dead to the world.

When I awoke, feeling much stronger and more confident, I climbed onto the floe. Earlier it had been difficult to
mount the floe to drive the stake in, as I had to cut steps out
of the side with an ax in order to get on top. I had been too
weak to jump up. Now it was much easier, and the sky had
lightened into a grey twilight. The wind, however, was still
screaming over the floes from the north, and once on top of
the floe, it was a job to remain upright.

I looked first to the north; what I saw was one of the
bitterest, most disappointing sights I have ever seen in my
life.

There, only forty yards from where I stood, on the other
side of an isthmus joining two huge fields of jammed-up
pack ice that stretched away as far as I could see east and
west, northeast and southwest, was another lead heading
north, and away, at the end of it, at its mouth, was a great
stretch of clear water right across the north horizon!

"Goddamn it, bugger it, and blast it!" I cursed myself,
the floes, the forty yards, everything. Then, more in anger
than in desperation, I clambered back onboard, grabbed the
big tree-felling ax, and started to hack away at the ice. But
after a few minutes the foolishness of trying to carve
through a forty-yard-thick wall of ice twelve feet deep
became obvious. I sat down on the ice. Tears were futile in
this temperature, for they would freeze as soon as they left
my eyes. Then I thought of what would happen if these two
fields of ice, each higher than the boat, came together.

There was only one solution, for sailing back south was
out of the question. It would take days to overtake the miles
and miles of ice fields, and during those days they could
crush together anyway, especially if the westerly field hit
the fixed shore ice. I would not stand a chance. If I stayed
where I was, I was a dead man; if I tried to sail south, I was
probably a dead man. The third alternative, difficult though
it might be, was the only solution. I must try to get the boat

up onto the ice floe, about seven feet above sea level. But how?

There was only one possible way. I must hack a slipway out of the ice, wide enough for *Cresswell*'s hull to slide up, then I must lighten her bows, get her bows onto the ice whilst the stern was still loaded and low in the water, then unload all her other gear, and drag the empty hull up the incline.

And this is what I set to doing. I hacked away with the ax and shifted tons of ice, solid hard ice, until, after nine days' steady hard labor, I had a "ramp" leading from just below water level, back through the ice floe at a steady incline of about twenty-five degrees, back almost to the other side of the ice-floe isthmus. I worked all the daylight hours, axing, throwing, shoveling, slashing, until a fairly smooth ramp was created.

On the ninth of September I unloaded all the stores, all the sails, all the tools off the boat, having made a ladder out of some spare lumber, so I could climb off the deck straight onto the "deck" of the floe.

With the forefoot now above the waterline, I turned the boat bows onto the ramp and dragged her until the keel, just an inch of it, was resting on the ice. Then, I started to unload the midship parts of the boat, lifting the forefoot even higher above the bottom edge of the ice ramp.

Then, with much labor, I dug a five-foot hole in the ice at the inner end of the ramp, and into this I dropped the eighty-pound hurricane anchor. The chain from the anchor was secured to a three-inch-diameter nylon storm running line, a hundred fathoms of it—six hundred feet. I filled the anchor hole up with salt water and had a short sleep after a hearty meal of corned beef, rice, and porridge.

When I awoke the salt water in the anchor hole had frozen solid, and I had a good "deadman" to pull the boat up against. I had no winches in *Cresswell*, so the whole thing had to be done with blocks and tackles, five of them, six-inchers, with three sheaves apiece. I dug footholds into the top of the floe, reeved the storm line through the blocks, and set to pulling four and a half tons up the twenty-five-degree incline. It took me five days to get the forefront up to the chain, a matter of twenty-eight yards or so. The bottom of the keel was then only about a foot below the top of the floe. She was out of danger. She was sitting almost on top of the ice, exposed to a bitter cold wind, covered in frost and driven ice, but she was safe. That was the main thing. Wearily I reloaded my stores onboard, except for some of the cartons of corned beef, which would take up valuable space in the cabin. These I covered with an old sail, pegged down into the ice. Then I noticed that the northern exit from the floe had jammed up solidly with ice floes.

"One good thing about this situation, old son," I said to Nelson, as I clambered below to get a long rest, "at least we don't have to worry about the rigging freezing up now." But the ice would still have to be knocked off regularly, at least twice a day, to prevent its weight snapping the masts.

I made a big pot of burgoo, so I could rest thoroughly during the next day or two, and tacked up all my mutton cloths on the inner lining of the hull around the cabin, then fixed felt pads over the portholes and the skylights, while the tiny cabin warmed up with the heat of the cooking. Then I went topsides to have a last look around.

The wind had died at last, and there was little noise except for the distant cracking and crunching of the ice. The sun had dropped over the southwest horizon, changing the sky to pale blue, deepening into turquoise, Prussian blue, then Stygian black. In the north and east the stars shone so bright, so close, that it seemed as if they hung around my shoulders. The dryness of the atmosphere made the rays of the stars diffuse into each other. The effect was like standing under a great chandelier of a billion-trillion shining candles.

I decided it was too cold to piss in the open air. I would do it in the big wine demijohn, hermetically sealed, which I used in inclement weather. I touched the mizzen shrouds with my mittened hands. Small bits of glistening ice fell off the rigging wire. I made a mental note to clean my ice goggles later. I had removed them, for the twilight was deepening. The smell of a good stew simmered up the companionway hatch.

Although I had failed to reach Nansen's latitude of eighty-four degrees north, I had got very close—within eight degrees. I had reached a point only 850 miles from the North Pole itself, and despite the potentially terrifying situation *Cresswell* had been in only two weeks previously, she was now reasonably safe, unless the ice under her broke up.

As I turned to go below, I saw the bear. Twelve feet long, padding silently, swiftly over the snow-laden ice. He was only fifty yards away, coming straight at the boat!

Weary with toil, I haste me to my bed,
The dear repose for limbs with travel tired;
But then begins a journey in my head
To work my mind, when body's work's expired.
For then my thoughts, from far where I abide,
Intend a zealous pilgrimage to thee,
And keep my drooping eyelids open wide,
Looking on darkness which the blind do see.
Save that my soul's imaginary sight
Presents thy shadow to my sightless view,
Which like a jewel hung in ghastly night,
Makes black night beauteous, and her old face new.
  Lo, thus by day my limbs, by night my mind,
  For thee, and for myself, no quiet find.

Shakespeare, Sonnet 27.

18

Alone on the Ice

"Jesus Christ Almighty!" I said under my breath to Nelson, who was also on deck to perform his ablutions over the side. But he had gone stock rigid, his ears quivering, his eye glaring at the monster advancing towards us. Then, without thinking, I was down the companionway ladder, grabbing Nelson as I went.

For a second or two, slithering down the ladder, my mind was in a dither. Instinctively grabbing my harpoon, an eight-foot-long ash shaft with a fine, greased steel tip sharpened to a needlepoint, from its stowage on the deck head of the cabin, I turned to mount the ladder. Then my mind started to work. Fast.

"Move!" I shouted to Nelson. "Move, you silly sod. Make the bastard think you're a fox! Move!" Nelson jerked out of his stupor and jumped, then ran as fast as his three legs would carry him up the side-deck, to the fore deck, where he stood his ground, snarling.

By now the bear was hauling himself upright, with his great paws clawing at the guardrails. As his head, with its fierce fangs and glittering, menacing eyes, appeared over the gunwale, I jabbed at him with the harpoon from where I was standing in the companionway. My idea was to fight him off from there, where the lower part of my body was protected and I could duck if he made a swipe at me.

The bear jerked his head and body back in surprise, his

great massive claws tearing away the upper wire of the
guardrail, bending the one-inch-thick galvanized iron
stanchions as if they were putty. Then I realized that this
huge creature could, if he wished, literally tear the boat
apart with his strength. At the same time Nelson made a
gallant charge towards him aft along the side-deck, yapping, snarling, and barking. All hell broke loose. The bear
recovered from his shock and rebounded back, his whole
body thumping against the hull, which slid sideways, the
keel jarring against the side of the ramp. I reacted fast and
jabbed at his right paw, which was tearing at the canvas
deck cover, the huge nails ripping into the covering clear
through to the wood underneath. The harpoon struck
home. It went through the bear's forefoot and stuck in the
wood underneath. The bear let out a roar loud enough to
shake the boat to pieces. Then he ripped his paw, harpoon
and all, out of the deck and dropped down onto the ice. The
harpoon went flying, clattering over the floe. I could feel his
breath, hot and oily, like a cloud of steam from a locomo-
tive. For a second or two Nelson and I stook stock-still,
petrified with shock and alarm. The bear crawled on all
fours around the side of the boat, bumping the hull with his
shoulder. Then I remembered the Very rocket gun.

This is a device, shaped like a pistol, with a barrel eight
inches long and an inch and a half bore, into which flare
rockets are loaded. Fired by mariners in distress, the rocket
will rise into the sky up to four hundred feet and slowly
descend, its phosphorous flakes burning all the way back
down to the sea's surface. When I had sighted the first bear,
off Shannon Island, I had loaded the Very pistol in readi-
ness for just such an attack as this. Now I slithered below,
fumbled at the fireworks box, and grabbed the pistol, my
hands shaking badly.

The bear had climbed up above the ramp on the other
side of the boat and was pawing at the gunwale with one
forefoot, while swiping at Nelson, who was trying to lure
him forward away from me. I climbed the ladder and

turned to face the bear. Holding the Very pistol in one frozen hand, I slammed down as hard as I could on the doghouse roof with the other, fist clenched.

The bear turned his jaws towards me, showing his great fangs, his hungry, wicked eyes crackling with anger. I fired, sending the rocket straight into his throat, a great stream of red light particles. With a grunt, the bear threw himself backwards onto the ice floe, rolling in agony, for the phosphorus of the flare was burning fiercely in his gorge. Then, jumping up and down with tremendous force, he beat the ice with his paws, all the while weaving his upper body from side to side, while Nelson slithered onto the ice and snapped at his hindquarters. After a few more mighty thuds on the top of the ice floe, which actually shook the boat, the bear took off fast across the ice and dove into the water on the other side of the floe. This did not save him, however, because phosphorus burns underwater. There was a mighty splash in the distance and he disappeared.

Shivering with fright and excitement, I went below, still holding the pistol. Once below I found that my fingers were stuck to the rocket gun. Frostbite! I grabbed a flannel cloth in the galley, threw it into the still simmering stew, then fished it out again with a fork and slapped it, steaming, over my hand. I didn't feel a thing for about thirty seconds, until the circulation was restored, and then the hot stew started to scald the hand, and I knew it was safe. I checked my face, which had been exposed just below the eyes, above the icy scarf. There were two fish-belly white spots, one on each cheek. I repeated the burgoo-stew treatment, in my hurry splashing the hot, gooey liquid onto my eyelids, and in a few seconds the cure was made. The pain almost sent me through the roof.

By this time Nelson was back in the cabin, still shaking with fight-lust.

I threw him a bone and some hardtack, then, after closing the companionway door and hatch cover to try to warm the boat up again, I collapsed on the berth. "Jesus!" I thought,

"I hope there's no more of *those* around!"

Wearily I stood at the galley and doled out some stew, but I couldn't eat much. I felt sick with concern and relieved at the same time.

Sleep, when it came, was fitful and full of fantasy. But before I dropped off, I made two resolutions. One was that I would not, while on the ice, sleep more than two hours at a stretch, and then would always leave Nelson on guard in a box in the cockpit to protect him from the wind. The other was that before sleeping I would always, whenever possible, search the floe, out to a perimeter of a thousand yards, for signs of bear.

The Danes had told me that bears generally haunt broken floes and areas where there are many seals, and that, usually, where there is a bear, the white fox is never far behind, eating the scraps of seal left by the bear. Not only the tracks of bear in the ice would warn me of their presence, but also the much smaller spoor of the fox.

Seals are the bears' only food. They are supposed to catch fish, but none of the Danes I met in Iceland and Scoresby Sund had ever seen a bear fishing, neither had any of the Eskimos I met later. There is a conundrum here. If, as the dieticians tell us, fat is only fuel, and protein is the body-builder, how is it that the bear, whose only food (evidently) is seal meat, which is practically all fat, manages to build up such a huge, strong body?

During the short days which followed, I remembered everything that the Danes told me about bears. How they stalk a seal, with their great bulky bodies splayed down on the ice, surprisingly flat and inconspicuous from nose to tail. If it's a bearded seal, a great heavy animal, weighing up to six hundred pounds, the bear will satisfy his appetite, then he will leave the rest of the carcass and amble off to sleep. After two or three days' rest, he will return to the frozen seal remains, a great mass of solid hard blubber and bones, and gnaw it, grinding the rock-hard mass between his teeth till there is nothing left. That is if the foxes have not gotten to it while the bear is sleeping.

The bears are usually followed by the fox, as the lion is followed by the hyena and the jackal. But the two ignore each other. The bear knows he cannot catch the swift fox, and the fox knows the bear is too slow for him; so as he follows the bear, the fox runs around and around, playfully teasing the great, lumbering king of the Arctic. Ashore, the white fox tends to treat man in the same way as he does the bear, running round him with not a care in the world. The fox confuses man with the bear. The bear confuses dogs sleeping or lying down on the ice with the seal. The bear also confuses a still man, sitting or lying down, with the seal. The bear confuses a standing or running dog with the white fox. How he sees an active man is not quite clear. It is either as another bear or as another type of hunting animal. Whichever, out on the ice floes the polar bear will attack, because he cannot stand competition in the fight for survival.

During the short daylight hours, I obtained fair sun sights, and it was soon evident that the drift of the floe was more or less due south, at the rate of around half a knot. That is about twelve miles a day, but as the days progressed, this seemed to be slowing down, until by the end of September, it was down to six miles a day. The great ice field was moving steadily and surely, and I was by then at around latitude seventy-three, which put me somewhere near the wireless station at Myggbukta and Ella Island. I kept the boat clear of ice and driven snow as best I could to make her show up against the whiteness of the floe, in case a plane passed overhead. One day, during the twilight, I actually saw a flying boat heading northwest, but it was far away on the southern horizon, and with the bear threat I did not dare waste my signal flares trying to attract his attention. I had only eight flares with me and no idea how many bears might show up. But fortunately none did, although on two occasions I saw them through the binoculars, walking over distant ice floes.

By the first of October my floe, which I had christened *Ark Royal*, had started to break off here and there, with loud cracks, groans, and wheezes. The lead to the north of *Cresswell* was once again widening up. *Ark Royal* was shaped something like an hourglass, with the two sand vessels pointing east and west and *Cresswell* sitting on top of the narrow stem. If the western edge hit against the solid shore ice, the two "sand vessels" would part company, which would split the floe just about where *Cresswell* was.

I made plans to get *Cresswell* back afloat. It was pointless to slide her back down the ice ramp into the southern lead, for it no longer existed. Where the lead had been was a long line of tossed-up ice cakes and chunks piled up into the air for a distance of about two miles!

The only reasonable course was to dig another ramp through the ice over into the northern lead, then slide *Cresswell* down it and try to emerge from the ice field by way of that route, which seemed to be fairly loose, being low, flat, "young" ice, newly formed. If I could get her afloat again, there was a chance I could get out.

I was out on the ice, huddled up in my Eskimo gear, with a screaming storm coming up from the south, blowing ice particles so strong that I could feel them drumming on my caribou-skin jerkin, even through the inner layer of thick hair. Nelson circled me slowly, keeping watch just within visibility range, about fifty yards. I was probing the ice with the harpoon, plotting the course of the new ramp. Ahead, through a momentary gap in the flying ice, I saw a black lump stretched out on the floe, not more than fifty yards away. A seal! I dropped down flat onto the ice.

Nelson was behind me, out of eyeshot of the seal. I lifted my head up and looked around, trying to appear like a seal, jerking my hooded head in quick, sniffing motions. Nelson sat down in the driving ice. He had sensed something was afoot, even though the wind was blowing at an oblique angle from our side to the seal's. I waved my hand down and Nelson dropped prone, his nose twitching.

There, in front of me, was a highly sensitive animal, with built-in natural alarm systems; an animal which never slept for more than three minutes at a time, which continually was on the lookout for foes, and which could move with surprising speed over the ice and into the safe water. Behind me was another animal, highly intelligent at stalking, hunting, and recovering, courageous and bold, but crippled. His missing eye did not seem to affect his sight much. The trouble was the missing forefoot, which deprived him of the hunting dog's speed, though only by a small margin. In between was me, man, intelligent enough to develop weapons capable of killing a seal from a mile away, yet reduced now to becoming a seal himself until he could get near enough to strike.

Soon I was within forty yards of the seal. He raised his smooth head up, with his shoulders supported by his flippers, and slowly looked around. Then he dropped down on the ice. I watched him for a few seconds, then inched forward again. Every five minutes or so I raised my head, just as the seal was doing, and gazed around. Nelson stayed prone, but he too was slowly slithering forward right behind me, keeping my body between him and the seal. After another hour of inching forward little by little, I was within twenty yards of the seal. After several hard stares, each lasting about a minute, he no longer looked my way. He still rose up on his fins and looked around, but only at the quarters of his vision away from my direction. Then I realized that he had made up his mind that I was another seal.

I scrabbled quietly forward, keeping as close to the ice as I could. By this time my dark goggles had started to steam, and I longed to take them off and clean them, but of course this would have warned the seal. I moved ahead again, perched up, looked around. Nelson had stopped moving with me. He was too crafty to come near enough for the seal to see him and think he was a fox following a bear. Another hour, another ten yards, then a slow nudging forward over the smooth, twilit ice. The next five yards took about twenty minutes to cover, as I moved a little faster because the seal seemed to be getting restless and I was concerned in case he should suddenly take off.

By this time I could study him at close quarters. He was about nine feet long and must have weighed a good four hundred pounds. He was a bearded seal, what the Eskimos call an *ugrug*. Every now and then he would rise up, like a huge slug, and search the area away from me. At intervals his tail flapped lazily against the ice. He looked fat and satisfied; there was enough food on him to give me energy to build ten ramps. I edged closer, trying to make the same breathing noise as he, a sort of heavy wheeze, like a person snoring in his throat.

Fifteen feet away I raised my feet and slapped the ice, just as he was doing with his tail. As he rose to look around away from me, I slowly lifted the harpoon and flung it, hard as I could, straight at his neck. It went right through and he dropped like a stone, with no twitching, no jerking, nothing. His huge carcass just collapsed on the ice.

"Come on, boy!" I jumped up and fell on the harpoon handle, twisting it out. Nelson was up in a flash, snapping and snarling, standing just clear of the seal's head and throat, his back teeth bared, ready to bite. I plunged the harpoon again into the shoulder, as deep as I could. There was a slight resistance as the steel barb entered the tough skin, then it slid right in like a dart into a slab of lard.

Satisfied the seal was truly dead, I looked around for bear and then trudged back to the boat for a bucket and a box. In another two hours I had enough blubber laying alongside the boat to feed a small ship's crew for a fortnight and more.

After a meal and a reconnoiter around our perimeter, I had a sleep, with Nelson on guard, gnawing at a huge chunk of raw seal blubber.

Once awake, I started to dig the new ramp. A weary,

backbreaking job. On the first one I had great difficulty shifting the huge slabs of ice with mittened hands. I made a "longshoreman's hook" out of a great shark-fishing barb by fixing a wooden handle on it, and so I could now grab onto the ice and drag it clear. It took until October 15 to complete the ramp. For two days I was immobile, taking refuge from a raging blizzard. The next task was to start moving the boat.

The first thing was to dig out the hurricane anchor, then plant it again into another hole astern of the boat. Then the fifty-pound fisherman anchor had to be dug into yet another five-foot-deep hole just over the top of the ramp, about ten yards down. The idea was to use the fisherman to slide the boat forward, until she was sitting, bows forward, on top of the ramp, then brake the slide down into the water with the storm line secured to the hurricane hook.

Much easier said than done, but on October 16 all was ready and I started pulling the boat, using the great blocks, or pulleys, as landsmen call them, to inch the boat along the ice, after unloading two and a half tons of removable gear and food onboard. On the seventeenth, after many hours of hard labor in the freezing cold, interspersed with heavy meals of boiled curried seal blubber, biscuits, and porridge, with great dollops of strawberry jam smeared over the lot, the boat was teetering on the top of the ramp. I married up the brake line to the hurricane hook, gave the stern a mighty heave, grabbed the brake line to control it, and she was away, just like a ship being launched, only *Cresswell* went bows first. I had left a good amount of weight in the stern, and as she hit the water, the empty bows danced up into the air, the stern swung around sideways, and she was afloat, checked by the heavy line from colliding with the small ice floes in the water.

Then, using the ladder with a plank lashed along its length, I reloaded the boat, dragging the stores over the ice on a species of sled which I had knocked together during the comparatively idle day-nights on the floe. With me pulling on one rope and Nelson grasping the other in his teeth, we soon made a quick job of shifting and restowing all the gear. It was not easy, as it was very dark in the boat, with just two small kerosene lamps flickering.

After a short sleep and another meal, I went out to try the engine. It was frozen solid, despite all the attempts I had made to keep it warm. I had even constructed a chimney from the galley to the engine compartment to conduct warm air, but to no avail. The blowtorch onboard refused to operate despite an hour's fumbling with frozen fingers. There was only one solution. I laboriously dismantled the cabin stove and chimney and, in a matter of hours, had it fitted up in the engine compartment, with the fumes going through the engine exhaust outlet. This did the trick, and early on the eighteenth I had the engine running and was moving slowly out, through thin new ice, to the northwest. As I was on the lee side of the *Ark Royal* ice floe, the sea was flat calm, and by running the engine flat out, I shoved my way between the thin cakes floating like shining waterlilies on the surface of the freezing sea.

Sunrise on the eighteenth of October was around eleven in the morning, and there was daylight until around one in the afternoon, then twilight until about four. I made good time, for *Cresswell*'s hull was tough as an ox and I rammed my way through thin ice. Gradually the lead widened. Once I broke out of the pack ice field into comparatively open water, I intended to head south, and so out to a point where I could turn east for Iceland, or perhaps even make my way into one of the Greenland fiords, to winter there.

Suddenly, again, my fate was decided for me. There, on the western horizon, was a smudge of smoke, coming closer. I fired off one of my emergency signal flares. As I gazed at the ship's hull, which by now was plainly visible, with the lights shining from her cabins, I saw a brighter light flashing away from where I imagined the bridge was. They had seen my flares!

I patted Nelson on the back of his head. "Now behave yourself, mate, we've got company coming!"

The ship was soon very close, having broken a wide swath right through the thin ice. She was wearing the Danish flag and her name was *Gustav Holm*, her port of registry Copenhagen. Seeing my tattered, barely recognizable red ensign, one of her officers sang out in English over his megaphone.

"Where are you coming from?"

"Reykjavík—I was trying to make for Jan Mayen Island, only I got stuck."

"We can see—how was your trip?"

"Up and down, up and down."

He laughed. As the ship edged closer, I distinctly heard him say to the others crowded on the bridge deck, "Bloody Englishmen. Bloody crazy fools!"

"Hey, up there!" I hollered, between cupped mittens. "Hello, up there!"

"*Ja?*" he replied, bending down low over the bulwark, his gloved hand around his ear. I could plainly see his cleanshaven face under the clean parka hood.

"*Ja?*" he shouted again.

"*Welshman, if* you don't mind!"

For I'm going back to the frozen North,
To the land where spunk is spunk——
Not a trickling stream of lukewarm cream,
But a solid frozen chunk!

> Last verse of "The Ballad of Deadeye Dick
> and Eskimo Nell." There are ninety-two
> verses of this, written by an anonymous
> bard in the early 1900s and traditionally ren-
> dered at Royal Navy "Sods' Operas."

19

Trapped!

Clumsily, in my sealskin boots and Arctic gear, I clambered up the rope ladder which had been cast over the weather-streaked side of the *Gustav Holm*, clinging to the lines which were already stiffening in the cold. It was no strain, for my arms, after six weeks of hauling and digging in solid ice, were like steel-wire rope, and I soon clattered on deck, watched by the astonished crew and passengers.

I was met by Captain Svensson, who, shaking my mitten heartily, led me up to his cabin under the bridge. Soon I was doffing my caribou-skin jerkin in his warm cabin. My shirt underneath was filthy and stiff with frozen sweat. My beard was eight inches long.

"You have a bath, and I will get your clothes cleaned up," said the captain, who was surprisingly young, about thirty. And then I realized that when ships' captains appear young, it is a sign of one's own advancing age.

The steward showed me into the bathroom, and I looked around in wonder. This was the first bathroom I had seen for months, ever since leaving Iceland. The marvel of hot water pouring from a faucet at the turn of a tap delighted me. For half an hour I soaked in sudsy hot water; it was the first time in weeks that I had been really warm. Afterwards I inspected myself in the mirror. My eye had completely recovered from the blow on the voyage up from St. Kilda, and although tired, I felt fitter than I had for years.

"How was the bath?" asked the captain when I had done.

"For a small-boat voyager," I told him, "there is no finer welcome, no greater luxury."

The dinner, with the passengers and crew, was in the Danish fashion, and that night there was boiled ham. As usual among Northern Europeans, there was far too much on my plate for me to eat, and, as usual, I had to make apologies for my small needs. But the aquavit went down well, though I was careful not to overindulge.

During the meal the captain said, "You know, I can easily lift your boat out of the water and carry her onboard to Reykjavík."

That was the last thing I wanted. The authorities there had charged me mooring fees at fishing boat rates, a fantastic sum, about ten dollars per day. As I had not been in Icelandic waters for commercial reasons, as I had not been exploiting their fishing grounds, and as I had been out at anchor the whole while, using the port facilities only to the extent of drawing off forty gallons of water, this was daylight robbery. Besides, I was 360 miles north of Reykjavík, and if I could winter on the coast of Greenland, I would be in a favorable position to try another probe north early next summer, 1960. Generous as the captain's offer was, if there was rough weather it would not be possible to lower *Cresswell* back down into the sea before the *Gustav Holm* reached Reykjavík, and then, with the shipping company watching all, I would have a fat freight bill to pay, and my coffers were exceedingly low.

"Thank you very much for your offer, Captain Svensson, it is most kind, but I think I will try to get into one of the Greenland fiords. Our position now, you said, is about sixty miles southeast of the King Oscar fiord. What about if I try for there, go up the fiord and reach Ella Island? I can winter there, at the radio station."

He shook his head. "Impossible. We've just come out from there and it was all we could do to force our way through the piled-up shore ice in the fiord. We were very lucky not to be frozen in ourselves. You would stand no chance." After dinner, he led me up to the bridgehouse and showed me a chart of Eastern Greenland.

"Look," he said, "if you are determined on this, your best chance, probably your only chance, is to try to get into Scoresby Sund. There are a lot of bergs coming down from the glaciers inland, but the latest information is that the shore ice is still fairly loose. The pack ice is still moving, so there's a good chance you can find your way in to the wireless station. Anyway, I will signal them and tell them you are heading there, and if you don't reach there in a couple of days, they can set up a search with the Catalina flying boat from Angmagssalik."

"Sounds fair enough to me, captain. Look, I don't want to hold you up any longer. You have been most helpful and kind, and I surely do appreciate it. *Mange tak!*"

I climbed back down to the deck of my boat, gave Nelson a pat, cast off the lines, and was away. The *Gustav Holm* slid away to the southeast while her passengers and crew lined up, waving to me as she eased through the thin ice pack. Then I set off to follow the passage she had already broken up between the point where she had encountered me and the coast of Greenland.

The weather was cold, with a bitter wind of about fifteen knots blowing from the northeast. I soon had all working sail up and in two hours was out in fairly open water. After another twelve hours standing at the wheel in the freezing cold, trying to dodge behind rigged-up canvas shelters, I sighted, away to the southwest, the red light atop the Scoresby Sund wireless mast and, feeling my way around the edge of a great mass of broken-up shore ice, entered the great sound. Now I was within a few miles of a good wintering haven, and there would be company and warmth over the coming months of night.

But try as I would there was no passage through the ice to the shore. In the pale light of the twilit day, I estimated that the nearest I could approach the station was eight miles.

There, on the edge of the shore ice, I would be completely exposed to all the winter storms and to the huge, monstrous icebergs as they swept out to sea. There was only one thing to do; I must try to penetrate into the great long fiord and find a suitable spot, no matter how isolated, where I could perhaps beach the boat, thus keeping her from being crushed as the shore ice piled up. And so I made up by the Scoresby Sund, watching the tiny red light of warmth and cheer fading away beyond the shore fog. Even though I was shining a light, I knew the people in the wireless station would probably not see me through the fog. Then I remembered the great brass foghorn. I gave six toots on it—*"Dah dit dah; dah dit dah*: I wish to communicate with you"—then listened. No reply. Another six hoots, then I heard them— eight miles away. That's how noise carries in the dry Arctic air. They were signaling back slowly, in straight Morse. Their hoots were deep and melancholy. I listened carefully.

"Dit dah dah; dit dit dit dit; dit; dit dah dit; dit. Dit dah dit; dit, dit, dah. Dit dah dit; dah dah dit dah: Where R.U. Interrogative?"

I gave the hooter handle heavy jerks. "Due south; going up fiord; try Syd Kap."

The answer came after a brief pause. "C., *dah dit dah dit,* yes; R.AR. Message received. Ends."

That was the last communication I had with anyone but the Eskimos for well over a year. Slowly, I wended my way upstream under sail and engine, dodging the ice floes and bergs, this way and that, under the moon and stars, with the ice mountains gleaming and sparkling nine thousand feet up above the wide fiord. Progress was slow, and it was another two days before I sighted the umiak, forty feet long, made of skins, with five Eskimos onboard. They paddled over to meet me, for they were against the wind, and I was under very short sail, for fear of colliding with a floe. They waved and pointed towards the shore. At first it seemed there was nothing there but bare rock, but then I saw the huts, three of them, sitting on a small headland.

There were some children running over the ice on the shore. To the east of the huts, a smaller fiord dropped back from the main fiord. I sailed along it for about three hours. It was free of ice, right up to the beach!

After starting the engine I made my way in. I dropped the sails and slowly, holding the string to the very primitive throttle arrangement I had rigged up, steered the boat head on, at right angles to the pebble beach. She touched; then, with a rumble, her speed carried her gently about five yards onto the beach as she slid on her three keels. There is very little tide in Scoresby Sund, so there was no fear of the boat refloating and being carried away by the tide; in any case, I secured her with a stout mooring line to a nearby boulder. Then I went to sleep.

When I awoke there was a full storm heading in from the northeast, but going on deck it was obvious that I was in a very good spot, protected by high mountains all around, except due south, where there was a fetch of about thirty miles from the range of mountains which stretch out west to east across Knud Rasmussen Land. If there was to be any danger here, it would come from the south. While I made breakfast of eggs and bacon, courtesy of the captain of *Gustav Holm*, I thought about this problem.

The answer was soon obvious. The beach I was sitting on sloped up to the land at about the same angle as the ramp on the *Ark Royal* ice floe. About sixty feet ahead of the bows was a line of boulders, quite high, about thirty feet on average, and over at an angle of forty-five degrees northwest of the boat, about eighty feet away, was a gap. Behind that, when I went to look, I found sand. Further up, there was a slope of smooth rock, also strewn with lichen-covered boulders. There was no sign of a glacier above the rock hillside. Climbing up it, in the cold starlight, I was reminded of the great water catchments which cover the southern side of the Rock of Gibraltar.

I would haul the boat up through the gap and settle her in behind the rocks which followed the line of the shore.

There she would be protected from all winds, from any high seas brought in by a south wind, and from any ice which might drive ashore with the wind.

There was a problem here though, because unlike the glassy smooth ice of the floe, which had made it comparatively easy to slide the boat, the pebbles and sand would be much more difficult to haul the weight of the boat over. The first thing I would need was long balks of timber, two of them, to lay up the beach, then three heavy rollers. Securing the blocks to the rocks was simple, with a rope lashed right around the base of one of the boulders.

Even after the storm died, there was no sight of the Eskimos, though far in the distance, from the west, the sound of chopping and hammering carried over in the wind. I estimated that the Eskimo hamlet was about twelve miles away. I dared not leave the boat in the position she was in, half-ashore and half-afloat, so I started to make ready to haul her up the beach, first landing all the removable stores over the bow onto the beach, all two and a half tons. While I was doing this, the thought came to me that perhaps I could use the spars, the masts, the gaffs, and the booms to roll her up the beach. The mainmast was hollow for half its length only, but very strong; the mizzenmast completely solid.

It took me three hours to lower the mainmast and the mizzenmast; with a long line reeved through a block way up the beach and back to the mastheads, I had then to take the pins out of the tabernacles and slowly ease the mainmast down. The difficulty was to prevent the mast from crashing down once it was past an angle forty-five degrees from the vertical, so I rigged another line, from the mizzen head to the mainmast top, and, while easing away on the shore line, hauled in on the triatic line. Then, once the mast reached the critical forty-five-degree angle, the mizzen took the weight. Lowering away slowly, or "handsomely," as sailors say, with the triatic line, the whole of the mast was soon down on deck. Then, securing the shore line to the base of the mast, which was lying foot forward by now, I heaved away and dragged the mainmast over the bow onto the beach.

The mizzenmast was comparatively simple to lower, being only two-thirds the height of the main and only half the diameter. That, too, was soon lying up the beach. I packed the underside of the two masts with sails and blankets. Now I had my "railway"! The booms and gaffs were soon lying at right angles across the masts and I had my "wheels." Then I started hauling, with the three keels of the boat, only six inches deep below the hull, resting on the booms. She moved slowly but steadily as I hauled away, using the same five-block purchase I had used on the ice floe, and after six hours or so she was high and dry on the beach, close to the rock gap. Then I made ready to slew her around the corner of the far rock and tuck her in on the sand. But first I had a good meal of corned beef and rice, then a sleep of four hours or so. By the time the four next meals had been eaten, she was lying cozily tucked in, low behind the rock barricade, bows facing northeast and the masts and booms stowed on deck to make a frame for a tent rigged up from the older, spare sails and the canvas awnings. Between the booms I packed boxes of food stores to provide plenty of holding and supporting surface for the tent, which would soon be supporting snow and ice. This took another day.

After another meal and another sleep, with the wind again howling outside, I unshipped the heating stove from its engine-room berth and repositioned it in the cabin. It was the twenty-sixth of October. The sun had disappeared altogether, and there was only about two hours of pale, ghostly twilight. Other than that, all was night. When it was clear, bright with the reflected light of the moon and the stars from the ice and snow of the great massifs overhead, it was a sight of beauty; but when the sky was overcast or foggy, pitch-black and cold, with the bitter Arctic winds blowing blinding blizzards of snow and frozen rain, it was misery in the extreme. But I was ready; my winter haven was prepared. I set out southwest along the frozen, rocky beach to find the Eskimos.

Traveling on foot along the shore was much more difficult than I had imagined. Often there were rock tumbles, or crushed ice right up on the shore, which meant a long detour inland, up slippery, almost vertical, cliff faces. I had left Nelson onboard, on a loose line. The wind was slight, and I made good going. Considering the icy and rocky terrain, I thought I could reach Syd Kap in fourteen hours. I had taken along my sleeping bag and a small sea bag with some baked beans, corned beef, and sugar, just in case I got stuck in a blizzard—or, if the Eskimos were friendly and hospitable, I could exchange it for some food.

It is awkward to account for the passage of time when the "days" are so short, and the only way it can be done is by the twenty-four-hour clock system, used by seafarers and airmen. The normal days and nights fuse into one during the Arctic winter, and much of the time the visibility is better in the "night" hours than in the "day." I left the boat at 1600 hours and plodded first along the pebble beach, now mostly iced over, for two hours. Coming to a rockfall of huge boulders fallen down from the mountainside onto the shore, much too smooth and slippery to climb over, I wended my way up the steep rise of the moraine to circumvent the rocks. On my way down again, the wind piped up from the north and the sky darkened, with great masses of black clouds overhead. In a matter of minutes, there was a raging blizzard, snow sweeping down the mountainside out into the fiord below. A little later, as I took my bearings, worried lest I be marooned in a drift, visibility dropped to a matter of feet. All was black, with white snow swirling around. I could tell my direction because of the fall of the land and the direction of the wind, so I made my way slowly down to the upper edge of the rockfall. By 2350 I had found a gap between two boulders, one resting on top of the other, and crawled inside, freezing cold and shivering, despite the extra jersey under my parka. There was a space about eight feet long and as big as a coffin between the rocks, and in this I laid my sleeping bag, then crawled inside and scoffed another can of beans mixed with some sugar: Then I went to sleep with the driven snow and ice whistling past the end of the opening between the giant boulders.

I wasn't too worried about animals, as I had heard that bears were timid ashore and avoided man, even a sleeping man, while foxes or wolves mainly traveled alone. I packed some driven snow around the bag and dropped off, exhausted.

When I awoke the scene outside was beautiful. The wind had dropped entirely and all around were huge hummocks of snow under the moonlight. It was 0400 hours on November 1. I ate a can of corned beef and swung myself up onto the top of the boulder I had slept under. Peering all around in the freezing night, I found to my horror that I was trapped! The pile of boulders, about half a mile above the shore line, was completely isolated, surrounded by snow drifts of twenty feet or more. I scampered below again, into my rock cleft, lit a cigarette, and had a think. My hands shook as I doffed my outer mittens.

There were five cans of corned beef and three of beans in my pack, four packets of cigarettes and two pounds of sugar, which I had hoped to exchange with the Eskimos for useful items like seal oil. There was the harpoon, a can opener, a flashlight and a seaman's clasp knife, and six boxes of matches. And that was it. The chances of Eskimos coming within sight of me during the next few months were nil. There was only one thing for it, I must dig my way out through the snowdrifts!

I clambered again onto the top of the boulders and looked around. The nearest other rocks clear of snow were down towards the shore, about half a mile downhill, as far as I could tell in the darkness.

Back down in the rock crevice, I opened up two cans of

corned beef, laid the food down on the icy stone, and opened up the cans with the can opener, flattening them until they were sheets of thin metal. Then I punched holes in the metal with the seaman's knife. The next bit was tricky, because it meant completely undressing, cutting thin strips of my fawnskin underpants, made like long johns, and getting dressed again fast. The cold, as I took the clothes off, burned me all over.

With the thin strips of leather I lashed the plate metal to my harpoon handle. Now I had a primitive shovel. Then I set the sleeping bag, with its orange cover, out on the snow, pegged with slivers of wood hacked from the harpoon handle, as a signal for any casual observers from the air or the sea, and started shoveling. I made up my mind to follow a strict schedule: six hours' shoveling, back to the "cave," an ounce of brown sugar, a quarter of a can of beans, a spoonful of corned beef, two hours' sleep, then back to shoveling. I reckoned that if I followed this schedule, there was a good chance of reaching the lower boulder crop inside a week. That is, if the drifts were not deeper down on the lower stretches.

I started shoveling at 0600 hours on the first of November. It was heavy work, for I had to dig a path about four feet wide at the top, narrowing to about a foot where I could walk on the packed snow. At first I made my way forward at around fifty yards a session, then the snowdrift depth shallowed off to about ten feet, and I drove forward at one hundred yards a shift by 1200 hours on the third of November. But I was not very happy, because the heavy work and expenditure of energy without adequate replacement were beginning to tell. Sleeping inside the rock cleft, I was reasonably warm as long a I stayed still, but if I moved in my sleep the heat from my body melted the thin layer of ice inside the bag, making everything damp. This dampness in turn evaporated with the heat driven off and formed more ice on the part of the bag I was not resting against.

By the fifth of November I began to slow down. My determination to get out of my snow prison had not diminished, but it was obvious, from the ground I was covering, that I was sleeping longer and digging less. Once I conked out for five hours. Very unusual for me, and an obvious sign that something was wrong. Then sitting on the rock bed in utter silence, I heard it. A plane!

I grabbed the paper bag which the sugar had been in and went outside, onto the inner end of my dug channel. The bag was fairly large, of brown paper, and I had smeared it with grease from the corned beef and left sugar grains stuck to it. As the plane passed over the Schuchert Elv, from east to west, low over the water, I lit the paper bag and tied it to the end of the shovel. In the windless night it burned brightly for about a minute. After my eyes recovered from the glare of my signal, I peered after the plane. It carried on its course for a full minute. Exhausted and bitterly disappointed, I sat down on the snow, determined to dig on. By this time I had about two thousand feet, maybe seven hundred yards, still to go to the rock outcrop on the shore. I stretched up above the level of the snow, balancing on a rocky ledge protruding from the base of the home boulder, gazing after the plane. He had changed course!

He was coming straight for me. I kept shining the flashlight directly at him, and when he passed over the shore, his big landing lamp replied, shining a beam down on me, then on the trail I had so laboriously dug through the snow. Then he sent a white flare into the black sky, a parachute flare, which for a full five minutes lit up the whole scene, like daylight. He waggled his wings, then turned to the southwest, still shining his spotlight on my boulders.

I had been seen! To celebrate I ate a whole can of corned beef, then smoked a cigarette. "Shall I just sit here and wait?" I wondered. Then the answer came loud and clear—"No! Keep moving, keep digging. It's probably the one thing that's kept you alive and sane, so keep at it!"

The Eskimos arrived three hours later. I saw their long umiak wend into the shore ice. They clambered over the ice and the rocks, then four of them, mere black dots on the white snow surface, made their way, waddling on snowshoes, to the lower end of my trench. They came trudging up the trench, grinning. Two of them spoke Danish. "*Goddag, Goddag!*" they cried, grinning all over their faces.

I grabbed the mitten of the first one to arrive and shook it. I was too excited to speak anything else but English.

"Jesus Christ, mates, am I pleased to see you!"

All four grinned as they recovered my gear and fitted a pair of snowshoes on my feet. Then we set off down the trench. I tapped the rock-solid sides of the trench as we came to the far end. "It's a long way to Tipperary," I said, quietly. The Eskimo leader, Untuk, looked at me quizzically. I offered him an ounce of frozen brown sugar from my jerkin pocket. He accepted it, smiling, sniffed it, tasted it, then swallowed the lot, patting me on the shoulder.

I wasn't too concerned about Nelson. He wouldn't starve; he knew where the burgoo pot was, and there were plenty of peanuts in the engine compartment, where I'd left the hatch loose so he could get at them if I was away too long. But I reflected what a bloody fool I'd been, not to have brought the alarm flares, pistol, and snowshoes with me, and how lucky I was.

Wise men make life happier and more endurable by lightening their troubles with remembrances of their blessings, whereas most people, like sieves, let the worst things remain and stick to them while the best slip through. . . . And as for the things which are not by their nature evil but are made painful wholly and entirely by sheer imagination, we should treat them as we do the masks that frighten children—bring them near, put them in the children's hands and turn them over until we accustom them not to mind them. So by bringing our trouble close to us and using our reason we may discover how ephemeral and flimsy and exaggerated it is.

Plutarch, "Exile."

20

Safe and Sound

When the four Eskimo rescuers and I reached the edge of the shore, clambering over the rocky boulders and over the jumbled-up shore ice, then trudging another half-mile over the flat cake ice out on the water's edge, we met up with a waiting party of six more—three men and three women—though to be truthful I couldn't for the life of me tell the difference until they started to talk. They were all dressed more or less the same, all of fairly short stature, all with the same chubby faces. Carefully they handed me into the boat, where there were three more women. Then, with a female hugging each side of me and blankets thrown over my shoulders, we set off, with the women paddling the umiak out to sea, until they had enough sea room to hoist the sail.

The chief of the crew, who seemed also to be the oldest (though it is difficult to tell with Eskimos, as they do not show signs of age until well into their fifties), asked me in Danish how many passings of the moon I had been stranded. I counted up and it came to eight. Eight days! Then I came to the conclusion that if I had not attempted to dig my way out, if I had just sat there, moping, hoping for rescue, I probably would not have survived. The cold alone, after two hours' sleep, was enough to make one wish to die. The action made effort, effort made heat. The action also stopped me from feeling too sorry for myself, and self-pity is very dangerous.

212

He patted my head, then felt under my mouth-scarf of thin silk, which was covered with a layer of ice. He felt all around my face, then, coming to my beard, let out a yell and laughed. I dropped the scarf and the beard fell out, all ten inches of it. The Eskimos burst out chattering and laughing, until I covered my face again from the cold.

As we made our way down the Schuchert Elv fiord, dodging bergs and floes, I observed the umiak and how it was handled. The ladies sat on each side of me, paddling and warming my uncovered hands on their stomachs. Perhaps inspecting the boat would keep my mind off where my hands were.

The Eskimo boats, the umiak and the kayak, are not just vessels made to float and move through the water. They are highly efficient machines. They belong to the same family of membrane and frame vessels as did the ancient Irish curragh and the British coracle, which themselves were highly efficient, ocean-worthy vessels.

The curragh had more or less the same lines and appearance as the Iroquois bark canoe, but the umiak has the characteristics of the dory, one of the most seaworthy of all vessels. Therefore it follows that as the dory is more efficient than the bark canoe, especially in any kind of rough sea, then the Eskimo umiak must be more seaworthy than the ancient curragh.

Like the dory, the umiak is double-ended. The keel is carved out flat from a piece of driftwood and so are the pieces of wood lashed from fore to aft along the gunwale which keep the frames in position. The Eskimos told me that some of the umiak lashings are of long strips of whalebone, but the one I was in had rawhide lashings, very well served and tied.

I noticed that the men did not paddle the boat, but only steered or handled the sails. I later found that the Eskimos consider paddling to be women's work, and they even call the umiaks "the women's boats." The kayaks, smaller, more fragile, and much harder to handle, were known as "the men's boats," though I did occasionally see women handling kayaks at Syd Kap.

At Syd Kap I watched how the skin boats are made. When a seal is caught and killed, the skin and blubber is removed. The Eskimos put the skins into tubs until the hair rots away on one side and most of the blubber on the other. When the boatbuilder guesses that the rotting is enough, he scrapes the hair from one side and the blubber from the other. The skins are sewn together while still wet, the seams overlapping, and the stitching very fine indeed. The thread used is seal sinew, which swells when wet.

Then the pliable, wet skins are stretched over the frame of the boat. When a kayak is sewn together, the two sides must be held while the last seam is sewn. This is because the kayak is an enclosed vessel, about as wide as a coffin and twice as long. The wet sealskin cover is sewn up reasonably tight, and when it dries becomes as taut and resonant as a drumhead. Umiaks may be built of large sealskins, walrus or white whale hides, and it is a tough job to stretch these hard skins tight enough. This is done by pulling the skins over the gunwale of the frame and over-lapping it back onto its own part, then sewing one part to the other.

Before the Eskimo launches his skin boat, he leaves it out in the rain or snow for a while, to dampen it. After that it is as tight as a drum and no water will leak in. Because the sinews, with which the skins are sewn, rot after three or four days in fresh water, the skin boat is dragged onshore to dry out, turned upside down and placed on stones to allow ventilation. Overnight the sinews are restored, and the boat is good for another three or four days. When the boats are not in use, they are taken ashore and stood on their sides as extra protection from the wind. In salt sea water the umiak or the kayak stitching will last for ten days before having to be completely redried.

The Eskimos told me that the umiaks made of walrus skin are not as good as those made of white whale hide. The walrus skin rots faster and is much harder to stitch. The average life of an umiak is about three years in fresh water, but longer in sea water. The kayaks last a shorter time, but this is probably because they are used more often.

The umiaks I saw at Syd Kap carried an amazing cargo load, sometimes as much as four tons. The thirty-five-footers carried up to twenty passengers. This is because of their high sides. They could come right inshore because of their flat bottom and could be dragged up on the ice because of their light weight when unloaded; no more than half a ton. I realized that in choosing *Cresswell* for the Arctic cruise I had unwittingly followed the path of the umiak, for *Cresswell*, too, had all these attributes, with the exception of the light weight—being constructed of wood, she was heavier.

On the way to Syd Kap the umiak was forced by piled-up pack ice to take a detour down a lead quite close to the shore. She grazed a sharp rock which put a gash into her starboard bow. I was amazed to see one of the women get out a sewing needle made of whalebone, some sinew from a seal, a small sealskin patch, lean over the bow, and sew a patch on!

The sail used was a square sail, and I wondered if the Eskimos had learned of that from the Norsemen, or whether they had figured it out before the arrival of the Scandinavians. The Eskimos told me that they had tried out fore-and-aft sails, but that with an umiak they were dangerous in the swift gusts of the fiords, and that some fore-and-aft-rigged boats had been lost, but hardly any square-riggers.

I learned later that when the Eskimos take the umiaks up the rivers, if they come to a shallow part, they half unload the umiak, with its four-inch draft, then they get out into the water and lift the boat over the shallows! When they haul against the current, they secure the towing line half-way up the mast at one end, then to a dog team or some men at the other.

When we came out into the open, wide waters of the Halls Bredning fiord, where there was quite a sea, the women inflated eight sealskin bags and tied them to the hull outside the boat, four a little aft of the bows and four a little forward of the stern. This was to prevent the boat from being swamped. With so little wood in the frame, if she were swamped she'd go down like a brick unless she had buoyancy. The sealskin bags gave her an added 250 pounds of buoyancy each. I watched carefully, storing all these ideas at the back of my mind. As the roughness of the sea increased, a sealskin flap, which had been hanging down all round the inside of the freeboard, was raised and tied to the wooden rail fixed round the boat above the gunwale. They had even thought of the weathercloth! The dodger!

Once up, the weathercloth flaps were held in place by sticks jammed between the gunwale and the rail. All very seamanlike and simple.

But the most original thing about the skin boats is that if someone is stranded in one, or wrecked on one of the many rocks or ice floes, he need not starve. He can eat the uncured hide of which the boat is made! There's enough food in an umiak to last ten men for a month! True, it would be tough and taste like old rope, but hunger knows no taste.

There were only three huts in the Eskimo settlement, and these were almost completely surrounded by walls of turf bricks, about five feet high, acting as windbreaks. On arrival a meal was prepared of the two large codfish caught on the expedition. As guest of honor, following the Eskimo custom, I got the head. This I ate with relish. It was the first warm food I had had in over ten days.

The proper name of the people of the East Greenland Arctic is *Kalatdlit*, and this is how they refer to themselves. The meaning of *Kalatdlit* is not clear, but the meaning of *Eskimo* is. It means "eater of raw meat," and the Kalatdlit find this very insulting.

After the fish head, which I ripped from the bones, eyes and all, boiled salmon was served by the women, but I thought it unwise to eat too much after having had so little for so many days. I therefore asked for only a small portion. The Kalatdlit understood my reasons for this, and also for turning down an offering of raw narwhal blubber.

Around the inside of the wooden hut, there were pictures from Danish magazines and newspapers. Three small stone oil lamps burned seal oil, with a little wisp of black smoke rising from each one into the rafters above. There was a fairly large potbellied stove of iron, the only white man's influence I saw in Syd Kap, with the exception of the magazine pictures. Everything else had been made, caught, killed, or grown there.

Untuk, the chief, told me that caribou head and fish head are the best food, rabbit the worst. He gave me to understand that if one eats nothing but rabbit for six weeks one will die. Of course he's right. There's no fat on a rabbit. He showed me a caribou head ready for eating the next day. It had been skinned and two rawhide sinews threaded through the nostrils, from which it could be hung over an open fire outside.

It was interesting to see the Kalatdlits drying the fish in one of the other huts. They had mainly cod and salmon, which they first gutted, then took out the backbone with the head. The rest of the fish was split and the two halves tied together with sinew at the tail. The head and backbone were hung separately, those of the small fish for the dogs to eat and the larger ones for the old people. They did not salt the fish because any flesh, meat or fish or fowl, which is salted soon loses its antiscorbutic power.

Scurvy results partly from not eating enough food with the necessary antiscorbutic ingredients. Salt kills these. This is probably the reason for the many cases of whole ships' crews' dying of scurvy in the old days. Their main diet was salt beef and pork. Their main antidote to scurvy was lime juice, which is just about useless for anything except a thirst quencher! The way to combat scurvy is to cook food only as long as is necessary to make it digestible, or to make it taste pleasant, and to eat only enough salt to replace that lost by sweating. The cures for scurvy are many. If fresh fruit and vegetables are available, they will do the trick (if only because they do not have the antiscorbutics cooked out of them); but if, as in the Arctic, fruit and vegetables are not readily available, then raw meat (except rabbit) or bone marrow will serve the purpose.

Death by scurvy is by no means the most unpleasant death, at least with respect to pain. There is, in fact, hardly any suffering right up until the last few hours, except perhaps a mild form of toothache. But the last hours are distressing, as death is usually from internal hemorrhaging caused by broken blood vessels flooding the stomach and lungs, thus causing you to drown, as it were, in your own blood. The first symptoms are purple gums, loose teeth, and muscle ache. There are few other signs until close to death, for bowel elimination and even digestion remain normal throughout the whole process.

During the four days I stayed with the Kalatdlits of Syd Kap I learned many things: how to find a seal under the ice and harpoon him; how not to set my dog onto a bear (a live dog is much more useful than a dead bear); how to trap and kill arctic foxes; where the fishing was best around where the boat was hidden; where to find blueberries in the early spring; and a lot more advice on how to live in intense cold without a gun.

No matter how interested I was in their culture, it was tiring to be among people whose language I did not understand. Besides, I was concerned about *Cresswell* and anxious to get back to Nelson. So on the fourth "day" Untuk gathered an umiak paddling party of eight women and four men to return me to the boat, promising that he would send a party to visit me every month, if the weather was good.

I said my goodbyes to Untuk and his family, which was a big job, as he had eight children and six grandchildren, and returned in the umiak to *Cresswell* beach, where, after sliding along in the dark across the sea ice and brash, I donned the snowshoes which Untuk had presented to me and sloshed away up to the boat. The breeze was onshore, and as I said goodbye to the women, who stayed in the boat, I could hear Nelson barking, almost a mile away. He had my scent and knew I was returning.

As the four men and I clambered around the gap in the rock line, I had a shock, for at first I could not see the boat. Then a piece of sailcloth caught my attention. She was almost completely buried in a snowdrift. There was only a slight rise in the snow to show where she was! I scrambled along the top of the drift and up to the fluttering sailcloth. There, inside, on deck, Nelson was jumping up and down with joy and relief.

I made the Kalatdlit men some tea, gave them ten cans of corned beef and some sugar, then, as they tied on their snowshoes, bade them goodbye. They all grinned and waved as they disappeared around the gap between the boulders.

I surveyed the scene. I had chosen my hibernation hole well, for on the seaward side of the boulders great hummocks of ice had been forced up the beach by the pressure of the icebergs calving off the Elv glacier to the east. But the boat lay peaceful and unharmed, under three feet of snow. I cleared a hole for the stovepipe chimney, then went below. It was mid-November.

For the whole of the arctic winter I ventured very little out of the boat. When the wind dropped I would go out on the drift in my snowshoes, for exercise, or, if it was calm weather, to perform ablutions. The rest of the time I carried out boat maintenance chores inside the boat, in the warmth, slept, ate sparingly, and read a great deal (I went through the whole of Shakespeare twice). I listened to the radio for a couple of hours each day only, as I had to conserve the batteries. I also knitted two pairs of socks and one jersey. I had brought back from Syd Kap a stone seal-oil lamp and some oil, and this I rigged up, with a chimney passing through a wooden porthole "dummy" shield, to give me longer hours of light, for my kerosene ration only allowed four hours of lighting per twenty-four.

Sometimes I would see the awesome sight of the aurora borealis, the northern lights, great streaks of colored lights shooting through the blackness of the arctic sky, and I learned to watch for high cirrus clouds after the northern lights, which always indicated a storm pending. Then, cozily tucked up in my warm woolen indoor clothing and insulated by the mutton cloths tacked around the cabin and the yard-deep snow outside on deck, I would read by the light of my seal-oil lamp. Every few weeks, just as Untuk had promised, the Kalatdlits would come in their umiak to see me—sometimes only two or three, sometimes six or seven—and we would sit around for a few hours talking in poor Danish or sign language. But I learned to make them laugh, and they seemed to enjoy their visits as much as I did.

December came, then January and February and March. By early April the snowdrift around the boat had mostly blown away. In late February the sun reappeared—a wondrous sight, the first rays of light in the southeast sky, after almost four months of absolute night—and the ice out in the fiord started to break away from the shore. It was time to think about refloating the boat.

But first I delved into the chart locker and studied all my Arctic charts. I had failed to beat Nansen by going up the Greenland coast; now I would try the same route as he had.

The Gulf Stream, as it passes northwestward across the North Atlantic, sends an offshoot into the Arctic between Iceland and Britain. The warming effect of this water, coming all the way from the Caribbean, makes for much less ice to the north of Norway than is the case off Greenland. The ice line is much further north, and there are drastically fewer icebergs.

The warm current gradually cools as it heads north of Norway, then passing around the islands of Svalbard (or

Spitsbergen), it turns north, then northwest, towards the very high latitudes near the pole, moving the vast ice fields with it. If I could get *Cresswell* onto that ice field, the chances were that the movement of the ice would carry her further north than Nansen's ship *Fram* had reached. The estimated rate of current is twenty-five sea-miles a day, with the ice drift a good deal less, about six miles a day, and so if I wintered out over 1960 to 1961 on the ice, I would stand a very good chance of getting beyond latitude eighty-four north. The current from the Norwegian side of the pole turns southwest somewhere due north of Iceland and joins the southbound Greenland current, upon whose ice pack I had already had one free ride.

I made up my mind to get out of the Scoresby Sund as early as possible in May and to make for Svalbard. It would be somewhat risky passing through the eastern Greenland ice floes, but once out and as far east as the eastern tip of Iceland, the Gulf Stream offshoot would take me rapidly to Svalbard. Then I could tackle the Arctic region from a point further north.

I turned to find Nelson lying on the floor looking at me. He was absolutely fed up, as his only exercise had been walking round and round the deck under the tent and jumping up and down the companionway ladder. He could not go out in the snow yet, for fear of sinking into a hole. As I looked at him, his tail thumped on the floorboard. I patted him. "One good thing about not being able to go 'ashore,' mate; you won't get a bloody tapeworm!"

Nelson got up slowly and walked to his favorite spot, between the table and the forward bulkhead. Then, with a sigh, he laid his head down to doze again.

The next day, with two visiting Kalatdlits, I started digging a passage through the packed snow, now about three feet deep, and prepared to move the boat out of her nest. We unfroze the blocks and set the masts and spars out, then reversed the earlier hauling procedure. By April fifteenth we were hacking away at the small hummocks of ice down by the shore, then, on the eighteenth, at the sea ice to clear a passage through. When she was sitting with her bows over the fiord edge, we took the long storm line out and tied it right around a small berg about as big as a house. Heaving against that, the berg was soon aground and we had a good "deadman" to haul the boat against. By April twentieth *Cresswell* was back in the water, and on the twenty-first we hauled up the masts and rigged her for sailing.

Then, after resetting the stove up in the engine compartment, I rested three days, before setting off to try to reach the radio station at Scoresby Sund. The first place I made for, however, was Syd Kap, where all the Kalatdlits came onboard, men, women, and kids, and bade me a grand farewell. Their umiak escorted me about ten miles down the fiord, and then they turned and waved through the pale twilight of the weeks-long arctic dawn.

They were the last human beings I was to see for another fifteen months.

I met an ancient man who mushed
   With Peary to the Pole.
Said I: "In all that land so hushed
   What most inspired your soul?"
He looked at me with bleary eye,
   He scratched a hoary head:
"You know that Sourdoughs jest cain't lie,
   So here's the dope," he said.

"I saw it clear, I raised a cheer,
   I knowed the prize was won;
The huskies too, like wind they flew—
   Them critters sure could run.
The light was dim, the site was grim,
   But sunshine swept my soul,
To see—each husky lift a limb
   And . . . irrigate the Pole.

Robert Service
from "My Husky Team."

21

Across the Arctic Ocean

It is estimated that more icebergs flow out of Scoresby Sund than out of any other stretch of coast in the world. But in late April, with the spring thaw not yet set in, there were very few, and they were fairly small, not more than half-a-mile long and around four hundred feet high, moving slowly out to sea. The shore and pack ice, however, were jammed up solid against the coasts, out to a distance of ten miles or so; further out, the great flat floes and mighty bergs moved across the horizon. It was light for most of the twenty-four hours, a grey, funereal light as the weakling sun tried to penetrate the thick cloud cover. Low clouds hovered halfway up the giant cliffs, obscuring the peaks six thousand feet above the grey waters and dull ice.

When I reached the northern exit of the Sund, I found that the ice stretched out even further to sea than it had back in October—so far that there was no chance at all of communicating with the Danes. I was not too concerned, as I had sent a message to them through the Kalatdlits that I would try to get out of the Sund and make my way to Jan Mayen Island at the end of April. They, in turn, had sent a message advising against sailing too soon, as the exit from the great fiord was almost blocked by ice. But I realized that they were accustomed to dealing with the movement of much bigger craft, and, as they had said that there were leads through the blockage, I decided to have a go at escaping from the Greenland fiord. If I could get far enough to the east, beyond the ice line, and pick up the offshoot of the Gulf Stream, I stood a good chance of getting much further north, to Svalbard. There I could wait a while; then, in the late summer, when the ice line had receded to its north-ernmost point, I could emerge from hiding and head into the pack for the winter.

I rested the "night" under the lee of the ice piled up off Kap Brewster. It was far too deep there to anchor, so I landed on one of the floes, jumping from the boat onto the slippery ice in my sealskin boots, a sledgehammer tucked under my jerkin and an iron spike tied to my shoulders. Slithering around in the slushy snow, I drove the spike two feet into the ice, then tied the boat up. The wind held the boat off the floe; if another floe did touch *Cresswell*, she just swung around out of the way, sometimes quite violently, sometimes softly. With the southwest breeze, bitterly cold, blowing stronger as *Cresswell* sailed out of the lee of the mountains of Knud Rasmussen Land, I started to pick my way through the ever-increasing number of huge floating floes, swirling round slowly as the Greenland current picked them up and pushed them south.

Way out on the northeast horizon a great gap had shown in the southward-advancing ice field, so on the second of May I made my way out to sea. There was a good, strong, thirty-knot wind blowing from the southwest, and with all sail crowded, I made swift passage. Out to the north, through the grey gloom, I could see distant icebergs, mighty masses of ice, like mountains, under the low, black, heaped-up clouds. But when the sun shone it was glori-ously free sailing.

My plan was simple. If I got stuck in the ice, the current would carry me south. When the Greenland current met the Gulf Stream, the ice would break up and I could escape. If I was too far south, I would head from wherever I escaped to Iceland, and so on north from there. But if I could avoid being trapped, I would keep on eastward and meet the warmer Gulf Stream current in the waters northeast of Iceland.

After all the maintenance work done while she was aground in Schuchert Elv, the boat was in good shape, and I was well rested. The Kalatdlit had carried in stores for me, bought from the wireless station, and so there was now many months' supply of food onboard, plus fifty pounds of seal blubber and a hundred pounds or so of dried frozen fish—cod, halibut, and other kinds. My water supply was no problem, as the tops of the ice floes were almost devoid of salt. I was well rested, in fact too rested—for the last month or so, before launching the craft, I had been hard put to find enough work to fill my waking moments.

The wide, eastward-running gap turned north on the fourth of May. It was about eight miles wide. Here I was forced to make one of those decisions which a skipper has to make and which makes him a skipper. The question was whether to head north along the lead, or south, with it. I was now, by dead reckoning, about 150 miles east of the Liverpool Land coast of Greenland. All the ice, floes, bergs, and brash were moving south at a rate of around one knot. The patch of open water I was in was also moving south or southeast. To the east, the horizon was one solid line of ice. There might, or there might not be, a gap leading eastward further to the north of me. This was not certain.

I made the decision. I handed all the sail except the mizzen and turned the boat's head to point in line with the middle of the lead, southeast. She drifted on the current at almost the same rate as the ice surrounding her. By fiddling around with the mizzen and rigging the storm-jib forward, together with lashing the wheel, I arranged it so that the boat would hold herself roughly on course. Then I settled down to bide my time.

On the eighth of May I celebrated my thirty-sixth birthday by baking a small cake, which Nelson shared. As the heating stove was set up in the engine compartment, I was sleeping and warming myself there. Only six feet by five, it was nowhere near as roomy and comfortable as the cabin, but I managed to make a cozy enough berth by taking up the cabin floorboards and fixing them up across the beam of the engine room. In the cabin, with only the kerosene cooking stove to heat up the compartment, I found that water vapor formed on the top and sides of the cabin. Once the stove was turned off, this turned to ice, and when cooking recommenced and the cabin warmed up again, the ice melted, making everything damp—the bedding, my clothes, books, charts, everything. Then, when cooking was over, this dampness again turned into ice. It was like living alternately in a meat-market cold room and a Turkish bath. The most time I could spend on deck in one spell was about fifteen minutes in my normal seagoing, cold-weather clothes. Otherwise, it meant donning the full arctic Eskimo suit, which had to be removed below when I was in the engine compartment or I would start to sweat. This was dangerous, because as soon as I had been on deck for a few minutes, the sweat would start to freeze.

While the boat drifted in the calm water between the distant ice fields, I rigged the solid fuel stovepipe to pass through the cockpit. Now I could at least warm part of my body even when on deck. The extension to the stovepipe I made with cans, wired together and stuck with strong glue. During the winter months I had collected a great pile of driftwood and this kept dry in the bottom of the engine compartment, as an emergency fuel supply. I reckoned that if I kept the stove going for two spells of three hours each over the coming winter, I would have enough fuel to last for one year, possibly more.

The next few days were pleasant enough, despite the snow. There wasn't much movement inside the floating ice fields, and though the wind blew hard, there was a flat sea.

I drifted with the Greenland current for eight days, keeping an eye astern for floes and bergs which might overtake my rate of drift and collide with *Cresswell*. I spent much of the time fishing, but caught only two small halibut. My attempts at shrimp-catching were no more successful—out this far from the coast the shrimp are much deeper—but I managed to catch about one plateful in a week.

A very careful eye had to be kept on the ice growing on the masts and rigging, especially when any kind of wind was blowing. When sleet and snow fell, ice grew on the rigging wires at the rate of about a quarter of an inch a minute. Then I had to climb the main and mizzenmast every hour or so with a small ax and chop loose the ice, to prevent too much weight accumulating aloft. If this was not done, the "black ice" (as it is called) would continue to grow around the wires. The weight of the ice eventually would be greater than the weight of the keel and ballast, and the boat would overturn. No one can live for more than a few seconds in the icy cold water of the Greenland current.

I lashed a small hammer to a long pole and, in calm weather, used that to knock the black ice off the rigging. But in heavy wind it was impossible to use, and then it was a matter of slowly and carefully hauling myself up with the mainsail halyard on a bosun's chair, knocking the stuff off as I ascended. I dared not start at the top, in case the extra weight of my body at the masthead, along with the ice, should cause the boat to capsize. Climbing up a wildly swinging mast covered with ice, in a high wind, is a real circus performance.

During sleet and snowfalls, which were often heavy, the snow would land on deck and, unless shifted immediately, would turn into ice. It was a continuous effort. But most of the time the wind was slight, and it was a matter of clearing the rigging only twice every twenty-four hours.

On about the eighteenth of May I got a sun sight which put me 250 miles east-southeast of Scoresby Sund. The ice to the east was loosening up. I decided to have a go at following a long eastward gap. The wind was in the northwest, and again I crowded sail. The next day at 0400 hours, under the light of the midnight sun, I saw ice only to the west of me. After another twenty-four hours with no sight of anything but small floes, I realized that I was in the clear.

I had broken through two hundred miles of massed, moving ice. Immediately I changed my course northeast, for Jan Mayen Island.

By this time it was daylight for twenty-four hours. The skies had cleared, and the wind was from the southwest. I stayed in the cockpit, huddled against the stovepipe when it was warm, two blankets thrown over my Eskimo suit when it was not. It was good sailing, except for the cold. In fact it was so good that when I reached the point where I could have headed north, on the meridian of Jan Mayen, I decided to press on to the northwest. I could have done with the rest and human contact in Jan Mayen, but I wanted to reach Svalbard while this rare good weather persisted, so as to get to the edge of the ice field before the summer retreat north commenced. In this way I anticipated good prospects of reaching further than eighty-four degrees north.

Out of the ice-field area, the seas were now lively again, and *Cresswell*, with her shallow draft and narrow beam, was boisterous. It was, however, warm enough in the engine cuddy, and when the horizon was completely clear of any ice, I set the sails to self-steer and, together with Nelson, would go below. He would lie at the end of the shelf I had made, and I would take off the sealskin boots and stick my feet in between his legs and his belly. He made a grand foot-warmer.

By the eighteenth of May I was 130 miles to the west of Jan Mayen Island. Way out on the grey horizon I saw the smudge of smoke from a ship, but heard nothing on the radio. She was too far over the horizon to see me, but I could tell that she was heading to the east. I stared for two hours at the thin discoloration in the sky, thinking of all the millenia of effort and struggle it had taken to put her there, and wishing she were nearer, just so I would see somebody, and perhaps have a word with them. But she went on her way, unaware that I was there, and I settled down again, pushing north.

On the twenty-fifth of May I sighted, right across the

northern horizon, a long line, like a low shore. First it was grey, then, as the sun rose high in the south, it changed to deep blue, to aquamarine, then white, and finally gleaming silver—the edge of the ice pack! Soon, all around me, there were loose floes, but they did not seem to be moving. At first this puzzled me, until I figured that the southwest wind was holding them back from flowing southwest with the current. But then a question loomed. Was that the case, or was the ice, in fact, moving north?

I dropped the sails and hove to, under mizzen only, to wait a few hours and find out exactly what was happening. By noon I knew. The ice was actually moving north, but very slowly, and the edge of the ice field dropped back to the northeast. I decided to follow it, at a distance, just far enough away that I could see it, low on the horizon.

On the thirtieth of May I reached latitude seventy-six degrees ten minutes north. This was the furthest north I had reached in the previous year. I was elated. It was only the end of May, and I had clear water still to the north of me and all the months of June, July, and August for the ice to melt and break up, before it started to solidify again in September.

The wind increased that "night," and soon I was shortening sail. Under spitfire jib, trysail, and mizzen I headed due east, for I wanted to be far away from the ice should heavy weather blow up.

I switched on the radio, but got nothing in English. Back topsides, it seemed that a regular dusting was in the offing. I steered as straight as I could in the ever-steepening seas, to get clear of ice. By midnight it was blowing a twenty-four-carat bastard, with the wind howling, black clouds racing across the sky, and the sea getting up into a short, steep frenzy. I carried on to the east, staying on the wheel for a solid fifteen hours, unable to leave the helm for more than a few seconds at a time.

Eventually, with no sign of the storm abating, and with no ice having been sighted for twelve hours or so, I hove to, dowsing the spitfire jib and the trysail. Then I went below, to try to rest for a couple of hours and warm up a little. Sleep, in that sea, with the boat jerking and plunging, was impossible, but I did doze for a few minutes at a time. The smells from the diesel oil and lubricating oil in the engine compartment were sickening, and so I moved my blankets into the cabin, getting a great slop of icy cold Arctic Ocean water all over them in the process. But this soon froze, and I was at least warmer under the frozen blankets than I was outside. It was so cold during this storm that even Nelson, who was keeping watch while I rested, came down below every few minutes to warm himself up for a spell.

The storm raged for six days. It slashed, it howled, it screamed, driving the seas before it like berserk monsters. Soon the tops of the seas were so white with driven spume that it was impossible to tell if there were ice floes anywhere near the boat, and for a week I existed with the ever-present threat of death right in front of me, staring me full in the eye. To touch a floe with these seas running would be the end. Instant and very, very final. The great twenty-foot-high mountains of water would pick the boat up and throw her against the ice. She would be crushed like a matchbox. The only thing I could figure out as a possible safeguard was to slow the boat down to what I estimated would be the speed of a floe. Being low in the water, they move before the wind much more slowly than a boat. If I could stay at the speed of the average floe, chances were that I would not overtake one and drift close to it.

With the boat bouncing up and down like a crazy yo-yo, I delved into the after cuddy and dug out the long storm line. This was six hundred feet long. After leading the rope outboard through blocks on the gunwale at the chain plates, I secured both ends around the mast tabernacle, then cast the bight into the roaring sea, over the bow. The woven nylon line floated, and the bight created enough resistance to stop the boat drifting. However, the strain imposed on the hull, every time the sea lifted it up then dropped it forty feet, was *shocking*. She would rise up slowly, hover for about ten seconds as a great long, grey, icy sea ran under her, then slam down into the trough with force enough to lift me clear into the air if I was not securely tied down to the wheel binnacle. Where the storm line imparted the shocks to the hull, through the chain plate blocks, the sudden judders were great enough for me to wonder how long she could stand this treatment, strong as she was. But I had to accept the risk of the boat shaking to pieces as better than the risk that she would hurl down onto a floe.

During the storm I had not been able to get any sun, star, or moon sights to enable me to estimate my position, but by dead reckoning (that is, calculating the direction of course, drift, and the current, together with the speed), I had a rough idea. I was about 200 miles to the west-southwest of Prins Karls Forland, an island in the Svalbard group, and my latitude was approximately seventy-seven thirty north. Only 390 miles from the magical eighty-four degrees!

With the wind dropping and swinging to the southeast, I determined to head northeast. On the fifth of June I sighted, through a gap in the cloud cover, far away, the black mountains of the Barentzburg, on Spitsbergen. I got a bearing and went below. Checking up on the chart it was soon obvious that my previous dead-reckoned position had been way out, because I was only now at seventy-seven degrees forty north. When the horizon cleared up, it showed that the line of the ice field went clear across to the coast of Spitsbergen, and through the binoculars I could see plainly the settlement smoke of King's Bay. The entrance might be clear. I made sail again and headed for the smoke. The wind continued to swing to the east, and I was soon sailing in long zigzag tacks against the wind. Within six hours all hell broke loose again, with a fifty-knot wind blowing straight out of King's Bay dead against me. Before the sleet began to slash down, a quick gaze at the far-off shore showed that I must be around twenty miles off. The engine's ten-horsepower was useless against such a wind and sea, so I continued patiently and wearily, tacking all day. But the wind rose even more, and finally I had to admit defeat. After I had seen King's Bay and safety! I hove to. Again. All day on the sixth, the seventh, the eighth, and the ninth. Despite the storm line slowing her progress, the wind was blowing the boat away from Svalbard towards the ice field. Anxiously I watched astern, through the sheets of freezing hail and sleet, hour in, hour out. I had no idea what I would do if the ice field showed up, except perhaps rig the trysail and attempt to head south. But even with those sails up the wind would still blow the boat sideways, and the chances were that she would end up being flung against the awful ice. The only thing that I could hope for was that there was enough sea room astern of me, to the west.

Then I saw it; after many long, freezing hours of anxiety. I saw it, through a momentary clearing in the sleet, a great piled-up hump of frozen slabs, all thrown up into the air, this way and that. A mile long and seemingly a thousand feet high, glowering over the lashed, grey waters of the Arctic, and to each side of it, the frozen wall of the ice field, stretching back from here right across the top of the world, all the way to Alaska and the Bering Strait. Dead astern right in the way of the boat.

"Holy Jesus Christ Almighty!" I murmured to Nelson, as I crawled forward over the icy deck to hoist the trysail in a sixty-knot wind. "It looks like we've had it, old son."

Little by little, with the wind flogging the sail as I let go of the tiers and started to haul, up went the trysail. Then, hanging onto the ice-festooned boat with one hand, getting the spitfire jib up with the other frozen hand and my teeth, I struggled like a maniac. Then back to the cockpit, where I unlashed the wheel and heaved her over.

In a few seconds the wind picked up the sails and she was crashing over the immense moving mountains of white spume and grey green heaving water, straight for the ice.

After the first few minutes of shock, I peered again at the ice field, through another clearing in the sleet. Then, wiping the cluttered ice off my face, looked again. Another wipe over my eyebrows and lids, heavy with fluffy ice from my frozen tears. I looked again. There was an inlet behind the mountain of piled floes! There was a gap between the south end of the berg and the ice field. It was my only chance. I rammed the boat through the wind; she refused to go. I wore her, that is, turned off the wind; the trysail slammed across with a juddering shock, the spitfire came about with an explosion of ice particles and cold water, and she was over, heading for the gap!

And now the storm is over,
And we are safe and well;
We will walk into a public house
And drink and drink our fill;
We will drink strong ale and porter
And we'll make the rafters roar,
And when our money is all spent
We'll be off to sea once more!
(FINE GIRL YOU ARE!)
Ye're the girl I do adore,
And still we'll live in hopes to see,
The Holy Ground once more!

Old Liverpool halyard shanty. The Holy
Ground was the Scotland Road brothel area,
the landowner of which was the Roman
Catholic Church.

22

In the Arctic Icecap

The sail for the gap behind the iceberg was the kind I never want to make again as long as ever I live. To keep the boat moving northwest, beam onto the switchback seas, she had to carry all the sail she could. The course was uncertain. I did not know if there was submerged ice between me and the gap; I did not know if there was shallow water or other underwater hazards, such as protruding ice, near the ice field. All I knew was that this was a God-given chance of survival. I pushed her on, with the freezing spume off the tops of the seas blowing right over the boat, the spitfire jib dipping into the tops of the seas, picking up whole buckets of water and flinging them aft with the wind from its slipstream, the droplets freezing into hail as they flew with the wind straight at me, turning into a thousand burning daggers.

As visibility improved, I saw that the berg was, first of all, not as far away as it had seemed and, secondly, not as big as it had first appeared. Two hundred yards off the gap, I let fly the spitfire jib-sheets, to slow down the boat, and took stock, balancing myself up high in the mizzen shrouds. What I saw was incredible. There was a good clear passage, about forty yards wide, between the "hill," which rose about two hundred feet, and the piled-up pack ice on the other side. It all seemed to be clear of obstruction. Beyond the mouth of this inlet was a bay of flat water. I hauled in the sheet and steered a course right for the middle of the gap, bashing away over the great long thrusts of angry green seas.

Cresswell shot into the gap like a rat up a drainpipe. One minute she was in terrifyingly high, steep seas, with frozen spray flying all around, and the next minute she was becalmed, in the lee of the hill of ice, floating in calm water. Ahead was a small bay, reaching about two hundred yards deep between the hill and the ice field. The little bay was about one hundred yards wide.

I let go the sheets again and clambered below to start the engine. It had been shaken clear off its bed and was lying in the bilge, on its side. The strain imposed on the propeller shaft by the shock had bent the shaft like butter. I took one look below, then climbed aloft. I tested for depth with the sounding lead, all eight hundred feet of it. There wasn't any bottom! I could not drop an anchor (useless anyway, with the ice field moving over the top of the world). I had to make the boat secure to the ice!

I inflated the rubber dinghy (try getting rubber bungs into the air inlet valve holes while wearing two pairs of mittens!) and threw it over the side. Then I hopped into it with a long crowbar, a hammer, the mooring line, a small block, and the oars. Towing *Cresswell* almost a hundred yards was agony, for I was using up my reserves of strength, but eventually I made it to the middle of the bay, where the "shore" of the berg fell back. I rowed ashore, axed out footholes in the side of the berg, to get about ten feet above sea level, drove in the crowbar, and made fast the line. Then back to the boat to shorten the line and secure it to the knightheads. Over the side again with another line, I rowed over to the ice floes on the western side of the bay, clambered up the eight-foot sides, drove in a spike, made fast, and returned to the boat. Shortened up on the after line, and that was that, the boat was tied up secure, in flat calm water. I crawled down below so tired that I could not even find the strength to make a cup of tea or dish out some burgoo. I collapsed in the cabin, fully dressed, and fell asleep, to the noise of the wind, the ice floes grinding against the field, the seas crashing onto the ice floes, and Nelson padding around on deck. It was the tenth of June. In Britain the flowers were blooming; there was green, green grass, and trees, and towns with electric lights and buses. I drifted off. Outside it was broad daylight. Inside, with the felt pads over the decklights and portholes, with the companionway hatch shut, it was dark. Dark and cold, though under the blankets crackling with the cold as I moved in my sleep, it was warm enough. I was so weary I could have slept on a clothesline.

When I awoke, shivering, it was 0600 hours the next day. I lit the cooking stove, then carried it outside on deck and made a fine breakfast of corned beef hash and cocoa for me, the remainder of the burgoo, boiled up, for Nelson. Around, the wind was dying, but the seas were still colliding heavily with the floes outside the little bay. I lit the stove in the engine compartment, then sat down to smoke one of my six-a-day cigarettes and have a think.

There was plenty to do. But the first thing was to make sure that the boat was safe. This is always a skipper's highest priority. I made ready to climb the ice nearest to the boat and from there survey the scene. It was now obvious that what I had thought was one hill, was, in fact, three. These piles of ice did not look like the type of berg I had seen off Greenland. I concluded that this was a great chunk of ice which had escaped from the coast of Siberia, and was not a glacier-spawned berg, but in fact sea ice which had piled up on the coast far away somewhere.

Again, I gathered my ax, hammer, two spikelike chisels, rope and oars, and paddled over to the berg. The face at sea level was an overhanging wall of ice fifteen feet high. Climbing it to get a spike into the ice on the top of the wall took four hours. By the time that was done, and I had secured a block and rope onto the spike, I was about half-frozen, so I dropped into the dinghy and headed for the boat, to warm up for half an hour. Then, packing some food, corned beef and beans, with a block of freshwater ice in a small shoulder bag, I set off again.

From the overhanging edge of the berg's side, on top of which I had fixed the block, the hill overhung a platform, rearing up one hundred and eighty feet. To one side there was a slope of ice rising about fifty feet to a shoulder between two small peaks. The slope was at an angle of thirty degrees. Cold, shiny bright ice, with no handholes. Getting up the slope, driving one chisel in while standing on the one just driven in, was purgatory and it took three hours. When I got to the shoulder, I found myself once more in the wind, although by now it was down to about ten knots. Looking out "to sea," to the east, there was nothing but ice. To the north, the west, to the east, and as far as I could judge, to the southeast as well. To the south the broken ice floes were piled up against the bottom of the berg. Directly to the southwest the slope of the hill rose at around twenty degrees to a height of about two hundred feet. I started climbing, every now and then looking down. Thin ice was already forming a dull grey sheen all across the bay. It took another four hours to get to the top of the hill, the most southerly of the three. I promptly made a note to name them, from south to north, "England," "Wales," and "Scotland." The whole ice-mountain I christened "Brittania-Berg."

The scene from the top of "England" was astonishing. To the north, right around from east to west, there was nothing but ice. Most of it was flat, but at intervals other great hummocks appeared, similar to the one I was on, though not as big, except for one, in the far-off, hazy distance to the northeast, which was a giant. On the other side of the bay was a great jumble of ice floes, all heaving up and down separately as the monster sea-swell rolled in from the east, crashing, groaning, wheezing, and sighing. Then I looked at the mouth of the gap. It did not seem as wide as it had the day before. I made a note to check it in a few days' time. On top of the hill I firmly set a broom handle with a red ensign nailed to it to signal any searchers.

It took much less time to climb down "England" hill, as I had chopped out footholds in the ice. I was very careful though—one slip would mean death in the freezing water. I resolved that next time I climbed up I would bring a rope up all the way with me. I had chipped some of the ice and tasted it. Right on the top it was fresh, but on the shoulder it was salty. This confirmed my suspicions about the berg's origin.

By the time I got back down into the dinghy I was sweating. Supporting myself on a frozen line, over murderously cold water, I kicked out with my feet to bring the wildly swinging dinghy underneath me, so I could drop into it. Then, on my way back paddling over the bay, I hit ice. It was thick enough to support the weight of a man, whereas when I had left the boat it had been very thin. Weighing up the risks involved in heading out to sea with another easterly brewing as against being frozen in here, in what appeared to be a safe place, the answer was obvious. I would stay. A couple of hours later, when I paddled out to reconnoiter the entrance to the bay, I found that it was jammed solid with pack ice driven in by the wind.

Back on board, I set to making the boat shipshape for the coming months. I could not lower the mainmast, as there was nothing to rig a lowering line to. I unshipped the booms and slackened off all the standing rigging, so that by shaking it hard I could remove any ice which might accumulate. With the booms I made a frame for the old mainsail and the big canvas awning to act as a tent. These I lashed down firmly, at a steep angle, so that any snow falling on them would slide over the side. I made sure that the cockpit was well covered, so as to prevent snow from entering, thawing, and getting into the bilges. Then, after shifting the heating stove once more back into the cabin, I let the stove really rip, trying to drive out all the dampness.

After this I could once more live comfortably in the cabin.

My cooking stove I moved into the cockpit, so that the humidity from the burnt kerosene would dissipate in the open air.

By the time the "tent" was rigged, the weather was at storm force. Again hail and sleet slashed down. I rested below in the dry cabin, and let it scream overhead. Much better here than out at sea I thought to myself, as I set to, repairing the torn sails, cozy and warm.

It took three days for the storm to pass, and at the end of it the ice around the boat was a foot thick. I decided to lighten her as soon as the ice was strong enough to bear the weight of the stores. Meanwhile, I secured the engine back on its bed—hard work, as it weighed well over 180 pounds.

By the middle of July the days were getting shorter. I had seen very few signs of life—a seal, far away on the ice floes; one or two birds high up; and while out surveying the western floes, a few fish—nothing more. It was nowhere near as lively as the Greenland side.

When the weather was calm, I gingerly felt my way over the bay ice to the western side and made a sketch map of the ice floes, giving all the larger ones names, mainly from the alphabetical Morse code. If any wind was blowing, or if there was any sea movement, this was too risky, as the whole bed of ice would move around violently, like an animal in pain, and great long crevasses would appear and disappear continuously. By the end of July the ice in the bay was around two feet thick. By taking sun and moon sights, I knew that the drift of the ice was to the northwest, and it was obvious that we must be in a part of the Arctic Ocean where the Greenland current doubles back, coun- terclockwise, onto itself, which was why the cold water formed ice so rapidly.

I started to lighten the boat, unloading the ship's stores and food stores onto the ice, at the same time digging a narrow trench around the hull, so that as she lightened she lifted. Then, when I had her lightened by something like three tons, with the stern and bow almost out of the water, I let the ice freeze again. As soon as the boat was frozen into the ice, but eight inches higher than before, I started to load her once more, at least with the stuff I needed daily and for routine jobs. The rest I left out in the open, covered by the spare mainsail, well pegged down.

As her frames were on nine-inch centers, four-inch balks, the two feet of the boat's bottom now gripped in the ice was almost solid wood. *Cresswell's* bottom was round, and if she was gradually squeezed by the ice, she would lift up, vertically.

With the boat clear of gear inside, I started to clean her up. It proved impossible to get good fresh water, except when snow fell, which was not regular until late September, so I scraped and painted all the blocks instead, took weather observations, and navigated. With the awning over the boat, not much light got in, but I used my seal-oil lamp, with its chimney fixed up again in the porthole, so I could read by its glare for a few hours a day.

By the end of September the "days" were much shorter and it was obvious that the gap at the mouth of the bay was closing up rapidly. Every time there was a wind, any wind, except from due north, the ice floes would start to move and twist, crushing up against each other. The "Scotland" hill was breaking away from the main ice field, while "England" was steadily and surely heading west. In other words, the iceberg was revolving very slowly in a clockwise direction and making one hell of a noise doing it.

On 30 September my latitude was seventy-eight degrees fifty minutes north, 310 miles south of the *Fram's* furthest north! I was jubilant, for it seemed that at this rate I should pass the eighty-four-degree mark well before the ice turned with the current towards the southwest.

When the weather was calm, now that the dark hours were lengthening, I wandered out on the ice and watched the northern lights shining through the ice of the piled-up floes. A wondrous sight to behold. The great streaks of pure power and energy streaming across the night, right across the star-laden, blue black velvet sky of the Arctic is a vision which still comes into my mind every time I hear someone talk of miracles. But generally, the nights were far too cold to go out for more than a short while, so most of the time I was inside the cabin performing necessary chores. Alone, and having no idea if you are going to survive or not, the main thing is not to think about it too much. All the thinking in the world will not change the circumstances. Self-pity is the harbinger of despair, which, in turn, brings panic and fear. There is only one thing to do in these circumstances—think about and perform only the jobs in hand. If something I was reading dealt too heavily with the more profound aspects of existence, I put the book down and baked some bread, or repaired another sail, or had another go at straightening out the engine propeller shaft. A strict routine helped make time pass. Every "day" at 0900 I was up. Breakfast before ten, then repair and maintenance jobs until noon in clear weather. Then the latitude sight, then lunch until 1300 hours. Next, maintenance again; then tea and a longitude sight. Then read for an hour or so. Then a walk out on the ice with Nelson, or, if it had snowed, shoveling out the walkway. Later in the winter, of course, the snow became too thick for Nelson to walk very far safely, but I would still slog out there in snowshoes, in a wide circle, looking for tracks or anything else.

As the weather became colder, the simplest activities became more difficult. With very low temperatures it was no longer possible to have a shit on the ice. Instead it had to be done in the bucket down below, then carried out onto the ice. One minute's exposure in those temperatures was enough to cause frostbite.

Being alone is not being lonely. If you know there is no other human within a few hundred miles, it is much easier to accept than if there are millions and you know no one. Sex becomes very unimportant. I personally have not, during my long spells of being without relief for the sex urge, found that deprivation had any effect on my performance once back in the green pastures. In fact, the case is the exact reverse, or at least so I am told by impeccable authorities on the subject.

This seems to be the story with most of the other solo sailors that I know, and they all agree that the further away one is from possible partners, the less important sex becomes.

By mid-October the mouth of the bay was completely closed, both by the steady movement of the iceberg's southerly end in a westward direction, and by a jumbled mass of piled-up sea ice, stretching four or five miles to seaward. By the end of October, I hibernated inside the cabin, emerging only on clear nights to take star and moon shots.

So the weeks passed, with both Nelson and I eating sparingly from our diminishing food stocks. By mid-November all was darkness, and I was at latitude seventy-nine degrees fifteen minutes north. Only 285 miles from the target.

Again, on clear nights, when there was no precipitation in the form of falling ice and snow, I would sometimes watch the northern lights for a few minutes at a stretch, filling the whole sky with a display of wonder. I kept notes on how often this phenomenon was followed by strong winds and heavy weather. These events occurred about 90 percent of the time after the appearance of the aurora borealis. I came to the conclusion that there must be some connection between the northern lights and the weather, especially in the Arctic regions. The arctic wind-pressure system has a great bearing on the rest of the world's weather; if someone could find the connection, and the reasons for it, there might be a new, more accurate way of foretelling long-range climatic changes.

The boat was now completely frozen in. There was nothing but ice and darkness in all directions. Once, back in July, I had heard, far away, the drone of a plane, but there was no time to arrange a smoke signal as the ice was not then safe to step on. It had come, hummed for a few minutes in the cold clear air, and gone away again. That was the only sign of human presence in the world that I saw for ten months. Just a slight noise, anything up to forty miles away.

December 1: latitude seventy-nine, thirty-five.

December 18: latitude seventy-nine, forty-two.

December 25: latitude seventy-nine, *thirty-two*!

December 31: latitude seventy-nine, *sixteen*!

The direction of the flow of ice had changed! I was heading southwest! By January 10, 1961, I knew for certain: latitude seventy-eight, fifty-five. I had failed to beat the *Fram* by 285 miles! I had failed to get nearest to the Pole in a sailing craft. I had failed to beat Nansen! I had failed to reach nearer than 618 miles to the Pole!

I bent over my calculations, tears of defeat misting over the scribbled figures on the tattered page of my logbook. I stared, half-blind, at my grimed fist tightening over the pencil, squeezing it until it splintered into three shattered stubs—broken, like my dreams. I opened my palm and glared silently, bitterly, at the fragments. I threw the splinters down onto the table. Then, as I groped for my mug of tea, I glanced at the broken bits of wood and lead. I stared from one to the other and back again, like an idiot. I wiped my eyes, then stared again. A moment passed, then I picked up one of the pieces of wood.

The pencil, the *artifact*, the *result* of some man's dreaming effort somewhere, was destroyed, fragmented. But the man's dream survived! I stared closer, turning the splintered shard of wood around and around. The atoms of wood, the molecules of lead were still there; I could touch them. I could see them . . . only the man's dreams, only his ideas I could not see. Yet I could see the results of those dreams lying before me shattered. Yet the dream was not shattered, and *that's what mattered*!

Slowly I began to see that the realization of a dream, an ambition, was not of itself *essential*. It is the *conception* and *survival* of the dream, the idea, the ambition, that matters. But dreams, ideas, unlike atoms, cannot survive of themselves. The dreamer himself must survive to pass on his dream! Then, in the survival of my dream, in *my survival*, would lie my victory!

I picked up the shards of wood and lead and placed them carefully, reverently, in the pencil box. I would repair that bloody pencil!

Then I finished my tea and turned in.

Nelson stirred in his sleep, dreaming of some faraway bitch.

Everything that happens either happens in such a way that you are formed by nature to bear it or not to bear it. If what happens to you is within your strength to bear, bear it without complaining; if it is beyond your strength, do not complain, for it will perish after it has destroyed you. Remember, however, that you are formed by nature to bear everything which your own opinion can make endurable and tolerable, by thinking that it is either your interest or your duty to do so.

Marcus Aurelius, *Meditations* 10. 3.

23

An Embarrassing Predicament

During the eternal darkness of deep winter, on the edge of the icecap (although by now *Cresswell* was ten miles "inland"), the weather was calm for about four "days" out of ten. Then, the skies would clear and millions of stars shone bright, casting a diffused luminescence over the barren, cold, dead world of ice. High overhead Alkaid, Alcor, Alloth, Dhube, and Muscida, great blobs of shining light, delineated the backbone of the Great Bear, Ursa Major, while to one side, his cub, Ursa Minor, the Little Dipper, balancing on its unsure backpaws Kochab and Perkhab, pointed a grubby little claw-nail through Yildun at the paralyzed fish around which the whole sky revolved— Polaris—the pulse of the heart of the universe at a spot almost directly above my head.

To the east, the low horizon was obscured by the three mountainous humps of the Brittania-Berg thrusting their gleaming, pale white sugar loaves into the black velvet sky. In every other direction, north, west, and southwest, I could see stars so low in the firmament that they looked like ships passing by far away on a silver sea. Slowly they passed around the rim of the ice world—Vega, the lonely, shy virgin with her lyre, accompanied always by her handmaidens, Shelyak and Sulafat, tripping lightly along the dark corridors of infinity to escape muscle-bound Hercules. Cygnus, the Swan, his regal head picked out by

248

Deneb, with Gienah and Delta Cygni worn, jewellike, on the ends of his wings, led Vega to the court of Queen Cassiopeia, sitting regally in her celestial chair. Toward her, Perseus, the messenger, flew out of the ice horizon, bearing in his right hand the great flaming torch of Algol, the star of knowledge. This arrival of the light of learning at the feet of the eternal queen was watched joyously by her hand-maiden, Capella, together with Betelgeuse and Bellatrix, the two lovely wearers of the diamond-studded belt of Orion. Outside the palace door the gallant gladiators, Castor and Pollux, made way through the crowded lanes of the sky for beauteous Athena, while ahead of their proud progress, Leo Minor, the Lion Cub, scampered by the clumsy feet of the Great Bear.

As I stood, transfixed by the wonder of this sparkling spectacle, with my arms withdrawn from the sleeves of my jerkin to warm them against my chest, it was sometimes difficult to pick out the familiar stars against the sequin-spangled backdrop reaching to the other side of infinity. Draco, the dragon guard of the Little Bear, the playful favorite of the queen of the skies, was almost impossible to distinguish. Yet there he was, as faithful as ever, with his great tail flailing out from AlSafi, through Eta Draconis and Thuban, millions and trillions of miles across the reaches of space to his tail-tip, Giansar. While at the other end of his twisted frame, his fiery eyes, Eltanin and Alwaid, stared with defiant challenge at lovelorn Hercules wearily plodding through eternity after his virgin Vega.

All the themes of human emotions are shown in the sky. If a man can but tell a thousandth as much as the faintest, most obscure pinprick of light, as it shows its reflection of life, love, and hope to us from the nethermost corner of the most remote galaxy, he will have told more than all the greatest of men that ever lived here on earth.

Most of the moonrises I could not see, for they were obscured by the Brittania-Berg. But on two memorable occasions I did see the full moon rise in a calm arctic night, with not a sound except for the faint, faraway gnashing of the sea ice on the edge of the death white field. I was out on the western side of the bay, mapping the floes which had piled up there, watching for signs of possible leads opening up. This was a job which took twelve hours at a stretch, for the "terrain" over the floes, all jumbled up, was extremely difficult and hazardous. Some of the floes had frozen solid at an angle of sixty degrees from the horizontal. Often there was no way around these capsized slippery surfaces, and it was hard and heavy work to climb up glassy slopes the size of a soccer field. Then, having reached the top, I would have to sling a rope through a block and lower myself down the underside of the floe, which sometimes overhung the next floe. I always had the dinghy compass with me, for once beyond the "shore-side" floes, the frozen-in boat was completely out of sight. Snowstorms often closed in very suddenly, limiting vision to a matter of yards.

One night I reached the southern edge of the Brittania-Berg, or Gibraltar Point, as I called it. I was attempting to climb up England hill from the south, but this proved impossible. It was far too steeply angled and absolutely smooth. I was resting before making the four-hour scramble back to the boat, when, looking to the southeast, I saw the sky light up, very slowly. The horizon turned a cobalt color, then electric blue, next powder blue, shot with silver rays streaking up through the stars. A little while after, with the whole sky in the east gleaming with shot-silver, the ice accepted, like a woman handling a rich brocade, the moonlight. The tip of the moon's upper arc was actually shining through ten miles of piled-up ice! The light rays glittered, splintered, and slithered at odd angles, flashing right across the horizon. These shocks of pure silver were reflected on the base of the low, slow clouds over the sea, far away. It was as if the world would crack asunder with cold beauty. Then, slowly, the moon showed herself, her light shining horizontally over the cluttered masses of ice, casting long shadows. The whole surface of the world, as far as my eyes could see, became a vast panorama of speckled silver and black while the sky above was black with the speckled silver of twinkling stars. The moon seemed about twice the size she appears in the temperate zones, and the air was so clear I could see every freckle on her pockmarked face. Then, as she rose higher and higher, the shadows of the ice piles withdrew, and soon all was pale white and black again, with the moon's face cold, ghostly, and deathly alone as she became smaller and smaller, to hang in the sky like a crystal ball of ice, under the cold curtain of stars.

I shuddered, then put my arms back in the sleeves of my jerkin and headed off for the boat. Hours later, back over the ice barriers, onto the flat surface of frozen *Cresswell* bay, trudging wearily through the recently fallen, powdery snow, I saw a black shape advancing towards me. It was Nelson. Once alongside, he jumped up to greet this apparition. "I know, old son, it's alright. I know I look like a bloody Christmas tree!"

I hurried back to the warmth. There were a couple of dead spots on my cheeks, which did not feel my tears as I thought of other Christmases and the cheerful company of my sailor mates and the lasses we had loved.

Back in the galley, with the stove lit, I removed my goggles and warmed up my face. I inspected myself in the small looking glass. I looked wretched. Then I looked down at Nelson. Looking into the mirror, I said, "Right, you bastard, less of that crap, there's things to be done."

"What?" I asked myself.

"Well, for a start, feed the bloody dog."

"Right." I was getting to know me alright, and I was getting me shaped up, keeping control. But it was hard; it was terribly difficult to hold back the floodgates of self-pity and awful, soul-shrinking loneliness, and I took more and more to watching the stars and listening to their message in the stillness between raging blizzards.

After hot tea, ground-up peanuts, and porridge, I turned in, my head feeling the bump of the loaded Very pistol, broken at the breech, under the pillow. The whole time the boat was in the ice I was wary of a bear attack. If the bear off Greenland had been so aggressive while there was plenty of food available to him in the shape of fish and seals, what the devil would they be like out here, where there was apparently nothing?

All the time, in the ice, I was never very far from my ax, my hammer, a rope, and the Very pistol. Every time I left the boat, for whatever reason, even if it was only for ablutions on the calm, clear nights, my ax, my compass, the Very pistol, snowshoes, and two days' food went with me. Thick sheets of slashing snow and ice came down so fast that even yards away from the boat it was easy to be caught out and not be able to find the way back. Then it was necessary to find some kind of shelter under a cocked-up ice ledge and await the blizzard's tempering. But every move more than two yards from the boat was studied, every direction noted. I could not leave a lamp lit on the boat. For one thing, my fuel stock was low; for another, it would hardly show more than ten yards in a blizzard. Also I did not want to attract any possible prowlers, especially if I was absent from the boat. My shelter, my food, my warmth, my life. The center of my icy cold world. Each time I left the boat, I unwound a long line behind me, to show me the way back.

So the long, long procession of dark hours passed, week after week. I made it a rule to go over to the western ice-floe field whenever it was calm. Now it was a half-solid frozen mass, and I tried to follow the movement of the ice. It was always moving, not only en masse, everything together, but also bits and pieces, some as big as a city block, against the others. The Brittania-Berg moved clockwise, crushing into the western floes, which in turn had slowly transmitted the tremendous pressure of the berg onto the flat ice steppe beyond. Cracks and crevasses changed continuously towards the west of the boat, and this was where my attention was riveted, because I reckoned that when the breakup came (if it ever did), it would loosen the heavy floes and open a passage to the southwest.

Nine times out of ten, storms and blizzards were introduced by a display of power and light beyond imagination, as the northern lights flashed through the sky, like the fireworks of the gods, sending showers and fountains of streaking, liquid sparks across the black arch of the arctic sky. Hours later the wind started up—first a low moaning in the rigging, then rising to a whistle. This was the signal to batten everything down. Then the roar built to a scream of satanic anger. The vessel shook as the wind tore at the masts, trying to pluck them out of the snowbound hull. Now and again I peeped through the doghouse portholes, lifting the inch-thick felt insulators. Outside, a blinding white sheet of the wall of hell was zinging past the ice field, with the top ice breaking off under the strength of the mighty wind. On rare occasions I would brave the blast, well shielded with two extra blankets tied around my caribou-skin clothes, and through a tiny gap for my eyes, watch the ice blow over the top of Brittania-Berg, like a continuous spray of steam, clear over the top of the boat, onto the western side of *Cresswell* bay, where it filled the recently opened crevasses, changing the whole appearance of the ice-floe field.

Then I lit the seal-oil lamp and, putting some of my rapidly diminishing charcoal on the heating stove, settled down to read. This was my only relief from the arctic conditions of cold, anxiety, loneliness, and, when the weather was bad, idleness. My radio had given up the ghost just after Christmas, and though I fiddled with it for hours, it simply refused to speak to me any more. I came to the conclusion that the severe dampness in the cabin had got to one of the transistors. But after drying out all my volumes, I had plenty to read, and I was cozy enough, with the little stone lamp sending up its slow, tiny, wavering column of black smoke into the corned-beef-can chimney, and Nelson lying under the table, against my feet, with a bone held between his good paw and the stump of the missing limb.

Tiring of reading by the fitful lamp, I made plans for the long dawn, due to arrive about the end of February. I made ready a long line and a block, to fix a pulley up the steep northern slope of "England" on the Brittania-Berg. I made a new signal flag out of an ancient cockpit cover which I painted yellow and nailed to a frame. I hammered all my old empty food cans flat, then wired and glued them together, to make a sun reflector, a sort of heliograph. This was about a yard square, and I made a hole in it so I would be able to sight it at an airplane, and polished it, with emery paper and sand out of the bilge, until it shone like a mirror. When the sun rose high and the temperatures climbed, I planned to paint the big boat cover yellow and to make a separate signal to peg down onto the ice, away from the boat, out of the old awning. The food stores, in their boxes, together with the empty boxes, I pegged out in groups on the western side of the bay, while the ice held, to spell S.O.S. in Morse code, so it might be sighted from afar in the air.

Once a month, when the weather was calm, I baked bread, using the pressure cooker as an oven. I became quite expert at this, and the snow mixed with evaporated milk seemed to give the bread a good, light texture.

I do not know exactly what the lowest temperature I experienced was, as the alcohol in my outside thermometer had dropped out of sight by October, but I did find out later, from the Norwegian air force, that a plane within a hundred miles of my estimated position on New Year's Day of 1961 had registered, very close to sea level, something in the region of sixty-four degrees below zero Fahrenheit! Inside the cabin, with a domestic thermometer, I was able to raise the temperature as high as thirty-eight degrees Fahrenheit, but this was only for about five hours out of twenty-four. The rest of the time the temperature averaged around twenty-five degrees Fahrenheit.

The effects of cold and enforced idleness resulted in a slowing down of my whole system. I was not aware of this until one day I noticed that Nelson seemed to be moving much faster than he normally did. He was like a beast in an old-fashioned silent movie, jerking around, very fast. I stared at him for a while, then at myself, in the newly made sunlight reflector. It occurred to me that what had happened was that it was I who had slowed down; everything about me. This was interesting, and I lumbered over to the navigation cupboard and, after a few moments' thought (actually it was more like an hour), took out the chronometer to wind it up. I stared at it. Not only could I see the second hand moving fast, but I could see the minute hand moving quite steadily, and the *hour hand* moving! Time had warped my senses! I put the chronometer back and sat down to think this one out.

Was it the cold that was slowing me down? The loneliness? The enforced idleness? The diet? I puzzled out the reasons for a while, then decided to tackle the problem from another angle. Did the slowing down matter? Not if I was idle; in fact it was probably a good thing. Yes, if I had to get something done, and double-yes when and if the time ever came to get the boat out of this deathtrap.

From then on I made a conscious effort to increase the speed of all my movements and tried to vary my diet. Daily, I ate about eight ounces of greasy, rubbery seal blubber, raw. If it kept the Kalatdlits from getting scurvy, it would do the same for me. I left off frying food, even though I had still a good supply of lard on board, and tried to eat as much canned food as I could stomach, merely thawed out in the frying pan. I did these things by instinct, for I had never studied dietary rules, apart from getting hold of enough food to stay alive.

One thing I did learn during those months in the ice: the average westerner eats far too much and overcooks his food. I learned to eat what the body needed and no more, and to expend the energy given by the food before the next meal.

The other thing I learned was to play chess against myself without cheating. I had had a game going ever since I settled down in the ice, back in August, but it had been desultory, for I had to leave the board after each move and wait a week until I had forgotten the moves that I:a was going to make, then tackle the last move of I:a with I:b's fresh approach. The snag was that by the time I:b was ready to play his move, I:a had forgotten the moves in his future sequence of play. Gradually, however, over the weeks, the forgetting period of both the I's shrunk, and by December I could completely separate the two sets of tactics, blocking out I:a or I:b at will. At first this frightened me, and I gave up the game for a few days. But then I came to the conclusion that no human is only one "set of thoughts," that there are many sides to us, and so set to finish the game. Then a further complication arose, disturbing the first, until I became used to it. Not only were I:a and I:b well matched, but I was completely unbiased to either of them, merely watching the game from a spectator's point of view, objectively, forming separate and distinctive ideas as to what the future moves should be, yet not giving I:a or I:b a clue as to these thoughts. I cast encouragement or disapproval on both I:a and I:b as the move was made, without fear or favor.

One night, in between watching I:a form his strategy against the wily countermoves of I:b, I had to clamber topsides and shake the black ice off the loosened standing rigging wires, perform ablutions, and take my ghostly trek around the ghastly perimeter of smoking ice, watching the shooting stars fall from the heights of my mind and the stars and moon reflected on shining . . . shoulders . . . soldier boulders armies . . . dark winter's general campaign . . . over frozen steps . . . stepping-in-step across instant . . . bleached white covers . . . coniferous Conestoga wagons . . . wagons-lits . . . no wheels wheeling . . . blue shadows

lined . . . maligned . . . tramlines . . . butcher's apron . . .
ridged ice below . . . five-day growth . . . frostbitten jaws . . .
skull . . . icy white frozen . . . skull . . . icicles upside-down
in the empty eyesockets staring at bicycles cyclic cyclops . . .
traffic lights . . . policemen's whistles gristle . . . southwest
blizzards . . . gizzards, fried fish . . . chips smell . . . smelt . . .
from the . . . Brittania-Berg, Nelson limping after me
through the knee-high sheet of blown snow, beast snapping at my idol's legs with . . . walrus teeth and wasn't . . . it
. . . hot . . . in . . . the . . . bath tonight . . . because Ulli is
waiting . . . in the cabin . . . game just go on play up play up.
. . . I:a will move this pawn into *that* floe *there* . . . capture the
queen-boat . . . *Cresswell-Andromeda* . . . two ice chisels . . .
whoops! don't lose the hammer . . . Christ that's a hell of an
angle . . . it will need two . . . hundred . . . feet . . .
inch-and-a-half-nylon-line-in-the-spring, tra-la-la . . .
"I:b, you fucking idiot, why did you move that bloody rook,
your knight is day and day is night" . . . cold . . . cold . . .
and—"Jesus Christ!" I must have fallen flat on my face into
the bilge of the cabin, onto the slushy ice in the bilge,
hot-shocked into sanity with heart-freezing fear. Nelson
gasped—the boat was moving upwards and onto her side!
Outside the sky seemed to be caving in with noise! The deck
shot up, lifting me bodily.

"Holy fuck!" I staggered, drunkenly, to the hatchway,
trying to keep upright in the wildly heaving cabin. Then,
turning around and screaming, I grabbed the chessboard as
it slid across the table and heaved it against the forward
bulkhead. Now the boat was rearing up, *up* by the bow,
sinking down, *down* by the stern. Out in the cockpit after
what seemed like an aeon, I ripped the snowcover to one
side.

The ice field was in a frenzy of movement all around, as
far as I could see through the driving snow. I shook my
head and looked again, horrified, just in time to see all the
food boxes, two-thirds of my meager stock, slide down a
tilted floe into a widening crevasse and disappear as if

swallowed by some murderous, greedy beast. The noise was deafening. Cracks, thunder, explosions, then great loads of falling ice, in barrowloads at a time, truckloads, falling vertically down from the sky onto the heaving hull.

Barrowloads? Truckloads? What in the name of God?

I looked up. The sight I saw will haunt me until the last flicker of light leaves my weather-wracked soul. *The Brittania-Berg was capsizing!* It was turning over on its side, with "Wales," a great mass of ice, thousands of tons of the stuff, slowly falling, two hundred feet above the boat. Directly above the boat, and coming straight down onto the top, while *Cresswell* was being dragged by the shifting ice under her, right into the maw under the mountain of ice!

Was I going crazy? I shook my head as the boat was flung forward and upward again. *No, I wasn't. This nightmare was for real!*

What is a woman that you forsake her,
And the hearth-fire and the home-acre,
To go with the old grey Widow-maker?

She has no house to lay a guest in—
But one chill bed for all to rest in,
That the pale suns and the stray bergs nest in.

She has no strong white arms to fold you,
But the ten-times-fingering weeds to hold you—
Out on the rocks where the tide has rolled you.

Rudyard Kipling,
from "Harp Song of the Dane Women."

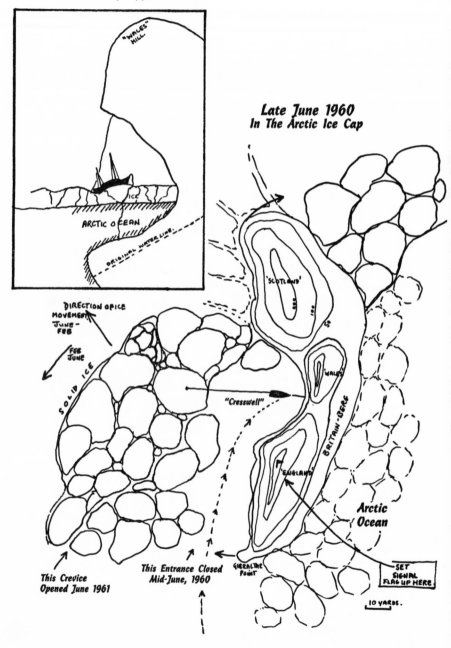

January 31st 1961
The Iceberg Tipped Over

"WALES" HILL.

ICE

ARCTIC OCEAN

ORIGINAL WATER LINE.

Late June 1960
In The Arctic Ice Cap

'SCOTLAND'

'WALES'

"Cresswell"

BRITAIN - BERG

'ENGLAND'

DIRECTION OF ICE MOVEMENT JUNE - FEB

FEB - JUNE

SOLID ICE

Arctic Ocean

GIBRALTER POINT

SET SIGNAL FLAG UP HERE

This Crevice Opened June 1961

This Entrance Closed Mid-June, 1960

10 YARDS.

24

Under the Ice

How long I stood gazing straight upwards, horror-struck, I
do not know. By the time I came to what senses I had left,
my mittens were frozen to the guardrail and the ice on my
snow goggles had completely obscured my vision. I remember thinking that this was death, this was the end. I
just stood there, unseeing, with *Cresswell* steadily tilting up
at the bow, waiting for her to go right over, hoping she
would, before the great ice-crash came and blotted out the
world, but this was more of a vision than a thought, more
like a sideways glance than a direct stare.

Suddenly *Cresswell* gave a great lurch downwards at the
bow, then froze. The racket around me was mind numbing;
it was as if all the tortured souls in hell were screaming for
mercy at the feet of Almighty God. It was not only the
volume of noise, it was the awful agony, the groans, the
crashes, the grinding *suffering* of it all.

I found myself working to free one hand from the rail,
which took a century, then fisting the ice from my goggles.
Just as they were clear and the world changed from dirty
black to blinding white again, the boat gave another lurch,
again the bows were thrown high up, and again they
smashed down. Even through the roars, bangs, and groans
of the ice my ears picked up the splintering crack as the
bowsprit smashed off, and the clatter of the forestay as it
swung wildly, free now, and smashed against the

doghouse. But I was not looking at the bow; my eyes were riveted on the berg. It suddenly stopped dropping and, with an almighty lurch, reared back again, hesitated for two or three seconds, then slowly settled down, coming to a halt with the peak of "Wales" at an angle about forty degrees from the vertical. There it hovered, 150 feet over the top of the masts. And stayed there! Bobbing.

Slowly I became aware of Nelson's whimpering and agitation, as he valiantly tried to keep his balance on the ice-covered deck of the heeled-over boat. I looked again at the berg around the boat. It was a shambles. The capsizing of the berg had meant that the wide ledge below the "Wales" peak had left a great gap under the overhanging summit. The pressure of the ice floes piled up against the western steppe had suddenly been released, and the whole mess had moved to the east, to take up the vacant space under the ice. With it, the boat had moved, the after line snapping like a piece of knitting wool. The forward mooring line, pegged to the edge of the berg's lower edge, had gone completely slack and was now hanging down vertically. With the pounding and smashing of the ice against the boat, the propeller, useless anyway with a bent shaft, had been snapped away. Fortunately, I had been able to unship the rudder before the boat had iced in. Now she was lying on her port side, at an angle of thirty-five degrees from the vertical, with her bow flung up, and the deck about forty degrees from the horizontal.

All around the ice was settling down again, and I realized that it would soon solidify into a frozen mass once more, until the berg moved over again onto the boat. My first resolution, once sanity returned, was to shift out of the boat as soon as the ice froze and make a refuge on the flat frozen steppe over to the west, from where I could watch both the berg and the boat. My second resolution was to cut my daily food ration down by a half. That would give me supplies for six months. I looked quickly at Nelson. "Then it'll be your turn, old son," I thought. He rubbed his good paw over his eyes. His tears were freezing, too.

Aware of the bitter cold, and giving one last look up at the tip of the ice peak hovering right overhead, I clambered below to survey the scene. It was chaos—clothes, books, charts, chess pieces, pans, cutlery, everything, lying wet in the icy slush of the bilges.

I set to picking up the bits and pieces of civilization out of the mucky slush. The first thing I did was to make a horizontal platform for the heating stove. Using the floor-boards from the engine compartment, I wedged them up with emptied boxes. Then I shortened the smoke-pipe and, finding some dry charcoal, soon had a little fire going to dry out all the gear. Then I mustered all the available food and worked out how to make it last for eight months. The collection was pitiful. Some seal blubber, six twenty-pound bags of peanuts, four pounds of sugar, twenty pounds of rice, thirty pounds of porridge, a block of salt, eighteen pounds of flour, twenty pounds of tea, ten pounds of cocoa, twenty cans of evaporated milk, twenty-four small cans of sardines, and eighteen large cans of beans, with twenty-two medium-sized cans of corned beef. I noted it all down, then, looking up at Nelson, thought *"and you."* He wagged his tail. And I did something I thought I'd never do again. I grinned at him. His tail bumped the deck.

I set to, tired and worn-out as I was, to tidy up the cabin. "Bugger it, mate," I said to him, as he lay down by the stove, out of the way. "If we're going to go, let's bloodywell go shipshape and Bristol fashion." I found that some sugar, out of the ready-use tin, had fallen under the navigation shelf, into the bilge. I spooned it out and set it on a tin plate to dry.

Then, when the cabin was squared away, I clambered up the crazily leaning companionway for a last look around. The first thing I looked at this time was not the ice around the boat. That had subsided now, and all was quiet, except for the faint hum of a low breeze through the rigging. My eyes went straight up vertically above my head, to the three thousand tons of hanging death hovering there. Polaris had shifted on its two-degree circular course around the celestial pole. Now it was over the peak of ice and shining *through* it. I gazed at the sight, fascinated.

As I watched, the first glares of the northern lights shot through the sky right above the hanging ice. Again I was petrified; would a strong wind blow the berg right over? Then the pyrotechnics of the heavens played across the night sky, sending sharp stabs of light into the Brittania-Berg, spears and daggers of pure energy. These, once they hit the ice, changed direction, scattering into the heart of the mass. I was fascinated, then wonder-struck, then delighted, so much that I yelled with pure joy at the sight, at the thought that the Spirit of the Universe was sending me this signal, this life, right across the vastness of space, just for me!

How long I was up there, gazing like an idiot at this display of awful power, I will never know, but finally I made my way below, intoxicated with the visual poetry of it all. Nelson opened his eye as I slithered down the drunkenly leaning hatch. "Well, old son, to die after seeing that—fuck it, *it's worth it!*"

Then I lay down on the level planks in front of the warm stove and went to sleep, thinking how beautiful, how very beautiful life is, so full of wonder.

The next "morning" was the twenty-fifth of January, and after the initial shock of finding the boat on her side and remembering the nightmare of the previous hours, I again stepped outside.

The berg was still there, all that ice straight overhead. It was steady and the ice all around was frozen solid, from the base of the berg to the ice field in the west. It was fairly clear by the starlight, and I looked over to the southwest. There, far up on the tilted ice mass of "England" hill, drooped the signal flag, hanging down right over the ice two hundred feet below. What had once been the high peak of the berg was now the side, fifty feet below the new peak! I grinned at the memory of having risked my life to reach the peak to plant the signal so many weeks before, when there was light in the world—and—I looked again at the peak of "Wales," then at the gap between it and "Scotland," to the north.

I peered, then removed the goggles.

There was—there was—light in the sky! A faint yellowish tinge, a mere touch of a glimmer of a glow! Not silver this time—gold! It was the sun, though still below the curve of the world. It was sunlight! It could not be the moon, for she was low in the ice rim to the west. It was Sol, it was light, and warmth; and the same light shone so far away on trees and unimaginable green things, grass and hedgerows, houses and—people! And it made the sea blue and green and the corn waving gold in the fields, and it was shining here, in this frozen hell of slow death, and it was shining for me! It was telling me that I would live and that I would follow it again and again, just as other men would follow other stars until the very hem of time turned into itself. The sight moved me to dance a slippery jig on the crazily canted deck. I shook the black ice free of the shrouds, shouting for joy. I rushed back, slithering, to call Nelson out. As he hobbled up the ladder, I grabbed his head and faced him to the whisps of gold in the black, star-studded sky. "There, it's there, old son, bloody daylight. We'll get out. We'll sodding well get out, I know we will!" Nelson jumped up and down as best he could.

By this time my position was approximately seventy-eight, forty latitude and one degree ten minutes east of the Greenwich Meridian. The whole ice mass was moving slowly but steadily southwest. I considered to myself that at this rate something was bound to happen during the next four months, as long as the direction and speed of the flow were maintained, and that that something was the gradual breakup of the ice floes on the edges of the field, then of the field itself. But if the direction changed to north again, I was probably a dead man, unless I could attract attention from some stray plane during the daylight season. Chances were that I was a dead man anyway, because if the weather deteriorated and piled more snow and ice on top of the Brittania-Berg it would capsize onto the boat. There was not much point in making a camp on the ice, because if the boat went I would not survive more than a few days in the ice. I had to stay with her and build a stack of wood close to her, laced with oil and covered from the snow, ready to light as a signal should I hear a plane.

I came to the conclusion that my best chance of getting out of this mess was to stick with *Cresswell*, keeping a close eye on the berg, and then if it seemed ready to capsize further, try my luck on the ice. But the dice would be loaded against me down to the quick.

I reckoned that February fourth would see the actual sunrise, and to watch it I scrambled for sixteen hours over the new jumble of piled ice, to a position north of "Scotland" peak. There I sheltered from the westerly wind and patiently waited for four hours until I saw the blood red glow, a tiny sliver of light, over the vast ice field to the southeast. Then, exhilarated, I clambered and slithered back for ten hours to the boat, and slept.

I made my mind up not to neglect the gear on the boat, and the first task towards this end, as soon as twilight filled the eastern half of the black dome of the sky, was to repair the bowsprit, which I did by gluing on a scarf made from one of the floor boards, and refix the spar to the knightheads. As the repaired sprit was slightly shorter than the original, I then had to shorten the forestay, which took several days, as it was difficult to splice wearing two pairs of mittens and working on a frozen wire. I could not get the forestay down to work below, because the mast was canted at an angle, and I dared not try climbing it as it was slippery with quick freezing ice.

By March first, twilight was upon us, and the ice mass

was moving faster. My position was now seventy-eight, fifteen north; zero degrees, sixteen minutes west. After a storm which lasted from March tenth to the fifteenth, I clambered out onto the western floe field and, looking far to the south through the binoculars from a high hummock, saw that the edges of the mass were indeed starting to break up. By March thirtieth, as the warmer water of the Gulf Stream offshoot passed under the ice field, the breakup began in earnest. From my lookout point, I found that the distance from where I stood, just near the southern tip of the Brittania-Berg, out to the "open" water (that is, ice with leads running between the floes) had diminished to approximately six miles. By April fifteenth, with the sun higher in the sky and more accurate sextant shots possible, the distance to the nearest open lead was about three miles from Brittania. The explosions of the separation of the floes could be heard from every direction around the clock. By May first, with the floes on the eastern side of Brittania-Berg opening up and drifting away to the south, the pressure was off the berg. It started to move, slowly at first, no more than a couple of feet a day, then more rapidly, two, four, six yards a day, in a counterclockwise direction. I was out at all hours, taking bearings on Gibraltar Point with the hand-bearing compass and noting the great mass of ice overhanging the boat gradually moving to the east. By the twenty-fifth of April the ice-in-the-sky was clear of the bow of the boat, and by the first of May the ice around the boat began to break up. On the eighth of May I celebrated my thirty-seventh birthday with an extra ration of seal blubber.

On the fifteenth of May, *Cresswell* suddenly fell down into a crevasse which opened below her. The shock was not too great, for, pitched bows up as she had been during the great upheaval, the stern was close to water level. The crevasse opened up from the west, and when it reached the stern, the boat, with a rumble, slid down into water. I anxiously searched below for leakage, but there seemed to be none or very little. The hull had held! I set to rigging spars and sails, tightening up the shrouds.

All this time I had been scrimping on food, eating no more than one small meal daily, with Nelson the same. It was no good getting out of the ice only to starve to death at sea. But now that the ice was breaking up, with cracks leading right out of the "bay" to the open sea only two miles away, I needed to build up my strength. So I increased my seal-blubber ration from eight ounces to ten, and the porridge from four ounces to six, while halving Nelson's ration of porridge for burgoo.

On June third, with a southeasterly storm heaving up the western floe field, it started to break up. The noise was enough to prevent any sleep; warily I watched for the slightest chance of springing the trap. By the tenth of June, after a long spell of high wind, which changed to a northerly, the ice floes southwest of *Cresswell* opened up and floated away like fishing boats leaving harbor on the evening tide.

The next day I managed to drag *Cresswell* astern by jumping onto the loose ice floes and pulling her with a mooring line, after cutting the bowline loose. Gradually, I maneuvered the boat until the bows were facing southwest. Then, driving the crowbar into a football-field-sized floe, I secured the boat's bowline and waited for the floe to move out when the wind dropped or shifted. The boat was a lot higher out of the water, for the food stores and ship's gear lost in the upheaval, together with food consumed for the past year, accounted for well over two tons. But weight lost meant easier hauling, and I soon had her ready to exit.

The southwest wind persisted for three days, pushing back loose floes into the open lead and jamming up the escape route. For three sunny days I waited patiently, willing the wind to change, while Nelson moped on deck, hungry on short rations. I put two lines over the side, baited with seal blubber.

Suddenly the wind dropped. We waited. One more day, the whole sunny night, half the next day. I was asleep in the

now much warmer cabin when it happened. A slight judder on the bowline. I was awake instantly. I crowded up the
ladder. She was moving—she was heading out—with the
great silver gleaming ice floe blinding me until I got the
goggles over my head. She was moving out! Ahead of our
"tug" the whole ice floe pack was shifting forward, away
from the great ice-field plateau. Behind us were a hundred
smaller floes, one of which was pushing against our rudder-
less stern. I didn't care. We were moving.

At the moment we rounded the south end of the Brittania-Berg, one of the fishing lines jerked. With a muffled
whoop, I leapt for it. There was a nice fat cod. Nelson
scampered for joy as I held it up, shining in the sunlight.
"Bugger it, old son, underway or not, this is going in the
pot!" I left the boat to fend for herself and lit the stove. With
the pot steaming merrily, I dashed topsides to look around
and found we were going at a surprising rate away from the
ice field, at least a knot and a half. The smell of cooking fish
wafted through the companionway. Soon the pan was out
on the bridge deck, with the pair of us scoffing cod-flesh
straight off the bone. We finished it all—flesh, eyes, head,
liver, fins; the whole fifteen pounds of it—the finest meal
we had seen for months. We drooled over it, tearing the
flesh away from the bones. The berg, and the three hills of
death, dropped astern. We were still surrounded by great
ice floes on all sides, and our position would be highly
dangerous if a storm blew up, but I wanted to be well clear
of the berg before turning to the southeast, to thread a way
through the massive jigsaw of floes.

"Well, mate, that's that!" I said to Nelson, as we glanced
back at the monstrous gravestone we had so narrowly
escaped. "Now we'll get some sea time in!"

Come cheer up, my lads, 'tis to glory we steer,
To add something new to this wonderful year,
'Tis to honor we call you, as free men, not slaves,
For who are so free as the sons of the waves?

Chorus: Heart of oak are our ships, heart of oak are our men;
We always are ready, steady, boys, steady;
We'll fight and we'll conquer again and again!

Royal Navy song, eighteenth century. It is
the lower-deckmen's marching tune.

25

By the Skin of My Teeth

Being underway was the most immense relief imaginable. Free at long, long last, after one year and a day locked in the ice field, 366 days—staring death right in its grisly skull-sockets. Even though the chance of collision with a floe was possible if a heavy wind piped up, I felt so unburdened, for the first three or four days, that I found myself taking risks which normally I never would dream of, steering straight for a floe, missing its leeward side by a matter of feet, and crowding on sail in forceful gusts.

The boat leaked like a sieve. The whole line of the garboard strake, where the hull joined the keel, had had the caulking shaken almost completely out of it during the wicked battering by the ice in the Brittania-Berg capsize. I had to pump her out almost continuously, though in calm weather I could take a rest, letting the boat take in two feet of freezing cold water. Then I would don my sea boots, reaching up to my thighs, go below the cockpit floorboards, and bucket the water out. It was heavy work and left no time for desperation or fear.

As soon as the wind picked up, I inflated the rubber dinghy below in the cabin, for extra flotation, just in case I fell asleep or was knocked unconscious. This made life below difficult, with a seven-foot dinghy stuck into the living space, but somehow I managed. It was cold, wet, miserable work, a great expenditure of my body's strength, meager as it was by this time. Mainly, it was willpower that enabled me to start bucketing once again.

I looked up at Nelson sniffing around the horizon during one spell of backbreaking bucketing. "Yes, you old bugger," I yelled at him, "and if you had two bloody forelegs, you'd be down here too." He frowned and again turned his snout to the far horizon, pretending to ignore me.

My position, when I broke out of the ice, was about 185 miles west-southwest of the main settlement of Svalbard, Kongsfjorden (King's Bay). As this was the nearest human abode, this is where I steered for, with a slight to moderate southwest wind pushing *Cresswell* before it over a kindly sea. On June thirteenth, four days after emerging from the ice trap, I obtained a position fix. I was only fifty miles from safety! The weather was much warmer now, some degrees above freezing for hours at a stretch. Becalmed from the thirteenth to the sixteenth, I managed to bail enough water out of the thawing tanks to wash three shirts, together with underwear and long sea-boot stockings. I used salt water to get the worst grime out, then rinsed them in fresh water. Then I trimmed my beard, which was all of nineteen inches long. It had served as a chest-warmer during the winter! Then my hair, which was down around my shoulders. It took me hours to unmat the hair and wash it before I could cut it, as the scissors were blunt and the whetstone was worn away entirely. The spare knife sharpener had gone to a watery grave with the other lost stores under the Brittania-Berg. This was the first time I had doffed the Eskimo-rig since entering the icecap, except for the three times I had had to remove it to peel off a sweat-frozen shirt. The fawnskin underwear came off like it was my skin itself peeling from my body, and underneath I was lily-white, while my face, around the eyes, was almost black. Naked, I looked like something out of a nudist-camp harlequin party. My weight had diminished, of course, but what I had been eating must have been good, for I'd no sunken gums, loose teeth, or falling hair, sure signs of scurvy. I was eliminating liquids about an hour after drinking and solids about twelve hours after eating, and my body muscles were like high-tensile steel wires. At first, my normal sea vision suffered. This ability always surprises landsmen (I can, after a day or two at sea, read a ship's name from four miles' distance). I knew this was the result of being in the dark cabin, straining my eyes with the seal-oil lamp, and, outside, wearing the snow goggles. But slowly my vision returned. My hearing was most acute. I was so accustomed to listening for the slightest boat noise or other unnatural sound, such as a possible airplane, that I could hear every one of the hundreds of separate wooden joints working in the hull. My sense of smell was almost as good as Nelson's. I was well rested, the boat steering herself, now clear of ice floes except for the odd maverick. I was warming up some porridge for peanut burgoo, when I smelt fish. It could not have been from the shore, as the wind was still southwest. I hopped topsides and looked around. There was nothing but a lone ice floe to the north. But I clearly smelled fish! Nelson was straining his nose around the compass, and finally settled for a direction to the west-southwest-by-west from our position. I stared hard, but, seeing nothing, went below to finish cooking the scrimpy meal.

By this time all the canned food had been eaten, with the exception of six cans of corned beef and six of sardines. We were down to porridge, peanuts, flour (I was out of yeast), and lard, together with the remnants of the seal blubber, about twelve pounds, stinking to high heaven. I fished diligently the whole time after leaving the ice, but caught only the cod on the way out and two small, poor-looking creatures the names of which I know not. They were so ugly that I was suspicious of them. I fed a boiled morsel of one to Nelson. He got sick, and I threw them back into the Arctic Ocean and gave him an extra helping of peanut burgoo.

Eating solids in the form of seal blubber, we both had the runs, but the color was not bad, and now that it was warmer, we could shit over the side, to leeward, without fear of frostbite, which was a great luxury.

One good thing about being alone in the Arctic, or out in the oceans anywhere, is that there are no cold germs, no lice, and no fleas. All the time I was up in cold latitudes I never had a headache. Nothing but my regular bouts of rheumatism when the weather gauge dropped and a stiff blow was on its way. Also "chinky toe-rot," as sailors call athlete's foot. How this came about I've no idea. It must have been from the previous owner of the sealskin boots, but the itch was murderous at first, until I finally ground up some chalk and cured it by that method.

But mentally and spiritually I had changed. The man who went into the ice was not the man who came out. Going in, I had not known the true nature of fear. I had not known, that is, the natural *animal* part of man, always lurking, waiting for the slightest chance to overcome his intelligence; always lurking in the shadows of man's mind, to spring upon him and drag him so easily, should he not purposefully resist, back into the murky dark cave from which he has so painfully, so slowly, so bloodily, so heroically, dragged himself over the millenia of human history.

When I went into the ice I had not known, either, the true nature of loneliness. Over the months of waiting for death, I had realized that the emotion we know as "loneliness" is, in fact, learned. *If there were no one to tell us we should be lonely, we would not be.*

Animals herd together for two main reasons: for protection and for procreation. Along with these two instincts man adds another: to try to hide from himself the fact that everyone, in the long run, is alone. *Absolutely alone.* In the whole vastness of the wastes of space, every human is on his own. To admit this, and to accept it, is the key to freedom from so-called loneliness. The more it is accepted, the more the company of other, likewise "alone" people can be appreciated, and the more they can be respected, liked, and even loved.

The intelligent man need never be "lonely." We can, if we are prepared to make the effort, keep the company of thousands of other intelligent men who have gone before us. We can learn from them, cry and laugh and hope with them, and recognize our places in the thrust of humanity from the corner of the cave to the outermost reaches of the firmament. Then we need never believe that any one of us is useless, disdained, or unwanted, for as long as there is blood in our veins, or a dream in our hearts, or a thought in our heads, we are, each one of us, an inescapable part of humanity, part of a whole. We are all a part of a spirit, a force, a *will*, which is irrepressible. A spirit which, even after inconceivable aeons of time, even after the whole universe collapses upon itself, will continue *to be*. A spirit the form of which is unknown to us; we have only an inkling, about which we can only guess.

It is towards this spirit, this unity, that we all strive. All humans, regardless of our faith or our political colorations, strive towards the eventual unity of the human spirit in eternity. We strive towards this, consciously or not. Some of us fail, some of us lean on others. Those of us who can perceive the paradox of our *alone-ness* and yet at the same time our *unity* with the Whole can defeat fear. We can triumph over the worst death of all, the death of the human spirit!

As *Cresswell* neared the haze of land to the east, I reflected on all that had passed, and wondered if I could rejoin the human race.

On the sixteenth of June, anxious and hopeful, I saw land. Magic, wonderful, solid, faithful, eternal land. True, it was the silver white, snow-topped peaks of the Barentzburg, but under the sinister white there was a glimpse, a shivering smudge of darkness down on the horizon. Rock! Terra-bloody-firma!

Excitedly, I trimmed the sheets and fussed about like a weekend racing man, even though the wind was very weak and the boat was hardly moving. I grabbed the bucket and the deck scrubber and went to it like a maniac, scrubbing the ice-gashed, torn canvas deck covering, wiping the spars, washing down the porthole lights, fussing and tidying the grubby, stinking blankets below, squaring up the oil-smeared books in the repaired library, nailing down the floorboards, a mass of broken wood, and running up the red ensign, hardly recognizable, just a pale pinkish yellow shaggy-edged rag. The treble-stitched cross and triangles of the Union Flag, now pure white, bleached out of their colors, were still whole and sound.

It took another thirty-six hours to reach the lee of Prins Karls Forland, even though the wind was up to gale force three hours after I sighted the land. I dared not push her too hard, for fear of opening the garboard strake even more. There was a serious risk that the amount of water leaking in would be more than I could get rid of, so I made my way into the channel between the Forland and the mainland of Spitsbergen under spitfire jib only. Of course this tiny sail would only move her very slowly, no more than two knots, but at least she was only pounding the seas, not dropping off them, as she would under the normal gale rig of mizzen, trysail, and spitfire.

On the evening of the eighteenth of June, I found myself in flat water, in the shallow sound east of the Forland. While I worked the boat through the fluky winds as they swept round the island, I stared about in wonder and delight. There were beaches, and rocks, seals, walruses, birds, and in the calm water by the shore of the island, hundreds of jumping fish. The temperature was just below freezing, and there was ice and snow to within yards of the beach. Above, the sky was black with storm clouds charging for Siberia. Rain stabbed down at intervals, but now and again sun-rays slanted down through the gaps.

No tropical island with white sandy beaches shining beyond the dazzling surf under the high sun of Capricorn ever looked to me as sweet, as inviting, as beautiful, as did this Godforsaken hump of half-frozen primeval rock, sitting in the raging, ice-spume-blown Arctic Ocean. The sound of the anchor chain coming out of the hawsepipe for the first time in fourteen months was to me like all the trumpet blasts of the heavenly hosts; the wind-torn wisps of ice-laden clouds whistling over the high ground of the Forland seemed like the very banners of Caesar's triumph; the walruses snouting out of the knife-thin ice by the shore and the birds gliding up on high, like a vast crowd of welcome. As I gazed around the small bay through the sleety rain, waiting to see the anchor dug in properly, I could feel the life force in everything about me. Suddenly my eyes blurred and I lifted my gloved hand to wipe away the sleet from my wet cheeks. But it wasn't raining.

I staggered down below, to sleep on the makeshift shelf I had fixed six inches below the top of the cabin, so that the rising water would not reach me if I overslept. Pulling the blankets, still damp from the washing, over me, I cried myself to sleep like a baby. I was safe from the clutches of death. I was back among living things, that swam and flew and *dreamed*.

Two hours after I fell asleep I was awakened by a far-off noise. It was an engine. I scrambled out of the blankets and clambered aloft. There, away to the south, was a boat, coming towards me. I delved into the after dodger for the siren and started to hoot. Then I realized that this was futile. They would not hear me at this distance, above the noise of the engine. Nelson jerked up and down on his foreleg, yelping a welcome. Sadly, I sunk down into the cockpit bilge to bail out two feet of icy water.

When the boat was only a mile away and I could sense the human presence, could feel the nearness of their souls, I hooted the siren, again and again. The answer came loud and clear through the now dying wind. I saw a figure waving from the small wheelhouse. It was a man! It was that wonder of all the wonders of a wonderful world—a human being!

I could not speak as they came onboard, and I could hardly see for the tears. The skipper sang out something, but I could not understand. In that state, at that moment, I would not have understood the Lord's Prayer in plain English. A crewman, a large, ruddy-faced, cleanshaven, blue-eyed giant, jumped onboard with a line, his heavy weight thudding on the deck. He looked at me and said quietly, "My God!"

He walked along the deck, to where I stood clutching the mizzen shrouds, tears streaming down my face, sobbing. He put his arm around my shoulder and spoke again. The sound of his voice, this rough fisherman on one of the most forlorn, remote, cold islands in the world, was overwhelming. He held me for a full minute, while I struggled to put a round turn and two half-hitches on my emotions.

It is said that when a man drowns he sees all his life flash through his mind's eye. The moment Olaf touched my shoulder, it seemed as if I could feel all of humanity, past, present, and future, pass, like an electric shock, through my whole being.

Then the skipper of the boat leaning through the wheelhouse noticed my ragged flag. He spoke to me in English—the first time I had heard it since Reykjavík, two years before. He called the time-honored words of welcome the world over.

"Hey, where you come from, friend?"

"Reykjavík, by way of Greenland!" I croaked.

The skipper repeated this in Norwegian to Olaf and the other two crewmen, who stared at the boat in disbelief. There was hardly a patch of paint left on her hull, she was all dirty grey wood where the ice had scraped and hammered her. Her wounds and gashes seemed to bleed.

"When you sail from Reykjavík?"

"July 1959!"

"Goddamn!" the skipper ejaculated, then turned and spoke rapidly to Olaf. Another crewman jumped onboard my boat. I was feeling claustrophobic with two other highly complex nervous systems observing, computing, and analyzing, so very close to me that their thoughts, as they silently poured out, almost seemed audible, touchable, and visible, like the balloons of speech in the cartoons of kids' comics. It was as if, all at once, I could feel every sensation, every emotion, that these men had felt all their waking lives, and see before me all the visions of their long-past dreams.

The voice of the skipper broke through. "I put Olaf and Gudar onboard your boat, and I tow you into King's Bay. You come onboard, come, eat, drink!"

"No, captain."

"It's okay. They good seamen, they bring her safe—come onboard, bring the dog!"

I shook my head. I wouldn't leave my boat until she was safe and sound at her destination. I wouldn't leave her, even if she sank under my feet. She was my vessel, she was my responsibility. That is the hard law of the sea, immutable and fixed. I came to, squaring my thin shoulders, and nodded to Olaf as he fixed the towing line around the tabernacle. I could see, as soon as he picked up the line, that he was a fine boatman. His mate looked horror-struck at the Arctic Ocean creeping up through the boat. Grabbing the pump, he worked away at clearing the bilge. I'd not been able to completely clear the boat of water for days. He did it in fifteen minutes flat.

I steered *Cresswell* in, with the fishing skipper taking it very slowly and easily, right down the deep fiord of King's Bay. There were all of twenty wooden structures! There were houses and buildings, and a church steeple even, and although it was lightly snowing, it seemed to me like we were going up under London Bridge, with the great city all around, or up the Hudson into New York harbor.

Olaf anchored the boat, while I deflated the dinghy and dragged it out of the cabin. Then Olaf reinflated it for me. But I went ashore in the fishermen's jolly boat, which they drove straight up onto the pebble beach. I didn't weep for joy as Nelson and I stepped our five feet onto the scrunching pebbles, but I surely felt like it. Instead I glanced back at wounded *Cresswell*, looking battered beyond belief.

All the inhabitants of the small outpost were on the beach to watch us go ashore. Within the hour I was sitting in Olaf's house with an electric light bulb shining miraculously over roast beef and creamed potatoes, cabbage and, the running gift of a breathless lady, Colman's Mustard! And the miracle of a hot bath with water from kettles boiling on the big potbellied stove.

During the three weeks in King's Bay I tried to explain what I'd been doing, but it came hard, because for the first days my mind simply refused to remember. I would try to recall a date, or the weather, and a curtain would drop, and then I could think of nothing but the immediate present and the future. Above all, I could think of little else besides getting away from the Arctic.

The Norwegians of Svalbard are quiet, sturdy, stolid folk, and they understood well enough how the long, long solitude had affected me. By instinct, for the first few days, they confined their solicitude for me to the needs of the moment. Did I sleep well enough? (I was sleeping dreams of relief.) Did I have enough to eat? (I was eating enough to feed a horse.) Was I warm enough? (I was warmer than I had been for many months.)

The rest of the time they left me to sit in a corner, silently drinking in the sights and sounds of human interplay, like a thirst-crazed man sipping cool water at an oasis. Then, little by little, I talked to Olaf and his mates, at first babbling away incoherently in basic English, about the Kalatdlits and the bear; about the stars and the ice; about escaping from the Arctic and the everlasting numbing cold, away from the ever-present threat of a soul-freezing death in the cold, cold darkness of glittering ice. I told them how I longed for warmth and the sunshine and gentle seas, and waving palm trees in the clear, starlit heavens of the tropics.

The Norwegian air force ran a weather station at King's Bay. Their doctor, when he examined me, was amazed at the complete absence of any fat on my body; yet, though skinny, I was very strong. He pronounced me fit and gave me some lotion for my rheumatism. Then he asked me what I was going to do.

"I'm sailing as soon as I can, before the weather closes in

again, before there's any chance I might get stuck here for a whole winter."

"But you can winter safely here. You have your boat up on the beach. You can take off in the early summer next year. We can even arrange work for you here, if you are concerned about earning money."

"No, doctor, I have enough money to buy five weeks' food. With what I already have, there will be enough to reach Canada, or, if worse comes to worst, Iceland. At least I'll be out of the Arctic Circle. I can work there a season, then sail on for Canada."

"Why Canada?"

"Well," I said, "look at all that bloody marvelous boat-building timber, pitch pine, Douglas fir——"

He patted my shoulder. "I know your type. We've got them, too. I won't try to stop you. You sense your destiny and you follow it."

I bought food: potatoes, dried egg, canned milk, canned meat, flour, sugar, chocolate, and canned vegetables and fruit. The kind folk of King's Bay, together with the air force men, donated another six cases of canned goods, and Olaf, with Gudar, helped me paint the boat and test the engine. On July tenth all the good folks in King's Bay turned up at the jetty to wish *Cresswell*, Nelson, and me farewell and Godspeed for Canada.

"Send me a card!" cried Olaf.

"A card?" I called back. "I'll send you a book!"

"When?" He and all the crowd were laughing.

"When I've something to write about!"

I patted Nelson. The breeze picked up. *Cresswell* lurched to the first wavelets beyond the pier. The new, blood red ensign fluttered. We were off on the long trail again, across the ocean!

Envoi: A last thought from and for America—

Wild Nights—Wild Nights!
Were I with thee
Wild Nights should be
Our luxury!

Futile — the Winds—
To a Heart in port—
Done with the Compass—
Done with the Chart!

Rowing in Eden—
Ah, the Sea!
Might I but moor—Tonight—
In Thee!

Emily Dickinson, "Wild Nights."

Doulas: Best Medicine for Labor?

Think three's a crowd? For many couples, not when it comes to labor and delivery. More and more are opting to share their birth experience with a doula, a woman trained as a labor companion. And for good reason. Studies have shown that women supported by doulas are much less likely to require cesarean deliveries, induction, and pain relief. Births attended by doulas may also be shorter, with a lower rate of complications.

Doula is a term that comes from ancient Greece, where it was used to describe the most important female servant in the household, the one who probably helped mom out the most during childbirth. What exactly can a doula do for you and your birth experience? That depends on the doula you choose, at what point in your pregnancy you hire her, and what your preferences are. Some doulas become involved well before that first contraction strikes, helping with the design of a birth plan and easing prelabor jitters. Many, on request, come to the house to help a couple through early labor. Once at the hospital or birthing center, the doula takes on a variety of responsibilities, again depending on your needs and wishes. Typically, her primary role is as a continuous source of comfort, encouragement, and support (both emotional and physical) during labor. She'll serve as a soothing voice of experience (especially valuable if you're first-timers), help with relaxation techniques and breathing exercises, offer advice on labor positions, and do her share of massage, hand holding, pillow plumping, and bed adjusting. A doula can also act as a mediator and an advocate, ready to speak for you as needed, to translate medical terms and explain procedures, and to generally run interference with hospital personnel. She won't take the place of your coach (and a good doula won't make him feel like she's taking his place, either) or the nurse on duty; instead, she will augment their support and services (especially important if the nurse assigned to you has several other patients in labor at the same time or if labor is long and nurses come and go as shifts change). She will also likely be the only person (besides the coach)

often). So chances are the test your practitioner ordered is just routine.

And it's simple, too, especially if you have a sweet tooth. You'll be asked to drink a very sweet glucose drink, which usually tastes like flat orange soda, one hour before having some blood drawn; you don't have to be fasting when you do this. Most women chugalug the stuff with no problem and no side effects; a few, especially those who don't have a taste for sweet liquids, feel a little queasy afterward.

If the blood work comes back with elevated numbers, which suggests the possibility that you might not be producing enough insulin to process the extra glucose in your system, the next level of test—the glucose tolerance test—is ordered. This fasting three-hour test, which involves a higher-concentration glucose drink, is used to diagnose gestational diabetes.

Gestational diabetes occurs in about 4 to 7 percent of expectant mothers, which makes it one of the most common pregnancy complications. Fortunately, it's also one of the most easily managed. When blood sugar is closely controlled through diet, exercise, and, if necessary,

Your Main Squeeze

Your baby might not be ready for delivery yet, but it isn't too soon to start getting your body—and your pelvic floor muscles, in particular—geared up for the big day. Never thought much about your pelvic muscles—or maybe never even realized you had any? It's time to start paying attention. They're the muscles that support your uterus, bladder, and bowels, and they're designed to stretch so your baby can come out. They're also the muscles that keep your urine from leaking when you cough or laugh (a skill set you're only likely to appreciate when it's gone, as can happen with postpartum incontinence). These multitalented muscles can also make for a much more satisfying sexual experience.

Luckily, there are exercises that can easily work these miracle muscles, whipping them into shape with minimal time and minimal effort (no workout clothes necessary, no visit to a gym required, and you don't even have to break a sweat). Just 5 minutes of these amazing exercises, called Kegels, three times a day and you'll tone your way to a long list of both short- and long-term benefits. Toned pelvic floor muscles can ease a host of pregnancy and postpartum symptoms from hemorrhoids to urinary and fecal incontinence. They can help you prevent an episiotomy or even a tear during delivery. Plus doing your Kegels faithfully during pregnancy will help your vagina snap back more gracefully after your baby's grand exit.

Ready to Kegel? Here's how: Tense the muscles around your vagina and anus and hold (as you would if you were trying to stop the flow of urine), working up to 10 seconds. Slowly release and repeat; shoot for three sets of 20 daily. Keep in mind when you Kegel that all your focus should be on those pelvic muscles—and not any others. If you feel your stomach tensing or your thighs or buttocks contracting, your pelvics aren't getting their full workout. Make this exercise your main squeeze during pregnancy (doing them each time you stop at a traffic light, while you check your e-mail, in line at the ATM, while waiting for the cashier to ring up your groceries, or while working at your desk), and you'll reap the benefits of stronger pelvic floor muscles. Try doing them during sex, too—both you and your partner will feel the difference (now that's a workout you can get excited about!).

birth plan, should you decide to fill one out, are listed below. You can use it as a general guideline, then flesh it out as needed (you can refer to the appropriate pages before making your decisions). For a more detailed list and sample birth plan, see the *What to Expect Pregnancy Journal and Organizer.*

- How far into your labor you would like to remain at home and at what point you would prefer to go to the hospital or birthing center

- Eating and/or drinking during active labor (page 369)

- Being out of bed (walking around or sitting up) during labor

- Personalizing the atmosphere with music, lighting, items from home

- The use of a still camera or video camera

- The use of a mirror so you can see the birth

- The use of an IV (intravenous fluid administration; page 372)

- The use of pain medication and the type of pain medication (page 301)

- External fetal monitoring (continuous or intermittent); internal fetal monitoring (page 372)

- The use of oxytocin to induce or augment contractions (page 368)

- Delivery positions (page 376)

- Use of warm compresses and perineal massage (pages 352 and 375)

- Episiotomy (page 374)

- Vacuum extractor or forceps use (page 375)

- Cesarean delivery (page 398)

- The presence of significant others (besides your spouse) during labor and/or at delivery

- The presence of older children at delivery or immediately after

- Suctioning of the newborn; suctioning by the father

- Holding the baby immediately after birth; breastfeeding immediately

- Postponing cutting the cord, weighing the baby, and/or administering eye drops until after you and your baby greet each other

- Having the father help with the delivery and/or cut the cord

- Cord blood banking (page 330)

You may also want to include some postpartum items on your birth plan, such as:

- Your presence at the weighing of the baby, the pediatric exam, and baby's first bath

- Baby feeding in the hospital (whether it will be controlled by the nursery's schedule or your baby's hunger; whether supplementary bottles and pacifiers can be avoided if you're breastfeeding)

- Circumcision (see *What to Expect the First Year*)

- Rooming-in (page 431)

- Other children visiting with you and/or with the new baby

- Postpartum medication or treatments for you or your baby

- The length of the hospital stay, barring complications (page 430)

Of course, the most important feature of a good birth plan is flexibility. Since childbirth—like most forces of nature—is unpredictable, the best-laid plans don't always go, well, according to plan. Though chances are very good that your plan can be carried out just the way you drew it up, there's always the chance that it won't. There is no way to predict precisely how labor and delivery will progress (or not progress) until those contractions start coming, so a birth plan you design in advance may not end up being obstetrically or

Don't Hold It In

Making a habit of not urinating when you feel the need increases the risk that your inflamed bladder may irritate the uterus and set off contractions. Not going when you've got the urge could also lead to a UTI, another cause of preterm contractions. So don't hold it in. When you gotta go, go . . . promptly.

Lifesaving Screenings for Newborns

Most babies are born healthy and stay that way. But a very small percentage of infants are born apparently healthy and then suddenly sicken. Luckily, there are ways to screen for such metabolic disorders. Most babies born in the U.S. live in states that require screening for at least 21 life-threatening disorders—and there is an effort under way to push all 50 states to screen for 29 universally recommended diseases. These include phenylketonuria (PKU), congenital hypothyroidism, congenital adrenal hyperplasia, biotinidase deficiency, maple syrup urine disease, galactosemia, homocystinuria, and sickle cell anemia.

If your state doesn't offer at least the core group of these tests, you can request that a private lab arrange testing. The lab will use blood that's collected in the hospital during your baby's routine heel stick (when drops of blood are drawn from

baby's heel after a quick stick with a needle).

In the very unlikely event your baby screens positive for any of the disorders, your baby's pediatrician and a genetic specialist can verify the results and begin treatment, if necessary (there is a high rate of false positives, so any positive result should be followed up by retesting). Early diagnosis and intervention can make a tremendous difference in the prognosis. For more information on private lab screening and newborn screening in general, contact Baylor University Medical Center: (800) 4BAYLOR (422-9567); baylorhealth.com/medicalspecialties/metabolic/newbornscreening.htm; or Pediatrix Screening: (954) 384-0175; pediatrixscreening.com.

To find out if your state screens for the 29 conditions that the March of Dimes recommends, go to genes-r-us.uthscsa.edu/.

medically wise, and it may have to be adjusted at the last minute. After all, there's no greater priority than your well-being and your baby's—and if your birth plan doesn't end up being consistent with that priority, it'll have to take a backseat. A change of mind (yours) can also prompt a change of plan (you were dead set against having an epidural, but somewhere around 4 cm, you become dead set on having one).

Bottom line: Birth plans, though by no means necessary (you can definitely decide to go with the flow when it comes to childbirth, and you'll give birth with or without one), are a great option, one that more and more expectant parents are taking advantage of. To find out more, and to figure out whether a birth

plan is right for you, talk it over with your practitioner at your next visit.

Glucose Screening Test

"My practitioner says I need to take a glucose screening test to check for gestational diabetes. Why would I need it, and what does the test involve?"

Don't feel too picked on. Almost all practitioners screen for gestational diabetes in almost all patients at about 24 to 28 weeks (though those at higher risk for gestational diabetes, including older or obese mothers or those with a family history of diabetes, are screened earlier in their pregnancies and more who will stay by your side through-out labor and delivery—a friendly and familiar face from start to finish. And many doulas don't stop there. They can also offer support and advice postpar-tum on everything from breastfeeding to baby care.

Though an expectant father may fear that hiring a doula will relegate him to third-wheel status, this isn't the case. A good doula is also there to help your coach relax so he can help you relax. She'll be there to answer ques-tions he might not feel comfortable broaching with a doctor or nurse. She'll be there to provide an extra set of hands when you need your legs and back mas-saged at the same time, or when you need both a refill on ice chips and help breathing through a contraction. She'll be an obliging and cooperative member of your labor team—ready to pitch in, but not to push dad (or the medical or midwife team) aside and take over.

How do you locate a doula? Many birthing centers and hospitals keep lists of doulas, and so do some practition-ers. Ask friends who've recently used a doula for recommendations, or check online for local doulas. Once you've tracked down a candidate, arrange a consultation before you hire her to

make sure both of you are comfortable with her. Ask her about her experience, her training, what she will do and what she won't do, what her philosophies are about childbirth (if you're planning on asking for an epidural, for instance, you won't want to hire a doula who dis-courages the use of pain relief), whether she will be on call at all times and who covers for her if she isn't, whether she provides pregnancy and/or postpartum services, and what her fees are (some doulas command hefty fees, especially those in big cities). For more informa-tion or to locate a doula in your area, contact Doulas of North America: (888) 788-DONA (788-3662); dona.org.

An alternative to a doula, which could also be beneficial, is a female friend or relative who has gone through pregnancy and delivery herself and with whom you feel totally comfort-able. The plus: Her services will be free. The drawback: She probably won't be quite as knowledgeable. One way to remedy that is having a "lay doula," a female friend who goes through four hours of training in doula techniques (ask if your hospital has such a training course). Researchers have found that a "lay doula" can provide the same ben-efits as a professional one.

medication, women with gestational dia-betes are likely to have perfectly normal pregnancies and healthy babies. See page 546 for more.

A Low-Birthweight Baby

"I've been reading a lot about the high incidence of low-birthweight babies. Is there anything I can do to be sure I won't have one?"

Some cases of low birthweight are preventable, so you can do a lot—

and, inasmuch as you're reading this book, chances are good you already are. Nationally, 8 of every 100 newborns are categorized as low birthweight (under 5 pounds 8 ounces, or 2,500 grams), and slightly more than 1 in 100 babies as very low birthweight (3 pounds 5 ounces, or 1,500 grams, or less). But that rate is much lower among women who are conscien-tious about both medical care and self-care (and are lucky enough to be able to afford the first and informed enough to do a good job on the second). Most of the common causes of low birthweight—use of tobacco, alcohol, or drugs (particularly

Signs of Preterm Labor

Though the chances of your baby arriving early are pretty low, it's a good idea for every expectant mom to be familiar with the signs of premature labor, since early detection can have a tremendous impact on outcome. Think of the following as information you'll probably never use but should know, just to be on the safe side. Read this list over, and if you experience any of these symptoms before 37 weeks, call your practitioner immediately:

- Persistent cramps that are menstrual-like, with or without diarrhea, nausea, or indigestion

- Regular painful contractions coming every 10 minutes (or sooner) that do not subside when you change positions (not to be confused with the Braxton Hicks contractions you might be already feeling, which don't indicate early labor; see page 311)

- Constant lower back pain or pressure or a change in the nature of lower backache

- A change in your vaginal discharge, particularly if it is watery or tinged or streaked pinkish or brownish with blood

- An achiness or feeling of pressure in the pelvic floor, the thighs, or the groin

- Leaking from your vagina (a steady trickle or a gush)

Keep in mind that you can have some or all of these symptoms and not be in labor (most pregnant women experience pelvic pressure or lower back pain at some point). In fact, the majority of women who have symptoms of preterm labor do not deliver early. But only your practitioner can tell for sure, so pick up the phone and call. After all, it's always best to play it safe.

For information on preterm labor risk factors and prevention, see pages 44–47. For information on the management of preterm labor, see page 557.

---

cocaine), poor nutrition, extreme emotional stress (but not normal stress levels), and inadequate prenatal care, for example—are preventable. Many others, such as chronic maternal illnesses, can be controlled by a good working partnership between the mother and her practitioner. A major cause—premature labor—can sometimes be prevented.

Of course, sometimes a baby is small at birth for reasons that no one can control: the mother's own low weight when she was born, for example, or an inadequate placenta, or a genetic disorder. A very short interval (less than nine months) between pregnancies may also be a factor. But even in these cases, excellent diet and

prenatal care can often compensate and tip the scales in baby's favor. And when a baby does turn out to be small, the top-notch medical care currently available gives even the very smallest an increasingly good chance of surviving and growing up healthy.

If you think you have real reason to worry about having a low-birthweight baby, share your concern with your practitioner. An exam and/or an ultrasound will probably reassure you that your fetus is growing at a normal pace. If it does turn out that your baby is on the very small side, steps can be taken to uncover the cause and, if possible, correct it. See page 550 for more information.

Easing Labor Pain

Let's face it. Those 15 or so hours it takes to birth a baby aren't called labor because it's a walk in the park. Labor (and delivery) is hard work—hard work that can hurt, big time. And if you actually consider what's going on down there, it's really no wonder that labor hurts. During childbirth, your uterus contracts over and over again to squeeze a relatively big baby through one relatively tight space (your cervix) and out through an even tighter one (your vagina, the same opening you once thought was too small for a tampon). Like they say, it's pain with a purpose—a really cute and cuddly purpose—yet it's pain nonetheless.

But while there may be no getting around the pain of labor altogether (unless you're scheduled for a cesarean delivery, in which case you'll be skipping labor and labor pain), there are plenty of ways to get through it. As a laboring mom, you can select from a wide menu of pain-relief options, both the medicinal kind and the nonmedicinal variety (and you can even opt for a combo from both columns). You can choose to go unmedicated throughout your entire labor or just through part of labor (like those easier first centimeters). You can turn to alternative medicine and nondrug approaches to manage the pain (acupuncture, hypnosis, or hydrotherapy, for instance). Or you can birth your baby with a little help—or a lot of help—from an analgesic, such as the very popular epidural (which leaves you with little or no pain during labor but allows you to remain awake during the entire process).

Which option is for you? To figure that out, look into them all. Read up on childbirth pain management (the section that follows covers the gamut). Talk to your practitioner. Get insights from friends who have recently labored. And then do some thinking. Remember that the right option for you might not be one option but a combination of several (reflexology with an epidural chaser, or a variety of relaxation techniques topped off with a round of acupuncture). Remember, too, the value of staying flexible—and not just so you can stretch yourself into some of those pushing positions you learned in childbirth class. After all, the option or options you settle on now may not sit well later, and may need to be adjusted midlabor (you were planning on an epidural but found you could handle the pain—or vice versa). Most of all, remember that (barring any obstetrical situation that would dictate how you labor and deliver), it's completely your choice to make—your birth, your way.

Managing Your Pain with Medications

When it comes to pain relief during labor, there's a wide variety of medications to choose from, including anesthetics (substances that produce loss of sensation or put you to sleep), analgesics (pain relievers), and ataraxics (tranquilizers). In most circumstances, it'll be up to you to select the pain medication you want to make your labor and delivery as comfortable as possible, though your choice may be limited depending on the stage of labor, whether it's an emergency situation, or your past health history or your present condition (and that of your baby) precludes a particular drug, and the anesthesiologist's preference and expertise.

Something else to keep in mind as you begin to explore your options: How effective a drug is in relieving pain will depend on how it affects you (different drugs affect different people differently), the dosage, and other factors. There's always a remote chance that a drug won't provide you with the relief you're looking for, or that it might not give you any at all. Most of the time, though, pain medications work exactly the way they are supposed to—offering up just what you (and your practitioner) ordered.

Here are the most commonly used labor and delivery pain medications:

Epidural. The epidural is the pain relief of choice for two thirds of all laboring women delivering at hospitals. The major reasons for the epidural's current surge in popularity are its relative safety (only a small amount of medication is needed to achieve the desired effect), its ease of administration, and its patient-friendly results (local pain relief in the lower part of the body that allows you to be awake during the birth and alert enough to greet your baby immediately after it). It's also considered safer for your baby than other anesthetics because the epidural is injected directly into the spine (technically, into the epidural space, which is located between the ligament that sheathes the vertebrae and the membrane that covers the spinal cord), which means the drug barely reaches the bloodstream (unlike other anesthetics). And even better news: An epidural can be given to you as soon as you ask for one—no need to wait until you're dilated a certain amount (3 or 4 cm, for instance). Studies show that even an early epidural doesn't increase the chances of a C-section as was once believed, nor does it slow down labor significantly. And even if labor does slow down a bit with an epidural, your doctor can give you Pitocin (a synthetic version of oxytocin, the hormone that triggers contractions naturally) to help get your labor back up to speed again.

Here's what you can expect if you're having an epidural:

- Before the epidural is administered, an IV of fluids is started (this is done to prevent a drop in blood pressure, a side effect some women have with an epidural; fluids will keep your blood pressure from going too low).

- In some hospitals (policies vary), a catheter (tube) is inserted into the bladder just before or just after administration of the epidural and stays in place to drain urine while the epidural is in effect (since the medication may suppress the urge to urinate). In other hospitals, the bladder is just drained intermittently with a catheter as needed.

- Your lower and midback are wiped with an antiseptic solution and a small area of the back is numbed with a local anesthetic. A larger needle is placed through the numbed area into the epidural space of the spine, usually while you're lying on your side or sitting up and leaning over a table or being supported by your spouse, coach, or nurse. Some women feel a little pressure as the needle is inserted. Others feel a little tingling or a momentary shooting pain as the needle finds the correct spot. If you're lucky (and many women are), you might not feel a thing while the epidural is being administered. Besides, compared to the pain of contractions, any discomfort from a needle poke is likely to be pretty minimal.

- The needle is removed, leaving a fine, flexible catheter tube in place. The tube is taped to your back so you can move from side to side. Three to five minutes following the initial dose, the nerves of the uterus begin to numb. Usually after 10 minutes, you'll begin to feel the full effect (hopefully, sweet relief). The medication numbs the nerves in the entire lower part of the body, making it hard to feel any contractions at all (and that's the point).

- Your blood pressure will be checked frequently to make sure it's not dropping too low. IV fluids and lying on your side will help counteract a drop in blood pressure.

- Because an epidural is sometimes associated with slowing of the fetal heartbeat, continuous fetal monitoring is usually required as well. Though such fetal monitoring limits your movements somewhat, it allows your practitioner to monitor the baby's heartbeat and allows you to "see" the frequency and intensity of your contractions (because, ideally, you won't be feeling them).

Happily, there are few side effects with an epidural, though some women might experience numbness on one side of the body only (as opposed to complete pain relief). Epidurals also might not offer complete pain control if you're experiencing back labor (when the fetus is in a posterior position, with its head pressing against your back).

Combined spinal epidural (aka "walking epidural"). The combined spinal epidural delivers the same amount of pain relief as a traditional epidural does, but it uses a smaller amount of medication to reach that goal. Not all anesthesiologists or hospitals offer this type of epidural (ask your practitioner if it'll be available to you). The anesthesiologist will start you off with a shot of analgesic directly into the spinal fluid to help relieve some pain, but because the medication is delivered only in the spinal fluid, you'll

---

Pushing Without the Pain

Does pushing have to be a pain? Not always. In fact, many women find they can push very effectively with an epidural, relying on their coach or a nurse to tell them when a contraction is coming on so they can get busy pushing. But if pain-free pushing isn't getting you (or your baby) anywhere—with the lack of sensation hampering your efforts—the epidural can be stopped so you can feel the contractions. The medication can then be easily restarted after delivery to numb the repair of a tear.

---

still feel and be able to use the muscles in your legs (which is why it's called a walking epidural). When you feel you need more pain relief, more medication is placed into the epidural space (through a catheter that was inserted at the same time the spinal medication was administered). Though you'll be able to move your legs, they'll probably feel weak, so it'll be unlikely you'll actually want to walk around.

Spinal block (for cesarean delivery or instrument-assisted vaginal delivery) or saddle block (for instrument-assisted vaginal delivery). These regional blocks, which are rarely used these days, are generally administered in a single dose just prior to delivery (in other words, if you didn't have an epidural during labor but want pain relief for the delivery, you'll get the fast-acting spinal block). Like the epidural, these blocks are administered with you sitting up or lying on your side while an anesthetic is injected into the fluid surrounding the spinal cord.

Pudendal block. Occasionally used to relieve early second-stage pain, a pudendal block is usually reserved for the vaginal delivery itself. Administered through a needle inserted into the vaginal area, the medication reduces pain in the region but not uterine discomfort. It's useful when forceps or vacuum extraction is used, and its effect can last through episiotomy (if needed) and repair of an episiotomy or tear.

General anesthesia. General anesthesia is rarely used for deliveries these days and only used in specific cases for emergency surgical births. An anesthesiologist in an operating/delivery room injects drugs into your IV that put you to sleep. When you come to, you may be groggy, disoriented, and restless. You may also have a cough and sore throat (due to the tube that's routinely inserted through the mouth into the throat) and experience nausea and vomiting.

The major downside to general anesthesia (besides the fact that mom has to miss the birth) is that it sedates the baby along with the mother. The medical team will minimize those sedative effects by administering the anesthesia as close to the actual birth as possible. That way the baby can be delivered before the anesthetic has reached him or her in amounts large enough to have an effect.

Demerol. Demerol is one of the most frequently used obstetrical analgesics. This shot (sometimes given in the buttocks) or IV-administered drug is used to dull the pain and relax the mother so she is better able to cope with contractions. It can be repeated every two to four hours, as needed. But not all women like the drowsy feeling Demerol imparts, and some find they are actually less able to cope with labor pains while under the effects of Demerol.

There may be some side effects (depending on a woman's sensitivity), including nausea, vomiting, and a drop in blood pressure. The effect Demerol will have on the newborn depends on the total dose and how close to delivery it has been administered. If it has been given too close to delivery, the baby may be sleepy and unable to suck; less frequently, respiration may be depressed and supplemental oxygen may be required. Any effects on the newborn are generally short-term and, if necessary, can be treated.

Demerol is not generally administered until labor is well established and false labor has been ruled out, but no later than two to three hours before delivery is expected.

Nitrous oxide. This dentist office staple, more commonly known as laughing gas, doesn't eliminate the pain from contractions entirely, but it does take the edge off them and could be a good alternative for women who choose not to go for an epidural. You're able to self-administer the laughing gas during labor—taking a few puffs when you feel the need for a little pain relief and setting it aside when you feel the pain is manageable.

Tranquilizers. These drugs (such as Phenergan and Vistaril) are used to calm and relax an extremely anxious mom-to-be so that she can participate more fully in childbirth. Tranquilizers can also enhance the effectiveness of analgesics such as Demerol. Like analgesics, tranquilizers are usually administered once labor is well established, and well before delivery. But they are occasionally used in early labor if a mother's anxiety is slowing down the progress of her labor. Reactions to the effects of tranquilizers vary. Some women welcome the gentle drowsiness; others find it interferes with their control and with their memory of this memorable experience. Dosage definitely makes a difference. A small dose may serve to relieve anxiety without impairing alertness. A larger dose may cause slurring of speech and dozing between contraction peaks, making it difficult to use prepared childbirth techniques. Though the risks to a fetus or newborn from tranquilizers are minimal, most practitioners prefer to stay away from tranquilizers unless they're really necessary. If you think you might be extremely anxious during labor, you may want to try learning about some nondrug relaxation techniques now (such as meditation, massage, hypnosis; see below), so you won't end up needing this kind of medication.

Managing Your Pain with CAM

Not every woman wants traditional pain medication, but most still want their labor to be as comfortable as possible. And that's where complementary and alternative medicine (CAM) therapies can come in. These days, it's not just CAM practitioners who are touting the benefits of these techniques. More and more traditional physicians are hopping on board the CAM bandwagon, too. Many recommend CAM techniques to their patients—either as an alternative to pain medication or as a relaxing supplement to it. Even

---

Just Breathe

Hoping to skip the meds but can't—or don't want to—CAM? Lamaze (or other kinds of natural childbirth techniques) can be very effective in managing the pain of contractions. See page 279 for more.

---

if you're sure there's an epidural with your name on it waiting at the hospital, you may want to explore the world of CAM, too. (And to explore it well before your due date, since many of the techniques take practice—or even classes—to perfect, and most take plenty of planning.) But remember to seek out CAM practitioners who are licensed and certified, not to mention ones who have plenty of experience with pregnancy, labor, and delivery.

Acupuncture and acupressure. Scientific studies now back up what the Chinese have known for thousands of years: Acupuncture and acupressure are effective forms of pain relief. Researchers have found that acupuncture, through the use of needles inserted in specific locations, triggers the release of several brain chemicals, including endorphins, which block pain signals, relieving labor pain (and maybe even helping boost labor progress). Acupressure works on the same principle as acupuncture, except that instead of poking you with needles, your practitioner will use finger pressure to stimulate the points. Acupressure on the center of the ball of the foot is said to help back labor. If you're planning to use either during labor, let your prenatal practitioner know that your CAM practitioner will be with you through labor.

Reflexology. Reflexologists believe that the internal organs can be accessed through points on the feet. By massaging the feet during childbirth, a reflexologist can relax the uterus and stimulate the pituitary gland, apparently reducing the pain of childbirth and even shortening the duration of labor. Some of the pressure points are so powerful that you should avoid stimulating them unless you *are* in labor.

Physical therapy. From massage and hot compresses to ice packs and intense

2lsier

tin

vedevced

counterpressure on your sore spots, physical therapy during labor can ease a lot of the pain you're feeling. Massage at the hands of a caring coach or doula or a skilled health professional can bring relaxing relief and can help diminish pain.

Hydrotherapy. There's nothing like a warm bath—especially one with jets kneading your sore spots and particularly if you're in labor. Settle into a jetted tub (or merely a soaking tub) for a session of hydrotherapy during your labor to reduce pain and relax you. Many hospitals and birthing centers now provide such tubs to labor—or even deliver—in.

Hypnobirthing. Though hypnosis won't mask your pain, numb your nerves, or quell contractions, it can get you so deeply relaxed (some women describe it as becoming like a floppy rag doll) that you are totally unaware of any discomfort. Hypnosis doesn't work for everyone; you have to be highly suggestible (some clues are having a long attention span, a rich imagination, and if you enjoy—or don't mind—being alone). Still, more and more women these days are seeking the help of a medically certified hypnotherapist (you'll want to shy away from someone without such credentials) to train them to get through labor by self-hypnosis; sometimes, you can have a hypnotherapist with you during the process. It's not something you can just start when that first contraction hits; you'll have to practice quite a bit during pregnancy to be able to achieve total relaxation, even with a certified therapist at your side (and while you're practicing, you can use hypnosis to get relief from pregnancy aches, pains, and stress, too). One big benefit of hypnobirthing is that while you're completely relaxed, you're also completely awake and aware of every moment of your baby's birth. There are also no physical effects on the baby (or on you).

Distraction. Even if you're not the type to try hypnosis (or you didn't plan far enough ahead), you can still try to get your mind off the pain of labor by using distraction techniques. Anything—watching TV, listening to music, meditating—that takes your mind off the pain can decrease your perception of it. So can focusing on an object (an ultrasound picture of your baby, a soothing landscape, a photo of a favorite place) or doing visualization exercises (for example, picturing your baby being pushed gently by contractions, preparing to exit the uterus, excited and happy). Keeping your pain in perspective is also key to an easier labor. Staying rested, relaxed, and positive (remember that the pain of a contraction is actually accomplishing something—each one getting you closer to your baby—and keep telling yourself that it won't last forever) will help you stay more comfortable.

Transcutaneous electrical nerve stimulation (TENS). This technique uses electrodes that deliver low-voltage pulses to stimulate nerve pathways to the uterus and cervix, supposedly blocking pain. Studies aren't clear on whether TENS is really effective at reducing labor pain, but some do show that it leads to a shorter first-stage labor and less need for pain meds.

Making the Decision

You now have the lowdown on pain relief options for labor and delivery—the information you'll need to make an informed decision. But before you decide what's best for you and your baby, you should:

- Discuss the topic of pain relief and anesthesia with your practitioner long before labor begins. Your practitioner's expertise and experience make him or her an invaluable partner—though not usually the deciding vote—in the decision-making process. Well before your first contraction, find out what kinds of drugs or CAM techniques he or she uses most often, what side effects may be experienced, when he or she considers medication absolutely necessary, and when the option is yours.

- Consider keeping an open mind. Though it's smart to think ahead about what might be best for you under certain circumstances, it's impossible to predict what kind of labor and delivery you'll have, how you will respond to the contractions, and whether or not you'll want, need, or have to have medication. Even if you're absolutely convinced that you'll

want an epidural, you may not want to close the door completely to trying some CAM approaches—either first, or on the side. After all, your labor may turn out to be more manageable (or a lot shorter) than you'd thought. And even if you're sold on an all-med-free delivery, you may want to think about leaving the medication window open—even if it's just a crack—in case your labor turns out to be tougher than you'd bargained for.

Most important of all, remember, as you sort through those pain relief options, to keep your eye on the bottom line—a bottom line that has a really cute bottom. After all, no matter how you end up managing the pain of childbirth—and even if you don't end up managing it the way you planned to or the way you really hoped to—you'll still manage to give birth to your baby. And what could be a better bottom line than that?

The
Eighth
Month

Approximately 32 to 35 Weeks

I N THIS NEXT-TO-LAST MONTH, YOU may still be relishing every expectant moment, or you may be growing increasingly weary of, well, growing—and growing. Either way, you're sure to be preoccupied with—and super-excited about—the much-anticipated event: your baby's arrival. Of course, along with that heaping serving of excitement (the baby's almost here!), you and your partner are likely experiencing a side of trepidation (the baby's almost here!)—especially if this is your first foray into parenthood. Talking those very normal feelings through—and tapping into the insights of friends and family members who've preceded you into parenthood—will help you realize that everyone feels that way, particularly the first time around.

Your Baby This Month

Week 32 This week your baby is tipping the scales at almost 4 pounds and topping out at just about 19 inches. And growing isn't the only thing on the agenda these days. While you're busy getting everything ready for baby's arrival, baby's busy prepping for that big debut, too. In these last few weeks, it's all about practice, practice, practice, as he or she hones the skills needed to survive outside the womb, from swallowing and breathing to kicking and sucking. And speaking of sucking, your little one has been able to suck his or her thumb for a while now (okay, maybe it's not a survival skill, but it sure is cute). Another change this week: Your baby's skin is no longer see-through. As more and more fat accumulates under the skin, it's finally opaque (just like yours!).

Week 33 Baby's gaining weight almost as fast as you are these days (averaging out

Your Baby, Month 8

to about half a pound a week), which puts the grand total so far at more than 4½ pounds. Still, your baby has plenty of growing up (and out) to do. He or she may grow a full inch this week alone and may come close to doubling in weight by D-day. And with that much baby inside your uterus now, your amniotic fluid level has maxed out (there's no room for more fluid now). Which explains why those pokes and kicks are sometimes extremely uncomfortable: There's less fluid to cushion the blows. Antibodies are also being passed from you to your baby as your little one continues to develop his or her own immune system. These antibodies will definitely come in handy on the outside and will protect your baby-to-be from many of those playground germs.

Week 34 Your baby could be as tall as 20 inches right now and weighs about 5 pounds. Got male (a male baby, that is)? If you do, then this is the week that his testicles are making their way down from his abdomen to their final destination: his scrotum. (About 3 to 4 percent of boys are born with undescended testicles, which is nothing to worry about; they usually make the trip down south before the first birthday.) And in other baby-related news, those tiny little fingernails have probably reached the tip of his or her fingers by this week, so make sure you have baby nail clippers on your shopping list!

Week 35 Your baby stands tall this week—if he or she could stand, that is—at about 20 inches, and continues to follow the ½-pound-a-week plan, weighing in at about 5½ big ones. While growth will taper off when it comes to height (the average full-termer is born at about 20 inches), your baby will continue to pack on the pounds up until delivery day. Something else he or she will be packing on in the few weeks that remain are brain cells. Brain development continues at a mind-boggling pace, making baby a little on the top-heavy side. And speaking of tops, it's likely your baby's bottom is. Most babies have settled into a head-down, bottoms-up position in Mom's pelvis by now, or will soon. That's a good thing, since it's easier on you if baby's head (the biggest part of his or her body) exits first during delivery. Here's another plus: Baby's head may be big, but it's still soft (at least, the skull is), allowing that tight squeeze through the birth canal to be a little less tight.

What You May Be Feeling

As always, remember that every pregnancy and every woman is different. You may experience all of these symptoms at one time or another, or only a few of them. Some may have continued from last month; others may be new. Still others may be hardly noticed because you've become so used to them. You may also have other, less common, symptoms. Here's what you might experience this month:

Physically

- Strong, regular fetal activity

- Increasing vaginal discharge

- Increased constipation

- Heartburn, indigestion, flatulence, bloating

- Occasional headaches, faintness, or dizziness

- Nasal congestion and occasional nosebleeds; ear stuffiness

- Sensitive gums

- Leg cramps

- Backache

- Pelvic pressure and/or achiness

- Mild swelling of ankles and feet, and occasionally of hands and face

- Varicose veins of legs

- Hemorrhoids

- Itchy abdomen

- Protruding navel

- Stretch marks

- Increasing shortness of breath as the uterus crowds the lungs, which eases when the baby drops

- Difficulty sleeping

- Increasing "practice" (Braxton Hicks) contractions

- Increasing clumsiness

- Enlarged breasts

- Colostrum, leaking from nipples (though this premilk substance may not appear until after delivery)

Emotionally

- Increasing eagerness for the pregnancy to be over

- Apprehension about labor and delivery

- Increasing absentmindedness

- Trepidation about becoming a parent, if it's your first time

- Excitement—at the realization that it won't be long now

A Look Inside

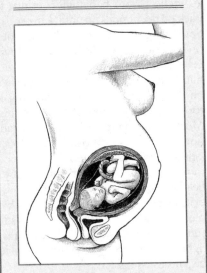

An interesting bit of pregnancy trivia: Measurement in centimeters from the top of your pubic bone to the top of your uterus roughly correlates with the number of weeks you're up to; so, at 34 weeks, your uterus measures close to 34 cm from the pubic bone.

What You Can Expect at This Month's Checkup

After the 32nd week, your practitioner may ask you to come in every two weeks so your progress and your baby's can be more closely watched. You can expect the following to be checked, depending on your particular needs and your practitioner's style of practice:

- Weight and blood pressure

- Urine, for sugar and protein

- Fetal heartbeat

- Height of fundus (top of uterus)

- Size (you may get a rough weight estimate) and position of the fetus, by palpation (feeling from the outside)

- Feet and hands for swelling, and legs for varicose veins

- Group B strep test

- Symptoms you have been experiencing, especially unusual ones

- Questions and problems you want to discuss—have a list ready

What You May Be Wondering About

Braxton Hicks Contractions

"Every once in a while my uterus seems to bunch up and harden. What's going on?"

It's practicing. With delivery right around the corner, your body is warming up for the big day by flexing its muscles—literally. Those uterine calisthenics you're feeling are called Braxton Hicks contractions—practice-for-labor contractions that usually begin sometime after the 20th week of pregnancy (though they're more noticeable in the last few months of pregnancy). These rehearsal contractions (typically experienced earlier and with more intensity in women who've had a previous pregnancy) feel like a tightening sensation that begins at the top of your uterus and then spreads downward, lasting from 15 to 30 seconds, though they can sometimes last as long as two minutes or more.

If you check out your belly while you're having a Braxton Hicks, you might even be able to see what you're feeling; your usually round abdomen might appear pointy or strangely bunched up. Weird to watch, but normal.

Though Braxton Hicks contractions are not true labor, they may be difficult to distinguish from real labor—especially as they become more intense, which they often do as pregnancy draws to a close. And though they're not efficient enough to deliver your baby (even when they get really uncomfortable), they may give you a leg up on labor by getting effacement and early dilation of the cervix started when the time is right.

To relieve any discomfort you may feel during these contractions, try changing your position—lying down and relaxing if you've been on your feet, or getting up and walking around if you've been sitting. Be sure, too, that you're getting enough to drink. Dehydration (even minor dehydration) can sometimes cause contractions, including these practice ones. You can also use this labor rehearsal to practice your breathing exercises and the various other childbirth techniques you've learned, which can make it easier to deal with the real contractions when they do arrive.

If the contractions don't subside with a change in activity, and if they become progressively stronger and more regular, you may be in real labor, so be sure to put in a call to your practitioner. A good rule of thumb: If you have more than four Braxton Hicks in an hour, call your practitioner and let him or her know. If you're having a hard time distinguishing Braxton Hicks contractions from the real thing—especially if this is your first pregnancy and you've never experienced the real thing—read up about the different kinds of contractions on page 359 and give your practitioner a call, being sure to describe exactly what you're feeling.

Not-So-Funny Rib Tickling

"It feels as though my baby has his feet jammed up into my rib cage, and it really hurts."

In the later months, when fetuses run out of stretching room in their cramped quarters, the resourceful little creatures often do seem to find a snug niche for their feet between their mother's ribs, and that's one kind of rib tickling that doesn't tickle. Changing your own position may convince your baby to change his or hers. A gentle nudge from you or a few pelvic tilts may dislodge him. Or try relocating him with this exercise: Take a deep breath while you raise one arm over your head, then exhale while you drop your arm; repeat a few times with each arm.

If none of these tactics works, hang in there. When your little pain-in-the-ribs engages, or drops into your pelvis, which usually happens two or three weeks before delivery in first pregnancies (though often not until labor begins in subsequent ones), he probably won't be able to stretch his toes quite so high up.

Another reason for rib cage pain that you can't blame on your baby—at least not directly—comes from a loosening of the joints in the area, courtesy of pregnancy hormones. Acetaminophen (Tylenol) can help ease the ache, but also avoid heavy lifting, which can make it worse (and which you shouldn't be doing now anyway).

Shortness of Breath

"Sometimes I have trouble breathing, even when I'm not exerting any energy. Why is that happening to me? And does it mean my baby isn't getting enough oxygen?"

It's not surprising you're feeling a little spare on air these days. Your ever-expanding uterus is now crowding out all your other internal organs in an effort to provide spacious-enough accommodations for your ever-growing baby. Among those organs feeling the crunch are your lungs, which your uterus has compressed, limiting their ability to expand fully when you take a breath. This, teamed with the extra progesterone that has already been leaving you breathless for months, explains why a trip upstairs these days can make you feel as if you've just run a marathon (winded, big time). Fortunately, while this shortness of breath may feel very uncomfortable to you, it doesn't bother your baby in the least. He or she is kept well stocked with all the oxygen he or she needs through the placenta.

Choosing a Pediatrician

Choosing a pediatrician (or a family practitioner) is one of the most important decisions you'll make as a parent—and actually, you shouldn't wait until you become a parent to make it. Sifting through your choices and making your selection now, before your baby starts crying inexplicably at 3 A.M., will ensure that your transition to parenthood will be that much easier. It will also allow for an informed—not hasty—decision.

If you're not sure where to begin your search, ask your practitioner (if you've been happy with his or her care) or friends, neighbors, or coworkers who have young children for recommendations. Or contact the hospital or birthing center where you'll be delivering (you can call the labor and delivery floor or pediatrics, and ask a nurse on duty for some suggestions; no one gets a better look at doctors than nurses do). Of course, if you're on a health insurance plan that limits your choices, you'll have to choose from that list.

Once you've narrowed your choices down to two or three, call for consultations; most pediatricians or family practitioners will oblige. Bring a list of questions about issues that are important to you, such as office protocol (for instance, whether there are call-in hours for parents or when you can expect calls to be returned), breastfeeding support, circumcision, the use of antibiotics, whether the doctor handles all well-baby visits or whether they are typically handled by nurse-practitioners in the practice. Also important to know: Is the doctor board certified? Which hospital is the doctor affiliated with, and will he or she be able to care for the newborn in the hospital? For more questions to ask and issues to consider, check out the *What to Expect Pregnancy Journal and Organizer.*

Relief from that winded feeling usually arrives toward the end of pregnancy, when your baby drops into your pelvis in preparation for birth (in first pregnancies this generally occurs two to three weeks before delivery, in subsequent deliveries often not until labor begins). Until then, you may find it easier to breathe if you sit straight up instead of slumped over and sleep in a semi-propped-up position, bolstered by two or three pillows.

Sometimes breathlessness can be a sign that iron stores are low, so check in with your practitioner about it. Call immediately (or head to the ER) if shortness of breath is severe and accompanied by rapid breathing, blueness of the lips and fingertips, chest pain, and/or rapid pulse.

Lack of Bladder Control

"I watched a funny movie last night and I seemed to be leaking urine every time I laughed. Why is that?"

As if frequent bathroom runs weren't annoying enough lately, the third trimester has added another bladder issue to the mix: stress incontinence. This lack of bladder control—causing you to spring a small leak when you cough, sneeze, lift something heavy, or even laugh (though there's nothing funny about that)—is the result of the mounting pressure of the growing uterus on the bladder. Some women also experience urge incontinence, the sudden, overwhelming need to urinate (gotta go *now!*) during late pregnancy. Try these tips to help prevent or control stress or urge incontinence:

- Empty your bladder as completely as possible each time you pee by leaning forward.

- Practice your Kegel exercises. Being faithful to your Kegels will help strengthen the pelvic muscles and prevent or correct most cases of pregnancy-induced incontinence—plus, looking ahead, they'll also help prevent postpartum incontinence. For a Kegel how-to, see page 295.

- Do Kegels or cross your legs when you feel a cough, sneeze, or laugh coming on.

- Wear a panty liner if you need one, or you're afraid you'll need one. Graduate to a maxipad when leaks might be especially inconvenient.

- Stay as regular as you can, because impacted stool can put pressure on the bladder. Also, straining hard during bowel movements (as you're likely to do when you're constipated) can weaken pelvic floor muscles. For tips on fighting constipation, see page 173.

- If it's the urge that's driving you crazy (and sending you to the bathroom in a hurry all the time), try training your bladder. Urinate more frequently—about every 30 minutes to an hour—so that you go before you feel that uncontrollable need. After a week, try to gradually stretch the time between bathroom visits, adding 15 minutes more at a time.

- Continue drinking at least eight glasses of fluids a day, even if you experience stress incontinence or frequent urges. Limiting your fluid intake will not limit leaks and it may lead to UTIs and/or dehydration. Not only can either of these lead to a lot of other problems (including preterm contractions), but UTIs can exacerbate stress incontinence. See page 499 for tips on keeping your urinary tract healthy.

To be sure that the leak you've sprung is urine (which it almost certainly is) and not amniotic fluid, it's smart to initially give it the sniff test. If the liquid that has leaked doesn't smell like urine (which has an ammonia-like smell; amniotic fluid has a sweet smell), let your practitioner know as soon as possible.

How You're Carrying

"Everyone says I seem to be carrying small and low for the eighth month. My midwife says everything's fine, but what if my baby isn't growing the way she should be?"

The truth is, you can't tell a baby by her mom's belly. How you're carrying has much less to do with the bulk of your baby and much more to do with these factors:

- Your own bulk, shape, and bone structure. Bellies come in all sizes, just like expectant moms do. A petite woman may carry more compactly (small, low, and out in front) than a larger woman. On the other hand, some very overweight moms never seem to pop out much at all. That's because their babies have lots of growing room available in mom's already ample abdomen.

- Your muscle tone. A woman with very tight muscles may not pop as soon or as much as a woman with slacker muscles, particularly one who's already had a baby or two.

- The baby's position. How your fetus is positioned on the inside may also affect how big or small you look on the outside.

- Your weight gain. A bigger maternal weight gain doesn't necessarily predict a bigger baby, just a bigger mom.

The only assessments of a fetus's size that are worth paying attention to are medical ones—the ones you get from your practitioner at your prenatal visits, not the ones you get from your sister-in-law, your colleague at work, or perfect strangers in the supermarket checkout line. To evaluate your baby's progress more accurately at each prenatal visit, your practitioner won't just take a look at your belly. She'll routinely measure the height of your fundus (the top of the uterus) and palpate your abdomen to locate your baby's cute little body parts and estimate her size. Other tests, including ultrasound, may also be used as needed to approximate size.

Carrying Baby, Eighth Month

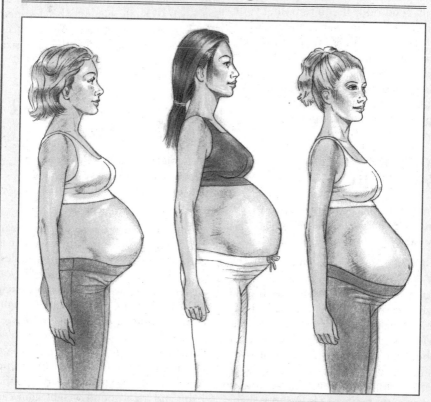

These are just three of the very different ways that a woman may carry near the end of her eighth month. The variations are even greater than earlier in pregnancy. Depending on the size and position of your baby, as well as your own size and weight gain, you may be carrying higher, lower, bigger, smaller, wider, or more compactly.

In other words, it's what's inside that counts—and apparently, what's inside your petite belly is a baby who's plenty big enough.

"Everyone says I'm having a boy because I'm all belly and no hips. I know that's probably an old wives' tale, but is there any truth to it at all?"

Predictions about the baby's sex—by old wives or others—have about a 50 percent chance of coming true. (Actually, a little better than that if a boy is predicted, since 105 boys are born for every 100 girls.) Good odds if you're placing a bet in Las Vegas; not necessarily good odds if you're basing your nursery theme and baby names on it.

That goes for "boy if you're carrying up front, girl if you're carrying wide," "girls make your nose grow, boys don't," and every other prediction not made from the pages of a baby's genetics report or from an ultrasound.

Your Size and Your Delivery

"I'm five feet tall and very petite. I'm afraid I'll have trouble delivering my baby."

When it comes to your ability to birth your baby, size matters—but inside size, not outside size. It's the size and shape of your pelvis in relation to the size of your baby's head that determines how difficult (or easy) your labor will be, not your height or your build. And just because you're extra petite doesn't necessarily mean you've got an extra-petite pelvis. A short, slight woman can have a roomier (or more accommodatingly configured) pelvis than a tall, full-figured woman.

How will you know what size your pelvis is (after all, it doesn't come with a label: small, medium, extra-large)? Your practitioner can make an educated guess about its size, usually using rough measurements taken at your first prenatal exam. If there's some concern that your baby's head is too large to fit through your pelvis while you're in labor, ultrasound may be used to get a better view (and measurement).

Of course, in general, the overall size of the pelvis, as of all bony structures, is smaller in people of smaller stature. Luckily, nature doesn't typically present an undersized woman with an oversized baby. Instead, newborns are usually pretty well matched to the size of their moms and their moms' pelvises at birth (though they may be destined for bigger things later on). And chances are, your baby will be just the right size for you.

Your Weight Gain and the Baby's Size

"I've gained so much weight that I'm afraid my baby will be very big and difficult to deliver."

Just because you've gained a lot of weight doesn't necessarily mean your baby has. Your baby's weight is determined by a number of variables: genetics, your own birthweight (if you were born large, your baby is more likely to be, too), your prepregnancy weight (heavier women tend to have heavier babies), and the kinds of foods you've gained the weight on. Depending on those variables, a 35- to 40-pound weight gain can yield a 6- or 7-pound baby and a 25-pound weight gain can net an 8-pounder. On average, however, the more substantial the weight gain, the bigger the baby.

By palpating your abdomen and measuring the height of your fundus (the top of the uterus), your practitioner will be able to give you some idea of your baby's size, though such guesstimates can be off by a pound or more. An ultrasound can gauge size more accurately, but it may be off the mark, too.

Even if your baby does turn out to be on the big side, that doesn't automatically predict a difficult delivery. Though a 6- or 7-pound baby often makes its way out faster than a 9- or 10-pounder, most women are able to deliver a large baby (or even an extra-large baby) vaginally and without complications. The determining factor, as in any delivery, is whether your baby's head (the largest part) can fit through your pelvis. See the previous question for more.

Baby's Position

"How can I tell which way my baby is facing? I want to make sure he's the right way for delivery."

Playing "name that bump" (trying to figure out which are shoulders, elbows, bottom) may be more entertaining than the best reality TV has to offer, but it's not the most accurate way of figuring out your baby's position. Your practitioner will be able to give you a better idea by palpating your abdomen for recognizable baby parts. The location of the baby's heartbeat is another clue to its position: If the baby's presentation is head first, the heartbeat will usually be heard in the lower half of your abdomen; it will be loudest if the baby's back is toward your front. If there's still some doubt, an ultrasound offers the most reliable view of your baby's position.

Still can't resist a round of your favorite evening pastime (or resist patting those round little parts)? Play away—and to make the game more interesting (and to help clue you in), try looking for these markers next time:

- The baby's back is usually a smooth, convex contour opposite a bunch of little irregularities, which are the "small parts"—hands, feet, elbows.

- In the eighth month, the head has usually settled near your pelvis; it is round, firm, and when pushed down bounces back without the rest of the body moving.

- The baby's bottom is a less regular shape, and softer, than the head.

Breech Baby

"At my last prenatal visit, my doctor said he felt my baby's head up near my ribs. Does that mean she's breech?"

Even as her accommodations become ever more cramped, your baby will still manage to perform some pretty remarkable gymnastics during the last weeks of gestation. In fact, although most fetuses settle into a head-down position between weeks 32 and 38 (breech

Turn, Baby, Turn

Some practitioners recommend simple exercises to help turn a breech baby into a delivery-friendly, heads-down position. Ask your practitioner whether you should be trying any of these at home: Rock back and forth a few times on your hands and knees several times a day, with your buttocks higher than your head; do pelvic tilts (see page 224); get on your knees (keep them slightly apart), and then bend over so your butt's up and your belly's almost touching the floor (stay in that position for 20 minutes three times a day if you can, for best results).

Face Forward

It's not just up or down that's important when it comes to the position of your baby—it's also front or back. If baby's facing your back, chin tucked onto his or her chest (as most babies end up positioned come delivery), you're in luck. This so-called occiput anterior position is ideal for birth because your baby's head is lined up to fit through your pelvis as easily and comfortably as possible, smallest head part first. If baby's facing your tummy (called occiput posterior, but also known by the much cuter nickname "sunny-side up"), it's a setup for back labor (see page 367) because his or her skull will be pressing on your spine. It also means your baby's exit might take a little longer.

As delivery day approaches, your practitioner will try to determine which way (front or back) your baby's head is facing—but if you're in a hurry to find out, you can look for these clues. When your baby is anterior (face toward your back), you'll feel your belly hard and smooth (that's your baby's back). If your little one is posterior, your tummy may look flatter and softer because your baby's arms and legs are facing forward, so there's no hard, smooth back to feel.

Do you think—or have you been told—that your baby is posterior? Don't worry about back labor yet. Most babies turn accommodatingly to the anterior position during labor. Some midwives recommend giving baby a nudge before labor begins by getting on all fours and doing pelvic rocks; whether these exercises can successfully flip a baby is unclear (research has yet to back it up, so to speak), but it certainly can't hurt. At the very least, it might help relieve any back pain you might be experiencing right now.

---

presentations occur in fewer than 5 percent of term pregnancies), some don't let on which end will ultimately be up until a few days before birth. Which means that just because your baby is bottoms down now doesn't mean that she will be breech when it comes time for delivery.

If your baby does stubbornly remain a breech as delivery approaches, you and your practitioner will discuss possible ways to attempt to turn your baby head down and the best method of delivery (see below).

"If my baby is breech, can anything be done to turn him?"

There are several ways to try to coax a bottoms-down baby heads up. On the low-tech side, your practitioner may recommend simple exercises, such as the ones described in the box, page 317. Another option (moxibustion) comes from the CAM camp and uses a form of acupuncture and burning herbs to help turn a stubborn fetus.

If your baby still seems determined not to budge, your practitioner may suggest a somewhat higher-tech, yet hands-on approach to manipulating your baby into the coveted heads-down position: external cephalic version (ECV). ECV is best performed around week 37 or 38 or very early in labor when the uterus is still relatively relaxed; some physicians prefer to attempt the procedure after an epidural has been given. Your practitioner (guided by ultrasound and usually in a hospital) will apply his or her hands to your abdomen (you'll feel some pressure, but probably no pain—especially if you've had an epidural) and try to gently

How Does Your Baby Lie?

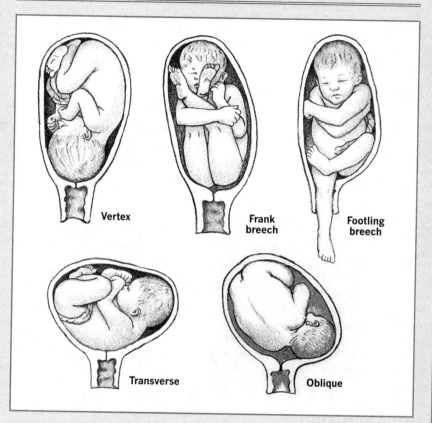

Vertex

Frank breech

Footling breech

Transverse

Oblique

Location, location, location—when it comes to delivery, a baby's location matters a lot. Most babies present head first, or in a vertex position. Breech presentations can come in many forms. A frank breech is when the baby is buttocks first, with his or her legs facing straight up and flat against the face. A footling breech is when one or both of the baby's legs are pointing down. A transverse lie is when the baby is lying sideways in the uterus. An oblique lie is when the baby's head is pointing toward mom's hip instead of toward the cervix.

turn your baby downward. Continuous monitoring will ensure that everything's okay while the maneuver's completed.

The chances of success are pretty high. About two thirds of all ECV attempts are successful (and the success rate is even higher for those who have delivered before, thanks to those laxer uterine and abdominal muscles). Some babies refuse to turn at all, and a small number of contrary fetuses turn and then flip back into a breech position.

"If my baby stays in a breech position, how will that affect labor and delivery? Will I still be able to try for a vaginal birth?"

Whether you'll be able to give vaginal birth a chance will depend on a variety of factors, including your practitioner's policy and your obstetrical situation. Most obs routinely perform a C-section when a baby's in a breech position (in fact, only 0.5 percent of breech babies end up arriving vaginally) because many studies have suggested it's a safer way to go. There are some doctors and midwives, however, who feel it's reasonable to attempt a vaginal delivery under some circumstances (such as when your baby is in a frank breech position and it's clear your pelvis is roomy enough to accommodate).

The bottom line if your baby remains bottom down: You'll need to be flexible in your childbirth plans. Even if your practitioner green-lights a trial of labor, it's just that—a trial. If your cervix dilates too slowly, if your baby doesn't move down the birth canal steadily, or if other problems come up, you'll likely wind up having a C-section. Talk the options over with your practitioner now so you'll be prepared for any possibility come delivery day.

Other Unusual Presentations

"My doctor said that my baby's in an oblique position—what's that and what does it mean for delivery?"

Babies can squirm their way into all kinds of unusual positions, and oblique is one of them. What this means is that your baby's head (though down) is pointed toward either of your hips, rather than squarely on your cervix. An oblique position makes a vaginal exit difficult, so your practitioner might do an external cephalic version (see page 318) to try to coax your baby's head straight down. Otherwise, he or she will probably opt for a C-section.

Yet another tight spot a baby can get into is a transverse position. This is when your baby's lying sideways, across your uterus, instead of vertically. Again, an ECV will be done to try and turn baby up and down. If that doesn't work, your baby will be delivered via cesarean.

Cesarean Delivery

"I was hoping for a vaginal birth, but my doctor just told me I'll probably have to have a cesarean. I'm really disappointed."

Even though it's still considered major surgery (and the happiest kind you can have), a cesarean is a very safe way to deliver, and in some cases, the safest way. It's also a more and more common way. Thirty-four percent of women are having C-sections these days, which means the chances that your baby will end up arriving via the surgical route are more than 1 in 3, even if you don't have any predisposing factors.

That said, if you had your heart set on a vaginal delivery, the news that your baby may need to arrive surgically instead can be understandably disappointing. Visions of pushing your baby out the way nature intended—and perhaps the way you'd always pictured—can be displaced by concerns about the surgery, about being stuck in the hospital longer, about the tougher recovery, and about the scar that comes standard issue.

But here are some things to consider if your practitioner ultimately decides that your baby's best exit strategy is through your abdomen: Most hospitals now strive to make a cesarean delivery as family friendly as possible, with mom awake (but appropriately numb), dad in the room by her side, and a chance to take a good look at your baby and even do a little quick kissing and caressing right afterward if there's no medical reason to preclude it. (More serious cuddling and nursing usually have to wait until you're in recovery—after you've been stitched back up.) So a surgical birth experience may be more satisfying than you're imagining. And while the recovery will be longer and the scar unavoidable (though usually placed unobtrusively), you'll also be delivering with your perineum intact and your vaginal muscles unstretched. The plus side for baby in a cesarean delivery is purely cosmetic—and temporary; because there's no tight squeeze through the birth canal, he or she will have an initial edge in appearance over vaginally delivered babies (think round head, not pointy).

But by far the most important thing to keep in mind as your baby's arrival approaches: The best birth is the one that's safest—and when it's medically necessary, a cesarean birth is definitely safest.

And after all, any delivery that brings a healthy baby into the world and into your arms is a perfect delivery.

"Why does it seem everyone I know (my sister, my friends, plus just about every celebrity) is having C-sections these days?"

With cesarean rates in the United States at an all-time high (over 30 percent of women can expect to have a surgical delivery), just about everyone knows somebody who's had one. And if the past few years are any indication of future trends, you can expect those numbers to continue climbing—and to hear more and more C-section birth stories from the recently delivered around you.

Many factors contribute to these rising cesarean rates, including:

Safety. Cesarean delivery is extremely safe—for both mom and baby—especially with today's better technology (such as the fetal monitor and a variety of other tests) that can more accurately indicate when a fetus is in trouble.

Bigger babies. With more expectant mothers exceeding the recommended weight gain of 25 to 35 pounds, and with the rate of gestational diabetes increasing, more large babies, who may be more difficult to deliver vaginally, are arriving.

Bigger moms. The C-section rate has also risen with the obesity rate. Being obese (or gaining too much weight during pregnancy) significantly increases a woman's chance of needing a C-section, partly because of other risk factors that accompany obesity (gestational diabetes, for instance), partly because obese women tend to have longer labors, and longer labors are more likely to end up on the operating table.

Older mothers. More and more women in their late 30s (and well into their 40s) are now able to have successful pregnancies, but they are more likely to require cesarean deliveries. The same is true of women with chronic health problems.

Repeat C-sections. Though VBAC (vaginal birth after cesarean; see page 325) is still considered a viable option in a few cases, fewer doctors and hospitals are allowing women to try one, and more are scheduling surgeries over a trial of labor.

Fewer instrumental deliveries. Fewer babies are being born with the help of vacuum extraction and even fewer with forceps, which means doctors are turning to surgical deliveries more often when they might have turned to instruments for help in the past.

Requests by moms. Since cesareans are so safe and can prevent the pain of labor while keeping the perineum neatly intact, some women—particularly those who've had one before—prefer them to vaginal deliveries and actually ask ahead for one (see page 323).

Be in the Know

The more you know, the better your birth experience will be. And that goes for a surgical birth experience, too. Here are a few topics you might want to bring up with your practitioner before the first contraction kicks in:

- If labor isn't progressing, will it be possible to try other alternatives before moving to a C-section—for example, oxytocin to stimulate contractions or squatting to make pushing more effective?

- If the baby is a breech, will attempts to turn the baby (using ECV or another technique) be tried first? Are there times when a breech vaginal birth might be possible?

- What kind of incision will likely be used?

- Can your coach be with you if you're awake? If you are asleep?

- Can your nurse-midwife or doula be with you, too?

- Will you and your spouse be able to hold the baby immediately after birth, and will you be able to nurse in the recovery room?

- If the baby doesn't need special care, can he or she room-in with you?

- How much recovery time will you need both in and out of the hospital? What physical discomforts and limitations can you expect?

To find out what you can expect at a cesarean delivery, see page 398.

Satisfaction. Family-friendly policies have made for a much more satisfying surgical birth experience. Since mom can be wide awake and alert during a cesarean section and family-friendlier hospital policies allow dad to be right alongside her, baby meet-and-greets can often take place right on the delivery table. What's more, a C-section is very quick, lasting a mere 10 minutes or less for the delivery itself (suturing mom back up takes about another 30 minutes).

Even with C-section rates as high as they are these days (and they're far lower for midwives, who attend only low-risk births), keep in mind that surgical deliveries still comprise the minority of births. After all, two out of three women can expect to deliver their babies vaginally.

"Do you generally know in advance that you are going to have a cesarean delivery, or is it usually last minute? What are the reasons you might have one?"

Some women won't find out whether they're having a C-section until they're well into labor, others will get the heads-up ahead of time. Different doctors follow different protocols when it comes to surgical deliveries. The most common reasons for a scheduled C-section include:

- A previous cesarean delivery, when the reason for it still exists (Mom has an abnormally-shaped pelvis, for example), or when a vertical incision was used before (instead of the more common low horizontal, which can better withstand the pressure of labor); a C-section is also called for when labor has to be induced in a woman who's already had a cesarean delivery

- When a fetus's head is believed to be too large to fit through mom's pelvis (cephalopelvic disproportion)

- Multiple births (almost all triplets or more are delivered by C-section; many twins are delivered by C-section)

- Breech or other unusual fetal presentation

- A fetal condition or illness (heart disease, diabetes, preeclampsia) in the mother that may make labor and vaginal delivery risky

- Maternal obesity

- An active herpes infection, especially a primary one, or an HIV infection

- Placenta previa (when the placenta partially or completely blocks the cervical opening) or placental abruption (when the placenta separates from the uterine wall too soon)

Sometimes the C-section decision isn't made until well into labor for reasons such as:

- Failure of labor to progress, such as when the cervix hasn't dilated quickly enough, or it's taking too long to push the baby out. (In most cases, physicians will try to give sluggish contractions a boost with oxytocin before resorting to a cesarean.)

- Fetal distress

- A prolapsed umbilical cord

- A ruptured uterus

If your practitioner says that a C-section will be necessary—or will probably be necessary—ask for a detailed explanation of the reasons. Ask, too, if any alternatives are open to you.

Elective Cesareans

"I've heard some women say they chose to have a C-section—is that something I should consider, too?"

Cesareans on demand may be more in demand than ever these days, but that doesn't mean you should sign up for yours. Opting for a surgical delivery when one isn't medically necessary isn't a decision you should take lightly (and definitely one you shouldn't base on trends). It deserves careful consideration—and plenty of discussion with your practitioner about the potential pros and cons.

Though you might have plenty of reasons for wanting a C-section, make sure you consider both sides of the equation. If you're . . .

. . . scared about the pain of a vaginal birth, keep in mind that electing to have a C-section isn't the only way to deliver without pain. There are many effective pain-relief options available to women having a vaginal birth (see page 302).

. . . worried about the aftereffects of a vaginal birth, like pelvic wear and tear or lax vaginal muscles, remember that regular pelvic floor exercises (aka Kegels) can significantly reduce the risk of those effects. What's more, a vaginal birth isn't any more likely to leave you with urinary incontinence issues than a C-section is (which means your baby's exit route doesn't impact the chances that you'll spring a leak postpartum).

. . . hoping to give birth when it's convenient for you, be sure you also consider the longer recovery time and hospital stay plus the increased risk from surgery for you and your baby if you select a C-section. That's not exactly convenient.

. . . going to have another baby, understand that opting for a C-section now

Scheduled Classes for Scheduled C's

Think a scheduled C-section means you won't have to schedule childbirth classes? Not so fast. Sure, you won't need to become an expert on breathing exercises or pushing techniques, but childbirth education classes still have plenty to offer you and your coach (including plenty on what to expect with a C-section—and with an epidural). Most classes also offer invaluable advice on taking care of your baby (which you'll have to master no matter which exit your baby takes), breastfeeding, and possibly getting back into shape postpartum. And don't tune out when the teacher's going over the labor breathing routine with the other students. You might find those skills come in handy postpartum when you're confronted with afterpains (as your uterus contracts back to its original size) or when baby's trying to feed off your painfully engorged breasts. Relaxation techniques also help all new moms (and dads).

may limit your options next time around. Some doctors and hospitals limit VBACs (vaginal births after cesarean) these days, which means you might not be able to choose a vaginal birth for your second baby, if you decide later on that C-sections aren't for you after all.

Something else to consider when contemplating a scheduled cesarean that's not medically necessary: The best time for your baby to make his or her exit from your uterus is when he or she is ready. When an elective delivery is planned, there's always the possibility that the baby will inadvertently be born too soon (particularly if the dates are off to begin with).

If, after careful consideration, you're still interested in signing up for an elective cesarean delivery, talk with your practitioner and decide together whether it's the choice that's right for you and your baby.

Repeat Cesareans

"I've had two cesareans and want to go for my third—and maybe my fourth child. Is there a limit on the number of C-sections you can have?"

Thinking of having lots of babies— but not sure whether you'll be allowed to make multiple trips to the hospital's happiest operating room? Chances are you'll be able to. Limits are no longer arbitrarily placed on the number of cesarean deliveries a woman can undergo, and having numerous cesareans is generally considered a much safer option than it once was. Just how safe depends on the type of incision made during the previous surgeries, as well as on the scars that are formed following the procedures, so discuss the particulars in your case with your practitioner.

Depending on how many incisions you've had, where you've had them, and how they've healed, multiple C-sections can put you at somewhat higher risk for certain complications. These include uterine rupture, placenta previa (a low-lying placenta), and placenta accreta (an abnormally attached placenta). So you'll need to be particularly alert for any bright red bleeding during your pregnancies, as well as the signs of oncoming labor (contractions, bloody show, ruptured membranes). If any of these occur, notify your practitioner right away.

Vaginal Birth After Cesarean (VBAC)

"I had my last baby by cesarean. I'm pregnant again and I'm wondering if I should try for a vaginal delivery this time."

The answer to your question depends on who you talk to. When it comes to determining whether it's safe for women to try for a VBAC (vaginal birth after cesarean; pronounced vee-back), the pendulum of opinions—expert or otherwise—continues to swing VBAC and forth. At one time, doctors and midwives were routinely encouraging pregnant women who'd had a C-section in the past to at least try for a vaginal birth (a trial of labor). But then came a study that warned of the risks (of uterine rupture or of the incision coming apart) if VBAC was attempted, leaving many pregnant women—and their practitioners—confused and unsure about what to do when it comes to childbirth after a C-section.

Looking at the statistics, though, your chances of having a successful VBAC are still pretty good. More than 60 to 80 percent of women who have had C-sections and who are candidates for a trial of labor are able to go through a normal labor and a vaginal delivery in subsequent deliveries. Even women who have had two cesarean deliveries have a good chance of being able to deliver vaginally, as long as the proper precautions are taken. And the study that caused the VBAC backlash actually showed that uterine rupture is really quite rare—it happens less than 1 percent of the time. What's more, that risk is only higher for certain women in certain circumstances, such as those who have a vertical uterine scar instead of a low transverse (95 percent of incisions are low transverse; check the records of your previous cesarean delivery to find

out for sure which type of incision you had), or those whose labors are induced by prostaglandins or other hormonal stimulants (these make contractions stronger). Which means that a VBAC is worth a shot if your practitioner and hospital are willing (many hospitals have strict rules about who can or can't attempt a VBAC and some have stopped allowing VBACs altogether).

If you do decide you'd like to attempt a VBAC, you'll need to find a practitioner who backs you up on your decision (midwives are more open to VBACs and often more successful at making them work). Most important if you're pushing for pushing out your baby is to learn everything you can about VBAC, including what your options will be when it comes to pain relief (some physicians limit pain medications during VBAC, some offer epidurals). Keep in mind, too, that if your labor ends up having to be induced, your practitioner will likely veto VBAC.

If, despite all your best efforts, you end up having a repeat C-section, don't be disappointed. Remember that even the woman who has never had a cesarean before has a nearly 1 in 3 chance of needing one. Don't feel guilty, either, if you decide ahead of delivery (in consultation with your practitioner) that you'd rather schedule an elective second cesarean delivery than attempt VBAC. About a third of all C-sections are repeats, and many are actually performed at the request of the mother. Again, what's best for your baby—and best for you—is what matters.

"My ob is encouraging me to try for a VBAC, but I'm not sure why I should bother."

While your feelings definitely factor into the decision of whether or not to give VBAC a shot, your ob does have a point—and a point you might want to consider. The risks of a VBAC are very low, and a C-section, after all, is still major surgery. A vaginal birth means a shorter hospital stay, a lower risk of infection, no abdominal surgery, and a faster recovery—all good reasons to favor a VBAC. So it makes sense to weigh the pros and cons of VBAC and a repeat cesarean delivery before you make your decision.

If, after you've thought and talked it over, you're still convinced that VBAC's not for you, let your ob know your decision and your reasons—and schedule your cesarean delivery without feeling guilty.

Group B Strep

"My doctor is going to test me for group B strep infection. What does this mean?"

It means that your doctor's playing it safe, and when it comes to group B strep, safe is a very good way to play it.

Group B strep (GBS) is a bacterium that can be found in the vaginas of healthy women (and it's not related to group A strep, which causes the throat infection). In carriers (about 10 to 35 percent of all healthy women are carriers), it causes no problems at all. But in a newborn baby, who can pick it up while passing through the vagina during childbirth, GBS can cause very serious infection (though only 1 in every 200 babies born to GBS-positive mothers will be affected).

If you're a GBS carrier, you won't have any symptoms (that's a plus). But that also means you're unlikely to know you're a carrier (that's a minus—one that could potentially spell trouble for your baby come delivery). Which is why expectant moms are routinely tested for GBS between 35 and 37 weeks (testing done before 35 weeks isn't accurate in predicting who will be carrying GBS at the time of delivery). Coming soon to a hospital near you (though not yet widely available) is a rapid GBS test that can screen women during labor and provide results within the hour, which might make a test at 35 to 37 weeks unnecessary.

So how's the test currently done? It's performed like a Pap smear, using vaginal and rectal swabs. If you test positive (meaning you're a carrier), you'll be given IV antibiotics during labor—and this treatment completely eliminates any risk to your baby. (GBS can also show up in your urine during a routine pee-in-cup test at a prenatal checkup. If it does, it'll be treated right away with oral antibiotics.)

If your practitioner doesn't offer the GBS test during late pregnancy, you can request it. Even if you weren't tested but end up in labor with certain risk factors that point to GBS, your practitioner will just treat you with IV antibiotics to be sure you don't pass the infection on to your baby. If you've previously delivered a baby with GBS, your practitioner may also opt not to test you at 35 to 37 weeks and merely

---

Eat Up

Okay, you may be feeling like a cow these days, and that's all the more reason to keep grazing. Fitting your meals—and baby's nutrient shipments—into that uterus-cramped stomach of yours is likely getting more and more challenging. Which means that more than ever, the Six-Meal Solution is for you. So graze on, Mom.

proceed straight to treatment during labor.

Playing it safe through testing—and, if necessary, treatment—means that your baby will be safe from GBS. And that's a very good thing.

Taking Baths Now

"Is it okay for me to take a bath this far along into my pregnancy?"

Not only is it okay, but a warm bath can provide welcome relief from those late pregnancy aches and pains after a long day (and what day isn't long when you're eight months pregnant?). So hop—or rather, gingerly hoist yourself and your mountain of a belly—into the tub and enjoy a good soak.

If you're worried about bathwater entering your vagina (you may have heard that one through the pregnancy grapevine), don't be. Unless it's forced—as with douching or jumping into a pool, two things you shouldn't be doing anyway these days—water can't get where it shouldn't go. And even if a little water does make its way up, the cervical mucous plug that seals the entrance to the uterus effectively protects its precious contents from invading infectious organisms, should there be any floating around in your tub.

Even once you're in labor and the mucous plug is dislodged, you can still spend time in the bath. In fact, hydrotherapy during labor can provide welcome pain relief. You can even opt to give birth in a tub (see page 24).

One caveat when you're tubbing for two, especially this late in the pregnancy game: Make sure the tub has a nonslip surface or mat on the bottom so you don't take a tumble. And as always, avoid irritating bubble baths—as well as too-warm ones.

Driving Now

"I can barely fit behind the wheel. Should I still be driving?"

You can stay in the driver's seat as long as you fit there; moving the seat back and tilting the wheel up will help with that. Assuming you've got the room—and you're feeling up to it—driving short distances is fine up until delivery day.

Car trips lasting more than an hour, however, might be too exhausting late in pregnancy, no matter who's driving. If you must take a longer trip, be sure to shift around in your seat frequently and to stop every hour or two to get up and walk around. Doing some neck and back stretches may also keep you more comfortable.

Don't, however, try to drive yourself to the hospital while in labor (a really strong contraction may prove dangerous on the road). And don't forget the most important road rule on any car trip, whether you are driver or passenger (and even if you're a passenger being driven to the hospital or birthing center in labor): Buckle up.

Traveling Now

"I may have to make an important business trip this month. Is it safe for me to travel this late in pregnancy, or should I cancel?"

Before you schedule your trip, schedule a call or visit to your practitioner. Different practitioners have differing points of view on last-trimester travel. Whether yours will encourage you or discourage you from hitting the road—or the rails or the skies—at this point in your pregnancy will probably depend on that point of view, as well as on several other factors. Most important is the kind of pregnancy you've been having: You're more likely to get the green light if yours has been uncomplicated. How far along you are (most practitioners advise against flying after the 36th week) and whether you are at any increased risk at all for premature labor will weigh into the recommendation, too. Also very important is how you've been feeling. Pregnancy symptoms that multiply as the months pass also tend to multiply as the miles pass; traveling can lead to increased backache and fatigue, aggravated varicose veins and hemorrhoids, and added emotional and physical stress. Other considerations include how far and for how long you will be traveling (and how long you will actually be in transit), how demanding the trip will be physically and emotionally, as well as how necessary the trip is (optional trips or trips that can be easily postponed until well after delivery may not be worth making now). If you're traveling by air, you'll also need to factor in the restrictions—if any—of the airline you choose. Some will not let you travel in the ninth month without a letter from your practitioner affirming that you are not in imminent danger of going into labor while in flight; others are more lenient.

If your practitioner gives you the go-ahead, there are still plenty of other arrangements you'll need to make besides the travel ones. See page 250 for tips to ensure happy (and safer and more comfortable) trails for the pregnant you. Getting plenty of rest will be especially important. But most critical will be making sure you have the name, phone number, and address of a recommended practitioner (and the hospital or birthing center where he or she delivers) at your destination—one, of course, whose services will be covered by your insurance plan should you end up requiring them. If you're traveling a long distance,

you may also want to consider the possibility of bringing along your spouse on the remote chance that if you do end up going into labor at your destination, at least you won't have to deliver without him.

Making Love Now

"I'm confused. I hear a lot of contradictory information about whether sex in the last weeks of pregnancy is safe—and whether it triggers labor."

It's not like there hasn't been a lot of research done about sex in late pregnancy. It's just that most of it is conflicting, leaving you and all your very pregnant peers unsure of how to proceed—that is, if you're still in the mood to proceed. It is widely believed that neither intercourse nor orgasm alone triggers labor unless conditions are ripe, though many impatient-to-deliver couples have enjoyed trying to prove otherwise. If conditions are ripe, it's been theorized, the prostaglandins in semen might be able to help get the labor party started. But even that's not a sure thing—or a theory you can necessarily bank on taking you to the birthing room, even under the right, ripe conditions. In fact, one study found that low-risk women who had sex in the final weeks of pregnancy actually carried their babies slightly longer than those who abstained from sex during that time. Are you confused yet?

Based on what's known, most physicians and midwives allow patients with normal pregnancies to make love right up until delivery day. And most couples apparently can do so without any problems arising, so to speak.

Check with your practitioner to see what the latest consensus is and what's safe in your situation. If you get a green light (chances are, you will), then by all means hit the sheets—if you have the will and the energy (and the gymnastic skills that might be necessary at this point). If the light is red (and it probably will be if you are at high risk for premature delivery, have placenta previa, or are experiencing unexplained bleeding), try getting intimate in other ways. While you still have some evenings to yourselves, rendezvous for a romantic candlelit dinner or a starlit stroll. Cuddle while you watch TV, or soap each other in the shower. Or use massage as the medium. Or do everything but—use your hands and your mouths to your heart's content, assuming your practitioner hasn't red-lighted orgasm for you. This may not quite satisfy like the real thing, but try to remember you have a whole lifetime of lovemaking ahead—though the pickings may continue to be slim in that department at least until baby's sleeping through the night.

Your Twosome

"The baby isn't even born yet, and already my relationship with my husband seems to be changing. We're both so wrapped up in the birth and the baby, instead of in each other, the way we used to be."

Babies bring a lot of things when they arrive in a couple's lives—joy, excitement, and a lot of dirty diapers, for starters. But they also bring change—and considering they're only pint-size, they bring a whole bunch of change.

Not surprisingly, your relationship with your spouse is one place where you'll notice that change, and it sounds like you've glimpsed it already. And that's actually a really good thing. When baby makes three, your twosome is bound to undergo some shifting of dynamics and reshuffling of priorities. But this predictable upheaval is usu-

ally less stressful—and easier to adapt to—when a couple begins the natural and inevitable evolution of their relationship during pregnancy. In other words, the changes to your relationship are more likely to represent a change for the better if they begin before baby's arrival. Couples who don't anticipate at least some disruption of romance-as-usual—who don't realize that wine and roses will often give way to spit-up and strained carrots, that lovemaking marathons will place (well) behind baby-rocking marathons, that three's not always as cozy as two, at least not in the same way—often find the reality of life with a demanding newborn harder to handle.

So think ahead, plan ahead—and be ready for change. But as you get yourselves into nurture mode, don't forget that baby won't be the only one who'll need nurturing. As normal—and healthy—as it is to be wrapped up in the pregnancy and your expected extra-special delivery, it's also important to reserve some emotional energy for the relationship that created that bundle of joy in the first place. Now is the time to learn to combine the care and feeding of your baby with the care and feeding of your marriage. While you're busily feathering your nest, make the effort to regularly reinforce romance. At least once a week, do something together that has nothing to do with childbirth or babies. See a movie, have dinner out, play miniature golf, hit the flea market. While you're out shopping for tiny onesies, buy a little something special (and unexpected) for your other special someone. Or surprise him with a pair of tickets for a show or a game you know he'd love to see. At dinner, spend at least some time asking about his day, talking about yours, discussing the day's headlines, reminiscing about your first date, dreaming about a

Considering Cord Blood Banking

As if you don't have enough to think about before baby's born, here's another decision you'll have to make: Should you save your baby's umbilical cord blood—and if so, how?

Cord blood harvesting, a painless procedure that takes less than five minutes and is done after the cord has been clamped and cut, is completely safe for mother and child (as long as the cord is not clamped and cut prematurely). A newborn's cord blood contains stem cells that in some cases can be used to treat certain immune system disorders or blood diseases. And research is under way to determine if these stem cells can also be useful in treating other conditions, such as diabetes, cerebral palsy, even heart disease.

There are two ways to store the blood: You can pay for private storage or you can donate the blood to a public storage bank. Private storage can be expensive, and the benefits for low-risk families—in other words, those who do not have any familial immune disorders—are not completely clear yet.

For these reasons, ACOG recommends doctors present the pros and cons of cord blood banking, and the American Academy of Pediatrics (AAP) doesn't recommend *private* cord blood storage unless a family member has a medical condition that might be helped by a stem cell transplant now or in the near future. These conditions include leukemia, lymphoma, and neuroblastoma; sickle cell anemia, aplastic anemia, and thalassemia illness; Gaucher disease and Hurler syndrome; Wiskott-Aldrich syndrome; and severe hemoglobinopathy. The AAP does, however, support parents donating the cord blood to a bank for general use by the public. This costs the donor nothing and could save a life.

Investigate your family's medical history to see if private cord blood banking makes sense for you. Or if you feel the potential future benefits are worth the cost, no matter what your family history, sign up for private banking (see below). You can also talk the cord blood options over with your practitioner.

For general information on cord blood banking, visit parentsguidecordblood.com. For information on donating cord blood, contact the International Cord Blood Registry at (650) 635-1452, cordblooddonor.org; or the National Marrow Donor Program at (800) MARROW2 (627-7692), marrow.org. For private banking options, contact the Cord Blood Registry at (888) 932-6568, cordblood.com; or ViaCord at (877) 535-4148, viacord.com.

second honeymoon (even if it won't be in the cards for many moons), all without mentioning the b-word. Bring massage oil to bed now and then, and rub each other the right way; even if you're not in the mood for sex—or it's seeming too much like hard work these days—any kind of touching can keep you close. None of this flame fanning will make the upcoming wonderful event any less anticipated, but it will remind you both that there's more to life than Lamaze and layettes.

Keeping this very important thought in mind now will make it easier to keep the love light burning later when you're taking turns walking the floor at 2 A.M. And that love light, after all, is what will make the cozy nest you're busily preparing for your baby—and the one you'll soon be sharing as a family of three—a happy and secure one.

Breastfeeding

For the past 30-odd weeks, you've likely seen (and felt) your breasts grow . . . and grow . . . and grow. If you've given any thought to what's going on underneath those giant cups you've now traded up for, you probably know that your breasts aren't growing randomly but are gearing up for one of nature's most important jobs: baby feeding.

It's clear that your breasts are already on board with breastfeeding. Whether you are, too, or whether you're still weighing your baby-feeding options, you'll probably want to learn more about this amazing process, a process that turns breasts (your breasts!) into the perfect purveyors of the world's most perfect infant food. You'll get some valuable highlights and insights here, but for much more on breastfeeding (from the why-to's to the how-to's), see *What to Expect the First Year.*

Why Breast Is Best

Just as goat's milk is the ideal food for kids (goat kids, that is), and cow's milk is the best meal for young calves, your human breast milk is the perfect meal for your human newborn. Here are the reasons why:

It's custom-made. Tailored to meet the nutritional needs of human infants, breast milk contains at least 100 ingredients that aren't found in cow's milk and that can't be precisely replicated in commercial formulas. The protein in breast milk is mostly lactalbumin, which is more nutritious and digestible than the major protein component of cow's milk, caseinogen, which is what formula is made from. The amount of fat in the two milks is similar, but the fat in mother's milk is more easily broken down and used by a baby. Infants also have an easier time absorbing the important micronutrients in breast milk than in cow's milk.

It's safe. You can be sure that the milk served up directly from your breast isn't improperly prepared, contaminated, tampered with, or spoiled. It never gets pulled from the shelves or overstays its sell-by date.

It's a tummy soother. Nursed babies are almost never constipated, thanks to the easier digestibility of breast milk. They also rarely have diarrhea, since breast milk seems both to destroy some diarrhea-causing organisms and to encourage the growth of beneficial flora in the digestive tract, which further discourage digestive upset. On a purely aesthetic note, the bowel movements of a breastfed baby are sweeter smelling (at least until solids are introduced). They're also less apt to cause diaper rash.

It's a fat flattener. Not only is breastfeeding less likely to cause overweight infants, but having been nursed for at least six months (or better, at least a year) appears to be related to lower rates of obesity later in life. It may also be linked to lower cholesterol readings in adulthood.

It's a brain booster. Breastfeeding appears to slightly increase a child's IQ. This may be related not only to the brain-building fatty acids (DHA) it contains, but to the closeness and mother-baby interaction that is built into breastfeeding, which naturally fosters intellectual development.

It keeps allergies on hold. Virtually no baby is allergic to breast milk (though once in a while an infant can have an allergic reaction to a certain food or foods in mom's diet, including cow's milk). On the other hand, beta-lacto-globulin, a substance contained in cow's milk, can trigger an allergic response, with a variety of possible symptoms ranging from mild to severe. Soy milk formulas, which are often substituted when an infant is allergic to cow's milk, stray even further in composition from what nature intended and can also cause an allergic reaction. Studies show, too, that breastfed infants are less likely to get childhood asthma than those babies fed formula.

It's an infection preventer. Breastfed babies are less subject not only to diarrhea but to infections of all kinds—including UTIs and ear infections. In fact, a number of studies suggest that a very wide range of diseases may be somewhat lower in breastfed children, including bacterial meningitis, SIDS, diabetes, some childhood cancers, Crohn's disease, and other chronic digestive diseases. Protection is partially provided by the transfer of immune factors in breast milk and in the premilk substance, colostrum.

It builds stronger mouths. Because nursing at the breast requires more effort than sucking on a bottle, breastfeeding may encourage optimum development of jaws, teeth, and palate. Also, recent studies show that babies who are breastfed are less likely to get cavities later on in childhood than those who are not.

It expands the taste buds early on. Want to raise an adventurous eater? Start at the breast. Developing those little taste buds on breast milk, which takes on the flavor of whatever you've been eating, may acclimate a baby early on to a world of flavors. Researchers have found that nursed babies are less likely to be timid in their tastes than their formula-fed peers once they graduate to the high chair—which means they may be more likely to open wide to that spoonful of yams (or that forkful of curried chicken) later on.

Breastfeeding offers a pile of perks for Mom, too:

Convenience. Breastfeeding requires no advance planning, packing, or equipment; it's always available (at the park, on an airplane, in the middle of the night), at just the right temperature. When you're nursing, you can pack up the baby and hit the road without having to pack up and lug around bottles, nipples, cleaning supplies, and so on; your breasts will always come along for the ride (you can't forget to pack them). You can also skip 2 A.M. trips to the kitchen for a formula refill; late-night feedings require nothing more complicated than an easy-access nightie and a cozy, sleepy snuggle with your little one. When you and baby aren't together (if you work outside the home, for instance), milk can be expressed in advance and stored in the freezer for bottle-feedings as needed.

Economy. Breast milk is free, and so is its delivery system.

Speedy recovery. When baby sucks on your breasts, it triggers the release of the hormone oxytocin, which helps speed the shrinking of the uterus back to its prepregnant size and may decrease the flow of lochia (postpartum vaginal bleeding), which means less blood loss. Nursing also enforces rest periods for you—particularly important, as you'll discover, during the first six postpartum weeks.

Speedy return to prepregnancy shape. And speaking of shrinking, all those extra calories your baby is draining out of you means that even though you'll

Prepping for Breastfeeding

Luckily, nature has worked out all the details, so there's not much you'll need to do to get ready for breastfeeding while you're still expecting (other than read up as much as you can). Some lactation experts recommend that during the last months of pregnancy you skip the soap on your nipples and areolas—just rinse with water, instead (it's not like they get that dirty, anyway). Soap tends to dry the nipples, which may lead to cracking and soreness early in breastfeeding. If your breasts are dry or itchy, a mild cream or lotion may feel soothing, but avoid getting it on the nipple or areola. If your nipples are dry, you can apply a lanolin-based cream such as Lansinoh.

The no-prep-necessary rule applies even to women with small or flat nipples. Flat nipples don't need to be prepped for nursing with breast shells, hand manipulation, or a manual breast pump during pregnancy. Not only are these prepping techniques often less effective than no treatment, but they can do more harm than good. The shells, besides being embarrassingly conspicuous, can cause sweating and rashes. Hand manipulation and pumping can stimulate contractions and, occasionally, even trigger breast infection.

One possible exception: You may want to think about planning ahead if your nipples are inverted (in other words, they retract when you squeeze the areola), which can make nursing a little trickier. Breast shells may help draw nipples out, but you probably won't want to use them frequently, for the reasons above. Ask your practitioner for the name of a lactation consultant who may be able to advise you, or contact your local La Leche League.

---

be adding more calories to your diet to make milk, you won't be piling on the pounds—and you might start seeing that waistline of yours sooner.

Period postponement. Your period will be slower to return, and who could complain about that? But unless you want your children very closely spaced—or enjoy surprises—you should *not* rely on breastfeeding as your only form of contraception. Most mothers who exclusively breastfeed—and whose babies are not sucking often on pacifiers—are probably protected for a few postpartum months. But they can begin menstruating as early as four months after giving birth and may be fertile before that first period.

Bone building. Nursing can improve mineralization in your bones after weaning and may reduce the risk of hip fracture after menopause, assuming you're taking in enough calcium to fill your needs and milk-making requirements.

Health benefits. Feeding your baby via the breast can reduce your risk of some cancers down the road. Women who breastfeed have a lower risk of developing ovarian cancer and breast cancer. Nursing also seems to reduce your risk of developing type 2 diabetes.

The biggest and best bonus. Breastfeeding brings you and your baby together, skin to skin, eye to eye, at least six to eight times a day. The emotional gratification, the intimacy, the sharing of love and pleasure, can not only be very fulfilling and make for a strong mother-child relationship, but it may also enhance your baby's brain development. (A note to mothers

The Breast: Sexual or Practical?

Or can it be both? If you think about it, having two or even more roles in life is not unusual—even roles that are very different, that require different skill sets and different attitudes (lover and mother, for example). You can look at the different roles of the breast—one sexual and one practical—in the same way: Each is important; neither is mutually exclusive. You can have one and the other, too (and in fact, breastfeeding makes lots of women—and their partners—feel especially sensuous). In deciding whether or not to breastfeed, keep this in mind.

of twins: All the advantages of breastfeeding are doubled for you. See page 447 for tips on tandem breastfeeding.)

For more information on breastfeeding, contact your local La Leche League, (800) La Leche (525-3243), or visit LLLUSA.org.

Why Some Opt for the Bottle

Maybe you've decided that breastfeeding definitely isn't for you. Or maybe there's a reason you won't be able to breastfeed, at least not exclusively. Don't feel guilty about choosing the bottle over the breast (or even combining the two; see page 336). Here are some of the pros of bottle-feeding:

More shared responsibility. Bottle-feeding allows dad to share the feeding responsibilities and its bonding benefits more easily. (Although the father of a breastfed baby can derive the same benefits, assuming his baby will take a bottle at all, by feeding a bottle of expressed mother's milk, as well as by taking charge of other baby-care activities, such as bathing, changing, and rocking.)

More freedom. Bottle-feeding doesn't tie a mom down to her baby. She's able to work outside the home without worrying about pumping and storing milk. She can travel a few days without the baby, even sleep through the night, because someone else can feed her baby. (Of course, these options are also open to breastfeeding moms who express milk or supplement with formula.)

Potentially, more romance. Bottle-feeding doesn't interfere with a couple's sex life (except when baby wakes up for a feeding at the wrong time). Breastfeeding can, to some extent. First, because lactation hormones can keep the vagina relatively dry (though vaginal lubricants can remedy the problem); and second, because leaky breasts during lovemaking can be a cold shower for some couples. For bottle-feeding couples, the breasts can play their strictly sensual role rather than their utilitarian one.

Fewer limitations on your diet. Bottle-feeding doesn't cramp your eating style. You can eat all the spicy foods and cabbage you want (though many babies don't object to these tastes in breast milk, and some actually lap them up), you can have a daily glass of wine or a cocktail without factoring in the next feeding, and you don't have to worry about as many nutritional requirements.

No public displays. If you're uncomfortable about the possibility of nursing in public, breastfeeding may be hard to imagine. That hangup, though, is often quickly hung up; many women who opt to try breastfeeding soon find it becomes second nature (and easy to accomplish discreetly), even in the most public places.

Less stress. Some women worry that they're too impatient or tense by nature to breastfeed. Given a try, you may find, however, that nursing is actually very relaxing: a stress-buster, not a stress-inducer (at least once it's well established).

Making the Choice to Breastfeed

For more and more women today, the choice is clear. Some know they'll opt for breast over bottle long before they even decide to become pregnant. Others, who never gave it much thought before pregnancy, choose breastfeeding once they've read up on its many benefits. Some women teeter on the brink of indecision right through pregnancy and even delivery. A few women, convinced that nursing isn't for them, still can't shake the nagging feeling that they ought to do it anyway.

Undecided? Here's a suggestion: Try it—you may like it. You can always quit if you don't, but at least you will have cleared up those nagging doubts. Best of all, you and your baby will have reaped some of the most important benefits of breastfeeding, if only for a brief time.

Nursing After Breast Surgery

Many women who have had breast reductions are able to breastfeed, though most don't produce enough milk to nurse exclusively. Whether you will be able to breastfeed your baby—and how much you'll need to supplement your milk supply with formula—will depend at least in part on how the procedure was performed. Check with your surgeon. If care was taken to preserve milk ducts and nerve pathways, chances are good that you'll be able to produce at least some milk. (The same applies if you had breast surgery because of breast cancer or because of fibrocystic breasts.)

If your surgeon is reassuring, increase your chances of success by reading up on breastfeeding and working with a lactation consultant who is familiar with the challenges of nursing after a breast reduction. Closely monitoring your baby's intake (by keeping an eye on growth and the number of dirty and wet diapers) will be especially important. If you don't end up making enough milk, supplement with bottles of formula (do the combo). Also consider using a nursing supplementation system, which allows you to breastfeed and supplement with formula at the same time and can encourage milk production while ensuring that your baby gets enough to eat. Remember, any amount of breastfeeding—even if it doesn't turn out to be baby's only or even primary source of nutrition—is beneficial. Visit bfar.org for more information on breastfeeding after reduction.

Breast augmentation is far less likely to interfere with breastfeeding than a breast reduction, but it depends on the technique, the incision, and the reason why it was done. While many women with implants are able to nurse exclusively, a significant minority may not produce enough milk. To make sure your supply meets your baby's demand, you'll need to keep close tabs on his or her growth and the number of dirty and wet diapers accumulated daily.

Got Pierced?

You're all set to nurse your baby-to-be, but there's one wrinkle—or rather, one ring, or one stud—that you're not sure what to do with. If you have a nipple piercing, good news: No evidence shows that nipple piercing has any effect on a woman's ability to breastfeed. But experts (in both the lactation and the piercing businesses) agree that you should remove any nipple jewelry before you nurse your baby. This is not only due to the potential for infection for you; it's also because the jewelry could pose a choking hazard for your baby or injure his or her tender gums, tongue, or palate during feedings.

But do be sure to give breastfeeding a fair trial. The first few weeks can be challenging, even for the most enthusiastic breastfeeders, and are always a learning process (though getting help from a lactation consultant or a sister or friend who has breastfed could make things easier if you're having a hard time). A full month, or even six weeks, of nursing is generally needed to establish a successful feeding relationship and give a mom the chance to figure out whether breast is best for her.

Mixing Breast and Bottle

Some women who choose to breastfeed find—for one reason or another—that they can't or don't want to do it exclusively. Maybe exclusive breastfeeding doesn't turn out to be practical in the context of their lifestyle (too many business trips away from home or a job that otherwise makes pumping a logistical nightmare). Maybe it proves to be too physically challenging. Fortunately, neither breastfeeding nor bottle-feeding is an all-or-nothing proposition—and for some women, combining the two is a compromise that works. If you choose to do the combo, keep in mind that you'll need to wait until breastfeeding is well established (at least two to three weeks) before introducing formula. For more information on combining breast and bottle, see *What to Expect the First Year.*

When You Can't or Shouldn't Breastfeed

Unfortunately, the option of breastfeeding isn't open to every new mother. Some women can't or shouldn't nurse their newborns. The reasons may be emotional or physical, due to the mother's health or the baby's, temporary (in which case breastfeeding can sometimes begin later on) or long term. The most common maternal factors that may prevent or interfere with breastfeeding include:

- Serious debilitating illness (such as cardiac or kidney impairment, or severe anemia) or extreme underweight, though some women manage to overcome the obstacles and breastfeed their babies.

- Serious infection, such as active untreated tuberculosis; during treatment, breasts can be pumped so a supply will be established once breastfeeding resumes.

- Chronic conditions that require medications that pass into the breast milk and might be harmful to the baby, such as antithyroid, anticancer, or antihypertensive drugs or mood-altering drugs, such as lithium, tranquilizers, or sedatives. If you take any kind of medication, check with your physician if you're considering breastfeeding. In some cases, a change of medication or spacing of doses may make breastfeeding possible. A temporary need for medication, such as penicillin, even at the time you begin nursing, doesn't usually have to interfere with breastfeeding. Women who need antibiotics during labor or due to a breast infection (mastitis) can continue to breastfeed while on the medication.

- Exposure to certain toxic chemicals in the workplace; check with OSHA (see page 194).

- Alcohol abuse. An occasional drink is okay, but too much alcohol can cause problems for a nursing baby.

- Drug abuse, including the use of tranquilizers, cocaine, heroin, methadone, or marijuana.

- AIDS, or HIV infection, which can be transmitted via body fluids, including breast milk.

Some conditions in the newborn may make breastfeeding difficult, but not (with the right lactation support) impossible. They include:

- A premature or very small baby, who may have difficulty sucking or latching on properly. A preemie who is sick and has to spend time in the NICU (neonatal intensive care unit) also may not be able to nurse, though you can pump to establish a good milk supply and feed the breast milk to the baby with the help of the hospital staff.

- Disorders such as lactose intolerance or PKU in which neither human nor cow's milk can be digested. In the case of PKU, babies can be breastfed if they also receive supplemental phenylalanine free formula; with lactose intolerance (which is extremely rare at birth),

When Father Knows Breast

It only takes two to breastfeed, but it often takes three to make it happen. Researchers have found that when fathers are supportive of breastfeeding, moms are likely to give it a try 96 percent of the time; when dads are ambivalent, only about 26 percent give it a try. What's more, say researchers, keeping dad in the breastfeeding loop (by providing him with lots of nursing know-how so he can better support you) can help extend the length of time you end up breastfeeding—plus it could make nursing easier overall. Dads: Take note, and join the breastfeeding team!

mother's milk can be treated with lactase to make it digestible.

- Cleft lip or other mouth deformities that interfere with sucking. Though the success of breastfeeding depends somewhat on the type of defect, with special help, nursing is usually possible. (Babies with cleft palates won't be able to breastfeed but will still be able to be fed pumped breast milk.)

Very rarely, the milk supply isn't adequate, perhaps because of insufficient glandular tissue in the breast, and breastfeeding just doesn't work—no matter how hard mother and baby work at it.

If you end up not being able to nurse your baby—even if you very much wanted to—there's no reason to add guilt to your disappointment. In fact, it's important that you don't, to avoid letting those feelings interfere with the very important process of getting to know and love your baby—a process that by no means must include breastfeeding.

CHAPTER 14

The
Ninth
Month

Approximately 36 to 40 Weeks

FINALLY, THE MONTH YOU'VE BEEN waiting for, working toward, and possibly worrying about just a little bit is here at long last. Chances are you're at once very ready (to hold that baby . . . to see your toes again . . . to sleep on your stomach!) and not ready at all. Still, despite the inevitable flurry of activity (more practitioner appointments, a layette to shop for, projects to finish at work, paint colors to pick for baby's room), you may find that the ninth month seems like the longest month of all. Except, of course, if you don't deliver by your due date. In that case, it's the tenth month that's the longest.

Your Baby This Month

Week 36 Weighing about 6 pounds and measuring somewhere around 20 inches tall, your baby is almost ready to be served up into your arms. Right now, most of baby's systems (from circulatory to musculoskeletal) are just about equipped for life on the outside. Though the digestive system is ready to roll, too, it hasn't really gotten a work-out yet. Remember, up until this point, your baby's nutrition has been arriving via the umbilical cord—no digestion necessary. But that's soon to change. As soon as baby takes his or her first suckle at your breast (or suck from the bottle), that digestive system will be jump-started—and those diapers will start filling.

Week 37 Here's some exciting news: If your baby were born today, he or she would be considered full term. Mind you, that doesn't mean he or she is finished growing—or getting ready for life on the outside. Still gaining weight at about a half pound a week, the average fetus this age weighs about 6½ pounds (though size varies quite a bit from fetus to fetus, as it does from newborn to newborn). Fat continues to accumulate on your baby, forming kissable dimples in those cute elbows, knees, and shoulders, and adorable creases and folds in the neck and wrists. To keep busy until the big debut, your baby is practicing to make perfect: inhaling and exhaling amniotic fluid (to get the lungs ready for that first breath), sucking on his or her thumb (to prepare for that first suckle), blinking, and pivoting from side to side (which explains why yesterday you felt that sweet little butt on the left side and today it's taken a turn to the right).

Your Baby, Month 9

Week 38 Hitting the growth charts at close to 7 pounds and the 20-inch mark (give or take an inch or two), your little one isn't so little anymore. In fact, baby's big enough for the big time—and the big day. With only two (or four, max) weeks left in utero, all systems are (almost) go. To finish getting ready for his or her close-up (and all those photo ops), baby has a few last-minute details to take care of, like shedding that skin-protecting vernix and lanugo. And producing more surfactant, which will prevent the air sacs in the lungs from sticking to each other when your baby begins to breathe—something he or she will be doing very soon. Baby will be here before you know it!

Week 39 Not much to report this week, at least in the height and weight department. Fortunately for you and your overstretched skin (and aching back), baby's growth has slowed down—or even taken a hiatus until after delivery. On average, a baby this week still weighs in at around 7 or 8 pounds and measures up at 19 to 21 inches (though yours may be a little bigger or smaller). Still, progress is being made in some other areas, especially baby's brain, which is growing and developing up a storm (at a rapid pace that will continue during the first three years of life). What's more, your baby's pink skin has turned white or whitish (no matter what skin your baby will ultimately be in, since pigmentation doesn't occur until soon after birth). A development that you may have noticed by now if this is your first pregnancy: Baby's head might have dropped into your pelvis. This change of baby's locale might make for easier breathing (and less heartburn), but could also make it harder for you to walk (make that to waddle).

Week 40 Congratulations! You've reached the official end of your pregnancy (and perhaps the end of your rope). For the record, your baby is fully full term and could weigh in anywhere between the 6- and 9-pound mark and measure anywhere from 19 to 22 inches, though some perfectly healthy babies check in smaller or bigger than that. You may notice when your baby emerges that he or she (and you'll know for sure at that momentous moment which) is still curled into the fetal position, even though the fetal days are over. That's just sheer force of habit (after spending nine months in the cramped confines of your uterus, your baby doesn't yet realize there's room to spread out now) and comfort (that snug-as-a-bug position feels good). When you do meet your new arrival, be sure to say hello—and more. Though it's your first face-to-face, your baby will recognize the sound of your voice—and that of dad's. And if he or she doesn't arrive on time (choosing to ignore the due date you've marked in red on your calendar), you're in good—though anxious—company. About half of all pregnancies proceed past the 40-week mark, though, thankfully, your practitioner will probably not let yours continue beyond 42 weeks.

Weeks 41–42 Looks like baby has opted for a late checkout. Fewer than 5 percent of babies are actually born on their due date—and around 50 percent decide to overstay their welcome in Hotel Uterus,

thriving well into the tenth month (though you may have lost that "thriving" feeling long ago). Remember, too, that most of the time an overdue baby isn't overdue at all—it's just that the due date was off. Less often, a baby may be truly postmature. When a postmature baby does make a debut, it's often with dry, cracked, peeling, loose, and wrinkled skin (all completely temporary). That's because the protective vernix was shed in the weeks before, in anticipation of a delivery date that's since come and gone. An "older" fetus will also have longer nails, possibly longer hair, and definitely little or none of that baby fuzz (lanugo) at all. They are also more alert and open-eyed (after all, they're older and wiser). Just to be sure all is well, your practitioner will likely monitor an overdue baby closely through nonstress tests and checks of the amniotic fluid or biophysical profiles.

What You May Be Feeling

You may experience all of these symptoms at one time or another, or only a few of them. Some may have continued from last month; others may be new. Still others may hardly be noticed because you are used to them and/or because they are eclipsed by new and more exciting signs indicating that labor may not be far off:

Physically

- Changes in fetal activity (more squirming and less kicking, as your baby has progressively less room to move around)

- Vaginal discharge becomes heavier and contains more mucus, which may

be streaked red with blood or tinged brown or pink after intercourse or a pelvic exam or as your cervix begins to dilate

- Constipation

- Heartburn, indigestion, flatulence, bloating

- Occasional headaches, faintness, dizziness

- Nasal congestion and occasional nosebleeds; ear stuffiness

- Sensitive gums

- Leg cramps at night

- Increased backache and heaviness

A Look Inside

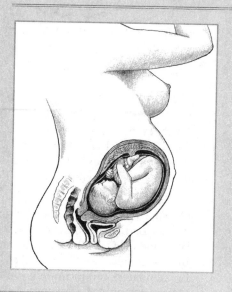

Your uterus is right under your ribs now, and your measurements aren't really changing that much from week to week anymore. The top of your uterus is around 38 to 40 cm from the top of your pubic bone. Your weight gain slows down or even stops as D-day approaches. Your abdominal skin is stretched as far as you think it can go, and you're probably waddling more now than ever, possibly because the baby has dropped in anticipation of impending labor.

- Buttock and pelvic discomfort and achiness

- Increased swelling of ankles and feet, and occasionally of hands and face

- Itchy abdomen, protruding navel

- Stretch marks

- Varicose veins in your legs

- Hemorrhoids

- Easier breathing after the baby drops

- More frequent urination after the baby drops, since there's pressure on the bladder once again

- Increased difficulty sleeping

- More frequent and more intense Braxton Hicks contractions (some may be painful)

- Increasing clumsiness and difficulty getting around

- Colostrum, leaking from nipples (though this premilk substance may not appear until after delivery)

- Extra fatigue or extra energy (nesting syndrome), or alternating periods of each

- Increase in appetite or loss of appetite

Emotionally

- More excitement, more anxiety, more apprehension, more absentmindedness

- Relief that you're almost there

- Irritability and oversensitivity (especially with people who keep saying "Are you still around?")

- Impatience and restlessness

- Dreaming and fantasizing about the baby

What You Can Expect at This Month's Checkup

You'll be spending more time than ever at your practitioner's office this month (stock up on some good waiting-room reading if you've already plowed through the office collection), with appointments scheduled weekly. These visits will be more interesting—the practitioner will estimate baby's size and may even venture a prediction about how close you are to delivery—with the excitement growing as you approach the big day. In general, you can expect your practitioner to check the following, though there may be variations, depending on your particular needs and your practitioner's style of practice:

- Your weight (gain generally slows down or stops)

- Your blood pressure (it may be slightly higher than it was at midpregnancy)

- Your urine, for sugar and protein

- Your feet and hands for swelling, and legs for varicose veins

- Your cervix (the neck of your uterus), by internal examination, to see if effacement (thinning) and dilation (opening) have begun

- The height of the fundus

- The fetal heartbeat

- Fetal size (you may get a rough weight estimate), presentation (head or buttocks first), position (front or rear facing), and descent (is presenting part engaged?) by palpation (feeling with the hands)

- Questions and concerns you want to discuss, particularly those related to labor and delivery—have a list ready. Include frequency and duration of Braxton Hicks contractions, if you've noticed any, and other symptoms you have been experiencing, especially unusual ones.

You can also expect to receive a labor and delivery protocol (when to call if you think you are in labor, when to plan on heading to the hospital or birthing center) from your practitioner; if you don't, be sure to ask for these instructions.

What You May Be Wondering About

Urinary Frequency— Again

"During the last few days, it seems like I'm in the bathroom constantly. Is it normal to be urinating this frequently now?"

Having a little first-trimester déjà vu? That's because your uterus is right back where it started: down low in your pelvis, pressing squarely on your bladder. And this time, the weight of your uterus is significantly greater, which means the pressure on your bladder is greater, too—as is that need to pee. So you go, girl—again, and again, and again. As long as frequency isn't accompanied by signs of infection (see page 498), it's completely normal. Don't

THE NINTH MONTH

343

be tempted to cut back on fluids in an attempt to cut back on your trips to the bathroom—your body needs those fluids more than ever. And, as always, go as soon as you feel the urge (and can find a bathroom).

Leaky Breasts

"A friend of mine says she had milk leaking from her breasts in the ninth month; I don't. Does this mean I won't have any milk?"

Milk isn't made until baby's ready to drink it—and that's not until three to four days after delivery. What your friend was leaking was colostrum, a thin, yellowish fluid that is the precursor to mature breast milk. Colostrum is chock-full of antibodies to protect a newborn baby and has more protein and less fat and milk sugar (the better to digest it) than the breast milk that arrives later.

Some, but far from all, women leak this phenomenal fluid toward the end of their pregnancies. But even women who don't experience leakage of colostrum are still producing it. Not leaking, but still curious? Squeezing your areola may allow you to express a few drops (but don't squeeze with a vengeance—that'll only result in sore nipples). Still can't get any? Don't worry. Your baby will be able to net what he or she needs when the time comes (if you plan to breastfeed). Not leaking isn't a sign that your supply won't ultimately keep up with demand.

If you are leaking colostrum, it's probably just a few drops. But if you're leaking more than that, you may want to consider wearing nursing pads in your bra to protect your clothes (and to prevent potentially embarrassing moments). And you might as well get used to the wet T-shirt look, since this is just a glimpse of leaky breasts—and wet bras, nightgowns, and shirts—to come.

Spotting Now

"Right after my husband and I made love this morning, I began to spot a little. Does this mean that labor is beginning?"

Don't order the birth announcements yet. Pinkish-stained or red-streaked mucus appearing soon after intercourse or a vaginal examination, or brownish-tinged mucus or brownish spotting appearing within 48 hours after the same, is usually just a normal result of the sensitive cervix being bruised or manipulated, not a sign that labor's about to start up. But pinkish- or brownish-tinged or bloody mucus accompanied by contractions or other signs of oncoming labor, whether it follows intercourse or not, could be signaling the start of labor (see page 359).

If you notice bright red bleeding or persistent red spotting after intercourse—or any time, for that matter—check in with your practitioner.

Water Breaking in Public

"I'm really worried that my water will break in public."

Most women worry about springing an amniotic leak—especially a public one—late in pregnancy, but few ever do. Contrary to popular pregnancy belief, your "water" (more accurately, your membranes) isn't likely to "break" (more accurately, rupture) before labor begins. In fact, more than 85 percent of women enter the birthing room with their membranes fully intact. And even if you end up being among the 15 percent who do spring a prelabor leak, you won't have to fear a public puddle at your feet. Unless you're lying down (something you probably don't do much in public anyway), amniotic

Baby's Crying Already?

The most joyous sound a new parent hears is that first cry the baby makes after he or she is born. But would you believe that your little one is already crying inside you? It's true, according to researchers, who found that third-trimester fetuses show crying behaviors—quivering chin, open mouth, deep inhalations and exhalations, and startle responses—when a loud noise and vibration were sounded near the mom's belly. It's known that the crying reflex is well developed even in premature infants, so it's not surprising that babies are perfecting this skill long before they're ready to emerge (and it explains why they're so good at crying once they come out!).

fluid is less likely to go with the flow, and more likely to come out as a slow trickle—or at most a small gush. That's because when you're upright (standing, walking, even sitting), your baby's head acts like a cork in a bottle, blocking the opening of the uterus and keeping most of the amniotic fluid in. In other words, it's probable that the forecast for the rest of your pregnant future will remain "mainly dry."

Something else to keep in mind: If you do actually experience a noticeable public gush of fluid, you can be sure that no one around you will stare, point, or chuckle. Instead, they will either offer you help or discreetly ignore you. After all, no one is likely to overlook the fact that you're pregnant, so it's just as unlikely they'll mistake amniotic fluid for anything else.

The bright side of a water break (in public or at home) is that it's usually followed by labor, typically within 24 hours. If labor doesn't start spontaneously within that time, your practitioner will probably start it for you. Which means your baby's arrival will be just a day away, either way.

Though it really isn't necessary, wearing a panty liner or maxipad in the last weeks may give you a sense of security, as well as keep you fresh as your vaginal discharge increases. You also might want to place heavy towels, a plastic sheet, or hospital bed pads under your sheets in the last few weeks, just in case your water breaks in the middle of the night.

Baby Dropping

"If I'm past my 38th week and haven't dropped, does it mean I'm going to be late?"

Just because your baby doesn't seem to be making his or her way toward the exit doesn't mean that exit will be late. "Dropping," also called "lightening," is what happens when a baby descends into mom's pelvic cavity, a sign that the presenting part (first part out, usually the head) is engaged in the upper portion of the bony pelvis. In first pregnancies, dropping generally takes place two to four weeks before delivery. In women who have had children previously, it usually doesn't happen until they go into labor. But as with almost every aspect of pregnancy, exceptions to the rule are the rule. You can drop four weeks before your due date and deliver two weeks late, or you can go into labor without having dropped at all. You can even drop and then undrop. Your baby's head can appear to settle in and then float up again (meaning it's not really fixed in place yet).

Often, dropping is obvious. You might not only see the difference (your belly seems lower—perhaps a lot lower—and tilted farther forward), you might feel the difference, too. As the upward pressure of the uterus on your diaphragm is relieved, you can breathe more easily, literally. With your stomach less crowded, you can eat more easily, too—and finish up your meals without a side of heartburn and indigestion. Of course, these welcome changes are often offset by a new set of discomforts, including pressure on the bladder (which will send you to the bathroom more frequently, again), the pelvic joints (which will make it harder to walk . . . or waddle), and the perineal area (sometimes causing pain); sharp little shocks or twinges on the pelvic floor (thanks to baby's head pressing hard on it); and a sense of being off-balance (because your center of gravity has shifted once more).

It is possible, however, for baby to drop unnoticed. For instance, if you were carrying low to begin with, your pregnant profile might not change noticeably after dropping. Or if you never experience difficulty breathing or getting a full meal down, or if you always urinate frequently, you might not detect any obvious difference.

Your practitioner will rely on two more indicators to figure out whether or not your baby's head is engaged: First, he or she will do an internal exam to see whether the presenting part—ideally the head—is in the pelvis; second, he or she will feel that part externally (by pressing on your belly) to determine whether it is fixed in position or still "floating" free.

How far the presenting part has progressed through the pelvis is measured in "stations," each a centimeter long. A fully engaged baby is said to be at "zero station"; that is, the fetal head has descended to the level of the prominent bony landmarks on either side of the midpelvis. A baby who has just begun to descend may be at −4 or −5 station. Once delivery begins, the head continues on through the pelvis past 0 to +1, +2, and so on, until it begins to "crown" at the external vaginal opening at +5. Though a woman who goes into labor at 0 station probably has less pushing ahead than the woman at −3, this isn't invariably true, since station isn't the only factor affecting the progression of labor.

Though the engagement of the fetal head strongly suggests that the baby can get through the pelvis without difficulty, it's no guarantee. Conversely, a fetus that is still free floating going into labor isn't necessarily going to have trouble negotiating the exit. And in fact, the majority of fetuses that haven't yet engaged when labor begins come through the pelvis smoothly. This is particularly true in moms who have already delivered one or more babies.

Changes in Baby's Movements

"My baby used to kick so vigorously, and I can still feel him moving, but he seems less active now."

When you first heard from your baby, way back in the fifth month or so, there was ample room in the uterus for acrobatics, kickboxing, and punching. Now that conditions are getting a little cramped, his gymnastics are curtailed. In this uterine straitjacket, there is little room for anything more than turning, twisting, and wiggling—which is probably what you've been feeling. And once your baby's head is firmly engaged in your pelvis, he will be even less mobile. But this late in the game, it's not important what kind of fetal

Going Down?

You may be in for a surprise—and a treat—at one of this month's weigh-ins. Most expectant moms who reach the end of pregnancy also reach the end of pregnancy weight gain. Instead of watching the numbers on the scale go up (and up), you may start seeing those numbers go nowhere—or even go down—over the last few weeks. What's up (or rather, down) with that? After all, your baby isn't losing weight—and your ankles (not to mention your hips) are still plenty puffy, thank you very much. What's happening, actually, is perfectly normal. In fact, this weight gain standstill (or downward trend) is one way that your body gets ready for labor. Amniotic fluid starts to decrease (less water equals less weight), and loose bowels (common as labor approaches) can also send the numbers down, as can all that sweating you're doing (especially if you've been nesting overtime). And if you think this weight loss is exciting, wait until delivery day. That's when you'll experience your biggest one-day weight-loss total ever!

movement you feel (or even if it's only on one side), as long as you feel some every day. If, however, you feel no activity (see next question) or a sudden spurt of very panicky, frantic, jerky, or violent activity, check with your practitioner.

"I've hardly felt the baby kick at all this afternoon. What does that mean?"

Chances are your baby has settled down for a nap (older fetuses, like newborns, have periodic interludes of deep sleep) or that you've been too busy or too active to notice any movements. For reassurance, check for activity using the test on page 289. You may want to repeat this test routinely twice a day throughout the last trimester. Ten or more movements during each test period mean that your baby's activity level is normal. Fewer suggest that medical evaluation might be necessary to determine the cause of the inactivity, so contact your practitioner if that's the case. Though a baby who is relatively inactive in the womb can be perfectly healthy, inactivity at this point sometimes indicates fetal distress. Picking up this distress early and taking steps to intervene can often prevent serious consequences.

"I've read that fetal movements are supposed to slow down as delivery approaches. My baby seems as active as ever."

Every baby's different, even before he or she is born—especially when it comes to activity levels, and particularly as delivery day approaches. While some babies move a bit less as they get ready to arrive, others keep up an energetic pace right until it's time for that first face-to-face. In late pregnancy, there is generally a gradual decline in the number of movements, probably related to tighter quarters, a decrease in amniotic fluid, and improved fetal coordination. But unless you're counting every single movement, you're not likely to notice a big difference.

Nesting Instinct

"I've heard about the nesting instinct. Is it pregnancy legend, or is it for real?"

The need to nest can be as real and as powerful an instinct for some humans as it is for our feathered and four-legged friends. If you've ever witnessed the birth of puppies or kittens, you've probably noticed how restless the laboring mother becomes just before delivery—frantically running back and forth, furiously shredding papers in a corner, and finally, when she feels all is in order, settling into the spot where she will give birth. Many expectant mothers do experience the uncontrollable urge to ready their nests, too, just prior to childbirth. For some it's subtle. All of a sudden, it becomes vitally important to clean out and restock the refrigerator and make sure there's a six-month supply of toilet paper in the house. For others, this unusual burst of manic energy plays itself out in behavior that is dramatic, sometimes irrational, and often funny (at least, to those watching it)—cleaning every crevice of the nursery with a toothbrush, rearranging the contents of the kitchen cabinets alphabetically,

washing everything that isn't tied down or being worn, or folding and refolding baby's clothes for hours on end.

Though it isn't a reliable predictor of when labor will begin, nesting usually intensifies as the big moment approaches—perhaps as a response to increased adrenaline circulating in an expectant mom's system. Keep in mind, however, that not all women experience the nesting instinct, and that those who don't are just as successful in bearing and caring for their nestlings as those who do. The urge to slump in front of the television during the last few weeks of pregnancy is as common as the urge to clean out closets, and just as understandable. Make that more understandable.

If a nesting urge does strike, make sure it's tempered by common sense. Suppress that overwhelming urge to paint the baby's nursery yourself; let someone else climb the ladder with the bucket and roller while you oversee

Getting Ready

These days, it almost goes without saying that becoming educated about childbirth is one of the best ways to prepare for this momentous experience. So by all means make sure you and your coach are as educated as you can be: Read the next chapter, along with any other materials on labor and delivery you can get your hands on; watch DVDs; take a childbirth class together. But don't let your preparedness stop there. Be as prepared for matters practical and aesthetic, and plan, too, for your entertainment. Consider, for example: Are you interested in having the event videotaped (if that's allowed where you're delivering), or will a few photos suffice? Will music

soothe your soul when your soul needs it most, or will you prefer some peace and quiet? What will distract you best between contractions—playing poker with your partner or solitaire on your cell phone, checking e-mail on your laptop, or watching reruns of your favorite sitcoms on TV? (Of course, also be prepared for the possibility that once those contractions begin, you may have little patience for distractions.) Don't forget to include the materials you'll need for the activities you've planned (including batteries for that camera, plus your phone charger) in the suitcase you'll be taking to the hospital or birthing center (see page 356 for a complete packing list).

How Is Baby Doing?

As your pregnancy nears its end (yes, it *will* end), your practitioner will be keeping a closer eye on your health and that of your baby—especially once you pass the 40-week mark. That's because 40 weeks is the optimum uterine stay for babies; those who stick around much longer can face potential challenges (becoming too big to arrive vaginally, experiencing a decline in their placenta's function, or a dip in amniotic fluid levels). Luckily, your practitioner can tap into plenty of tests and assessments of fetal well-being to make sure all's well and will end well:

Kick counts. Your record of fetal movements (see page 289), though not foolproof, can provide some indication of how your baby is doing. Ten movements an hour is usually reassuring. If you don't notice enough activity, other tests are then performed.

The nonstress test (NST). You'll be hooked up to a fetal monitor (the same kind that's used during labor) in your practitioner's office to measure the baby's heart rate and response to movement. You will be holding a clicker contraption (like a buzzer on a game show), and each time you feel the baby move, you'll click it. The monitoring goes on for 20 to 40 minutes and is able to detect if the fetus is under any stress.

Fetal acoustical stimulation (FAS) or vibroacoustic stimulation (VAS). This nonstress test, in which a sound-and-vibration-producing instrument is placed on the mother's abdomen to determine the fetus's response to sound or vibrations, is useful if there's a question about how to interpret a standard NST.

The contraction stress test (CST) or oxytocin challenge test (OCT). If the results of a nonstress test are unclear, your practitioner may order a stress test. This test, done at a hospital, tests how the baby responds to the "stress" of uterine contractions to get some idea of how the baby will handle full-blown labor. In this somewhat more complex and time-consuming test (it may take a number of hours), you're hooked up to a fetal monitor. If contractions are not occurring on their own, you'll be given a low-dose IV of oxytocin (or you'll be asked to stimulate your nipples) to jump-

from a comfy chair. Don't let overzealous home cleaning exhaust you, either—you'll need energy reserves for both labor and a new baby. Most important of all, keep the limitations of your species in mind. Although you may share this nesting instinct with members of the animal kingdom, you are still only human—and you can't expect to get everything done before that little bundle of joy arrives at your nest.

When You Will Deliver

"I just had an internal exam and the doctor said I'll probably be going into labor very soon. Can she really tell exactly how close I am?"

Your practitioner can make a prediction about when you'll give birth, but it's still just an educated guess—just as your original due date was. There are clues that labor is getting closer, which start the contractions. How the fetus responds to contractions indicates its probable condition and that of the placenta. This rough simulation of the conditions of labor can, if the results are unequivocal, allow a prediction to be made about whether or not the fetus can safely remain in the uterus and whether it can meet the strenuous demands of true labor.

A biophysical profile (BPP). A BPP generally evaluates, through the use of ultrasound, four aspects of life in the uterus: fetal breathing, fetal movement, fetal tone (the ability of your baby to flex a finger or toe), and amniotic fluid volume. When all these are normal, the baby is probably doing fine. If any of these are unclear, further testing (such as a CST or a VAS) will be given to provide a more accurate picture of the baby's condition.

The "modified" biophysical profile. The "modified" biophysical profile combines the NST with an evaluation of the quantity of amniotic fluid. A low level of amniotic fluid may indicate that the fetus is not producing enough urine and the placenta may not be functioning up to par. If the fetus reacts appropriately to the nonstress test and levels of amniotic fluid are adequate, it's likely that all is well.

Umbilical artery Doppler velocimetry. This test uses ultrasound to look at the flow of blood through the umbilical artery. A weak, absent, or reverse flow indicates the fetus is not getting adequate nourishment and probably not growing well.

Other tests of fetal well-being. These include regular ultrasound exams to document fetal growth; amniotic fluid sampling (through amniocentesis); fetal electrocardiography or other tests (to assess the fetal heart); and fetal scalp stimulation (which tests how a fetus reacts to pressure on, or pinching of, the scalp).

Most of the time, fetuses pass these tests with flying colors, which means they can continue to stay put until they're good and ready to make their debuts. Rarely, the test results can be labeled "nonreasurring," which really isn't as unreassuring as it sounds. Because these tests yield plenty of false positives, a nonreassuring result doesn't definitely diagnose distress, but it will mean that your practitioner will continue to test your baby, and if it turns out that there's any indication of fetal distress, will induce your labor. (For information on labor induction, see page 368.)

a practitioner looks for beginning in the ninth month, both by palpating the abdomen and doing an internal exam. Has lightening or engagement taken place? What level, or station, has the baby's presenting part descended to? Have effacement (thinning of the cervix) and dilation (opening of the cervix) begun? Has the cervix begun to soften and move to the front of the vagina (another indicator that labor is getting closer) or is it still firm and positioned to the back?

But "soon" can mean anywhere from an hour to three weeks or more. A practitioner's prediction of "you'll be in labor by this evening" could segue into a half month more of pregnancy, whereas a forecast of "labor's weeks away" could be followed hours later by birth. The fact is that engagement, effacement, and dilation can occur gradually, over a period of weeks or even a month or more in some women—and overnight in others. Which means that these clues

Do-It-Yourself Labor Induction?

So what happens if you're overdue, and still as pregnant as ever (make that more pregnant than ever), with your baby showing no signs of budging? Should you just let nature take its course, no matter how long that course takes? Or should you take matters into your own hands, and try some do-it-yourself labor induction techniques? And if you do take matters into your own hands, will it even work? While there are plenty of natural methods you can use to try to bring on labor (and plenty of old wives' tales to go along with them), it's hard to prove that any of them will do the trick. Some women swear by them, but none of the home-grown methods passed from mom-to-be to mom-to-be has been documented as consistently effective. That's probably at least partly due to the fact that when they do appear to work, it's difficult to establish whether they actually worked—or whether labor, coincidentally, started on its own at the same time.

Still, if you're at the end of your rope (and who isn't by 40 weeks?), you might want to give these a try:

Walking. It has been suggested that walking can help ease the baby into the pelvis, thanks perhaps to the force of gravity or the swaying (or waddling) of your hips. Once your baby puts pressure on the cervix—literally—labor just might get going. If it turns out that your stroll doesn't jump-start labor, you'll be no worse for the wear. In fact, you might be in better shape for labor, whenever it actually does begin.

Sex. Sure you're the size of a small hippo, but hopping (make that hoisting yourself) into bed with your partner may be an effective way to mix business with pleasure. Or not. Some research shows that semen (which contains prostaglandins) can stimulate contractions, while other research has found that women who continue to have sex late in pregnancy might carry their babies even longer than those who abstain.

are far from sure bets when it comes to pinpointing the start of labor.

So feel free to pack your bags, but don't keep the car running. Like every pregnant woman who preceded you into the birthing room, you will still have to play the waiting game, knowing for certain only that your day, or night, will come—sometime.

The Overdue Baby

"I'm a week overdue. Is it possible that I might never go into labor on my own?"

The magic date is circled in red on the calendar; every day of the 40 weeks that precede it is crossed off with great anticipation. Then, at long last, the big day arrives—and, as in about half of all pregnancies, the baby doesn't. Anticipation dissolves into discouragement. The stroller and crib sit empty for yet another day. And then a week. And then, in about 10 percent of pregnancies, most often those of first-time mothers, two weeks. Will this pregnancy never end?

Though women who have reached the 42nd week might find it hard to believe, no pregnancy on record ever went on forever, even before the advent

The bottom line? Go for your bottom lines, if you're game to try (and get a good laugh while you're at it). After all, it may be the last time in a long time that you'll actually be able (or willing) to have sex. If getting busy brings on labor, great—if it doesn't, still great.

Other natural methods have potential drawbacks (even though they've been passed down from midwives to old wives to new doctors). So before you try these at home, discuss them with your practitioner first:

Nipple stimulation. Interested in some nipple tweaking (ouch)? How about some nipple twisting (double ouch)? Stimulating your nipples for a few hours a day (yes, hours) can release your own natural oxytocin and bring on contractions. But here's the caveat: Nipple stimulation—as enticing as hours of it may sound (or not)—can lead to painfully long and strong uterine contractions. So unless your practitioner advises it and is monitoring your progress, you may want to think four times—twice for each nipple—before you or your spouse attempt nipple stimulation.

Castor oil. Hoping to sip your way into labor with a castor oil cocktail? Women have been passing down this yucky-tasting tradition for generations on the theory that this powerful laxative will stimulate your bowels, which in turn will stimulate your uterus into contracting. The caveat for this one: Castor oil (even mixed with a more appetizing drink) can cause diarrhea, severe cramping, and even vomiting. Before you chug-a-lug, be sure you're game to begin labor that way.

Herbal teas and remedies. Raspberry leaf tea, black cohosh—these herbal remedies might be just what your grandmother orders to bring on labor, but since no studies have been done to establish the safety of any herbal treatments as labor inducers, don't use any without getting the green light from your practitioner first.

And while you're pondering the effectiveness of the do-it-yourself methods, remind yourself that you *will* go into labor—either on your own or with a little help from your practitioner—in a week or two.

of labor induction. Studies show that about 70 percent of apparent post-term pregnancies aren't post-term at all. They are only believed to be late because of a miscalculation of the time of conception, usually thanks to irregular ovulation or a woman's uncertainty about the exact date of her last period. And in fact, when early ultrasound examination is used to confirm the due date, diagnoses of post-term pregnancy drop dramatically from the long-held estimate of 10 percent to about 2 percent.

Even if you do end up among those 2 percent of women who are truly overdue, your practitioner won't let your pregnancy pass the 42-week mark. In fact, most practitioners won't even let a pregnancy continue that long, choosing instead to induce by the time your baby has clocked in 41 uterine weeks. And, of course, if at any point test results show that the placenta is no longer doing its job well or that the amniotic fluid levels have dipped too low—or if there are any other signs that baby might not be thriving—your practitioner will take action, and depending on the situation, either induce labor or perform a cesarean delivery. Which means that even if you don't end up going into labor on your own, you won't be pregnant forever.

"I've heard that overdue babies don't continue to thrive. I just passed my 40th week—does that mean my baby should be delivered?"

Just because your pregnancy has exceeded those 40 allotted weeks doesn't necessarily mean that your baby has worn out his or her uterine welcome—or that a speedy exit is called for. Many babies actually continue to grow and thrive well into the tenth month. But when a pregnancy goes post-term (technically, at the 42-week mark), the once ideal environment in a womb can become less hospitable. The aging placenta can fail to supply enough nutrition and oxygen, and production of amniotic fluid can drop off.

Babies born after spending time in such an inhospitable environment are called postmature. Their skin is dry, cracked, peeling, loose, and wrinkled, having already shed the cheesy vernix coating that previously protected it. Being "older" than other new arrivals, they have longer nails and more hair, and are generally open-eyed and alert. Because they are usually larger than term babies, with wider head circumferences, and because they may sometimes be in distress, postmature babies are more likely to be delivered by cesarean. They may also need some special care in the neonatal intensive care nursery for a short time after birth. So, though the majority of post-term babies arrive home a little later than scheduled, they arrive completely healthy.

To prevent postmaturity, many practitioners choose to induce labor

Massage It, Mama

Got nothing but time on your hands as you wait for baby's arrival? Put your hands (or a special someone else's hands) to good use—and give yourself a rub. Perineal massage can help gently stretch a first timer's perineum (that area of skin between your vagina and rectum), which in turn can minimize the "stinging" that occurs when baby's head crowns during childbirth. And here's another plus you'll appreciate: It may also help you avoid an episiotomy and tearing, according to some experts.

Here's how to give your perineum the right rub: With clean hands (and short nails) insert your thumbs or index fingers (lubricated with a little K-Y jelly if you'd like) inside your vagina. Press down (toward your rectum) and slide your fingers across the bottom and sides of your perineum. Repeat daily during the last weeks of pregnancy, five minutes (or longer) each time. Not in the mood for a perineal massage? It's certainly not something you have to do. Don't bother if you don't feel comfortable with the concept, it seems too weird, or you just don't have the time. Though anecdotal evidence has long supported its effectiveness, clinical research has not yet backed it up. Even without the rubbing, your body will still stretch when the time comes. And don't bother with perineal massage if you've already popped out a baby or two. Your perineum doesn't need, and probably won't benefit from, the extra stretching.

One word to the wise: If you do go the massage route, proceed gently. The last thing you want to do right before labor is to pull too hard, scratch yourself, or irritate the sensitive skin down there. Bottom line: Massage with care.

when it's certain that a pregnancy is past 41 weeks and the cervix is found to be ripe (soft and ready to dilate) or sooner if there are complications of any kind. Other practitioners may choose to wait it out a bit longer, performing one or more assessment tests (see box, page 348) to see if the baby is still doing well in the uterus, and repeating these tests once or twice a week until labor begins. Ask your practitioner what game plan he or she usually goes with when a baby's late.

Of course, chances are good your baby will decide to check out of your womb sooner than later—and without any prompting.

Inviting Others to the Birth

"I'm really excited about having my baby and I want to share the experience with my sisters and best friends—and, of course, my mom. Would it be weird to have them all in the birthing room with me and my husband?"

Someone's having a birth day party (your baby, in fact), and if you're like more and more moms-to-be, the guest list is getting longer and longer. There's definitely nothing weird about wanting to have those who are closest to you by your side on the big day—and, in fact, it's a trend that's gaining popularity in birthing circles.

Why is more merrier for some women on labor day? For one, the widespread use of epidurals has made labor less laborious for many. With little or no pain to deal with—or breathe through—there's more opportunity to socialize (plus, it's a lot easier to be in a party mood if you're not groaning and panting). For another, hospitals and birthing centers are also enabling the

---

Foods to Bring It On?

Hungry for labor? Ready to do—or eat—anything that might trigger that first real contraction? Though there's no science backing them up, plenty of old wives (or old friends) will tell you about a last supper that ended with a trip down labor lane. Among the often heard: If your stomach can take the heat, dip into something spicy. Or order something that gets your bowels—and hopefully your uterus—in an uproar (a crate of bran muffins, chased down by a bucket of prune juice, perhaps?). Not in the mood for something so stimulating? Some women swear by eggplant, tomatoes, and balsamic vinegar (not necessarily together); others say pineapple buys a ticket on the Labor Express. Whatever you dig into, remember that unless your baby and your body are ready to take the labor plunge, it's unlikely that dinner's going to pull the trigger.

---

maternity mob, making some birthing rooms bigger (more equipped to handle the overflow of guests) and more comfortable (complete with sofas and extra chairs for visitors to plop down on while they're waiting for the headliner to make his or her debut). Some even have Internet access to keep guests busy when there's a break in the action. Policies have become more lenient, too—and at some hospitals and birthing centers, even open door (for as many as can fit in the door, that is). And having a gaggle of girlfriends and relatives may be just what the doctor—

Sounds Like a Plan

How far along in labor should you be before calling your practitioner? Should you call if your water breaks? How can you make contact if the contractions start outside of regular office hours? Should you call first and then head for the hospital or birthing center? Or the other way around?

Don't wait until labor starts to get the answers to these important questions. Discuss all of these and other labor logistics with your practitioner at your next appointment, and write down all the pertinent info; otherwise, you'll be sure to forget the instructions once those contractions kick in.

Also, be sure you know the best route to your place of delivery, roughly how long it will take to get there at various times of the day, and what kind of transportation is available if you don't have someone to drive you (don't plan on driving yourself). And if there are other children at home, or an elderly relative, or a pet, be sure you've made plans for their care in advance.

Keep a copy of all the above information in the bag you're likely to be using and in the suitcase you've packed, as well as on your refrigerator door or bedside table.

or midwife—ordered, too. Many practitioners reason that having more distraction, support, and back-rubbing hands makes a mom-to-be happier and more relaxed during labor—always a good thing, whether it's a medicated birth or not.

Clearly, there are lots of good reasons why you might want an encouraging entourage in the birthing room with you. Still, there are a few caveats to consider before you issue the invites: You'll have to get the medical-powers-that-be to sign off on your guest list (not all practitioners are mob friendly, and some hospitals cap the number of guests you're allowed). You'll also have to be sure your spouse is on board with the guest list (remember, even though you'll be doing most of the work, both of you are co-hosting the party, and he won't want to be relegated to B-list). Think about, too, whether you'll really be comfortable with so many eyes on you during

a very private moment (there will be moaning, grunting, peeing, probably a little pooping—and you will be half-naked). Something else to ponder: Will those you've invited (your brother, your father-in-law, for example) be comfortable with what you're inviting them to view—and might their discomfort put you on edge when you most need to be relaxed? Will you want everyone standing around chatting when you're craving peace and quiet (and rest)? Will you feel obligated to entertain your guests when you need to be focused on birthing your baby?

If you decide you'd like the company, just remember to put flexibility on the list, too. Remember (and remind your guests) that there's always the possibility your intended uneventful vaginal birth may turn into an unexpected C-section, in which case only the expectant dad will be allowed to follow the party into the OR. Or that you'll decide—say somewhere around the second hour of pushing—that you're not up to guests anymore and they might be shown to the door for delivery. (And if you do end up regretting your decision to invite a crowd, don't worry about hurting anyone's feelings by sending the guests packing; as a woman in labor, your feelings are the only ones that matter.)

Not feeling like inviting a crowd? Don't let trends—or pushy relatives—guilt you into a full birthing room. What feels right for you and your spouse is the right decision.

Another Long Labor?

"I had a 30-hour labor my first time around and finally delivered after three hours of pushing. Though we both came out of it fine, I dread going through that again."

Anyone brave enough to go back into the ring after such a challenging first round deserves a break. And chances are good that you'll get one. Of course, though the odds of an easier childbirth are significantly improved the second time around, there are no sure bets in labor and delivery rooms. Your baby's position or other factors may alter these odds. Short of a crystal ball, there's no way to predict precisely what will happen this time around.

But second and subsequent labors and deliveries are usually easier and shorter than first ones—often dramatically so. Less resistance will be met from your now-roomier birth canal and your laxer muscles, and though the process won't be effortless—it rarely is—it probably will seem like less of an ordeal. The most marked difference may be in the amount of pushing you have to do; second babies often pop out in a matter of minutes rather than hours.

Mothering

"Now that the baby's almost here, I'm beginning to worry about how I'm going to take care of her. I've never even held a newborn before."

Most women aren't born mothers—any more than men are born fathers—instinctively knowing how to soothe a crying baby, change a diaper, or give a bath. Motherhood—parenthood, for that matter—is a learned art, one that requires plenty of practice to make perfect (or actually, near-perfect—since there's no such thing as a perfect parent).

Time was, women routinely practiced on other people's babies, caring for younger siblings or other infants in the family or the neighborhood, before they had their own. These days, though, many women—just like you—have never held a newborn until they hold their own. Their training for motherhood comes on the job, with a little help from parenting books, magazines, and websites, and, if they're lucky enough to find one locally, from a baby-care class. Which means that for the first week or two—and often much longer—a new mom can feel out of her element as the baby does more crying than sleeping, the diapers leak, and many tears are shed over the "no-tears" shampoo (on both sides of the bottle).

Slowly but surely—one dirty diaper, one marathon feeding session, one sleepless night at a time—every new mom (even the greenest) begins to feel like an old pro. Trepidation turns to assurance. The baby she was afraid to hold (won't it break?) is now cradled casually in her left arm while her right pays bills online or pushes the vacuum cleaner. She can dispense vitamin drops, give baths, and slip squirming arms and legs into onesies in her sleep—literally, sometimes. As she hits her maternal stride and settles into

What to Take to the Hospital or Birthing Center

Though you could show up with just your belly and your insurance card, traveling that empty-handed to the hospital or birthing center probably isn't the best idea. Traveling light, however, is (no need to lug a huge suitcase along with that big belly), so pack only what you think you'll really use or need. Be sure to pack that bag early (so you won't be turning the house upside down for your iPod when the contractions are coming five minutes apart) with as many—or as few—of the following as you'd like:

For the Labor or Birthing Room

- This book and *The What to Expect Pregnancy Journal and Organizer,* which has ample room for labor-and-delivery and meet-the-baby note keeping. A pen and pad may also be useful for jotting down questions and answers on procedures and on your condition and your baby's; instructions for when you go home; and the names of staff members who have taken care of you.

- Several copies of your birth plan, if you're using one (see page 294).

- A watch with a second hand or any digital timer for timing contractions. Better yet, make sure your coach has one handy at all times during the last few weeks of your pregnancy.

- Any personal audio player, equipped with your favorite tunes, if music soothes and relaxes you. Don't forget extra batteries and/or chargers.

- A camera and/or video equipment, if you don't trust your memory to capture the moment (and if the hospital or birthing center rules allow media coverage of births—most do). Don't forget extra batteries and/or chargers.

- Entertainment: a laptop or tablet to use your favorite apps, read books, watch movies, and play games on (and also so you can issue updates to and stay connected with friends and family); magazines; knitting; or whatever diversions might help pass the time. Don't forget any necessary chargers.

- Favorite lotions or oils for massages.

- A tennis ball or back massager, for firm countermassage, should lower backache be a problem.

- A pillow of your own to make you more comfortable.

- Sugarless lollipops or candies to keep your mouth moist.

- A toothbrush, toothpaste, mouthwash, face wipes, and body wipes (you may find yourself desperate for a freshen-up).

- A cell phone and charger (in some hospitals, cell phone use is restricted and service spotty).

a somewhat predictable rhythm, parenting an infant becomes second nature. She starts to feel like the mom she is, and—difficult though it may be to imagine right now—you will, too.

Though nothing can make those first days with a first baby a cinch, starting the learning process before your newborn is placed in your arms (and in your round-the-clock care) can make them seem a little less overwhelming. Any of the following can help moms- (and dads-) to-be ease into their new roles: visiting a newborn nursery and

- Heavy socks, should your feet become cold.

- Comfortable slippers with nonskid bottoms, in case you feel like doing some walking during labor, and so you can do some strolling in the halls later, between baby feedings.

- A scrunchie, clip, or hairband, if your hair is long, to keep it out of your face and tangle free. A hairbrush, too, if you think it'll come in handy.

- A couple of sandwiches or other snacks for your coach, so he won't have to leave your side when his stomach starts growling.

- A change of clothes for your coach, for comfort's sake and if he plans to sleep over in the hospital.

- A cell phone and charger (though you might not be allowed to use a cell in the room).

For Postpartum

- A robe and/or nightgowns/pj's, if you'd rather wear your own than the hospital's. Make sure it opens in the front if you'll be breastfeeding. Keep in mind, however, that though pretty nightgowns or comfy pj's can boost your spirits, they may get bled on and stained.

- Toiletries, including shampoo and conditioner, body wash, deodorant, hand mirror, makeup, and any other essentials of beauty and hygiene.

- Your favorite brand of maxipads, though the hospital will also provide some (skip the tampons).

- A couple of changes of underwear and a nursing bra.

- All the entertainment listed above, plus books (including a baby-name book if that decision's still up in the air).

- A supply of snacks: trail mix, soy chips, cereal bars, and other healthy treats to keep you from starving when the hospital food doesn't cut it or hunger strikes between meals.

- A list of phone numbers of family and friends to call with the good news; a phone card or calling card number in case you have no cell phone reception or the hospital doesn't allow cell phone usage.

- A going-home outfit for you, keeping in mind that you'll still be sporting a sizable belly (you'll probably look like you're at least five or six months pregnant right after the birth; plan accordingly).

- A going-home outfit for baby: a kimono or stretchie, T-shirt, booties, a receiving blanket, and a heavy bunting or blanket if it's cold; diapers will probably be provided by the hospital, but bring along an extra, just in case.

- Infant car seat. Most hospitals will not let you leave with the baby unless he or she is safely strapped into an approved rear-facing infant car seat. Besides, it's the law.

viewing the most recent arrivals; holding, diapering, and soothing a friend's or family member's infant; reading up on a baby's first year; visiting first-year websites and message boards (no one can teach you more about being a mom than another mom; check out whatto-expect.com) and watching a DVD or taking a class in baby care (and baby CPR). For even more reassurance, talk to friends who have recently become parents. You'll be relieved to know that just about everybody comes into the job with the same new-mom (or new-dad) jitters.

Fill 'Er Up

Your kitchen, that is. Though shopping for strollers, diapers, and pint-size clothing understandably has been your priority these days, don't forget to take a time-out at the market. Even with swollen ankles and a super-size belly weighing you down, grocery and staple shopping is easier nine months pregnant than it will be again for a long time—so take advantage and stock up now so you won't have to later with baby (and car seat, and diaper bag) in tow. Fill your pantry, fridge, and freezer to the brim with healthy foods that are easy to serve—cheese sticks, individual containers of yogurt, frozen fruit bars, frozen fruit for making smoothies, cereal, granola bars, soups, dried fruit and nuts. Don't forget the paper products, too (you'll be using paper towels by the crateful, and disposable plates and cups can fill in when you don't get around to emptying the dishwasher). And while you're in the kitchen—and have the time—cook up some extra servings of your favorite freezer-friendly foods (lasagna, mini meatloaves, chili, pancakes, muffins), and store them in clearly marked single-meal containers in the freezer. They'll be ready to pop in the microwave when you're pooped (and hungry) postpartum.

ALL ABOUT
Prelabor, False Labor, Real Labor

It always seems so simple on TV. Somewhere around 3 A.M., the pregnant woman sits up in bed, puts a knowing hand on her belly, and reaches over to rouse her sleeping husband with a calm, almost serene, "Honey, it's time."

But how, you wonder, does this woman know it's time? How does she recognize labor with such cool, clinical confidence when she's never been in labor before? What makes her so sure she's not going to get to the hospital, be examined by the resident, found to be nowhere near her time, and be sent home, amid snickers from the night shift, just as pregnant as when she arrived? The script, of course.

On our side of the screen (with no script in hand), we're more likely to awaken at 3 A.M. with complete uncertainty. Are these really labor pains or just more Braxton Hicks? Should I turn on the light and start timing? Should I bother to wake my spouse? Do I drag my practitioner out of bed at 1 A.M. to report what might really be false labor? If I do and it isn't time, will I turn out to be the pregnant woman who cried "labor" once too often, and will anybody take me seriously when it's for real? Or will I be the only woman in my childbirth class not to recognize labor? Will I leave for the hospital too late, maybe giving birth in the back of a taxicab (and ending up on the evening news)? The questions multiply faster than the contractions.

The fact is that most women, worry though they might, don't end up misjudging the onset of their labor. The vast majority, thanks to instinct, luck, or no-doubt-about-it killer contractions, show up at the hospital or birthing center neither too early nor too late, but at just about the right time. Still, there's no reason to leave your judgment up to chance. Becoming familiar in advance with the signs of prelabor, false labor, and real labor will help allay the concerns and clear up the confusion when those contractions (or are they?) begin.

Prelabor Symptoms

Before there's labor, there's prelabor—a sort of preshow that sets things up before the main event. The physical changes of prelabor can precede real labor by a full month or more—or by only an hour or so. Prelabor is characterized by the beginning of cervical effacement and dilation, which your practitioner can confirm on examination, as well as by a wide variety of related signs that you may notice yourself:

Dropping. Usually somewhere between two and four weeks before labor starts in first-time mothers, the fetus begins to settle down into the pelvis. This milestone is rarely reached in second or later births until labor is about to kick off.

Sensations of increasing pressure in the pelvis and rectum. Crampiness (similar to menstrual cramps) and groin pain are common—and particularly likely in second and later pregnancies. Persistent low backache may also be present.

Loss of weight or no gain. Weight gain might slow down in the ninth month; as labor approaches, you might even lose a bit of weight, up to 2 or 3 pounds.

A change in energy levels. Some ninth-monthers find that they are increasingly exhausted. Others experience energy spurts. An uncontrollable urge to scrub floors and clean out closets has been related to the "nesting instinct," in which the female of the species—that's you—prepares the nest for the impending arrival (see page 346).

A change in vaginal discharge. If you've been keeping track, you may find that your discharge increases and thickens.

Loss of the mucous plug. As the cervix begins to thin and open, the "cork" of mucus that seals the opening of the uterus becomes dislodged (see page 362). This gelatinous chunk of mucus can be passed through the vagina a week or two before the first real contractions, or just as labor begins.

Pink, or bloody, show. As the cervix effaces and dilates, capillaries frequently rupture, tinting the mucus pink or streaking it with blood (see page 363). This "show" usually means labor will start within 24 hours—though it could be as much as several days away.

Intensification of Braxton Hicks contractions. These practice contractions (see page 311) may become more frequent and stronger, even painful.

Diarrhea. Some women experience loose bowel movements just before labor starts.

False Labor Symptoms

Is it or isn't it? Real labor probably has not begun if:

- Contractions are not at all regular and don't increase in frequency or severity. Real contractions won't necessarily fall into a neat textbook pattern, but they will become more intense and more frequent over time.

- Contractions subside if you walk around or change your position (though this can sometimes be the case in early "real" labor, too).

- Show, if any, is brownish. This kind of discharge is often the result of an internal exam or intercourse within the past 48 hours.

- Fetal movements intensify briefly with contractions. (Let your practitioner know right away if activity becomes frantic or jerky.)

Keep in mind that false labor (though it isn't the real thing) isn't a waste of time—even if you've driven all the way to the hospital or birthing center. It's your body's way of getting pumped, primed, and prepped for the main event, so when the time comes, it'll be ready—whether you are or not.

Real Labor Symptoms

No one knows exactly what triggers real labor (and more women are concerned with "when" than "why"), but it's believed that a combination of factors are involved. This very intricate process begins with the fetus, whose brain sets off a relay of chemical messages (which probably translate into something like, "Mom, let me out of here!") that kick off a chain reaction of hormones in the mother. These hormonal changes in turn pave the way for the work of prostaglandins and oxytocin, substances that trigger contractions when all labor systems are "go."

You'll know that the contractions of prelabor have been replaced by true labor if:

- The contractions intensify, rather than ease up, with activity and aren't relieved by a change in position.

- Contractions become progressively more frequent and painful, and generally (but not always) more regular. Every contraction won't necessarily be more painful or longer (they usually last about 30 to 70 seconds) than the last one, but the intensity does build up as real labor progresses. Frequency doesn't always increase in regular, perfectly even intervals, either—but it does increase.

- Early contractions feel like gastrointestinal upset, or like heavy menstrual cramps, or like lower abdominal pressure. Pain may be just in the lower abdomen or in the lower back and abdomen, and it may also radiate down into the legs (particularly the upper thighs). Location, however, is not as reliable an indication, because false labor contractions may also be felt in these places.

- You have show and it's pinkish or blood-streaked.

In 15 percent of labors, the water breaks—in a gush or a trickle—before labor begins. But in many others, the membranes rupture spontaneously during labor, or are ruptured artificially by the practitioner.

When to Call the Practitioner

Your practitioner has likely told you when to call if you think you're in labor (when contractions are five to seven minutes apart, for instance). Don't wait for perfectly even intervals; they may never come. If you're not sure you're in real labor—but the contractions are coming pretty regularly—call anyway. Your practitioner will probably be able to tell from the sound of your voice, as you talk through a contraction, whether it's the real thing—but only if you don't try to cover up the pain in the name of good phone manners. Even if you've checked and rechecked the above lists and you're still unsure, call your practitioner. Don't feel guilty about waking him or her in the middle of the night (people who deliver babies for a living don't expect to work only 9 to 5) or be embarrassed if it turns out to be a false alarm (you wouldn't be the first expectant mom to misjudge her labor signs, and you won't be the last). Don't assume that if you're not sure it's real labor, it isn't. Err on the side of caution and call.

Also call your practitioner immediately if contractions are increasingly strong but your due date is still weeks

Ready or Not

To make sure you're ready for your baby's arrival when he or she is ready to arrive, start reading up now about labor and delivery in the next chapter.

away, if your water breaks but labor hasn't begun, if your water breaks and it has a greenish-brown tint, if you notice bright red blood, or if you feel the umbilical cord slip into your cervix or vagina.

A REMINDER

It's time to pick up a copy of WHAT TO EXPECT® THE FIRST YEAR

This all-in-one, month-by-month guide clearly explains everything you need to know about that first amazing year with baby—from first cuddle to first smile to first steps. Packed with the most reassuring answers and the most practical and realistic tips on all things baby, including:

- Feeding for every age and stage
- Sleep strategies that really work
- Decoding and comforting crying
- Stimulating (and having fun with) your infant

- Making the transition to parenthood
- Plus an illustrated Baby Care Primer, comprehensive sections on first aid, safety, keeping your baby healthy, and much more

CHAPTER 15

Labor and Delivery

ARE YOU COUNTING DOWN THE days? Eager to see your feet again? Desperate to sleep on your stomach—or just plain desperate to sleep? Don't worry—the end (of pregnancy) is near. And as you contemplate that happy moment—when your baby will finally be in your arms instead of inside your belly—you're probably also giving a lot of thought to (and coming up with a lot of questions about) the process that will make that moment possible: labor and delivery. When will labor start, you're likely wondering? More important, when will it end? Will I be able to handle the pain? Will I need an epidural (and when can I have one)? A fetal monitor? An episiotomy? What if I want to labor—and deliver—while squatting? Without any meds? What if I don't make any progress? What if I progress so quickly that I don't make it to the hospital or birthing center in time?

Armed with answers to these (and other) questions—plus the support of your partner and your birth attendants (doctors, midwives, nurses, doulas, and others)—you'll be prepared for just about anything that labor and delivery might bring your way. Just remember the most important thing that labor and delivery will bring your way (even if nothing else goes according to plan): that beautiful new baby of yours.

What You May Be Wondering About

Mucous Plug

"I think I lost my mucous plug. Should I call my doctor?"

Don't send out for the champagne just yet. The mucous plug—the clear, globby, gelatinous blob-like barrier that has corked your cervix throughout your pregnancy—occasionally becomes dislodged as dilation and effacement begin. Some women notice the passage of the mucous plug (what exactly *is* that in the toilet?); others don't (especially if you're the flush-and-rush type). Though the passage of the plug is a sign that your body's preparing for the big day, it's not a reliable signal the big day has arrived—or even that it's around the corner. At this point, labor could be one or two days, or even weeks, away, with your cervix continuing to open gradually over that time. In other words, there's no need to call your practitioner or frantically pack your bags just yet.

No plug in your pants or your toilet? Not to worry. Many women don't lose it ahead of time (and others overlook it), and that doesn't predict anything about the eventual progress of labor.

Bloody Show

"I have a pink mucousy discharge. Does it mean labor's about to start?"

Sounds like it's bloody show time—and happily, this particular production is a preview of labor, not of a gory horror movie. Passing that bloody show, a mucous discharge tinged pink or brown with blood, is usually a sign that the blood vessels in the cervix are rupturing as it dilates and effaces and the process that leads to delivery is well under way (and that's something to applaud!). Once the bloody show has made its debut in your underwear or on the toilet paper, chances are your baby's arrival is just a day or two away. But since labor is a process with an erratic timetable, you'll be kept in suspense until the first true contractions strike.

If your discharge should suddenly become bright red, contact your practitioner right away.

Your Water Breaking

"I woke up in the middle of the night with a wet bed. Did I lose control of my bladder, or did my water break?"

A sniff of your sheets will probably clue you in. If the wet spot smells

sort of sweet (not like urine, which has the harsher odor of ammonia), it's likely to be amniotic fluid. Another clue that the membranes surrounding your baby and containing the amniotic fluid he or she's been living in for nine months have probably ruptured: You continue leaking the pale, straw-colored fluid (which won't run dry because it continues to be produced until delivery, replacing itself every few hours). Another test: You can try to stem the flow of the fluid by squeezing your pelvic muscles (Kegel exercises). If the flow stops, it's urine. If it doesn't, it's amniotic fluid.

You are more likely to notice the leaking while you are lying down; it usually stops, or at least slows, when you stand up or sit down, since the baby's head acts as a cork, blocking the flow temporarily. The leakage is heavier—whether you're sitting or standing—if the break in the membranes is down near the cervix than if it is higher up.

Your practitioner has probably given you a set of instructions to follow if your water breaks. If you don't remember the instructions or have any doubts about how to proceed—call, night or day.

"My water just broke, but I haven't had any contractions. When is labor going to start, and what should I do in the meantime?"

It's likely that labor's on the way—and soon. Most women whose membranes rupture before labor begins can expect to feel the first contraction within 12 hours of that first trickle; most others can expect to feel it within 24 hours.

About 1 in 10, however, find that labor takes a little longer to get going. To prevent infection through the ruptured amniotic sac (the longer it takes for labor to get going, the greater the risk), most practitioners induce labor within 24 hours of a rupture, if a mom-to-be is at or near her due date, though a few induce as early as six hours after. Many women who have experienced a rupture actually welcome a sooner-than-later induction, preferring it to 24 hours of wet waiting.

The first thing to do if you experience a trickle or flow of fluid from your vagina—besides grab a towel and a box of maxipads—is call your practitioner (unless he or she has instructed otherwise). In the meantime, keep the vaginal area as clean as possible to avoid infection. Don't have sex (not that there's much chance you'd want to right now), use a pad (not a tampon) to absorb the flow, don't try to do your own internal exam, and, as always, wipe from front to back when you use the toilet.

Rarely, when the membranes rupture prematurely and the baby's presenting part is not yet engaged in the pelvis (more likely when the baby is breech or preterm), the umbilical cord can become "prolapsed"—it is swept into the cervix, or even down into the vagina, with the gush of amniotic fluid. If you can see a loop of umbilical cord at your vaginal opening, or think you feel something inside your vagina, call 911. For more on what to do if the cord is prolapsed, see page 565.

Darkened Amniotic Fluid

"My membranes ruptured, and the fluid isn't clear—it's greenish brown. What does this mean?"

Your amniotic fluid is probably stained with meconium, a greenish-brown substance that is actually your baby's first bowel movement. Ordinarily, meconium is passed after birth as the baby's first stool. But sometimes—such as when the

fetus has been under stress in the womb, and more often when it is past its due date—the meconium is passed before birth into the amniotic fluid.

Meconium staining alone is not a sure sign of fetal distress, but because it suggests the possibility of distress, notify your practitioner right away. He or she will likely want to get labor started (if contractions aren't already in full swing) and will monitor your baby very closely throughout labor.

Low Amniotic Fluid During Labor

"My doctor said that my amniotic fluid is low and she needs to supplement it. Should I be concerned?"

Usually, nature keeps the uterus well stocked with a self-replenishing supply of amniotic fluid. Fortunately, even when levels do run low during labor, medical science can step in and supplement that natural source with a saline solution pumped directly into the amniotic sac through a catheter inserted through the cervix into the uterus. This procedure, called amnioinfusion, can significantly reduce the possibility that a surgical delivery will become necessary due to fetal distress.

Irregular Contractions

"In childbirth class we were told not to go to the hospital until the contractions were regular and five minutes apart. Mine are less than five minutes apart, but they aren't at all regular. I don't know what to do."

Just as no two women have exactly the same pregnancies, no two women have exactly the same labors. The labor often described in books, in childbirth education classes, and by practitioners is what is typical—close to what many women can expect. But far from every labor is true-to-textbook, with contractions regularly spaced and predictably progressive.

If you're having strong, long (20 to 60 seconds), frequent (mostly 5 to 7 minutes apart or less) contractions, even if they vary considerably in length and time elapsed between them, don't wait for them to become regular before calling your practitioner or heading for the hospital or birthing center—no matter what you've heard or read. It's possible your contractions are about as regular as they're going to get and you're well into the active phase of your labor.

Calling Your Practitioner During Labor

"I just started getting contractions and they're coming every three or four minutes. I feel silly calling my doctor, who said we should spend the first several hours of labor at home."

Better silly than sorry. It's true that most first-time mothers-to-be (whose labors are generally slow-going at first, with a gradual buildup of contractions) can safely count on spending the first several hours at home, leisurely finishing up their packing and their baby prep. But it doesn't sound like your labor's fitting that typical first-timer pattern. If your contractions have started off strong—lasting at least 45 seconds and coming more frequently than every 5 minutes—your first several hours of labor may very well be your last (and if you're not a first-timer, your labor may be on an even faster track). Chances are that much of the first stage of labor has

passed painlessly and your cervix has dilated significantly during that time. This means that not calling your practitioner, chancing a dramatic dash to the hospital or birthing center at the last minute—or not getting there in time— might be considerably sillier than picking up the phone now.

So by all means call. When you do, be clear and specific about the frequency, duration, and strength of your contractions. Since your practitioner is used to judging the phase of labor in part by the sound of a woman's voice as she talks through a contraction, don't try to downplay your discomfort, put on a brave front, or keep a calm tone when you describe what you're experiencing. Let the contractions speak for themselves, as loudly as they need to.

If you feel you're ready but your practitioner doesn't seem to think so, ask if you can go to the hospital/birthing center or to your practitioner's office and have your progress checked. Take your bag along just in case, but be ready to turn around and go home if you've only just begun to dilate—or if nothing's going on at all.

Not Getting to the Hospital in Time

"I'm afraid that I won't get to the hospital in time."

Fortunately, most of those sudden deliveries you've heard about take place in the movies and on TV. In real life, deliveries, especially those of first-time mothers, rarely occur without ample warning. But once in a great while, a woman who has had no labor pains, or just erratic ones, suddenly feels an overwhelming urge to bear down; often she mistakes it for a need to go to the bathroom.

Emergency Delivery if You're Alone

You'll almost certainly never need the following instructions—but just in case, keep them handy.

1. Try to remain calm. You can do this.

2. Call 911 (or your local emergency number) for the emergency medical service. Ask them to call your practitioner.

3. Find a neighbor or someone else to help, if possible.

4. Start panting to keep yourself from pushing.

5. Wash your hands and the vaginal area, if you can.

6. Spread some clean towels, newspapers, or sheets on a bed, sofa, or the floor, and lie down to await help (unlock the door so help can get in easily).

7. If despite your panting the baby starts to arrive before help does, gently ease him or her out by pushing each time you feel the urge.

8. As the top of the baby's head begins to appear, pant or blow (do not push), and apply very gentle counterpressure to your perineum to keep the head from popping out suddenly. Let the head emerge gradually—don't pull it out. If there is a loop of umbilical cord around the baby's neck, hook a finger under it and gently work it over the baby's head.

9. Next, take the head gently in two hands and press it very slightly downward (do not pull), pushing the baby out at the same time, to deliver the front shoulder. As the upper arm appears, lift the head carefully, feeling for the rear shoulder to deliver. Once the shoulders are free, the rest of your baby should slip out easily.

10. Place the baby on your abdomen or, if the cord is long enough (don't tug at it), on your chest. Quickly wrap the baby in blankets, towels, or anything else that's clean.

11. Wipe baby's mouth and nose with a clean cloth. If help hasn't arrived and the baby isn't breathing or crying, rub his or her back, keeping the head lower than the feet. If breathing still hasn't started, clear out the mouth some more with a clean finger and give two quick and extremely gentle puffs of air into his or her nose and mouth.

12. Don't try to pull the placenta out. But if it emerges on its own before emergency assistance arrives, wrap it in towels or newspaper, and keep it elevated above the level of the baby, if possible. There is no need to try to cut the cord.

13. Keep yourself and your baby warm and comfortable until help arrives.

As remote as the possibility is that this will happen to you, it's a good idea for both you and your coach to become familiar with the basics of an emergency delivery (see boxes, above and on page 370). Once that's done, relax, knowing that a sudden and quick delivery is an extremely remote possibility.

Having a Short Labor

"I always hear about women who have really short labors. How common are they?"

While they make for really good labor stories, not all of the short labors you've heard about are as short as they seemed. Often, an expectant mom who appears to have a quickie labor has actually been having painless contractions for hours, days, even weeks, contractions that have been dilating her cervix gradually. By the time she finally feels one, she's well into the final stage of labor.

That said, occasionally the cervix dilates very rapidly, accomplishing in a matter of minutes what the average cervix (particularly a first-time mom's cervix) takes hours to do. And happily, even with this abrupt, or precipitous, kind of labor (one that takes three hours or less from start to finish), there is usually no risk to the baby.

If your labor seems to start with a bang—with contractions strong and close together—get to the hospital or birthing center quickly (so you and your baby can be monitored closely). Medication may be helpful in slowing contractions a bit and easing the pressure on your baby and on your own body.

Back Labor

"The pain in my lower back since my contractions began is so bad that I don't see how I'll be able to make it through labor."

What you're probably experiencing is known in the birthing business as "back labor." Technically, back labor occurs when the fetus is in a posterior position, with its face up and the back of its head pressing against your sacrum, or the back of your pelvis. (Ironically, this position is nicknamed "sunny-side up" in birthing circles—though there's nothing cheerful about back labor.) It's possible, however, to experience back labor when the baby isn't in this position or to continue to experience it after the baby has turned

to a head-to-the-front position—possibly because the area has already become a focus of tension.

When you're having this kind of pain—which often doesn't let up between contractions and can become excruciating during them—the cause doesn't matter much. How to relieve it, even slightly, does. If you're opting to have an epidural, go for it (there's no need to wait, especially if you're in a lot of pain). It's possible that you might need a higher dose than usual to get full comfort from the back labor pain, so let the anesthesiologist know about it. Other options (such as narcotics) also offer pain relief. If you'd like to stay med free, several measures may help relieve the discomfort of back labor; all are at least worth trying:

Taking the pressure off. Try changing your position. Walk around (though this may not be possible once contractions are coming fast and furious), crouch or squat, get down on all fours, do whatever is most comfortable and least painful for you. If you feel you can't move and would prefer to be lying down, lie on your side, with your back well rounded—in a sort of fetal position.

Heat or cold. Have your coach (or doula or nurse) use warm compresses, a heating pad, or ice packs or cold compresses—whichever soothes best. Or alternate heat and cold.

Counterpressure and massage. Have your coach experiment with different ways of applying pressure to the area of greatest pain, or to adjacent areas, to find one or more that seem to help. He can try his knuckles, the heel of one hand reinforced by pressure from the other hand on top of it, a tennis ball, or a back massager, using direct pressure or a firm circular motion. Pressure or a firm massage can be applied while you're sitting or while you're lying on your side. Cream, oil, or powder can be applied periodically to reduce possible irritation.

Reflexology. For back labor, this therapy involves applying strong finger pressure just below the center of the ball of the foot.

Other alternative pain relievers. Hydrotherapy can definitely ease the pain somewhat. If you've had some experience with meditation, visualization, or self-hypnosis for pain, try these, too. They often work, and they certainly couldn't hurt. Acupuncture can also help, but you'll have to arrange ahead of time to have a therapist on call when you go into labor.

Labor Induction

"My doctor wants to induce labor. But I'm not overdue yet and I thought induction was only for overdue babies."

Sometimes Mother Nature needs a little help making a mother out of a pregnant woman. About 20 percent of pregnancies end up needing that kick in the maternity pants, and though a lot of the time induction is necessary because a baby is overdue, there are many other reasons why your practitioner might feel that nature needs a nudge, such as:

- Your membranes have ruptured and contractions have not started on their own within 24 hours (though some practitioners induce much sooner).

- Tests suggest that your uterus is no longer a healthy home for your baby because the placenta is no longer functioning optimally or amniotic fluid levels are low, or for another reason.

- Tests suggest that the baby isn't thriving and is mature enough to be delivered.

- You have a complication, such as preeclampsia or gestational diabetes, or a chronic or acute illness, that makes it risky to continue your pregnancy.

- There's a concern that you might not make it to the hospital or birthing center on time once labor has started, either because you live a long distance away or because you've had a previous very short labor.

If you're still unsure about your doctor's reasons for inducing labor, ask for a better explanation. To find out all you'll need to know about the induction process, keep reading.

"How does induction work?"

Induction, like naturally triggered labor, is a process—and sometimes a pretty long process. But unlike naturally triggered labor, your body will be getting some help with the heavy lifting if you're induced. Labor induction usually involves a number of steps (though you won't necessarily go through all of them):

- First, your cervix will need to be ripened (or softened) so that labor can begin. If you arrive with a ripe cervix, great—you'll probably move right on to the next step. If your cervix is not dilated, not effaced, and not soft at all, your practitioner will likely administer a hormonal substance such as prostaglandin E in the form of a vaginal gel (or a vaginal suppository in tablet form) to get things started. In this painless procedure, a syringe is used to place the gel in the vagina close to your cervix. After a few hours or longer of letting the gel do its work, you'll be checked to see if your cervix is getting softer and beginning to efface and dilate. If it isn't, a second dose of the prostaglandin gel is administered. In many cases, the gel is enough to get contractions and labor started. If your cervix is ripe enough but contractions have not begun, the induction process continues. (Some practitioners use mechanical agents to ripen the cervix, such as a catheter with an inflatable balloon, graduated dilators to stretch the cervix, or even a botanical—called Laminaria japonicum—that, when inserted, gradually opens the cervix as it absorbs fluid around it.)

- If the amniotic sac is still intact, your practitioner may strip the membranes by swiping a finger across the fine membranes that connect the amniotic sac to the uterus to release prostaglandin (this process isn't always pain free, and while it isn't meant to break your water, it sometimes does). Or he or she may artificially rupture your membranes (see page 373) to try to get labor started, which could speed things up.

- If neither the prostaglandin nor the stripping or rupturing of the membranes has brought on regular contractions, your practitioner will slowly administer intravenous Pitocin, a synthetic form of the hormone oxytocin (which is produced naturally by the body throughout pregnancy and also plays an important role in labor), until contractions are well established. The drug misoprostol, given through the vagina, might be used as an alternative to other ripening and induction techniques. Some research shows giving misoprostol decreases the amount of oxytocin needed and shortens labor.

- Your baby will be continuously monitored to assess how he or she is dealing with labor. You'll also be monitored to make sure the drug isn't overstimulating your uterus, triggering contractions that are too long or powerful. If that happens, the rate of infusion can be reduced or the process can be discontinued entirely. Once your contractions are in full swing, the oxytocin may be stopped or the dose decreased, and your labor should progress just as a noninduced labor does.

- If, after 8 to 12 hours of oxytocin administration, labor hasn't begun or progressed, your practitioner might stop the induction process to give you a chance to rest before trying again or, depending on the circumstances, the procedure may be stopped in favor of a cesarean delivery.

Eating and Drinking During Labor

"I've heard conflicting stories about whether it's okay to eat and drink during labor."

Should eating be on the agenda when you're in labor? That depends on who you're talking to. Some practitioners red-light all food and drink during labor, on the theory that food in the digestive tract might be aspirated, or "breathed in," should emergency general anesthesia be necessary. These practitioners usually okay ice chips only, supplemented as needed by intravenous fluids. Many other practitioners (and ACOG guidelines) allow liquids and light solids (read: no stuffed-crust pizza) during a low-risk labor, reasoning that a woman in labor needs both fluids and calories to stay strong and do her best work, and that the risk of aspiration (which only exists if general anesthesia is used, and it rarely is except in emergency situations) is extremely low: 7 in 10 million births. Their position has even been backed up by research, which shows that women who are allowed to eat and drink during labor have shorter labors by an average of 90 minutes, are less likely to need

Emergency Delivery: Tips for the Coach

At Home or in the Office

1. Try to remain calm while at the same time comforting and reassuring the mother. Remember, even if you don't know the first thing about delivering a baby, a mother's body and her baby can do most of the job on their own.

2. Call 911 (or your local emergency number) for the emergency medical service; ask them to call the practitioner.

3. Have the mother start panting, to keep from pushing.

4. If there's time, wash your hands and the vaginal area with soap and water (use an antibacterial product, if you have one handy).

5. If there is time, place the mother on the bed (or desk or table) so her buttocks are slightly hanging off, her hands under her thighs to keep them elevated. If available, a couple of chairs can support her feet. A few pillows or cushions under her shoulders and head will help to raise her to a semi-sitting position, which can aid delivery. If you are awaiting emergency help and the baby's head hasn't appeared, having the mother lie flat may slow delivery until help arrives.

Protect delivery surfaces, if possible, with a plastic tablecloth, shower curtain, newspapers, towels, or similar material. A dishpan or basin can be placed under the mother's vagina to catch the amniotic fluid and blood.

6. If there's no time to get to a bed or table, place newspapers or clean towels or folded clothing under the mother's buttocks. Protect delivery surfaces, if possible, as described in number 5.

7. As the top of the baby's head begins to appear, instruct the mother to pant or blow (not push), and apply very gentle counterpressure to her perineum (the area between the vagina and the anus) to keep the head from popping out suddenly. Let the head emerge gradually—never pull it out. If there is a loop of umbilical cord around the baby's neck, hook a finger under it and gently work it over the baby's head.

8. Next, take the head gently in two hands and press it very slightly downward (do not pull), asking the mother to push at the same time, to deliver the front shoulder. As the upper arm appears, lift the head carefully, watching for the rear shoulder to deliver. Once the shoulders are free, the rest of the baby should slip out easily.

9. Place the baby on the mother's abdomen or, if the cord is long enough (don't tug at it), on her chest. Quickly wrap the baby in blankets, towels, or anything else that's clean.

oxytocin to speed up labor, require fewer pain medications, and have babies with higher Apgar scores than women who fast. Check with your practitioner to find out what will and won't be on the menu for you during labor.

Even if your practitioner gives you the go-ahead on eating, chances are you won't be in the market for a major meal once the contractions begin in earnest (and besides, you'll be pretty distracted). After all, labor can really spoil your appetite. Still, an occasional light, easy-to-digest snack during the early hours of labor—Popsicles, Jell-O, applesauce, cooked fruit, plain pasta, toast with jam, or clear broth are ideal choices—may help keep your energy

10. Wipe baby's mouth and nose with a clean cloth. If help hasn't arrived and the baby isn't breathing or crying, rub his or her back, keeping the head lower than the feet. If breathing still hasn't started, clear out the mouth some more with a clean finger, and give two quick and extremely gentle puffs of air into his or her nose and mouth.

11. Don't try to pull the placenta out. But if it emerges on its own before emergency assistance arrives, wrap it in towels or newspaper, and keep it elevated above the level of the baby, if possible. There is no need to try to cut the cord.

12. Keep both mother and baby warm and comfortable until help arrives.

En Route to the Hospital

If you're in your car and delivery is imminent, pull over to a safe area. If you have a cell phone with you, call for help. If not, turn on your hazard warning lights or turn signal. If someone stops to help, ask him or her to call 911 or the local emergency medical service. If you're in a cab, ask the driver to radio or use his cell phone to call for help.

If possible, help the mother into the back of the car. Place a coat, jacket, or blanket under her. Then, if help has not arrived, proceed as for a home delivery. As soon as the baby is born, proceed to the nearest hospital.

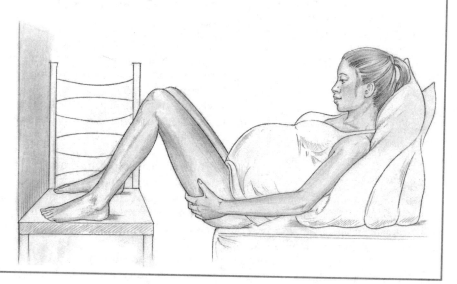

up at a time when you need it most (you probably won't be able to, or won't want to, eat during the later parts of active labor). When deciding—with your practitioner's help—what to eat and when, also keep in mind that labor can make you feel pretty nauseous. Some women throw up as labor progresses, even if they haven't been eating.

Whether you can chow down or not during labor, your coach definitely can—and should (you don't want him weak from hunger when you need him most). Remind him to have a meal before you head off to the hospital or birthing center (his mind's probably on your belly, not his) and to pack a bunch of snacks to take along so he won't have to leave your side when his stomach starts growling.

Routine IV

"Is it true that I'll be hooked up to an IV as soon as I'm admitted into the hospital when I'm in labor?"

That depends a lot on the policies of the hospital you'll be delivering in. In some hospitals, it's routine to give all women in labor an IV, a flexible catheter placed in your vein (usually in the back of your hand or lower arm) to drip in fluids and medication. The reason is precautionary—to prevent dehydration, as well as to save a step later on in case an emergency arises that necessitates medication (there's already a line in place to administer drugs—no extra poking or prodding required). Other hospitals and practitioners omit routine IVs and instead wait until there is a clear need before hooking you up. Check your practitioner's policy in advance, and if you strongly object to having a routine IV, say so. It may be possible to hold off until the need, if any, comes up.

You'll definitely get an IV if an epidural is on the agenda. IV fluids are routinely administered before and during the placement of an epidural to reduce the chance of a drop in blood pressure, a common side effect of this pain relief route. The IV also allows for easier administration of Pitocin should labor need to be augmented.

If you end up with a routine IV or an IV with epidural that you were hoping to avoid, you'll probably find it's not all that intrusive. The IV is only slightly uncomfortable as the needle is inserted and after that should barely be noticed. When it's hung on a movable stand, you can take it with you to the bathroom or on a stroll down the hall. If you very strongly don't want an IV but hospital policy dictates that you receive one, ask your practitioner whether a heparin lock might be an option for you.

With a heparin lock, a catheter is placed in the vein, a drop of the blood-thinning medication heparin is added to prevent clotting, and the catheter is locked off. This option gives the hospital staff access to an open vein should an emergency arise but doesn't hook you up to an IV pole unnecessarily—a good compromise in certain situations.

Fetal Monitoring

"Will I have to be hooked up to a fetal monitor the whole time I'm in labor? What's the point of it anyway?"

For someone who's spent the first nine months of his or her life floating peacefully in a warm and comforting amniotic bath, the trip through the narrow confines of the maternal pelvis will be no joyride. Your baby will be squeezed, compressed, pushed, and molded with every contraction. And though most babies sail through the birth canal without a problem, others find the stress of being squeezed, compressed, pushed, and molded too difficult, and they respond with decelerations in heart rate, rapid or slowed-down movement, or other signs of fetal distress. A fetal monitor assesses how your baby is handling the stresses of labor by gauging the response of its heartbeat to the contractions of the uterus.

But does that assessment need to be continuous? Most experts say no, citing research showing that for low-risk women with unmedicated deliveries, intermittent fetal heart checks using a Doppler or fetal monitor are an effective way to assess a baby's condition. So if you fit in that category, you probably won't have to be attached to a fetal monitor for the entire duration of your labor. If, however, you're being induced, have an epidural, or have certain risk factors (such as meconium staining), you're most likely going to be hooked up to an electronic fetal monitor throughout your labor.

There are three types of continuous fetal monitoring:

External monitoring. In this type of monitoring, used most frequently, two devices are strapped to the abdomen. One, an ultrasound transducer, picks up the fetal heartbeat. The other, a pressure-sensitive gauge, measures the intensity and duration of uterine contractions. Both are connected to a monitor, and the measurements are recorded on a digital and paper readout. When you're connected to an external monitor, you'll be able to move around in your bed or on a chair nearby, but you won't have complete freedom of movement, unless telemetry monitoring is being used (see this page).

During the second (pushing) stage of labor, when contractions may come so fast and furious that it's hard to know when to push and when to hold back, the monitor can be used to accurately signal the beginning and end of each contraction. Or the use of the monitor may be all but abandoned during this stage, so as not to interfere with your concentration. In this case, your baby's heart rate will be checked periodically with a Doppler.

Internal monitoring. When more accurate results are required—such as when there is reason to suspect fetal distress—an internal monitor may be used. In this type of monitoring, a tiny electrode is inserted through your vagina onto your baby's scalp, and a catheter is placed in your uterus or an external pressure gauge is strapped to your abdomen to measure the strength of your contrac-

tions. Though internal monitoring gives a slightly more accurate record of the baby's heart rate and your contractions than an external monitor, it's only used when necessary (since its use comes with a slight risk of infection). Your baby may have a small bruise or scratch where the electrode was attached, but it'll heal in a few days. You'll be more limited in your movement with an internal monitor, but you'll still be able to move from side to side.

Telemetry monitoring. Available only in some hospitals, this type of monitoring uses a transmitter on your thigh to transmit the baby's heart tones (via radio waves) to the nurse's station—allowing you to take a lap or two around the hallway while still having constant monitoring.

Be aware that with both internal and external types of monitoring, false alarms are common. The machine can start beeping loudly if the transducer has slipped out of place, if the baby has shifted positions, if the monitor isn't working right, or if contractions have suddenly picked up in intensity. Your practitioner will take all these factors and others into account before concluding that your baby really is in trouble. If the abnormal readings do continue, several other assessments can be performed (such as fetal scalp stimulation) to determine the cause of the distress. If fetal distress is confirmed, then cesarean delivery is usually called for.

Artificial Rupture of Membranes

"I'm afraid that if my water doesn't break on its own, the doctor will have to rupture the membranes artificially. Won't that hurt?"

Most women actually don't feel a thing when their membranes are artificially ruptured, particularly if they're already in labor (there are far more significant pains to cope with then). If you do experience a little discomfort, it'll more likely be from the introduction into the vagina of the Amniohook (the long plastic device that looks like a sharp-pointed crochet hook and is used to perform the procedure) than from the rupture itself. Chances are, all you'll really notice is a gush of water, followed soon—at least that's the hope—by harder and faster contractions that will get your baby moving. Artificial rupture of the membranes is also performed to allow for other procedures, such as internal fetal monitoring, when necessary.

Artificial rupture of the membranes doesn't seem to decrease the need for pitocin but does seem to shorten the length of labor—at least in labors that are induced, and many practitioners will turn to artificial rupture in an attempt to help move a sluggish labor along. If there's no compelling reason to rupture them (labor's moving along just fine), you and your practitioner may decide to hold off and let them rupture naturally. Occasionally, membranes stay stubbornly intact throughout delivery (the baby arrives with the bag of waters still surrounding him or her, which means it will need to be ruptured right after birth), and that's fine, too.

An Episiotomy

"I heard episiotomies aren't routine anymore. Is that true?"

Happily, you've heard right. An episiotomy—a surgical cut in your perineum (the muscular area between your vagina and your anus) to enlarge the vaginal opening just before the baby's head emerges—is no longer performed routinely at delivery. These days, in fact, midwives and most doctors rarely make the cut without a good reason.

It wasn't always that way. The episiotomy was once thought to prevent spontaneous tearing of the perineum and postpartum urinary and fecal incontinence, as well as reduce the risk in the newborn of birth trauma (from the baby's head pushing long and hard against the perineum). But it's now known that infants fare just fine without an episiotomy, and mothers, too, seem to do better without it. An average total labor doesn't seem to be any longer, and mothers often experience less blood loss, less infection, and less perineal pain after delivery without an episiotomy (though you can still have blood loss and infection with a tear). What's more, research has shown that episiotomies are more likely than spontaneous tears to turn into serious third- or fourth-degree tears (those that go close to or through the rectum, sometimes causing fecal incontinence).

But while routine episiotomies are no longer recommended, there is still a place for them in certain birth scenarios. Episiotomies may be indicated when a baby is large and needs a roomier exit route, when the baby needs to be delivered rapidly, when forceps or vacuum delivery need to be performed, or for the relief of shoulder dystocia (a shoulder gets stuck in the birth canal during delivery).

If you do need an episiotomy, you'll get an injection (if there's time) of local pain relief before the cut, though you may not need a local if you're already anesthetized from an epidural or if your perineum is thinned out and already numb from the pressure of your baby's head during crowning. Your practitioner will then take surgical scissors and make either a median (also called midline) incision (a cut made directly toward the rectum) or a mediolateral incision (which slants away from the rectum).

After delivery of your baby and the placenta, the practitioner will stitch up the cut (you'll get a shot of local pain medication if you didn't receive one before or if your epidural has worn off).

To reduce the possibility that you'll need an episiotomy and to ease delivery without one, some midwives recommend perineal massage (see page 352) for a few weeks before your due date if you're a first-time mom. (If you've delivered vaginally before, you're already stretched, so do-ahead massage probably won't accomplish much.) During labor, the following can also help: warm compresses to lessen perineal discomfort, perineal massage, standing or squatting and exhaling or grunting while pushing to facilitate stretching of the perineum. During the pushing phase, your practitioner will probably use perineal support—applying gentle counterpressure to the perineum so your baby's head doesn't push out too quickly and cause an unnecessary tear.

If you haven't already, discuss the episiotomy issue with your practitioner. It's very likely he or she will agree that the procedure should not be performed unless there's a good reason. Document your feelings about episiotomies in your birth plan, too, if you like. But keep in mind that, very occasionally, episiotomies do turn out to be necessary, and the final decision should be made in the delivery or birthing room—when that cute little head is crowning.

Forceps

"How likely will it be that I'll need forceps during delivery?"

Pretty unlikely these days. Forceps— long curved tong-like devices designed to help a baby make his or her descent down the birth canal—are used in only a very small percentage of deliveries (vacuum extraction is more common; see next question). But if your practitioner does decide to use forceps, rest assured; they are as safe as a C-section or vacuum extraction when used correctly by an experienced practitioner (many younger doctors have not been trained in their use, and some are reluctant to use them).

Forceps are considered when a laboring mom is just plain exhausted or if she has a heart condition or very high blood pressure that might make strenuous pushing harmful to her health. They might also be used if the baby needs to be delivered in a hurry because of fetal distress (assuming the baby is in a favorable position—for example, close to crowning) or if the baby's in an unfavorable position during the pushing stage (the forceps can be used to rotate the baby's head to facilitate the birth).

Your cervix will have to be fully dilated, your bladder empty, and your membranes ruptured before forceps are used. Then you'll be numbed with a local anesthetic (unless you already have an epidural in place). You'll also likely receive an episiotomy to enlarge the vaginal opening to allow for placement of the forceps. The curved tongs of the forceps will then be cradled one at a time around the temples of the baby's crowning head, locked into position, and used to gently deliver the baby. There may be some bruising or swelling on the baby's scalp from the forceps, but it will usually go away within a few days after birth.

If your practitioner attempts delivery with forceps, but the attempt is unsuccessful, you'll likely undergo a C-section.

Vacuum Extraction

"My friend's ob used a vacuum extractor to help deliver her baby. Is that the same as forceps?"

It does the same job. The vacuum extractor is a plastic cup placed on the baby's head, and it uses gentle suction to help guide him or her out of the birth canal. The suction prevents the baby's head from moving back up the birth canal between contractions and can be used to help mom out while she is pushing during contractions. Vacuum extraction is used in about 5 percent of deliveries and offers a good alternative to both forceps and C-section under the right circumstances.

Your practitioner would use vacuum extraction for the same reason forceps would be used during delivery (see previous question). Vacuum deliveries are associated with less trauma to the vagina (and possibly a lower chance of needing an episiotomy) and less need for local anesthesia than forceps, which is another reason why more practitioners opt for them over forceps these days.

Babies born with vacuum extraction experience some swelling on the scalp, but it usually isn't serious, doesn't require treatment, and goes away within a few days. As with forceps, if the vac-uum extractor isn't working success-fully to help deliver the baby, a cesarean delivery is recommended.

If during delivery your doctor suggests the need for vacuum extraction to speed things up, you might want to ask if you can rest for several contractions (time permitting) before trying again; such a break might give you the second wind you need to push your baby out effectively. You can also try changing your position: Get up on all fours, or squat; the force of gravity might shift the baby's head.

Before you go into labor, ask your practitioner any questions you have about the possible use of vacuum extraction (or forceps). The more you know, the better prepared you'll be for anything that comes your way during childbirth.

Labor Positions

"I know you're not supposed to lie flat on your back during labor. But what position is best?"

There's no need to take labor lying down, and in fact, lying flat on your back is probably the least efficient way to birth your baby: first because you're not enlisting gravity's help to get your baby out, and second because there's the risk of compressing major blood vessels (and possibly interfering with blood flow to the fetus) when you're on your back. Expectant mothers are encouraged to labor in any other position that feels comfortable, and to change their position as often as they can (and want to). Getting a move on during labor, as well as varying your position often, not only eases discomfort but may also yield speedier results.

You can choose from any of the following labor and delivery postures (or variations of these):

Vacuum Extractor

Labor Positions

Sitting

Birthing ball

Hands and knees

Side lying

Squatting

Standing

Kneeling

Standing or walking. Getting vertical not only helps relieve the pain of contractions but also takes advantage of gravity, which may allow your pelvis to open and your baby to move down into your birth canal. While it's unlikely you'll be heading for the track once contractions are coming fast and furious, walking (or just leaning against a wall or your coach) during the early stages of labor can be an effective move.

Rocking. Sure, your baby's not even born yet, but he or she will still enjoy a little rocking—as will you, especially when those contractions start coming. Slip into a chair or remain upright, and sway back and forth. The rocking motion may allow your pelvis to move and encourage the baby to descend. And again, staying upright allows you to use the force of gravity to help in the process.

Squatting. You probably won't be able to stand and deliver, but once you get closer to the pushing phase of childbirth, you might want to consider squatting. There's a reason why women have delivered their babies in a squatting position for centuries: It works. Squatting allows the pelvis to open wide, giving your baby more room to move on down. You can use your partner for squatting support (you'll probably be a little wobbly, so you'll need all the support you can get), or you can use a squatting bar, which is often attached to the birthing bed (leaning on the bar will keep your legs from tiring out as you squat).

Birthing balls. Sitting or leaning on one of these large exercise balls can help open up your pelvis—and it's a lot easier than squatting for long periods.

Sitting. Whether in bed (the back of the birthing bed can be raised so you're almost sitting upright), in your partner's arms, or on a birthing ball, sitting can ease the pain of contractions and may allow gravity to help bring your baby down into the birth canal. You might also consider a birthing chair, if one is available, which is specifically designed to support a woman in a sitting or squatting position during delivery and, theoretically, speed labor. Another plus: Moms get to see more of the birth in this position.

Kneeling. Got back labor? Kneeling over a chair or over your spouse's shoulders is a great position when the back of the baby's head is pushing against your spine. It encourages the baby to move forward, taking that load off your back. Even if you don't have back labor, kneeling can be an effective labor and delivery position. Because kneeling allows you to shift and transfer some of the pressure toward the lower spine while you push your baby out, it seems to reduce childbirth pain even more than sitting does.

Hands and knees. Getting on all fours is another way to cope more comfortably with back labor—and to help get that puppy out faster. This position allows you to do pelvic tilts for comfort, while giving your spouse or doula access to your back for massage and counterpressure. You might even consider delivering in this position (no matter what kind of labor you're having), since it opens up the pelvis and uses gravity to coax baby down.

Side lying. Too tired to sit? Or squat? Just need to lie down? Lying on your side is much better than lying on your back, since it doesn't compress the major veins in your body. It's also a good delivery option, helping to slow a too-fast birth as well as easing the pain of some contractions.

Remember that the best labor position is the one that's best for you. And what's best in the early stages of labor might make you miserable when you're in the throes of transition, so change positions as often—or as little—as you want. If you're being continuously monitored, your positions are somewhat limited. It'll be hard to walk, for instance—but you'll have no problem squatting, rocking, sitting, getting on your hands and knees, or lying on your side. Even if you have an epidural, sitting, side lying, or rocking are options available to you.

Being Stretched by Childbirth

"I'm concerned about stretching during delivery. Will my vagina ever be the same again?"

Mother Nature definitely had mothers in mind when she thought up vaginas. Their incredible elasticity and accordion-like folds allow this amazing organ to open up for childbirth (and the passage of that 7- or 8-pound baby) and then—over a period of weeks following delivery—return to close to original size. In other words, your vagina's definitely designed to take it.

The perineum is also elastic but less so than the vagina. Massage during the months prior to delivery may help increase its elasticity and reduce stretching (though don't go overboard; see page 352). Likewise, exercising the pelvic muscles with Kegels during this period may enhance their elasticity, strengthen them, and speed their return to normal tone.

Most women find that the slight increase in vaginal roominess typically experienced postpartum is imperceptible and doesn't interfere at all with sexual enjoyment. For those who were previously too snug, that extra room can be a real plus—making sex more of a pleasure and in some cases, literally,

Apgar Score

The Apgar score is your baby's first test, and it's a way to quickly evaluate your newborn's condition. At one minute and again at five minutes after birth, a nurse, midwife, or doctor check the infant's Appearance (color), Pulse (heartbeat), Grimace (reflex), Activity (muscle tone), and Respiration. Babies who score above 6, which most babies do, are fine. Those who score between 4 and 6 often need resuscitation, which generally includes suctioning their airways and administering oxygen. Those who score under 4 require more dramatic lifesaving techniques.

less of a pain. Very occasionally, however, in a woman who was "just right" before, childbirth does stretch the vagina enough that sexual satisfaction decreases. Often, the vaginal muscles tighten up again in time. Doing Kegels faithfully and frequently helps speed that process. If six months after delivery you still find that your vagina's too slack for comfort, talk to your doctor about other possible treatments.

The Sight of Blood

"The sight of blood makes me feel faint. I'm not sure if I'll be able to handle watching my delivery."

Here's some good news for the squeamish. First of all, there isn't all that much blood during childbirth—not much more than you see when you've got your period. Second, you're not really a spectator at your delivery; you'll be a very active participant, putting every ounce of your concentration and energy into pushing your baby those last few inches. Caught up in the excitement and anticipation (and, let's face it, the pain and fatigue), you're unlikely to notice, much less be unsettled by, any bleeding. If you ask friends who are new mothers, few will be able to tell you just how much blood, if any, there was at their deliveries.

If you still feel strongly that you don't want to see any blood, simply keep your eyes off the mirror at the moment of birth (and look away, too,

if an episiotomy is performed). Instead, just look down past your belly for a good view of your baby as he or she emerges. From this vantage point, virtually no blood will be visible. But before you decide to opt out of watching your own delivery, watch someone else's by viewing a childbirth DVD. You'll probably be much more amazed than horrified.

Some fathers, too, worry about how they'll handle viewing the birth. If your spouse is anxious about this aspect of delivery, have him read page 483.

have him read page 483.

Childbirth

Delivering a baby is the challenge of a lifetime, but it's also an emotional and physical rush like no other. It's an experience that you may be looking ahead to with trepidation (and maybe a little dread), but that you'll

likely look back on—once it's all said, done, and delivered—with nothing but the purest joy (and maybe a little relief).

Fortunately, you won't be going it alone. In addition to the support of

Stages and Phases of Childbirth

Childbirth progresses in three stages: labor, delivery of the baby, and delivery of the placenta. Unless labor is cut short (or eliminated) by a C-section, all women go through the labor stage, which includes early labor, active labor, and transitional labor. The timing and intensity of the contractions can help pinpoint which phase of labor you're in at any particular time, and so can some of the symptoms you're experiencing along the way. Periodic internal exams will confirm the progress.

Stage One: Labor

Phase 1: Early (Latent)—thinning (effacement) and opening (dilation) of the cervix to 3 cm; contractions are 30 to 45 seconds long, 20 minutes apart or less.

Phase 2: Active—dilation of cervix to 7 cm; contractions are 40 to 60 seconds long, coming 3 to 4 minutes apart.

Phase 3: Transitional—dilation of cervix to 10 cm (fully dilated); contractions are 60 to 90 seconds long, about 2 to 3 minutes apart.

Stage Two: Delivery of the baby

Stage Three: Delivery of the placenta

your coach, you'll have plenty of medical professionals on the scene, too. But even with all that expertise in your camp, it'll help to have some know-how of your own.

After nine months at it—graduating from queasiness and bloating to heartburn and backache—you almost certainly know what to expect when you're expecting by now. But what should you expect when you're laboring and delivering?

That's actually hard to predict (make that impossible). Like every pregnancy before it, every labor and delivery is different. But just as it was comforting to know what you might expect during those months of growing your baby, it'll be comforting to have a general idea of what you might have in store for you during those hours of childbirth. Even if it turns out to be nothing like you expected (with the exception of that very happy and cuddly ending).

Stage One: Labor

Phase 1: Early Labor

This phase is usually the longest and, fortunately, the least intense phase of labor. Over a period of hours, days, or weeks (often without noticeable or bothersome contractions), or over a period of two to six hours of no-doubt-about-it contractions, your cervix will efface (thin out) and dilate (open) to 3 cm.

Contractions in this phase usually last 30 to 45 seconds, though they can be shorter. They are mild to moderately strong, may be regular or irregular (around 20 minutes apart, more or less), and become progressively closer together, but not necessarily in a consistent pattern.

During early labor, you might experience any or all of the following:

- Backache (either constant or with each contraction)
- Menstrual-like cramps
- Lower abdominal pressure
- Indigestion
- Diarrhea
- A sensation of warmth in the abdomen
- Bloody show (blood-tinged mucus)
- Rupture of the amniotic membranes (your water will break), though it's more likely that they'll rupture sometime during active labor.

Emotionally, you may feel excitement, relief, anticipation, uncertainty, anxiety, fear; some women are relaxed and chatty, others tense and apprehensive.

For the Record

Instead of grabbing the nearest piece of scrap paper to write down the timing of your contractions, flip open to the childbirth journal in *The What to Expect Pregnancy Journal and Organizer* to record all the info about your contractions and your labor experience (or better yet, have your spouse jot it down). This way you'll have a keepsake to help you remember the event—not that you'd ever forget.

What You Can Do. Of course you're excited (and nervous), but it's important to relax—or at least try to relax. This could take a while.

- If it's nighttime, try to sleep (you might not be able to later, when the contractions are coming fast and furious). If you can't sleep—what with all the adrenaline pumping—get up and do things around the house that will distract you. Cook a few more dishes to add to your freezer stash, fold some baby clothes, do the rest of the laundry so you can come home to an empty hamper (it'll fill up again soon enough), or log on to your favorite message board to see if anyone else is in the same boat. If it's daytime, go about your usual routine, as long as it doesn't take you far from home (don't go anywhere without your cell phone). If you're at work, you might want to head home (it's not like you're going to get anything done anyway). If you have nothing planned, find something relaxing to keep you occupied. Take a walk, watch TV, e-mail friends and family, finish packing your bag.

- Alert the media. Okay, maybe not the media (yet)—but you'll definitely want to put your spouse on alert if he's not with you. He probably doesn't have to rush to your side just yet if he's at work—unless he really wants to—since there's not much for him to do this early on. If you have hired a doula, it would be a good idea to issue a bulletin to her, too.

- Eat a light snack or meal if you're hungry (broth, toast with jam, plain pasta or rice, Jell-O, a Popsicle, pudding, a banana, or something else your practitioner has suggested)—now's the best time to stock up on energy foods. But don't eat heavily, and avoid hard-to-digest foods (burgers, potato chips).

You may also want to skip anything acidic, such as orange juice or lemonade. And definitely drink some water—it's important to stay hydrated.

- Make yourself comfortable. Take a warm shower; use a heating pad if your back is aching; take acetaminophen (Tylenol) if your practitioner approves. Don't take aspirin or ibuprofen (Advil, Motrin).

- Time contractions (from the beginning of one to the beginning of the next) for half an hour if they seem to be getting closer than 10 minutes apart and periodically even if they don't. But don't be a constant clock-watcher.

- Remember to pee often, even if you're not feeling the urge to. A full bladder could slow down the progress of labor.

- Use relaxation techniques if they help, but don't start any breathing exercises yet or you'll become bored and exhausted long before you really need them.

For the Coach: What You Can Do. If you're around during this phase, here are some ways you can help out. If a doula's also on site, she can share in any or all of these:

- Practice timing contractions. The interval between contractions is timed from the beginning of one to the beginning of the next. Time them periodically, and keep a record. When they are coming less than 10 minutes apart, time them more frequently.

- Spread the calm. During this early phase of labor, your most important function is to keep your partner relaxed. And the best way to do this is to keep yourself relaxed, both inside and out. Your own anxiety can be passed on to her without your real-

Call Your Practitioner If...

Your practitioner probably told you not to call until you're in more active labor, but may have suggested that you call early on if labor begins during the day or if your membranes rupture. Definitely call immediately, however, if your membranes rupture and the amniotic fluid is murky or greenish, if you have any bright red vaginal bleeding, or if you feel no fetal activity (it may be hard to notice because you are distracted by contractions, so try the test on page 289). Although you may not feel like it, it's best if you—not your coach—make the call and talk to your practitioner. A lot can be lost in third-party translations.

a silly sitcom or reality show, checking out celebrity birthday sites to see who baby might be celebrating with next year, baking something for the postpartum freezer stash, taking short strolls.

- Keep up your own strength so you'll be able to reinforce hers. Eat periodically but empathetically (don't go wolfing down a Big Mac when she's sticking to pudding). Prepare a sandwich to take along to the hospital or birthing center, but avoid anything with a strong or lingering odor. She won't be in the mood to be sniffing bologna or onions on your breath.

Phase 2: Active Labor

The active phase of labor is usually shorter than the first, lasting an average of 2 to 3½ hours (with, again, a wide range considered normal). The contractions are more concentrated now, accomplishing more in less time, and they're also increasingly more intense (in other words, painful). As they become stronger, longer (40 to 60 seconds, with a distinct peak about halfway through), and more frequent (generally 3 to 4 minutes apart, though the pattern may not be regular), the cervix dilates to 7 cm. With fewer breaks in the action, there's less opportunity to rest between contractions.

You'll likely be in the hospital or birthing center by now, and you can expect to feel all or some of the following (though you won't feel pain if you've had an epidural):

- Increasing pain and discomfort with contractions (you may not be able to talk through them now).

- Increasing backache.

- Leg discomfort or heaviness.

izing it, and it can be communicated not just through words but through touch—or even expressions (so no tensed-up foreheads, please). Doing relaxation exercises together or giving her a gentle, unhurried massage may help. It's too soon, however, to have her begin using breathing exercises. For now, just breathe.

- Offer comfort, reassurance, and support. She'll need them from now on.

- Keep your sense of humor, and help her keep hers; time flies, after all, when you're having fun. It'll be easier to laugh now than when contractions are coming fast and hard (she probably won't find very much of anything funny then).

- Try distraction. Suggest activities that will help keep both your minds off her labor: playing video games, watching

On to the Hospital or Birthing Center

Sometime near the end of the early phase or the beginning of the active phase (probably when your contractions are five minutes apart or less, sooner if you live far from the hospital or if this isn't your first baby), your practitioner will tell you to pick up your bag and get going. Getting to the hospital or birthing center will be easier if your coach is reachable anywhere, anytime by cell phone or beeper and can get to you quickly (do not try to drive yourself to the hospital or birthing center; take a taxi or ask a friend to drive you if your coach can't be reached); you've planned your route in advance; are familiar with parking regulations (if parking is likely to be a problem, taking a cab may be more sensible); and know which entrance will get you to the obstetrical floor most quickly. En route, recline the front seat as far back as is comfortable, if you'd like (remember to fasten your seatbelt). If you have chills, bring along a blanket to cover you.

Once you reach the hospital or birthing center, you can probably expect something like the following:

- To get registered: If you've preregistered (and it's best if you have), the admission process will be quick and easy; if you're in active labor and in no mood to answer questions, your coach can take care of it. If you haven't preregistered, you (or better yet, your coach) will have to go through a more lengthy process, so be prepared to fill out a bunch of forms and answer a lot of questions.

- Once on the labor and delivery floor, a nurse will take you to your room (most likely a labor, delivery, and recovery room, or LDR). Sometimes, you may be brought first to a triage (assessment) room, where your cervix will be checked, your baby's heart rate assessed, and your contractions monitored for some time to see if you're actively in labor or not. In some hospitals or birthing centers, your coach and other family members may be asked to wait outside while you are being admitted and prepped. Speak up if you'd rather your coach stay by your side; most hospitals or birthing centers are

- Fatigue.
- Increasing bloody show.
- Rupture of the membranes (if they haven't earlier), or they might be ruptured artificially now.

Emotionally, you may feel restless and find it more difficult to relax; or your concentration may become more intense, and you may become completely absorbed in your labor efforts. Your confidence may begin to waver ("How will I make it through?"), along with your patience ("Will this labor never end?"), or you may feel excited and encouraged that things are really starting to happen. Whatever your feelings, they're normal—just get ready to start getting "active."

During active labor, assuming all is progressing normally and safely, the hospital or birthing center staff will leave you alone (or stay out of your way, but in your room), checking and monitoring you as needed, but also allowing you to work through your labor with your coach and other support people without interference. You can expect them to:

flexible. (Note to the coach: This is a good time to make a few priority phone calls or to get a snack if you haven't brought one. If you aren't called into the room within 20 minutes or so, remind someone at the nurses' station that you're waiting. Be prepared for the possibility that you will be asked to put on a clean gown over your clothes.)

- Your nurse will take a brief history, asking, among other things, when the contractions started, how far apart they are, whether your membranes have ruptured, and, possibly, when and what you last ate.

- Your nurse will ask for your signature (or your spouse's) on routine consent forms.

- Your nurse will give you a hospital gown to change into and might request a urine sample. She will check your pulse, blood pressure, respiration, and temperature; look for leaking amniotic fluid, bleeding, or bloody show; listen to the fetal heartbeat with a Doppler or hook you up to a fetal monitor, if this is deemed necessary. She may also evaluate the fetus and its position.

- Depending on the policies of your practitioner and the hospital or birthing center (and, ideally, your preferences), an IV may be started.

- Your nurse, your practitioner, or a staff doctor or midwife will examine you internally to see how dilated and effaced your cervix is (if it wasn't already checked). If your membranes haven't ruptured spontaneously and you are at least 3 or 4 cm dilated (many practitioners prefer to wait until the cervix has dilated to 5 cm), your membranes may be artificially ruptured—unless you and your practitioner have decided to leave them intact until they break on their own or until later in labor. The procedure is generally painless; all you'll feel is a warm gush of fluid.

If you have any questions—about hospital or birthing center policy, about your condition, about your practitioner's plans—that haven't been answered before, now is the time for you or your coach to ask them. Your coach can also take this opportunity to hand a copy of your birth plan, if you have one, to the birth attendants.

- Take your blood pressure.

- Monitor your baby with a Doppler or fetal monitor.

- Time and monitor the strength of your contractions.

- Evaluate the quantity and quality of bloody discharge.

- Get an IV going if you're going to want an epidural.

- Possibly try to augment your labor if it's progressing very slowly by the use of Pitocin or by artificially ruptur-

ing the membranes (if they are still intact).

- Periodically examine you internally to check how labor is progressing and how dilated and effaced your cervix is.

- Administer pain relief if you choose to have some.

They'll also be able to answer any questions you might have (don't be shy about asking or having your coach ask) and provide additional support as you go through labor.

Are Things Slowing Down?

There's probably nothing you want more than to keep things moving along when it comes to labor. And making good progress during labor—which happens most of the time—requires three main components: strong uterine contractions that effectively dilate the cervix, a baby that is in position for an easy exit, and a pelvis that is sufficiently roomy to permit the passage of the baby. But, in some cases, labor doesn't progress by the book, because the cervix takes its time dilating, the baby takes longer than expected to descend through the pelvis, or pushing isn't getting you (or your baby) anywhere.

Sometimes, contractions slow down after an epidural kicks in, too. But keep in mind that expectations for the progress of labor are different for those who have an epidural (first and second stage may take longer, and that's typically nothing to worry about).

To get a stalled labor back up and running, there are a number of steps your practitioner (and you) can take:

- If you're in early labor and your cervix just isn't dilating or effacing, your practitioner may suggest some activity (such as walking) or just the opposite (sleep and rest, possibly aided by relaxation techniques). This will also help rule out false labor (the contractions of false labor usually subside with activity or a nap).

- If you're still not dilating or effacing as quickly as expected, your practitioner may try to rev things up by administering Pitocin (oxytocin), prostaglandin E, or another labor stimulator. He or she might even suggest a labor booster that you can take into your own hands (or your coach's): nipple stimulation.

- If you're already in the active phase of labor, but your cervix is dilating very slowly (less than 1 to 1.2 cm of dilation per hour in women having their first babies, and 1.5 cm per hour in those who've had previous deliveries), or if your baby isn't moving down the birth canal at a rate of more than 1 cm per hour in women having their first babies, or 2 cm per hour in others, your practitioner may rupture your membranes and/or continue administering oxytocin.

- If you end up pushing more than two hours (if you're a first-time mother who hasn't had an epidural) or three hours (if you have had an epidural), your practitioner will reassess your baby's position, see how you're feeling, perhaps attempt to birth your baby using vacuum extraction or (less likely) forceps, or decide to do a cesarean delivery.

To keep the ball (and the baby) rolling throughout labor, remember to urinate periodically, because a full bladder can interfere with the baby's descent. (If you have an epidural, chances are your bladder is being emptied by a catheter.) Full bowels may do the same, so if you haven't moved your bowels in 24 hours, give it a try. You might also try to nudge a sluggish labor along by utilizing gravity (sitting upright, squatting, standing, or walking). Ditto for trying to push along the pushing stage. A semi-sitting or semi-squatting position may be most effective for delivery.

Most physicians perform a C-section after 24 hours of active labor (sometimes sooner) if sufficient progress has not been made by that time; some will wait longer, as long as both mother and baby are doing well.

What You Can Do. It's all about your comfort now. So:

- Don't hesitate to ask your coach for whatever you need to get and stay as comfortable as possible, whether it's a back rub to ease the ache or a damp washcloth to cool your face. Speaking up will be important. Remember, as much as he's going to want to help, he's going to have a hard time anticipating your needs, especially if this is his first time.

- Start your breathing exercises, if you plan to use them, as soon as contractions become too strong to talk through. Didn't plan ahead and practice? Ask the nurse or doula for some simple breathing suggestions. Remember to do whatever relaxes you and makes you feel more comfortable. If the exercises aren't working for you, don't feel obligated to stick with them.

- If you'd like some pain relief, now's a good time to ask for it. An epidural can be given as early as you feel you need it.

- If you're laboring without pain relief, try to relax between contractions. This will become increasingly difficult as they come more frequently, but it will also become increasingly important as your energy reserves are taxed. Use the relaxation techniques you learned in childbirth class or try the one on page 142.

- Stay hydrated. With your practitioner's green light, drink clear beverages frequently to replace fluids and to keep your mouth moist. If you're hungry, and again, if you have your practitioner's okay, have a light snack (another Popsicle, for example). If your practitioner doesn't allow anything else by mouth, sucking on ice chips can serve to refresh.

Don't Hyperventilate

With all the breathing going on during labor, some women start to hyperventilate or over-breathe, causing low levels of carbon dioxide in the blood. If you feel dizzy or lightheaded, have blurred vision or a tingling and numbness of your fingers and toes, let your coach, a nurse, your practitioner, or your doula know. They'll give you a paper bag to breathe into (or suggest you breathe into your cupped hands). A few inhales and exhales will get you feeling better in no time.

- Stay on the move if you can (you won't be able to get around much if you have an epidural). Walk around, if possible, or at least change positions as needed. (See page 377 for suggested labor positions.)

- Pee periodically. Because of tremendous pelvic pressure, you may not notice the need to empty your bladder, but a full bladder can keep you from making the progress you'll definitely want to be making. No need to trek to the bathroom if you have an epidural (not that you could anyway), because you've probably been given a catheter to empty your bladder.

For the Coach: What You Can Do. If a doula is present, she can help out with many of these. Discuss ahead of time who will do what for your laboring spouse.

- Hand a copy of the birth plan to each nurse or other attendant at the birth, so everyone's on the same page about preferences. If the shift changes, make sure the new nurses receive a copy.

- If mom wants medication, let the nurse or practitioner know. Respect whatever decision she makes—to continue unmedicated or to go for pain relief.

- Take your cues from her. Whatever mom wants, mom should get. Keep in mind that what she'll want may change from moment to moment (the TV blaring one second, no TV the next). Ditto for her mood and her reaction to you. Don't take it personally if she doesn't respond to, doesn't appreciate—or is even annoyed by—your attempts to comfort her. Ease up, if that's what she seems to prefer—but be prepared to step it up 10 minutes later, if she wants. Remember that your role is important, even if you sometimes feel superfluous or in the way. She'll appreciate you in the morning (or whenever it's all over).

- Set the mood. If possible, keep the door to the room closed, the lights low, and the room quiet to promote a relaxed and restful atmosphere. Soft music may also help (unless she'd rather watch TV; remember, she's the boss). Continue encouraging relaxation techniques between contractions and breathing with her through the contractions—but don't push if she's not into them or if pushing the relaxation agenda is starting to stress her out. If distractions seem to help her, turn to cards or handheld video games, light conversation, or TV. But distract her only as much as she seems to want to be distracted.

- Pump her up. Reassure her and praise her efforts (unless your verbal reassurance is making her more edgy), and avoid criticism of any kind (even the constructive type). Be her cheerleader (but keep it low-key—she probably won't appreciate full-on exuberance). Particularly if progress is slow, suggest

that she take her labor one contraction at a time, and remind her that each pain brings her closer to seeing the baby. If she finds your cheers irritating, however, skip them. Stick to sympathy if that's what she seems to need.

- Keep track of the contractions. If she's on a monitor, ask the practitioner or the nurse to show you how to read it. Later, when contractions are coming one on top of the other, you can announce each new contraction as it begins—unless she starts to find that annoying. (The monitor may detect the tensing of the uterus before she can, and can let her know when she's having one if she can't feel them, thanks to an epidural.) You can also encourage your spouse through those tough contractions by telling her when each peak is ending. If there is no monitor, ask a nurse to show you how to recognize the arrival and departure of contractions with your hand on her abdomen (unless she doesn't want it there).

- Massage her abdomen or back, or use counterpressure or any other techniques you've learned, to make her more comfortable. Let her tell you what kind of stroking or touching or massage helps. If she prefers not to be touched at all, then it might be best to comfort her verbally. Remember, what feels good one moment might irk her the next, and vice versa.

- Remind her to take a bathroom break at least once an hour if she doesn't have a catheter. She might not feel the urge, but a full bladder can stand in the way of labor progress.

- Suggest a change of position periodically; take her for a hallway walk, if that's possible.

- Be the ice man. Find out where the ice machine is, and keep those chips coming. If she's allowed to sip on fluids or snack on light foods, offer them periodically. Popsicles may be especially refreshing; ask the nurse if there's a stash you can help yourself to.

- Keep her cool. Use a damp washcloth, wrung out in cold water, to help cool her body and face; refresh it often.

- If her feet are cold, offer to get out a pair of socks and put them on her (reaching her feet isn't easy for her).

- Be her voice and her ears. She has enough going on, so lighten her load. Serve as her go-between with medical personnel as much as possible. Intercept questions from them that you can answer, and ask for explanations of procedures, equipment, and use of medication, so you'll be able to tell her what's happening. For instance, now might be the time to find out if a mirror will be provided so she can view the delivery. Be her advocate when necessary, but try to fight her battles quietly, perhaps outside the room, so she won't be disturbed.

Phase 3: Transitional Labor

Transition is the most demanding phase of labor but, fortunately, typically the quickest. Suddenly, the intensity of the contractions picks up. They become very strong, 2 to 3 minutes apart, and 60 to 90 seconds long, with very intense peaks that last for most of the contraction. Some women, particularly women who have given birth before, experience multiple peaks. You may feel as though the contractions never disappear completely and you can't completely relax between them. The final 3 cm of dilation, to a full 10 cm, will probably take place in a very short time: on average, 15 minutes to an hour, though it can also take as long as 3 hours.

You'll feel plenty when you're in transition (unless, of course, you're numbed by an epidural or other pain relief), and may experience some or all of the following:

- More intense pain with contractions

- Strong pressure in the lower back and/or perineum

- Rectal pressure, with or without an urge to push or move your bowels (you might even feel the urge to grunt—so let it out!)

- An increase in your bloody show as more capillaries in the cervix rupture

- Feeling very warm and sweaty or chilled and shaky (or you might alternate between the two)

- Crampy legs that may tremble uncontrollably

- Nausea and/or vomiting

- Drowsiness between contractions as oxygen is diverted from your brain to the site of the delivery

- A tightening sensation in your throat or chest

- Exhaustion

Emotionally, you may feel vulnerable and overwhelmed, as though you're reaching the end of your rope. In addition to frustration over not being able to push yet, you may feel discouraged, irritable, disoriented, restless, and may have difficulty concentrating and relaxing (it might seem impossible to do either). You may also find excitement reaching a fever pitch in the midst of all the stress. Your baby's almost here!

What You Can Do. Hang in there. By the end of this phase, which is not far off, your cervix will be fully dilated, and it'll be time to begin pushing your baby out. Instead of thinking about the work ahead, try to think about how far you've come.

- Continue to use breathing techniques if they help. If you feel the urge to push, resist. Pant or blow instead, unless you've been instructed otherwise. Pushing against a cervix that isn't completely dilated can cause it to swell, which can delay delivery.

- If you don't want anybody to touch you unnecessarily, if your coach's once comforting hands now irritate you, don't hesitate to let him know.

- Try to relax between contractions (as much as is possible) with slow, deep, rhythmic breathing.

- Keep your eye on the prize: That bundle of joy will soon be arriving in your arms.

When you're a full 10 cm dilated, you'll be moved to the delivery room, if you aren't already there. Or, if you're in a birthing bed, the foot of the bed will simply be removed to prepare for delivery.

For the Coach: What You Can Do. Again, the doula, if one is present, can share these comforting techniques with you:

- If your laboring spouse has an epidural or other kind of pain relief, ask her if she needs another dose. Transition can be quite painful, and if her epidural is wearing off, she won't be a happy camper. If it is, let the nurses or the practitioner know. If mom's continuing unmedicated, she'll need you more now than ever (read on).

- Be there, but give her space if she seems to want it. Often, women in transition don't like being touched—but, as always, take your cues from her. Abdominal massage may be especially offensive now, though counterpressure applied to the small of her back may continue to provide some relief for back pain. Be prepared to back off—even from her back—as directed.

- Don't waste words. Now's not the time for small talk, and probably not for jokes, either. Offer quiet comfort, and help her with instructions that are brief and direct.

- Offer lots of encouragement, unless she prefers you to keep quiet. At this moment, eye contact or touch may communicate more expressively than words.

- Breathe with her through every contraction if it seems to help her through them.

- Help her rest and relax between contractions, touching her abdomen lightly to show her when a contraction is over. Remind her to use slow, rhythmic breathing in between contractions, if she can.

- If her contractions seem to be getting closer and/or she feels the urge to push—and she hasn't been examined recently—let the nurse or practitioner know. She may be fully dilated.

- Offer her ice chips or a sip of water frequently, and mop her brow with a cool damp cloth often. If she's chilly, offer her a blanket or a pair of socks.

- Stay focused on the payoff you're both about to get. It's been a long haul, but it won't be long before the pushing begins—and that anticipated bundle arrives in your arms.

Stage Two: Pushing and Delivery

Up until this point, your active participation in the birth of your child has been negligible. Though you've definitely taken the brunt of the abuse in the proceedings, your cervix and uterus (and baby) have done most of the work. But now that dilation is complete, your help is needed to push the baby the remainder of the way through the birth canal and out. Pushing and delivery generally take between half an hour and an hour, but can sometimes be accomplished in 10 (or even fewer) short minutes or in 2, 3, or even more very long hours.

The contractions of the second stage are usually more regular than the contractions of transition. They are still about 60 to 90 seconds in duration but sometimes further apart (usually about 2 to 5 minutes) and possibly less painful, though sometimes they are more intense. There now should be a well-defined rest period between them, though you may still have trouble recognizing the onset of each contraction.

Common in the second stage (though you'll definitely feel a lot less—and you may not feel anything at all—if you've had an epidural):

- Pain with the contractions, though possibly not as much

- An overwhelming urge to push (though not every woman feels it, especially if she's had an epidural)

- Tremendous rectal pressure (ditto)

- A burst of renewed energy (a second wind) or fatigue

- Very visible contractions, with your uterus rising noticeably with each

- An increase in bloody show

- A tingling, stretching, burning, or stinging sensation at the vagina as your baby's head emerges (it's called the "ring of fire" for good reason)

- A slippery wet feeling as your baby emerges

Emotionally, you may feel relieved that you can now start pushing (though some women feel embarrassed, inhibited, or scared); you may also feel exhilarated and excited or, if the pushing stretches on for much more than an hour, frustrated or overwhelmed. In a prolonged second stage, you may find your preoccupation is less with seeing the baby than with getting the ordeal over with (and that's perfectly understandable—and normal).

What You Can Do. It's time to get this baby out. So get into a pushing position (which one will depend on the bed, chair, or tub you're in, your practitioner's preferences, and, hopefully, what's most comfortable and effective for you). A semi-sitting or semi-squatting position is often the best because it enlists the aid of gravity in the birthing process and may afford you more pushing power. Tucking your chin to your chest when you're in this position will help you focus your pushes to where they need to be. Sometimes, if the pushing isn't moving your baby down the birth canal, it may be helpful to change positions. If you've been semi-inclined, for example, you might want to get up on all fours or try squatting.

Once you're ready to begin pushing, give it all you've got. The more efficiently you push and the more energy you pack into the effort, the more quickly your baby will make the trip

A Baby Is Born

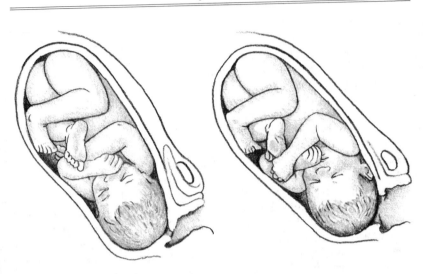

1. The cervix has thinned (effaced) somewhat but has not begun to dilate much.

2. The cervix has fully dilated and the baby's head has begun to press into the birth canal (vagina).

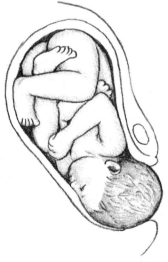

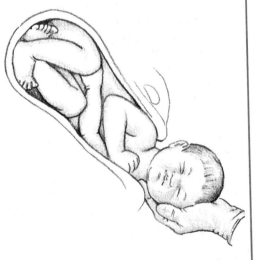

3. To allow the narrowest diameter of the baby's head to fit through the mother's pelvis, the baby usually turns sometime during labor. Here, the slightly molded head has crowned.

4. The head, the baby's broadest part, is out. The rest of the delivery should proceed quickly and smoothly.

through the birth canal. Frantic, disorganized pushing wastes energy and accomplishes little. Keep these pushing pointers in mind:

- Relax your body and your thighs and then push as if you're having a bowel movement (the biggest one of your life). Focus your energy on your vagina and rectum, not your upper body (which could result in chest pain after delivery) and not your face (straining with your face could leave you with black-and-blue marks on your cheeks and bloodshot eyes, not to mention do nothing to help get your baby out).

- Speaking of bowel movements, since you're bearing down on the whole perineal area, anything that's in your rectum may be pushed out, too; trying to avoid this while you're pushing can slow your progress. Don't let inhibition or embarrassment break the pushing rhythm. A little involuntary pooping (or passage of urine) is experienced by nearly everyone during delivery. No one else in the room will think twice about it, and neither should you. Pads will immediately whisk away anything that comes out.

- Take a few deep breaths while the contraction is building so you can gear up for pushing. As the contraction peaks, take a deep breath and then push with all your might—holding your breath if you want or exhaling as you push, whatever feels right to you. If you'd like the nurses or your coach to guide you by counting to 10 while you push, that's fine. But if you find it breaks your rhythm or isn't helpful, ask them not to. There is no magic formula when it comes to how long each push should last or how many times you should push with each contraction—the most important

thing is to do what comes naturally. You may feel as many as five urges to bear down, with each push lasting just seconds—or you may feel the urge to bear down just twice, but with each push lasting longer. Follow those urges, and you'll deliver your baby. Actually, you'll deliver your baby even if you don't follow your urges or if you find you don't have any urges at all. Pushing doesn't come naturally for every woman, and if it doesn't for you, your practitioner, nurse, or doula can help direct your efforts, and redirect them if you lose your concentration.

- Don't become frustrated if you see the baby's head crown and then disappear again. Birthing is a two-steps-forward, one-step-backward proposition. Just remember, you are moving in the right direction.

- Rest between contractions. If you're really exhausted, especially when the pushing stage drags on, your practitioner may suggest that you not push for several contractions so you can rebuild your strength.

- Stop pushing when you're instructed to (as you may be, to keep the baby's head from being born too rapidly). If you're feeling the urge to push, pant or blow instead.

- Remember to keep an eye on the mirror (if one is available) once there's something to look at. Seeing your baby's head crown (and reaching down and touching it) may give you the inspiration to push when the pushing gets tough. Besides, unless your coach is videotaping, there won't be any replays to watch.

While you're pushing, the nurses and/or your practitioner will give you support and direction; continue to monitor your baby's heartbeat, with either

A First Look at Baby

Those who expect their babies to arrive as round and smooth as a Botticelli cherub may be in for a shock. Nine months of soaking in an amniotic bath and a dozen or so hours of compression in a contracting uterus and cramped birth canal take their toll on a newborn's appearance. Those babies who arrived via cesarean delivery have a temporary edge as far as appearance goes.

Fortunately, most of the less-than-lovely newborn characteristics that follow are temporary. One morning, a couple of weeks after you've brought your wrinkled, slightly scrawny, puffy-eyed bundle home from the hospital, you'll wake to find that a beautiful cherub has taken its place in the crib.

Oddly shaped head. At birth, the infant's head is, proportionately, the largest part of the body, with a circumference as large as his or her chest. As your baby grows, the rest of the body will catch up. Often, the head has molded to fit through Mom's pelvis, giving it an odd, possibly pointed "cone" shape. Pressing against an inadequately dilated cervix can further distort the head by raising a lump. The lump will disappear in a day or two, the molding within two weeks, at which point your baby's head will begin to take on that cherubic roundness.

Newborn hair. The hair that covers the baby's head at birth may have little resemblance to the hair the baby will have later. Some newborns are virtually bald, some have thick manes, but most have a light cap of soft hair. All eventually lose their newborn hair (though this may happen so gradually that you don't notice), and it will be replaced by new growth, possibly of a different color and texture.

Vernix caseosa coating. The cheesy substance that coats the fetus in the uterus is believed to protect the skin from the long exposure to the amniotic fluid. Premature babies have quite a bit of this coating at birth; on-time babies just a little; postmature babies have almost none, except possibly in the folds of their skin and under their fingernails.

Swelling of the genitals. This can occur in both male and female new-

a Doppler or fetal monitor; and prepare for delivery by spreading sterile drapes and arranging instruments, donning surgical garments and gloves, and sponging your perineal area with antiseptic (though midwives generally just don gloves and do no draping). They'll also perform an episiotomy if necessary, or use vacuum extraction or, less likely, forceps if necessary.

Once your baby's head emerges, your practitioner will suction your baby's nose and mouth to remove excess mucus, then assist the shoulders and torso out. You usually only have to give one more small push to help with that—the head was the hard part, and the rest slides out pretty easily. The umbilical cord will be clamped (usually after it stops pulsating) and cut—either by the practitioner or by your coach—and your baby will be handed to you or placed on your belly. (If you've arranged for cord blood collection, it will be done now.) This is a great time for some caressing and skin-to-skin contact, so lift up your gown and bring baby close. In case you need a reason to do that, studies show borns. The breasts of newborns, male and female, may also be swollen (occasionally even engorged, secreting a white or pink substance nicknamed "witch's milk") due to stimulation by maternal hormones. The hormones may also stimulate a milky-white, even blood-tinged, vaginal secretion in girls. These effects are normal and disappear in a week to 10 days.

Puffy eyes. Swelling around the newborn's eyes, normal for someone who's been soaking in amniotic fluid for nine months and then squeezed through a narrow birth canal, may be exacerbated by the ointment used to protect the eyes from infection. It disappears within a few days. Caucasian babies' eyes are often, but not always, a slate blue, no matter what color they will be later on. In babies of color, the eyes are usually brown at birth.

Skin. Your baby's skin will appear pink, white, or even grayish at birth (even if it will eventually turn brown or black). That's because pigmentation doesn't show up until a few hours after birth. A variety of rashes, tiny "pimples," and whiteheads may also mar your baby's skin thanks to maternal hormones, but all are temporary. You may also notice skin dryness and cracking, due to first-time exposure to air; these, too, will pass.

Lanugo. Fine downy hair, called lanugo, may cover the shoulders, back, forehead, and temples of full-term babies. This will usually be shed by the end of the first week. Such hair can be more abundant, and will last longer, in a premature baby and may be gone in a postmature one.

Birthmarks. A reddish blotch at the base of the skull, on the eyelid, or on the forehead, called a salmon patch, is very common, especially in Caucasian newborns. Mongolian spots—bluish-gray pigmentation of the deep skin layer that can appear on the back, buttocks, and sometimes the arms and thighs—are more common in Asians, southern Europeans, and blacks. These markings eventually disappear, usually by the time a child is 4 years old. Hemangiomas, elevated strawberry-colored birthmarks, vary from tiny to about quarter size or even larger. They eventually fade to a mottled pearly gray, then often disappear entirely. Coffee-with-cream colored (café-au-lait) spots can appear anywhere on the body; they are usually inconspicuous and don't fade.

that infants who have skin-to-skin contact with their mothers just after delivery sleep longer and are calmer hours later.

What's next for your baby? The nurses and/or a pediatrician will evaluate his or her condition, and rate it on the Apgar scale at one minute and five minutes after birth (see box, page 379); give a brisk, stimulating, and drying rubdown; possibly take the baby's footprints for a keepsake; attach an identifying band to your wrist and to your baby's ankle; administer nonirri-tating eye ointment to your newborn to prevent infection (you can ask that the ointment be administered after you've had time to cuddle with your newborn); weigh, then wrap the baby to prevent heat loss. (In some hospitals and birthing centers, some of these procedures may be omitted; in others, many will be attended to later, so you can have more time to bond with your newborn.)

Then you'll get your baby back (assuming all is well) and you may, if you wish to, begin breastfeeding (but don't worry if you and/or your baby don't catch on immediately; see Getting Started Breastfeeding, page 435).

Sometime after that, it's off to the nursery for baby (if you've delivered in a hospital) for a more complete pediatric exam and some routine protective procedures (including a heel stick and a hepatitis B shot). Once your baby's temperature is stable, he or she will get a first bath, which you (and/or dad) may be able to help give. If you have rooming-in, your baby will be returned as soon as possible and tucked into a bassinet next to your bed.

For the Coach: What You Can Do. Once again, these responsibilities can be shared with a doula.

- Continue giving comfort and support (a whispered "I love you" can be more valuable to her during the pushing stage than anything else), but don't feel hurt if the object of your efforts doesn't seem to notice you're there. Her energies are necessarily focused elsewhere.

- Help her relax between the contractions—with soothing words, a cool cloth applied to forehead, neck, and shoulders, and, if feasible, back mas-

sage or counterpressure to help ease backache.

- Continue to supply ice chips or fluids to moisten her mouth as needed. She's likely to be parched from all that pushing.

- Support her back while she's pushing, if necessary; hold her hand, wipe her brow—or do whatever else seems to help her. If she slips out of position, help her back into it.

- Periodically point out her progress. As the baby begins to crown, remind her to keep an eye on the mirror so she can have visual confirmation of what she is accomplishing. When she's not looking, or if there's no mirror, give her inch-by-inch descriptions. Take her hand and touch baby's head together for renewed inspiration.

- If you're offered the opportunity to catch your baby as he or she emerges or, later, to cut the cord, don't be afraid. Both are relatively easy jobs, and you'll get step-by-step directions and backup from the attendants. You should know, however, that the cord can't be snipped like a piece of string. It's tougher than you may think.

Stage Three: Delivery of the Placenta

The worst is over, and the best has already come. All that remains is tying up the loose ends, so to speak. During this final stage of childbirth (which generally lasts anywhere from five minutes to half an hour or more), the placenta, which has been your baby's life support inside the womb, will be delivered. You will continue to have mild contractions approximately

a minute in duration, though you may not feel them (after all, you're preoccupied with your newborn!). The squeezing of the uterus separates the placenta from the uterine wall and moves it down into the lower segment of the uterus or into the vagina so it can be expelled.

Your practitioner will help deliver the placenta by either pulling the cord gently with one hand while pressing and kneading your uterus with the other or exerting downward pressure on the top of the uterus, asking you to push at the appropriate time. You might get some Pitocin (oxytocin) via injection or in your IV to encourage uterine contractions, which will speed expulsion of the placenta, help shrink the uterus back to size, and minimize bleeding. Once the placenta is out, your practitioner will examine it to make sure it's intact. If it isn't, he or she will inspect your uterus manually for placental fragments and remove any that remain.

Now that the work of labor and delivery is done, you may feel overwhelmingly exhausted or, conversely, experience a burst of renewed energy. If you've been deprived of food and drink, you are likely to be very thirsty and, especially if labor has been long, hungry. Some women experience chills in this stage; all experience a bloody vaginal discharge (called lochia) comparable to a heavy menstrual period.

How will you feel emotionally after you've delivered your baby? Every woman reacts a little differently, and your reaction is normal for you. Your first emotional response may be joy, but it's just as likely to be a sense of relief. You may be exhilarated and talkative, elated and excited, a little impatient at having to push out the placenta or submit to the repair of an episiotomy or a tear, or so in awe of what you're cuddling in your arms (or so beat, or a little bit of both) that you don't notice. You may feel a closeness to your spouse and an immediate bond with your new baby, or (and this is just as normal) you may feel somewhat detached (who is this stranger sniffing at my breast?), even a little resentful—particularly if the delivery was a difficult one (so this is the little person who made me suffer so much!). No matter what your response

now, you will come to love your baby intensely. These things just sometimes take time. (For more on bonding, see page 430.)

What You Can Do.

- Have a good cuddle with your new arrival! Once the cord is cut, you'll have a chance to breastfeed or just do some snuggling. Speak up, too. Since your baby will recognize your voice, cooing, singing, or whispered words will be especially comforting (it's a strange new world, and you'll be able to help baby make some sense out of it). Under some circumstances, your baby may be kept in a heated bassinet for a while or be held by your coach while the placenta is being delivered—but not to worry, there's plenty of time for baby bonding.

- Spend some time bonding with your coach, too—and enjoying your cozy new threesome.

- Help deliver the placenta, if necessary, by pushing when directed. Some women don't even have to push at all for the placenta to arrive. Your practitioner will let you know what to do, if anything.

- Hang in there during repair of any episiotomy or tears.

- Take pride in your accomplishment!

All that's left to do, then, is for your practitioner to stitch up any tear (if you're not already numbed, you'll get a local anesthetic) and clean you up. You'll likely get an ice pack to put on your perineum to minimize swelling—do ask for one if it's not offered. The nurse will also help you put on a maxipad or add some thick pads under your bottom (remember, you'll be bleeding a lot). Once you're feeling up to it, you'll be transferred to a postpartum room (unless you've delivered in an LDRP—a labor, delivery, recovery, and postpartum—room, in which case you'll get to stay put).

For the Coach: What You Can Do. If a doula is present, she can continue to help out, concentrating on the more practical aspects of postdelivery care while you spend some quality time with the two stars of the show.

- Offer some well-earned words of praise to the new mom—and congratulate yourself, too, for a job well done.

- Begin bonding with your little one—with some holding and cuddling, and by doing soft singing or talking. Remember, your baby has heard your voice a lot during his or her stay in the uterus and is familiar with its sound. Hearing it now will bring comfort in this strange new environment.

- Don't forget to do some cuddling and bonding with the new mom, too.

- Ask for an ice pack to soothe her perineal area, if the nurse doesn't offer one.

- Ask for some juice for the new mom; she may be very thirsty. After she's been rehydrated, and if both of you are in the mood, break out the bubbly—champagne or sparkling cider if you brought some along.

- If you've brought along the necessary equipment, take baby's first photos or capture your amazing newborn on video.

Cesarean Delivery

You won't be able to participate actively at a cesarean delivery the way you would at a vaginal one, and some would consider that a definite plus. Instead of huffing, puffing, and pushing your baby into the world, you'll get to lie back and let everybody else do all the heavy lifting. In fact, your most important contribution to your baby's cesarean birth will be preparation: The more you know, the more comfortable you'll feel. Which is why it's a good idea to look this section over ahead of time, even if you're not having a planned cesarean.

Thanks to regional anesthesia and the liberalization of hospital regulations, most women (and their coaches) are able to be spectators at their cesarean deliveries. Because they aren't preoccupied with pushing or pain, they're often able to relax (at least to some degree) and marvel at the birth. This is what you can expect in a typical cesarean birth:

- An IV infusion will be started (if it isn't already in) to provide speedy access if additional medications or fluids are needed.

- Anesthesia will be administered: either an epidural or a spinal block (both of which numb the lower part of your body but don't knock you out). In rare emergency situations, when a baby must be delivered immediately, a general anesthetic (which does put you to sleep) may be used.

- Your abdomen will be washed down with an antiseptic solution. A catheter (a narrow tube) will be inserted into your bladder to keep it empty and out of the surgeon's way.

- Sterile drapes will be arranged around your exposed abdomen. A screen will be put up at about shoulder level so you won't have to see the incision being made.

- If your coach is going to attend the delivery, he will be suited up in sterile garb. He will sit near your head so that he can give you emotional support and hold your hand; he may have the option of viewing the actual surgery.

- If yours is an emergency cesarean, things may move very quickly. Try to stay calm and focused in the face of all that activity, and don't let it worry you—that's just the way things work in a hospital sometimes.

- Once the physician is certain that the anesthetic has taken effect, an incision (usually a horizontal bikini cut) is made in the lower abdomen, just above the pubic hairline. You may feel a sensation of being "unzipped" but no pain.

- A second incision is then made, this time in your uterus. The amniotic sac is opened, and, if it hasn't already ruptured, the fluid is suctioned out; you may hear a sort of gurgling or swooshing sound.

- The baby is then eased out, usually while an assistant presses on the uterus. With an epidural (though not likely with a spinal block), you will probably feel some pulling and tugging sensations, as well as some pressure. If you're eager to see your baby's arrival, ask the doctor if the screen can be lowered slightly, which will allow you to see the actual birth but not the more graphic details.

- Your baby's nose and mouth are then suctioned; you'll hear the first cry, the cord will be quickly clamped and cut, and you'll be allowed a quick glimpse of your newborn.

- While the baby is getting the same routine attention that a vaginally delivered infant receives, the doctor will remove the placenta.

- Now the doctor will quickly do a routine check of your reproductive organs and stitch up the incisions that were made. The uterine incision will be repaired with absorbable stitches, which do not have to be removed. The abdominal incision may be closed with either stitches or surgical staples.

- An injection of oxytocin may be given intramuscularly or into your IV, to help contract the uterus and control bleeding. IV antibiotics may be given to minimize the chances of infection.

You may have some cuddling time in the delivery room, but a lot will depend on your condition and the baby's, as well as hospital rules. If you can't hold your baby, perhaps your spouse can. If he or she has to be whisked away to the NICU nursery, don't let it get you down. This is standard in many hospitals following a cesarean delivery and is more likely to indicate a precaution than a problem with your baby's condition. And as far as bonding is concerned, later can be just as good as sooner—so not to worry if the snuggles have to wait a little while.

*Congratulations—You've done it . . .
Now relax and enjoy your new baby!*

PART 3

Twins, Triplets & More

When You're Expecting Multiples

CHAPTER 16

Expecting More Than One

HAVE TWO (OR MORE) PAS-sengers aboard the mother ship? Even if you'd been hoping for multiples, your first response to the news that you're car-rying more than one can be all over the emotional map—ranging from disbelief to joy, from excitement to

---

Seeing Double—Everywhere?

If it looks like multiples are multiply-ing these days, it's because they are. In fact, about 3 percent of babies in the United States are now born in sets of two, three, or more, with the majority (about 95 percent) of these multiple births comprised of twins. At least twice as amazing, the number of twin births has jumped more than 50 percent in recent years, and higher-order multiple births (triplets and more) has risen an astonishing 400 percent.

So what's up with this multiple-baby boom? The surge in older moms has a lot to do with it. Moms over the age of 35 are naturally more likely to drop more than one egg at ovulation (thanks to greater hormone fluctuations, spe-cifically FSH, or follicle-stimulating hormone), upping the odds of having twins. Another factor is the increase in fertility treatments (also more common among older moms), which multiplies the chances of a multiple pregnancy. And yet another surprising factor, say some experts, might be the increase in obesity. Women with prepregnancy BMIs higher than 30 are significantly more likely to have fraternal twins than women with lower BMIs.

trepidation (make that fear). And in between all the whoops of delight and buckets of tears will come the questions: Will the babies be healthy? Will I be healthy? Will I be able to stick with my regular practitioner, or will I have to see a specialist? How much food will I have to eat, and how much weight do I have to gain? Will there be enough room inside of me for two babies? Will there be enough room in my house for two babies? Will I be able to carry them to term? Will I have to go on bed rest? Will giving birth be twice as hard?

Carrying one baby comes with its share of challenges and changes; carrying more than one—well, you've probably already done the math. But not to worry. You're up for it—or at least you will be once you're armed with the information in this chapter (and the support of your partner and your practitioner). So sit back (comfortably, while you still can) and get ready for your marvelous multiple pregnancy.

What You May Be Wondering About

Detecting a Multiple Pregnancy

"I just found out I'm pregnant and I have a feeling it's twins. How will I find out for sure?"

Gone are the days when multiples took their parents by surprise in the delivery room. Today, most parents-to-be of multiples discover the exciting news pretty early on. Here's how:

Ultrasound. The proof is in the picture—the ultrasound picture, that is. If you're looking for indisputable confirmation that you're carrying more than one baby, an ultrasound is the best way to get it. Even an early first-trimester ultrasound done at six to eight weeks (which you're very likely to have if your blood hCG level is high or if you've conceived using fertility treatments, though some practitioners also do them routinely) can sometimes detect multiples. But if you want to be absolutely sure you're seeing double, you'll want to look to an ultrasound done after the 12th week (because very early ultrasounds don't always uncover both babies).

Doppler. The beat goes on . . . and on. Your practitioner can usually pick up a baby's heartbeat sometime after the ninth week. And though it's hard to distinguish two heartbeats with just a Doppler, if your practitioner is an experienced listener and thinks he or she detects two distinct beats, there's a good chance that you're carrying multiples (an ultrasound will confirm the news).

Hormone levels. The pregnancy hormone hCG is detectable in your urine about 10 days postconception, and its level rises rapidly throughout the first trimester. Sometimes (but not always), a higher-than-usual hCG level may indicate multiple fetuses. That said, the range of normal hCG levels for twins also falls within the normal range for singletons, so an elevated level of hCG does not, in and of itself, indicate a multiple pregnancy.

Fraternal or Identical?

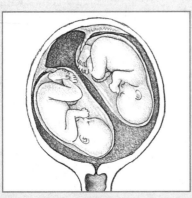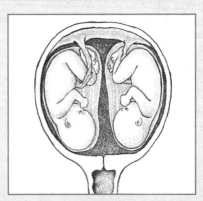

Fraternal twins (left), which result from two eggs being fertilized at the same time, each have their own placenta. Identical twins (right), which come from one fertilized egg that splits and then develops into two separate embryos, may share a placenta or—depending on when the egg splits—may each have their own.

Fraternal twins are the more common type of twin, with your chances of having fraternal twins increasing with your age and the number of children you have. Your chance of having twins in general increases if you have twins in your family on your mother's side.

Test results. An unusually high (positive) result on the triple (or quad) screen (see page 63) in the second trimester can sometimes indicate a multiple pregnancy.

Your measurements. Not surprisingly, the more babies, the bigger the uterus. At each visit, your practitioner feels for the height of the fundus (the top of your uterus) to measure that growth. Measuring larger than would be expected for gestational age may be a sign that you have more than one baby on board (but not always; see page 162).

Bottom line on your hunch: Lots of clues can point to a multiple pregnancy (including your mom-to-be instincts), but only an ultrasound can tell you for sure. Check with your practitioner.

Choosing a Practitioner

"I just found out I'm having twins. Can I use my regular ob-gyn, or do I need to see a specialist?"

If you're happy with your practitioner, there's no reason to trade in for a specialist's care just because you have two babies to care for. (Just make sure you are really happy with your practitioner, since you'll be spending more time with him or her during your twin pregnancy—more babies equals more office visits). Even if your regular practitioner is a midwife, you'll likely be able to continue seeing her as long as you also have a physician on board for regular checkups and for delivery.

Do you like your regular ob but also like the idea of extra-careful care? Many ob-gyn practices send patients who are pregnant with multiples to a specialist for periodic consultations—a good compromise if you'd like to combine the familiar comfort of your practitioner's care with the expertise of a specialist's. Moms-to-be of multiples who have specific special needs (such as advanced age, history of miscarriage, or a chronic health condition) may want to consider switching to a maternal-fetal medicine specialist (also known as a perinatologist). Talk that possibility over with your practitioner if your pregnancy falls into a higher risk category.

When choosing a practitioner for your multiple pregnancy, you'll also need to factor in his or her hospital affiliation. Ideally, you'll want a facility with the ability to care for premature babies (one with a neonatal intensive care unit) in case your bundles arrive early, as multiples often do.

Also ask about the practitioner's policy on topics specifically related to multiple births: Will you be induced at 37 or 38 weeks as a matter of course, or will you have the option of carrying beyond that time frame if all is going well? Will a vaginal birth be possible, or does the practitioner routinely deliver multiples via cesarean delivery? Will you be able to give birth in an LDR (labor and delivery room), or is it routine to deliver multiples in an OR as a precautionary measure?

For more general information about choosing a practitioner, see page 21.

Pregnancy Symptoms

"I've heard that when you're pregnant with twins, your pregnancy symptoms are worse than with just one baby. Is that true?"

Twice the babies sometimes spell twice the pregnancy discomforts, but not always. Every multiple pregnancy, like every singleton pregnancy, is different. An expectant mom of one may suffer enough morning sickness for two, while a mom-to-be of multiples might sail through her pregnancy without a single queasy day. The same with other symptoms, too.

But though you shouldn't expect a double dose of morning sickness (or heartburn, or leg cramps, or varicose veins), you can't count it out. The miseries do, on average, multiply in a multiple pregnancy, and that's not surprising given the extra weight you'll be carrying around and the extra hormones you're already generating. Among the symptoms that might be—but won't necessarily be—exponentially exacerbated when you're expecting twins or more:

- Morning sickness. Nausea and vomiting can be worse in a multiple pregnancy, thanks to—among other things—the higher levels of hormones circulating in a mom's system. Morning sickness can also start earlier and last longer.

- Other tummy troubles. Hello, heartburn, indigestion, and constipation. More gastric crowding (and more gastric overloading, since moms of multiples are eating for three or more) can lead to an increase in the kinds of digestive discomforts pregnancy's known for.

- Fatigue. This is a no-brainer: The more weight you're dragging around, the more you're likely to drag. Fatigue can also increase with the extra energy an expectant mom of multiples expends (your body has to work twice as hard to grow two babies). Sleep deprivation can also wear you out (it's difficult enough to settle down with a watermelon-size belly, let alone one that's the size of two watermelons).

- All those other physical discomforts. Every pregnancy comes with its share of aches and pains; your twin pregnancy might just come with a little more than its share. Toting that extra baby can translate to extra backache, pelvic twinges, crampiness, swollen ankles, varicose veins, you name it. Breathing for three or more can also seem an extra effort, especially as your babies get big enough to push up on your lungs.

• Fetal movement. Though every pregnant woman might feel at some point that she's expecting an octopus, the eight limbs you'll be carrying will really pack a punch. Make that many punches, and kicks.

Whether your pregnancy ends up bestowing you with double the discomforts or not, one thing's for sure—it'll also bestow you with twice the rewards. Not bad, for nine months' work.

Eating Well with Multiples

"I'm committed to eating well now that I'm pregnant with triplets, but I'm not sure what that means—eating three times as much?"

Belly up to the buffet table, Mom—feeding four means it's always time to chow down. While you won't literally have to quadruple your daily intake (any more than a woman expecting a single baby has to double it), you will need to do some serious eating in the months to come. Moms-to-be of multiples should indulge in an extra 150 to 300 calories a day per fetus, doctor's orders (good news if you're looking for a license to eat, not so good news if queasiness or tummy crowding has your appetite cramped). Which translates to an extra 300 to 600 calories if you're carrying twins, an extra 450 to 900 calories for triplets (if you've started out with

an average prepregnancy weight). But before you take that extra allotment as a free pass to Burritoville (extra guacamole for Baby A; extra sour cream for Baby B; refried beans for Baby C), think again. The quality of what you eat will be just as important as the quantity. In fact, good nutrition during a multiple pregnancy has an even greater impact on baby birthweight than it does during a singleton pregnancy.

So just how do you eat well when you're expecting more than one? Check out the Pregnancy Diet (see Chapter 5) and:

Keep it small. The bigger your belly gets, the smaller you'll want your meals to stay. Not only will grazing on five or six healthy mini meals and snacks ease your digestive overload (and your tummy crowding), but it'll keep your energy up—while delivering the same nutritional bottom line as three squares.

Make your calories count. Pick foods that pack plenty of nutrients into small servings. Studies show that a high-calorie diet that's also high in nutrients significantly improves your chances of having healthy full-term babies. Wasting too much of that premium space on junk food, on the other hand, means you'll have less room for nutritious food.

Go for extra nutrients. Not surprisingly, your need for nutrients multiplies with each baby—which means you'll have to tack on some extra servings to your Daily Dozen (see page 93). It's usually recommended that women carrying multiples get one extra serving of protein, one extra serving of calcium, and one extra serving of whole grains. Be sure to ask your practitioner what he or she recommends in your case.

Pump up the iron. Another nutrient you'll need to ramp up is iron, which helps your body manufacture red blood cells (you'll need lots of those for the increased blood your multiple-baby factory will be using) and helps keep you from becoming anemic, which often happens in multiple pregnancies. Red meat, dried fruit, pumpkin seeds, and spinach are great sources of iron (you can find more iron-rich foods on page 100). Your prenatal vitamin and possibly a separate iron supplement should fill in the rest; ask your practitioner.

Keep the water flowing. Dehydration can lead to preterm labor (something moms-to-be of multiples are already at risk for), so make sure you drink at least eight 8-ounce glasses of liquid a day.

For more information on eating well for multiples, check out *What to Expect: Eating Well When You're Expecting.*

Weight Gain

"I know I'm supposed to gain more weight with twins, but just how much more?"

Get ready to gain. Most practitioners advise a woman expecting twins to gain 35 to 45 pounds and a woman expecting triplets to gain an average of 50 pounds (a little less if you were over-weight prepregnancy; a little more if you were underweight). Sounds like a piece of cake, right? Or maybe two pieces of cake (or heck, maybe the whole cake). But the reality is, gaining enough weight isn't always as easy as it seems when you've got two—or more—on board. In fact, a variety of challenges you may face throughout your pregnancy can keep the numbers on the scale from climbing fast enough.

Standing between you and weight gain in the first trimester might be nausea, which can make it difficult to get food down—and then keep it down. Eating tiny amounts of comforting (and, hopefully, sometimes nutritious) food throughout the day can help get you through those probably queasy months. Aim for a pound-a-week gain through the first trimester, but if you find you can't gain that much, or have trouble gaining any at all, relax. You can have fun catching up later. Just be sure to take your prenatal vitamin and stay hydrated.

Use the second trimester (which will probably be your most comfortable one—and the easiest one for you to do some serious chowing down in) as your chance to load up on the nutrition your babies need to grow. If you gained no weight during the first trimester (or

---

What to Gain When You're Gaining for Two or More

Pregnancy Status	First-Trimester Weight Gain	Second-Trimester Weight Gain	Third-Trimester Weight Gain	Total Weight Gain
Normal with Twins	3–4 pounds	20–22 pounds	14–19+ pounds	37–54 pounds
Overweight with Twins	1–2 pounds	17–22 pounds	13–19+ pounds	31–50 pounds
Triplets	4–5 pounds	30+ pounds	11–15 pounds	45+ pounds

Multiple Time Line

Already counting down your
40 weeks? You might not
have to count that high after all. A
twin pregnancy may be considered
full-term a full 3 weeks earlier, at
37 weeks, which is certainly reason to celebrate (3 weeks less of
puffiness, heartburn—and waiting!). But just as 95 percent of all
singletons fail to arrive on their due
date, multiples keep their moms
and dads (and practitioners) guessing, too. They might just stay put
until 39 weeks (or longer)—or
they might make their appearance
before they've clocked in the full
37 weeks. In fact, the average multiple pregnancy lasts 35½ weeks.

If your babies do end up over-
staying their 37-week term, your
practitioner may elect to induce
at 38 weeks, depending on how
they're doing and how you're doing,
as well as his or her practice preferences. Be sure to have an end-game
discussion with your practitioner
long before the end is near, because
many differ on how they typically
handle the late stages of a multiple
pregnancy.

---

if you lost weight due to severe nausea
and vomiting), your practitioner may
want you to gain 1½ to 2 pounds per
week during this period for twins or 2
to 2½ per week for triplets. (If you've
been gaining steadily through the first
trimester, you'll only have to aim for
1½ pounds a week for twins or 2 per
week for triplets.) That may seem like a
lot of weight in a short time, and you're
right—it is. But it's weight that's important to gain. Supercharge your eating
plan with extra servings of protein, calcium, and whole grains. Heartburn and

indigestion starting to cramp your eating
style? Spread your nutrients out over
those six (or more) mini meals.

As you head into the home stretch
(aka, the third trimester), reach for a goal
of 1½ to 2 pounds per week through
your seventh month. By 32 weeks, your
babies may be 4 pounds each, which
won't leave much room in your crowded-
out stomach for food. Still, even though
you'll be feeling plenty bulky already,
your babies will have to bulk up quite
a bit more—and they'll appreciate the
nutrition a well-balanced diet provides.
So focus on quality over quantity, and
expect to taper down to a pound a week
or less in the eighth month and just a
pound or so total during the ninth. (This
makes more sense when you remember
that most multiple pregnancies don't
make it to 40 weeks.)

Exercise

**"I'm a runner, but now that I'm pregnant
with twins, can I keep on exercising?"**

Exercise can benefit most pregnancies,
but when you're staying fit for three,
you'll have to work out with care. If your
practitioner green-lights exercise during
the first and second trimesters (do be
sure to ask), he or she will probably steer
you toward more gentle options than running. You'll definitely be advised to avoid
any workout that puts a lot of downward
pressure on your cervix or raises your
body temperature significantly. ACOG
recommends that moms-to-be of multiples stay away from high-impact aerobic
exercise (which would include running)
because it can increase the risk of preterm
labor for them. This holds true for experienced runners, too.

Looking for a more sensible fitness routine for the three of you? Good
options include swimming or pregnancy
water aerobics, stretching, prenatal yoga,

light weight training, and riding a stationary bicycle, all exercises that don't require you to be on your feet while you do them. And don't forget your Kegels, the anywhere-anytime exercise designed to strengthen your pelvic floor (which needs extra reinforcement when there are extra babies inside).

No matter what you're doing during your workout, if the exertion is causing Braxton Hicks contractions or any other red flags listed on page 223, stop immediately, rest, drink some water, and call your practitioner if they don't subside in 20 minutes or more.

Mixed Feelings

"Everybody thinks it's so exciting that we're going to have twins, except us. We're disappointed and scared. What's wrong with us?"

Absolutely nothing. Prenatal daydreams don't usually include two cribs, two high chairs, two strollers, or two babies. You prepare yourself psychologically, as well as physically and financially, for the arrival of one baby—and when you suddenly discover you're having two, feelings of disappointment aren't unusual. Neither is trepidation. The impending responsibilities of caring for one new infant are plenty daunting without having them doubled.

While some expectant parents are happy to hear they're expecting more than one, others take some time getting used to the news. It's just as common to feel initial shock as initial joy—to experience a sense of loss for the intimacy and normalcy of the one-on-one relationship you'd have with a single baby but can't immediately see yourselves having with two. Instead of picturing yourselves rocking, feeding, and cuddling that one baby, you may have a hard time coming to terms with the thought of life with two

newborns. You may also be flooded by conflicted emotions—first asking "Why us?" then feeling guilty about questioning your double blessing (especially if becoming pregnant was a struggle to begin with). All of these feelings (and the others you might be experiencing) are a completely normal reaction to the news that your pregnancy and your lives are taking an unexpected and very special turn.

So accept the fact that you're ambivalent about the dual arrivals, and don't saddle yourselves with guilt (since your feelings are normal and understandable, there's absolutely nothing to feel guilty about). Instead, use the months before delivery to get used to the idea that you'll be having twins (believe it or not, you will get used to it—and you will become happy about it!). Talk openly and honestly to each other (the more you let your feelings out, the less they'll weigh you down and the faster you'll work through them). Talk to anyone you know who has twins, and if you don't know anyone, seek them out through groups and message boards. Sharing your feelings with others who've felt them, and recognizing that you're not the first expectant parents to experience them, will help you accept and, in time, become excited about this pregnancy and the two beautiful babies you'll be holding one day soon. Twins, you'll find, may be double the effort at first, but they're also double the pleasure down the road.

Insensitive Comments

"I can't believe it, but when I told my friends that we're expecting twins, one of them said to me, 'Better you than me.' I thought she'd be happy for me—why would she make such a nasty comment?"

That might be the first insensitive comment you've been ambushed by during your multiple pregnancy,

Multiple Connections

As a multiples mother-to-be, you're about to join a special club already filled with thousands of women just like you—women who are also expecting double the delight and, no doubt, experiencing double the anxiety. Never been a joiner? Membership in this particular club does come with plenty of rewards. By talking to other moms-to-be of multiples, you'll be able to share your fears, your joy, your symptoms, your funny stories (the ones nobody else would get) with women who know just how you're feeling. You'll also be able to score reassuring advice from other expectant moms who have more than one on the way (as well as from those who've already had their multi-stork delivery). Join a discussion group online (check out whattoexpect.com for a multiples message board) or ask your practitioner to hook you up with other pregnant-with-multiples women in his or her practice and start your own group. There are also national organizations that can provide you with contact information for local clubs, including the National Organization of Mothers of Twins Clubs, nomotc.org, or you can use an online search engine to find a local multiples chapter. You can also check out online sites that cater specifically to parents of multiples: mothersof multiples.com; twinstuff.com.

---

but it probably won't be the last. From coworkers to family members to friends to those perfect (make that not-so-perfect) strangers in the supermarket, you'll be amazed at the remarkably rude things people feel completely comfortable saying to an expectant mom of multiples, ranging from "Wow, you're so huge—you must have a litter in there!" to "Boy, you're in for it!" to "I could never manage more than one at a time."

What's up with the lack of tact? The truth is, many people don't know how to react to the news that you're carrying multiples. Sure, a simple "Congratulations!" might be in order, but most people assume that twins are special (they are) and therefore need to be recognized with a "special" comment. Curious about what it must be like to be pregnant with twins, in awe of what you'll be going through once they're born, they're clueless about the right response—so they dish out the completely wrong one. Their intentions are good, but their follow-through stinks.

The best way to react to the rudeness? Don't take it personally, and don't take it too seriously. Realize that even as your friend opened her mouth and inserted her foot, she was almost certainly trying to wish you well (and she probably has no idea that she offended you, so try not to take offense). Remember, too, that you're the best spokeswoman for moms of twins everywhere—and you'll have lots of chances to spread the wonderful word on multiples.

"People keep on asking me if twins run in my family or if I had fertility treatment. I'm not ashamed that I conceived my babies using a fertility drug, but it's also not something I want to share with strangers."

A pregnant woman brings out the nosy like no one else, but a woman expecting multiples becomes everybody's business. Suddenly, your pregnancy goes public—with people you hardly know (or don't know at all) prying into your personal life (and bedroom habits) and prodding you for personal information without thinking twice. But that's just the point—these people aren't really thinking twice—or even once. They're not asking to be intrusive, they're just curious (multiples are fascinating stuff, after all), and they haven't been educated in the fine art of twin etiquette. If you're open to spilling the juicy details, then by all means, go for it ("Well, first we tried Clomid, and when that didn't work we tried IVF, which means that my husband and I went to a fertility clinic . . ."). By the time you're halfway done with your story, the questioner will probably be bored to tears and looking for the nearest exit. Or, you can try one of these responses the next time someone asks about the conception of your twins:

- "They were a big surprise." This can be true whether you've conceived with or without fertility help.

- "Twins run in the family—now." This will shut them up while keeping them guessing.

- "We had sex twice in one night." Who hasn't at some point? Even if the last time was on your honeymoon, it's not a lie—and it'll be the end of the line for their line of questioning.

- "They were conceived with love." Well, that's a given, no matter what—and where do they go from there?

- "Why do you ask?" If they're TTC (trying to conceive) themselves, then maybe it'll open up a conversation that could help them (infertility can be a lonely road, as you probably know). If not, it could stop them in their nosy tracks. After all, they're not nearly as interested in talking about their own lives as they are about yours.

Not in the mood for a witty retort—or to even respond at all (especially after you've been asked the same question five times in a single day)? There's nothing wrong with letting the questioner know that the answer is none of her business, which it isn't. "That's a personal matter" says it all.

Safety in Numbers

"We'd barely adjusted to the fact that I was pregnant when we found out I'm carrying twins. Are there any extra risks for them, or for me?"

Extra babies do come with some extra risks, but not as many as you'd think. In fact, not all twin pregnancies are classified as "high risk" (though higher-order multiples definitely fall into that category), and most expectant mothers of multiples can expect to have relatively uneventful pregnancies (at least in terms of complications). Plus, entering your twin pregnancy armed with a little knowledge about the potential risks and complications can help you avoid many, and will prepare you should you encounter any. So relax (twin pregnancies are really safe), but read up.

For the babies, the potential risks include:

Early delivery. Multiples tend to arrive earlier than singletons. More than half of twins (59 percent of them), most triplets (93 percent), and practically all quadruplets are born premature. While women pregnant with only one fetus deliver, on average, at 39 weeks, twin delivery, on average, occurs at 35 to 36 weeks. Triplets usually come (again, on average) at 32 weeks, and quadruplets at 30 weeks. (Keep in mind that term for twins is considered 37 weeks, not 40.) After all, as cozy as it can be for your little ones in the uterus, it can also get pretty crowded as they grow. Be sure you know the signs of premature labor, and don't hesitate to call your practitioner right away if you're experiencing any of them (see page 300).

Low birthweight. Since many multiple pregnancies end early, most babies born of multiple pregnancies arrive weighing less than 5½ pounds, which is considered low birthweight. Most 5-pounders end up doing just fine healthwise, thanks to advances in caring for these small newborns, but babies born weighing less than 3 pounds are at increased risk for health complications as newborns, as well as for long-term disabilities. Making sure your prenatal health is in top-notch condition and your diet contains plenty of nutrients (including the right amount of calories) can help get your babies to a bigger birthweight. (See *What to Expect the First Year* for more on premature babies.)

Twin-to-Twin Transfusion Syndrome (TTTS). This in utero condition, which happens in about 15 percent of identical twin pregnancies in which the placenta is shared (fraternal twins are almost never affected because they never share a placenta), occurs when blood vessels in their shared placenta cross, resulting in one baby getting too much blood flow and the other too little. This condition is dangerous for the babies, though not to the mother. If it's detected in your pregnancy,

---

Multiple Benefits

Good news! There's never been a safer time to conceive, carry, and give birth to more than one baby, and for lots of reassuring reasons. Here's what you have going for you as a mom-to-be of multiples these days:

- A heads-up. Since the discovery that you're carrying multiples almost always comes early on in pregnancy these days, you've got extra time for planning and preparing for your babies, plus plenty of time to get the best possible prenatal care. And good prenatal care is the ticket to a healthy pregnancy—doubly so in a multiple pregnancy.

- Lots more practitioner visits. Good prenatal care starts with more frequent practitioner visits. You'll likely be seen every two to three weeks (rather than every four) up until your seventh month and more frequently after that. And those visits may get more in-depth as your preg-

nancy progresses. You'll get all the tests singleton moms get, but you may also get internal exams earlier than a singleton mom-to-be would get (to check for signs of preterm labor).

- Pictures, pictures, pictures. Of your babies, that is. You'll get extra ultrasounds to monitor your babies and make sure their development and growth is on track and the pregnancy is healthy. Which means extra reassurance, plus extra pictures for your baby book.

- Extra attention. Good prenatal care also means extra attention to your health to reduce your risk of certain pregnancy complications (like hypertension, anemia, placenta abruption, and preterm labor, which are all more common in multiple pregnancies). With all that extra attention, any problem that develops will be treated quickly.

your practitioner may opt to use amniocentesis to drain off excess fluid, which improves blood flow in the placenta and reduces the risk of preterm labor. Laser surgery to seal off the connection between the blood vessels is another option your practitioner may use. If you're dealing with TTTS, check out fetalhope.org for more information and resources.

A multiple pregnancy can also impact the health of the mother-to-be:

Preeclampsia. The more babies you're carrying, the more placenta you've got on board. This added placenta (along with the added hormones that come with two babies) can sometimes lead to high blood pressure, which may in turn progress to preeclampsia. Preeclampsia affects one in four mothers of twins and usually is caught early, thanks to careful monitoring by your practitioner. For more on the condition and treatment options, see page 548.

Gestational diabetes. Expectant multiple moms are slightly more likely to have gestational diabetes than a singleton mom. That's probably because higher hormone levels can interfere with a mother's ability to process insulin. Diet can usually control (or even prevent) this condition, but sometimes extra insulin is needed (see page 546 for more).

Placental problems. Women pregnant with multiples are at a somewhat higher risk for complications such as placenta previa (low-lying placenta) or placental abruption (premature separation of the placenta). Fortunately, careful monitoring (which you'll be getting) can detect previa long before it poses any significant risk. Abruption can't be detected before it happens, but because your pregnancy is being carefully watched, steps can be taken to avoid further complications should an abruption occur.

Bed Rest

"Will I have to be on bed rest just because I'm carrying twins?"

To bed rest or not to bed rest? That is the question many moms-to-be of multiples ask, and many practitioners don't always have an easy answer. That's because there really isn't an easy answer. The obstetrical jury is still out on whether bed rest helps prevent the kinds of complications sometimes associated with a multiple pregnancy (such as preterm labor and preeclampsia). So in the meantime, until more is known, some practitioners prescribe it in some cases. The more babies in a pregnancy, the more likely it will be prescribed, since the risk of complications increases with each additional fetus.

Be sure to have a discussion with your practitioner early in your pregnancy about his or her philosophy on bed rest. Some practitioners prescribe it routinely for all expectant mothers of multiples (often beginning between 24 and 28 weeks); more and more do it on a case-by-case basis, taking a wait-and-see approach.

If you are put on bed rest, see page 571 for tips on coping with it. And keep in mind that even if you aren't sent to bed, your practitioner will probably still advise you to take it easy, cut back on work, and stay off your feet as much as possible during the latter half of your pregnancy—so get ready to rest up.

Vanishing Twin Syndrome

"I've heard of vanishing twin syndrome. What is it?"

Detecting multiple pregnancies early using ultrasound technology has many benefits, because the sooner you and your practitioner discover you've got two (or more) babies to care for, the better care you'll be able to get. But there's sometimes a downside to knowing so soon. Identifying twin pregnancies earlier than ever also reveals losses that went undetected before the days of early ultrasound.

The loss of one twin during pregnancy can occur in the first trimester (often before the mother even knows she's carrying twins) or, less commonly, later in the pregnancy. During a first-trimester loss, the tissue of the miscarried twin is usually reabsorbed by the mother. This phenomenon, called vanishing twin syndrome, occurs in about 20 to 30 percent of multiple pregnancies. Documentation of vanishing twin syndrome has grown significantly over the past few decades, as early ultrasounds—the only way to be sure early in pregnancy that you're carrying twins—have become routine. Researchers report more cases of vanishing twin syndrome in women older than 30, though that may be because older mothers in general have higher rates of multiple pregnan-

cies, especially with the use of fertility treatments.

There are rarely any symptoms when the early loss of one twin occurs, though some mothers experience mild cramping, bleeding, or pelvic pain, similar to a miscarriage (though none of those symptoms is a sure sign of such a loss). Decreasing hormone levels (as detected by blood tests) may also indicate that one fetus has been miscarried.

The good news is that when vanishing twin syndrome occurs in the first trimester, the mother usually goes on to experience a normal pregnancy and delivers the single healthy baby without complication or intervention. In the much less likely case that a twin dies in the second or third trimester, the remaining baby may be at an increased risk of intrauterine growth restriction, and the mother may be at risk of preterm labor, infection, or bleeding. The remaining baby would then be watched carefully and the rest of the pregnancy monitored for complications.

For help coping with the loss of a twin in utero, see page 583.

see page 583.

ALL ABOUT
Multiple Childbirth

You're probably spending a lot of time wondering (okay, maybe you've been obsessing) about the day you'll actually give birth to your bundles of joy. Every delivery day is an unforgettable one, but if you're carrying twins (or more), yours probably won't be the typical birth story you've heard from moms who've delivered just one. Not surprisingly, things can get a little more complicated when you've got two babies or more heading for the exit—and a lot more interesting.

Will your labor and delivery be twice the effort? What will be the ideal way to deliver your multiple newborns into your two arms? The answers can depend on a lot of factors, such as fetal position, your health, the safety of the babies, and so on. Multiple births have more variables—and more surprises—than single births. But since you'll be getting two (or more) for the price of one labor, your multiple childbirth will be a pretty good deal no matter how it ends up playing out. And remember that whatever route your babies take from your snug womb to your even snugger embrace, the best way is the one that is the healthiest and safest for them—and for you.

Laboring with Twins or More

How will your labor differ from the labor of a mother-of-one? Here are a few ways:

- It could be shorter. Will you have to endure double the pain to end up cuddling double the pleasure? Nope. In fact, when it comes to labor, you're likely to catch a really nice break (for once). The first stage of labor is often shorter with multiples—which means that it may take less time to get to the point where you can start pushing, if you'll be delivering vaginally. The catch? You'll be hitting the harder part of labor sooner.

- Or it could be longer. Because a multiples mom's uterus is overstretched, contractions are sometimes weaker. And weaker contractions could mean that it might take longer to become fully dilated.

- It'll be watched more closely. Because your medical team will have to be twice as careful during your multiple delivery, you'll be monitored more during labor than most moms of singletons. Throughout labor, you'll likely be attached to two (or more) fetal monitors so your practitioner can see how each baby is responding to your contractions. Early on, the babies' heartbeats may be monitored with external belt monitors; this could allow you to go off the monitors periodically so you can walk around or hit the whirlpool tub to help ease your pain (if you're so

---

Twin Timing

Just how far apart will your multiples be born? With vaginal deliveries, most babies are born 10 to 30 minutes apart. With C-sections, it can be just seconds, or up to a minute or two, between births.

---

inclined). In the latter stages of labor, Baby A (the one closest to the exit) may be monitored internally with a scalp electrode while Baby B is still monitored externally. This will put an end to any wandering because you'll be tethered to a machine (but by this time, you may be well past the point of wanting to move around anyway). Be sure to discuss fetal monitoring and how it will affect your mobility with your practitioner.

- You'll probably have an epidural. If you've had your heart set on one anyway, you'll be happy to hear that epidurals are strongly encouraged—or even required—with multiple deliveries, in case an emergency C-section becomes necessary to deliver one or all of your babies. If you'd like to avoid an epidural, talk to your practitioner, because practitioner and hospital policies differ on this topic.

- You'll probably deliver in an operating room. Most hospitals require this, just to be on the safe side (and in case an emergency C-section becomes necessary), so ask ahead. Chances are you'll be able to labor in one of those comfy rooms with the pretty curtains and relaxing prints, but when it's time to push, you'll likely be wheeled into the OR.

Position, Position, Position

Quick . . . flip a coin. Heads (up) or tails (down)? Or maybe a combination of both? How multiples will end up at delivery time (and how you'll end up delivering) is anybody's guess. Here's a look at the possible ways your twins may be presenting and the likely delivery scenarios for each situation.

Vertex/vertex. This is the most cooperative position that twins can wind up in on delivery day, and they wind up in it about 40 percent of the time. If both your babies are vertex (heads down), you'll likely be able to go into labor naturally and attempt a vaginal birth. Keep in mind, however, that even perfectly positioned singletons sometimes need to be delivered by C-section. This goes double for twins.

Vertex/breech. The second best-case scenario if you're hoping for a vaginal birth for your twins is the vertex/breech setup. This means that if Baby A is head down and well positioned for delivery, it may be possible for your practitioner to manipulate Baby B from the breech position to vertex after Baby A is born. This can be done either by applying manual pressure to your abdomen (external version) or literally reaching inside your uterus to turn Baby B (internal version). The internal version sounds much more complicated than it is; because Baby A has essentially warmed up and stretched out the

birth canal already, the procedure's over pretty quickly. If Baby B remains stubbornly breech, your practitioner may do a breech extraction, in which your baby is pulled feet first right out the door.

Breech/vertex or breech/breech. If Baby A is breech or if both your babies are bottoms down, your physician will almost certainly recommend a C-section. Though external version is commonplace for breech singletons (and can work in the above-mentioned vertex/breech multiple pregnancy), it's considered too risky in this scenario.

Baby A oblique. Who knew there were so many positions for babies to lie in? When Baby A is oblique, it means his or her head is pointed down, but toward either of your hips rather than squarely on your cervix. In a singleton pregnancy with oblique presentation, a practitioner would probably try external version to bring the baby's head where it needs to be (facing the exit), but that's risky with twins. In this case, two things can happen: An oblique presentation can correct itself as contractions progress, resulting in a vaginal birth, or more likely, your practitioner will recommend a C-section to avoid a long, drawn-out labor that may or may not lead to a vaginal birth.

Transverse/transverse. In this setup, both babies are lying horizontally across your uterus. A double transverse almost always results in a C-section.

Delivering Twins

Here's what you can expect when delivering your twins:

Vaginal delivery. About half of all twins born these days come into the world

the old-fashioned way, but that doesn't mean the birthing experience is the same as it is for singleton moms. Once you're fully dilated, delivery of Baby A may be a cinch ("Three pushes was all it took!") or a protracted ordeal ("It took three hours!"). Though that latter scenario is far from a given, some research has shown that the pushing phase (stage two) is usually longer in a twin delivery than in a singleton delivery. The second twin in a vaginal delivery usually comes within 10 to 30 minutes of the first, and most mothers report that delivering Baby B is a snap compared to Baby A. Depending on the position of Baby B, he or she may need some help from the doctor, who can either reach in and move the baby into the birth canal (internal version) or use vacuum extraction to speed the delivery. The possibility of this kind of intervention is yet another reason why many doctors strongly recommend epidurals for multiple moms. (An arm reaching up into your uterus to pull out a baby isn't pretty without pain meds.)

Mixed delivery. In rare cases (very rare cases), Baby B must be delivered by C-section after Baby A has been delivered vaginally. This is usually done only when an emergency situation has come up that puts Baby B at risk, such as placental abruption or cord prolapse. (Those all-important fetal monitors tell your doctor just how well Baby B is doing after Baby A's arrival.) A mixed delivery is not fun for mom; in the moment, of course, it can be very scary, and after the babies are born, it means recovery from both a vaginal birth and major abdominal surgery, a big double ouch. But when it's necessary, it can be a baby-saving procedure, well worth the added recovery time.

Planned C-section. A scheduled C-section is discussed with your doctor in advance and a date is set. Possible reasons for this plan include a previous C-section (a VBAC is not common practice for multiples), placenta previa or other obstetrical or medical issues, or fetal positions that make vaginal delivery unsafe. With most planned C-sections, your spouse, partner, or coach can accompany you into the operating room, where you will probably be given a spinal block—a pumped-up version of the epidural used to block pain

Recovery from a Multiple Delivery

Besides having your hands twice as full, your recovery from a multiple delivery will be very similar to that of a singleton delivery, so be sure to read through Chapters 17 and 18. You can also expect these postpartum differences:

■ It'll likely take longer for your belly to return to normal size (it was stretched out more, after all). You'll likely have more extra skin to contend with, too, after all that stretching.

■ You may experience more lochia (vaginal bleeding) for a longer period of time. That's because more blood was stored up in your uterus during your pregnancy, and it all has to go now.

■ Getting back into shape will take longer—mostly because you were probably pretty inactive for the last three months of your pregnancy (no matter how physically fit, or not, you were before your pregnancy).

■ You'll be achier for longer because of all the extra weight you carried around during pregnancy. Not to mention all the extra carrying around you'll be doing after delivery.

Breastfeeding for Two Is Good for Mom, Too

You probably already know that breastfeeding is the best for your babies (see page 447 for tips on breastfeeding multiples). But did you know that it also does your postpartum body good? Breastfeeding releases hormones (oxytocin) that help your uterus contract to its normal size (and remember, yours was especially stretched). This in turn will also stem the flow of lochia, so you'll lose less blood. And if you're concerned about losing weight, just consider those little nurslings to be nature's liposuction machines: Breastfeeding two babies will burn fat and calories twice as fast, which means you'll also have license to continue eating more. Nurse three (or more) and the calorie bonuses multiply.

If your newborns are in the NICU, you probably won't be able to nurse them directly at first, but they'll benefit greatly from the ideal nutrition only you can provide (especially if they're preemies). So cozy up to an electric pump (they can likely be fed with the expressed milk), and continue pumping until they're released and ready to cozy up to your breasts.

in a vaginal birth. You may be surprised by how fast it all goes after you're numb: Baby A's and Baby B's birth times will be separated by anywhere from seconds to just a minute or two.

Unplanned C-section. An unplanned C-section is the other possible way your babies might enter the world. In this case, you may walk into your usual weekly prenatal appointment and find out that you're going to meet your babies the same day. Best to be prepared, so in those later weeks of pregnancy, be sure to get your bag packed and ready to go. Reasons for a surprise cesarean delivery include such conditions as intrauterine growth restriction (where the babies run out of room to grow) or a sharp rise in your blood pressure (preeclampsia). Another unplanned C-section scenario may arise if you labor for a very long time and don't progress at all. A uterus holding 10 or more pounds of babies may be too stretched to contract effectively, so a cesarean delivery might be the only way out.

Delivering Triplets

Wondering if your triplets are destined to take the abdominal route out? Cesarean delivery is most often used for triplets—not only because it's usually safest, but because C-sections are more common in high-risk deliveries (a category triplets always fall into) and because they're more common among older moms (who give birth to the majority of triplets). But some doctors say that vaginal delivery can be an option if Triplet A (the one nearest the "exit") is in a head-down presentation and there are no other complicating factors (such as preeclampsia in the mother or fetal distress in one or more of the babies). In some rare cases, the first baby or the first and second may be delivered vaginally, and the final one may require a cesarean delivery. Of course, more important than having all three of your babies exit vaginally is having all four of you leaving the delivery room in good condition—and any route to that outcome will be a successful one.

PART 4

After the Baby Is Born

CHAPTER 17

Postpartum: The First Week

CONGRATULATIONS! THE MOMENT you've awaited for 40 (or so) weeks has finally arrived. You've put months of pregnancy and long hours of childbirth behind you, and you're officially a mother, with a new bundle of joy in your arms instead of in your belly. But the transition from pregnancy to postpartum comes with more than just a baby. It also comes with a variety of new symptoms (good-bye pregnancy aches, pains, and discomforts, hello postpar-

tum ones) and a variety of new questions (Why am I sweating so much? Why am I having contractions if I've already delivered? Will I ever be able to sit again? Why do I still look six months pregnant? Whose breasts are these anyway?). Hopefully, you'll have a chance to read up on these and many more pertinent postpartum topics in advance. Once you're on full-time mom duty, finding the time to read anything (never mind use the toilet) won't be easy.

What You May Be Feeling

During the first week postpartum, depending on the type of delivery you had (easy or difficult, vaginal or cesarean) and other individual factors, you may experience all, or only some, of the following:

Physically

- Vaginal bleeding (lochia) similar to your period

- Abdominal cramps (afterpains) as your uterus contracts

- Exhaustion
- Perineal discomfort, pain, numbness, if you had a vaginal delivery (especially if you had stitches)
- Some perineal discomfort if you had a C-section
- Pain around the incision and, later, numbness in the area, if you had a C-section (especially a first one)
- Discomfort sitting and walking if you had an episiotomy, a repair of a tear, or a cesarean delivery
- Difficulty urinating for a day or two
- Constipation; discomfort with bowel movements for the first few days
- Hemorrhoids, continued from pregnancy, or new from pushing
- All-over achiness, especially if you did a lot of pushing
- Bloodshot eyes; black-and-blue marks around eyes, on cheeks, elsewhere, from too-vigorous pushing

- Sweating, and lots of it, particularly at night
- Breast discomfort and engorgement beginning around the third or fourth day postpartum
- Sore or cracked nipples, if you're breastfeeding

Emotionally

- Elation, blues, or swings between the two
- New-mom jitters; trepidation about caring for your new baby, especially if you're a first timer
- Frustration, if you're having a hard time getting started breastfeeding
- A feeling of being overwhelmed by the physical, emotional, and logistical challenges facing you
- Excitement about starting your new life with your new baby

What You May Be Wondering About

Bleeding

"I expected some bleeding after delivery, but when I got out of bed for the first time and saw the blood running down my legs, I was a little freaked out."

Grab a pile of pads, and relax. This discharge of leftover blood, mucus, and tissue from your uterus, known as lochia, is normally as heavy as (and often heavier than) a menstrual period for the first three to ten postpartum days. It may total up to 2 cups before it begins to taper off, and at times it may seem pretty profuse. A sudden gush when you stand up in the first few days is normal—it's just the flow that accumulates when you've been lying down or sitting. Because blood and an occasional blood clot are the predominant ingredients of lochia during the immediate postpartum period, your discharge can be quite red for anywhere from five days to three weeks, gradually turning to a watery pink, then to brown, and finally to a yellowish white. Maxipads, not tampons, should be used to absorb the flow, which may continue on and off for just a couple of weeks or as long as six weeks.

In some women, light bleeding continues for three months. The flow is different for everyone.

Breastfeeding—and/or intravenous Pitocin (oxytocin), which is routinely ordered by some doctors following delivery—may reduce the flow of lochia by encouraging uterine contractions. These postdelivery contractions help shrink the uterus back to its normal size more quickly while pinching off exposed blood vessels at the site where the placenta separated from the uterus. For more about these contractions, see the next question.

If you're in the hospital or birthing center and you think your bleeding may be excessive, notify a nurse. If you experience what seems to be abnormally heavy bleeding (see page 569) once you're home, call your practitioner without delay; if you can't reach him or her, go to the emergency room (in the hospital where you delivered, if possible).

Afterpains

"I've been having crampy pains in my abdomen, especially when I'm nursing. What's that about?"

Thought you'd felt the last of those contractions? Unfortunately, they don't end immediately with delivery—and neither does the discomfort they cause. Those so-called afterpains are triggered by the contractions of the uterus as it shrinks (from about 2⅓ pounds to just a couple of ounces) and makes its normal descent back into the pelvis following the birth of your baby. You can keep track of the shrinking size of your uterus by pressing lightly below your navel. By the end of six weeks, you probably won't feel it at all.

Afterpains can definitely be a pain, but they do good work. Besides helping the uterus find its way back to its usual size and location, those contractions help slow normal postpartum bleeding. They're likely to be more of a pain in women whose uterine muscles are lacking in tone because of previous births or excessive stretching (as with a multiple pregnancy). Afterpains can be more pronounced during nursing, when contraction-stimulating oxytocin is released (a good thing, actually, since it means your uterus is shrinking faster) and/or if you've had intravenous Pitocin (oxytocin) following delivery.

The pains should subside naturally within four to seven days. In the meantime, acetaminophen (Tylenol) should provide relief. If it doesn't, or if the pains persist for more than a week, see your practitioner to rule out other postpartum problems, including infection.

Perineal Pain

"I didn't have an episiotomy, and I didn't tear. Why am I so sore down below?"

You can't expect some 7 pounds of baby to pass unnoticed. Even if your perineum was left neatly intact during the baby's arrival, that area has still been stretched, bruised, and generally traumatized, and discomfort, ranging from mild to not so mild, is the very normal result. The pain may be worse when you cough or sneeze, and you may even find that it hurts to sit down for a few days. You can try the same tips given in the next answer for women with post-tear pain.

It's also possible that in pushing your baby out, you developed hemorrhoids and, possibly, anal fissures, which can range from uncomfortable to extremely painful. See page 272 for tips on dealing with hemorrhoids.

"I tore during delivery and now I'm incredibly sore. Could my stitches be infected?"

Everyone who delivers vaginally (and sometimes those who have a lengthy labor before delivering via cesarean) can expect some perineal pain. But, not surprisingly, that pain's likely to be compounded if the perineum was torn or surgically cut (aka an episiotomy). Like any freshly repaired wound, the site of a laceration or episiotomy will take time to heal, usually 7 to 10 days. Pain alone during this time, unless it is very severe, is not an indication that you've developed an infection.

What's more, infection (though possible) is really very unlikely if your perineal area has been well cared for since delivery. While you're in the hospital or birthing center, a nurse will check your perineum at least once daily to be certain there is no inflammation or other indication of infection. She'll also instruct you in postpartum perineal hygiene, which is important in preventing infection not only of the repair site but of the genital tract as well (germs can get around). For this reason, the same precautions apply for those who delivered completely intact. Here's the self-care plan for a healthy postpartum perineum:

- Use a fresh maxipad at least every four to six hours.

- Pour or squirt warm water (or an antiseptic solution, if one was recommended by your practitioner or nurse) over your perineum while you pee to ease burning, and after you're done on the toilet, to keep the area clean. Pat dry with gauze pads or with the paper wipes that come with some hospital-provided sanitary pads, always from front to back. Gently does it—no rubbing.

- Keep your hands off the area until healing is complete.

Though discomfort is likely to be greater if you've had a repair (with itchiness around the stitches possibly accompanying soreness), the suggestions below will likely be welcome no matter how you delivered. To relieve perineal pain:

Ice it. To reduce swelling and bring soothing relief, use chilled witch hazel pads, a surgical glove filled with crushed ice, or a maxipad with a built-in cold pack, applied to the site every couple of hours during the first 24 hours following delivery.

Heat it. Warm sitz baths (a bath in which only your hips and buttocks are submerged) for 20 minutes a few times a day or hot compresses will ease discomfort.

Numb it. Use local anesthetics in the form of sprays, creams, ointments, or pads recommended by your practitioner. Acetaminophen (Tylenol) may also help.

Keep off it. To keep the pressure off your sore perineum, lie on your side when possible, and avoid long periods of standing or sitting. Sitting on a pillow (especially one with an opening in the center) or inflated tube (usually marketed to hemorrhoid sufferers) may also help, as can tightening your buttocks before sitting.

Keep it loose. Tight clothing, especially underwear, can rub and irritate the area, plus slow healing. Let your perineum breathe as much as possible (for now, favor baggy sweats over spandex leggings).

Exercise it. Kegel exercises, done as frequently as possible after delivery and right through the postpartum period, will stimulate circulation to the area, promoting healing and improving muscle tone. Don't worry if you can't feel yourself doing the Kegels; the area will be numb right after delivery. Feeling

When to Call Your Practitioner Postpartum

Few women feel their physical (or emotional) best after delivering a baby—that's just par for postpartum. Especially in the first six weeks after delivery, experiencing a variety of aches, pains, and other uncomfortable (or unpleasant) symptoms is common. Fortunately, what isn't common is having a serious complication. Still, it's smart to be in the know. That's why all recent deliverees should be aware of symptoms that might point to a postpartum problem, just in case. Call your practitioner without delay if you experience any of the following:

- Bleeding that saturates more than one pad an hour for more than a few hours. If you can't reach your practitioner immediately, call your local emergency room and have the triage nurse assess you over the phone. He or she will be able to tell you whether or not you should come into the ER. While waiting

or en route to the ER, if necessary, lie down and keep an ice pack (or a ziplock plastic bag filled with ice cubes and a couple of paper towels to absorb the melting ice) on your lower abdomen (directly over your uterus, if you can locate it).

- Large amounts of *bright red* bleeding any time after the first postpartum week. But don't worry about light menstrual-like bleeding for up to 6 weeks (in some women as many as 12) or a flow that increases when you're more active or when you're nursing.

- Bleeding that has a foul odor. It should smell like a normal menstrual flow.

- Numerous or large (lemon-size or larger) clots in the vaginal bleeding. Occasional small clots in the first few days, however, are normal.

will return to the perineum gradually over the next few weeks—and in the meantime, the work's being done even if you can't feel it.

If your perineum becomes very red, very painful, and swollen, or if you detect an unpleasant odor, you may have developed an infection. Call your practitioner.

Delivery Bruises

"I look more like I've been in a boxing ring than in a birthing room. How come?"

Look and feel like you've taken a beating? That's normal postpartum. After all, you probably worked harder

birthing your child than most boxers work in the ring, even though you were only facing a 7- or 8-pounder. Thanks—or no thanks—to powerful contractions and strenuous pushing (especially if you were pushing with your face and chest instead of your lower body), you might be sporting a variety of unwelcome delivery souvenirs. These may include black or bloodshot eyes (dark glasses will do a cover-up job in public until your eyes return to normal, and cold compresses for 10 minutes several times a day may help speed that return) and bruises, ranging from tiny dots on the cheek to larger black-and-blue marks on the face or upper chest area. You may also be bringing home soreness in your chest

- A complete absence of bleeding during the first few postpartum days

- Pain or discomfort, with or without swelling, in the lower abdominal area beyond the first few days after delivery

- Persistent pain in the perineal area, beyond the first few days

- After the first 24 hours, a temperature of over 100°F for more than a day

- Severe dizziness

- Nausea and vomiting

- Localized pain, swelling, redness, heat, and tenderness in a breast once engorgement has subsided, which could be signs of mastitis or breast infection. Begin home treatment (page 446) while waiting to reach your practitioner.

- Localized swelling and/or redness, heat, and oozing at the site of a C-section incision

- After the first 24 hours, difficult urination; excessive pain or burning when urinating; a frequent urge to urinate that yields little result; scanty and/or dark urine. Drink plenty of water while trying to reach your practitioner.

- Sharp chest pain (not chest achiness, which is the usual result of strenuous pushing); rapid breath or heartbeat; blueness of fingertips or lips

- Localized pain, tenderness, and warmth in your calf or thigh, with or without redness, swelling, and pain when you flex your foot. Rest, with your leg elevated, while you try to reach your practitioner.

- Depression that affects your ability to cope or that doesn't subside after a few days; feelings of anger toward your baby, particularly if those feelings are accompanied by violent urges. See page 458 for more on postpartum depression.

and/or difficulty taking a deep breath, due to strained chest muscles (hot baths, showers, or a heating pad may ease it), pain and tenderness in the area of your tailbone (heat and massage may help), and/or general all-over achiness (again, heat may help).

Difficulty Urinating

"It's been several hours since I gave birth, and I haven't been able to pee."

Peeing doesn't come easily for most women during the first 24 postpartum hours. Some women feel no urge at all; others feel the urge but are unable to satisfy it. Still others manage to urinate, but with accompanying pain and burning. There are a host of reasons why basic bladder function often becomes too much like hard work after delivery:

- The holding capacity of the bladder increases because it suddenly has more room to expand—thus your need to pee may be less frequent than it was during pregnancy.

- The bladder may have been traumatized or bruised during delivery. Temporarily paralyzed, it may not send the necessary signals of urgency even when it's full.

- Having had an epidural may decrease the sensitivity of the bladder or your alertness to its signals.

- Pain in the perineal area may cause reflex spasms in the urethra (the tube through which the urine exits), making urination difficult. Swelling of the perineum may also stand between you and an easy pee.

- The sensitivity of the site of a tear or episiotomy repair can cause burning and/or pain with urination. Burning may be alleviated somewhat by standing astride the toilet while urinating so the flow comes straight down, without touching sore spots. Squirting warm water on the area while you pee can also decrease discomfort (use the squirt bottle the nurse probably gave you; ask for one if she didn't).

- Dehydration, especially if you didn't do any drinking during a long labor, and didn't receive any IV fluids.

- Any number of psychological factors may keep you from going with the flow: fear of pain, lack of privacy, embarrassment or discomfort over using a bedpan or needing assistance at the toilet.

As difficult as peeing may be after delivery, it's essential that you empty your bladder within six to eight hours to avoid urinary tract infection, loss of muscle tone in the bladder from over-distension, and bleeding (because an overfull bladder can get in the way of your uterus as it attempts the normal postpartum contractions that staunch bleeding). Therefore, the nurse will ask you frequently after delivery if you've accomplished this important goal. She may even request that you make that first postpartum pee into a container or bedpan, so she can measure your output, and may palpate your bladder to make sure it's not distended. To help get things flowing:

- Be sure you're drinking plenty of fluids: What goes in is more likely to go out. Plus, you lost a lot during delivery.

- Take a walk. Getting up out of bed and going for a slow stroll as soon after delivery as you're able will help get your bladder (and your bowels) moving.

- If you're uncomfortable with an audience (and who isn't?), have the nurse wait outside while you urinate. She can come back in when you've finished and give you a demonstration of perineal hygiene, if she hasn't already.

- If you're too weak to walk to the bathroom and you have to use a bedpan, ask for some warm water to pour over the perineal area (which may stimulate the urge). It will also help to sit on the pan, instead of lying on it. Privacy, again, will be key to success.

- Warm your perineal area in a sitz bath or chill it with ice packs, whichever seems to induce urgency for you.

- Turn the water on while you try. Running water in the sink really does encourage your own faucet to flow.

If all efforts fail and you haven't peed within eight hours or so after delivery, your practitioner may order a catheter (a tube inserted into your urethra) to empty your bladder—another good incentive to try the methods above.

After 24 hours, the problem of too little generally becomes one of too much. Most new moms usually begin urinating frequently and plentifully as the excess fluids of pregnancy are excreted. If you're still having trouble peeing, or if output is scant during the next few days, it's possible you have a urinary tract infection (see page 498 for signs and symptoms of a UTI).

"I can't seem to control my urine. It just leaks out."

The physical stress of childbirth can put a lot of things temporarily out of commission, including the bladder. Either it can't let go of the urine—or it lets go of it too easily, as in your case. Such leakage (called urinary incontinence) occurs because of loss of muscle tone in the perineal area. Kegel exercises, which are recommended for every postpartum mom anyway, can help restore the tone and help you regain control over the flow of urine. See page 454 for more tips on dealing with incontinence; if it continues, consult your practitioner.

That First Bowel Movement

"I delivered two days ago and I haven't had a bowel movement yet. I've actually felt the urge, but I've been too afraid of opening my stitches to try."

The passage of the first postpartum bowel movement is a milestone every newly delivered woman is anxious to put behind her (so to speak). And the longer it takes you to get past that milestone, the more anxious—and the more uncomfortable—you're likely to become.

Several physiological factors may interfere with the return of bowel-business-as-usual after delivery. For one thing, the abdominal muscles that assist in elimination have been stretched during childbirth, making them flaccid and sometimes temporarily ineffective. For another, the bowel itself may have taken a beating during delivery, leaving it sluggish. And, of course, it may have been emptied before or during delivery (remember that diarrhea you had prelabor? The poop that you squeezed out during pushing?), and probably stayed pretty empty because you didn't eat much solid food during labor.

But perhaps the most potent inhibitors of postpartum bowel activity are psychological: worry about pain; the unfounded fear that you'll split open any stitches; concern that you'll make your hemorrhoids worse; the natural embarrassment over lack of privacy in the hospital or birthing center; and the pressure to "perform," which often makes performance all the more elusive.

Just because postpartum constipation is common, though, doesn't mean you can't fight it. Here are some steps you can take to get things moving again:

Don't worry. Nothing will keep you from moving your bowels more effectively than worrying about moving your bowels. Don't worry about opening the stitches—you won't. Finally, don't worry if it takes a few days to get things moving—that's okay, too.

Request roughage. If you're still in the hospital or birthing center, select as many whole grains (especially bran cereal) and fresh fruits and vegetables from the menu as you can. Since those pickings may be slim, supplement with bowel-stimulating food brought in from outside, such as apples and pears, raisins and other dried fruit, nuts, seeds, and bran muffins. If you're home, make sure you're eating regularly and well—and that you're getting your fill of fiber. As much as you can, stay away from bowel-clogging foods (like those gift boxes of chocolates that are likely piling up on your bedstand or coffee table—tempting but, sadly, constipating).

Keep the liquids coming. Not only do you need to compensate for fluids you lost during labor and delivery, you need to take in additional liquids to help soften stool if you're clogged up. Water's always a winner, but you may also find apple or prune juice especially effective. Hot water with lemon can also do the trick.

Chew, chew, chew. Chewing gum stimulates digestive reflexes for some people and could get your system back to normal, so grab a stick of gum.

Get off your bottom. An inactive body encourages inactive bowels. You won't be running laps the day after delivery, but you will be able to take short strolls up and down the halls. Kegel exercises, which can be practiced in bed almost immediately after delivery, will help tone up not only the perineum but also the rectum. At home, take walks with baby; also, see page 465 for postpartum exercise ideas.

Don't strain. Straining won't break open any stitches you have, but it can lead to or aggravate hemorrhoids. If you already have hemorrhoids, you may find relief with sitz baths, topical anesthetics, witch hazel pads, suppositories, or hot or cold compresses.

Use stool softeners. Many hospitals send women home with both a stool softener and a laxative, for good reason. Both can help get you going.

The first few bowel movements may be a pain to pass, literally. But fear not. As stools soften and you become more regular, the discomfort will ease and eventually end—and moving your bowels will become second nature once again.

Excessive Sweating

"I've been waking up at night soaked with sweat. Is this normal?"

It's messy, but it's normal. New moms are sweaty moms, and for a couple of good reasons. For one thing, your hormone levels are dropping—reflecting the fact that you're no longer pregnant, as you might have noticed. For another, perspiration (like frequent urination) is your body's way of ridding itself of pregnancy-accumulated fluids after delivery—something you're bound to be happy about. Something you might not be happy with is how uncomfortable that perspiration might make you, and how long it might continue. Some women keep sweating up a storm for several weeks or more. If you do most of your perspiring at night, as most new moms do, covering your pillow with an absorbent towel may help you sleep better (it'll also help protect your pillow).

Don't sweat the sweat—it's normal. Do make sure, though, that you're drinking enough fluids to compensate for the ones you're losing, especially if you're breastfeeding but even if you're not.

Fever

"I've just come home from the hospital and I'm running a fever of about 101°F. Should I call my doctor?"

It's always a good idea to keep your practitioner in the loop if you're not feeling well right after giving birth. A fever on the third or fourth postpartum day could possibly be a sign of postpartum infection, but it could also be caused by a nonpostpartum-related illness. Fever can also occasionally be caused by the combination of excitement and exhaustion that's common in the early postpartum period. A brief low-grade fever (less than 100°F) occasionally accompanies engorgement when your milk first comes in, and it's nothing to worry about. But as a precaution, report to your practitioner any fever over 100°F that lasts more than a day during the first three postpartum weeks or that lasts more than a few hours if it's a higher fever—even if it's accompanied by obvious cold or flu symptoms or vomiting—so that its cause can be determined and any necessary treatment started.

Engorged Breasts

"My milk finally came in, leaving my breasts three times their normal size—and so hard and painful that I can't put on a bra. Is this what I have to look forward to until I wean my baby?"

Just when you thought your breasts couldn't get any bigger, they do. That first milk delivery arrives, leaving your breasts swollen, painfully tender, throbbing, granite hard—and sometimes seriously, frighteningly gigantic. To make matters more uncomfortable and inconvenient, this engorgement (which can extend all the way to the armpits) can make nursing painful for you and, if your nipples are flattened by the swelling, frustrating for your baby. The longer it takes for you and your baby to hook up for your first nursing sessions, the worse the engorgement is likely to be.

Happily, though, it won't last long. Engorgement, and all its miserable effects, gradually lessens once a well-coordinated milk supply-and-demand system is established, typically within a matter of days. Nipple soreness, too—which usually peaks at about the 20th feeding, if you're keeping count—generally diminishes rapidly as the nipples toughen up. And with proper care (see page 444), so does the nipple cracking and bleeding some women also experience.

Until nursing becomes second nature for your breasts—and completely painless for you—there are some steps you can take to ease the discomfort and speed the establishment of a good milk supply (read all about it starting on page 435).

Women who have an easy time getting started with breastfeeding (especially second timers) may not experience very much engorgement at all. As long as baby's getting those milk deliveries, that's normal, too.

Engorgement if You're Not Breastfeeding

"I'm not nursing. I've heard that drying up the milk can be painful."

Your breasts are programmed to fill (or make that overfill) with milk around the third or fourth postpartum day, whether you plan to use that milk to feed your baby or not. This engorgement can be uncomfortable, even painful—but it's only temporary.

Milk is produced by your breasts only as needed. If the milk isn't used, production stops. Though sporadic leaking may continue for several days, or even weeks, severe engorgement shouldn't last more than 12 to 24 hours. During this time, ice packs, mild pain relievers, and a supportive bra may help. Avoid nipple stimulation, expressing milk, or hot showers, all of which stimulate milk production and keep that painful cycle going longer.

Where's the Breast Milk?

"It's been two days since I delivered, and nothing comes out of my breasts when I squeeze them, not even colostrum. Is my baby going to starve?"

Not only is your baby not starving, he isn't even hungry yet. Babies aren't born with a big appetite or with immediate nutritional needs. And by the time your baby begins to hunger for a breastful of milk (on the third or fourth

Should I Stay or Should I Go Now?

Wondering when you'll be able to bring baby home? How long you and your baby stay in the hospital will depend on the kind of delivery you had, your condition, and your baby's condition. By federal law, you have the right to expect your insurer to pay for a 48-hour stay following a normal vaginal delivery and 96 hours following a cesarean delivery. If both you and your baby are in fine shape and you're eager to get home, you may be able to arrange with your practitioner for an early discharge. In that case, plan on having a home nurse visit (your insurance plan may pay for it) or taking your newborn for an office visit to the doctor within a few days, just to be sure no problems have cropped up. The baby's weight and general condition will be assessed (including a check for jaundice). There should also be an evaluation of how feeding is going—keeping and bringing along a feeding diary will help.

If you do stay the full 48 or 96 hours, take advantage of the opportunity to rest as much as possible. You'll need that energy stash for when you get home.

day postpartum), you'll undoubtedly be able to serve it up.

Which isn't to say that your breasts are empty now. Colostrum, which provides your baby with enough nourishment (for now) and with important antibodies his or her own body can't yet produce (and also helps empty baby's digestive system of excess mucus and his or her bowels of meconium), is definitely present in the tiny amounts necessary. A

teaspoon or so per feeding is all your baby needs at this point. But until the third or fourth postpartum day, when your breasts begin to swell and feel full (indicating the milk has come in), it's not that easy to express by hand. A day-old baby, eager to suckle, is better equipped to extract this premilk than you are.

Bonding

"I expected to bond with my baby as soon as she was born, but I'm not feeling anything at all. Is something wrong with me?"

Moments after delivery, you're handed your long-anticipated bundle of joy, and she's more beautiful and more perfect than you ever dared to imagine. She looks up at you and your eyes lock in a heady gaze, forging an instant maternal-child bond. As you cradle her tiny form, breathe in her sweetness, cover her soft face with kisses, you feel emotions you never knew you had, and they overwhelm you in their intensity. You're a mom in love.

And most likely, you were dreaming—or, at least, pregnant daydreaming. Birthing-room scenes like this one are the stuff dreams—and sappy commercials—are made of, but they don't play out for a lot of new moms. A possibly more-realistic scenario: After a long, hard labor that's left you physically and emotionally drained, a wrinkled, puffy, red-faced stranger is placed in your awkward arms, and the first thing you notice is that she doesn't quite resemble the chubby-cheeked cherub you'd been expecting. The second thing you notice is that she doesn't stop squalling. The third, that you have no idea how to make her stop squalling. You struggle to nurse her, but she's uncooperative; you try to socialize with her, but she's more interested in squalling than in sleeping—and frankly, at this point, so are you. And you can't help wondering (after you've woken up): "Have I missed my opportunity to bond with her?"

Absolutely, positively not. The process of bonding is different for every parent and every baby, and it doesn't come with a use-by date. Though some moms bond faster than others with their newborns—maybe because they've had experience with infants before, their expectations are more realistic, their labors were easier, or their babies are more responsive—few find that attachment forming with super glue speed. The bonds that last a lifetime don't form overnight. They form gradually, over time—something you and your baby have lots of ahead of you.

So give yourself that time—time to get used to being a mother (it's a major adjustment, after all) and time to get to know your baby, who, let's face it, is a newcomer in your life. Meet your baby's basic needs (and your own), and you'll find that love connection forming—one day (and one cuddle) at a time. And speaking of cuddles, bring 'em on. The more nurturing you do, the more like a nurturer you'll feel. Though it may not seem like it's coming naturally at first, the more time you spend cuddling, caressing, feeding, massaging, singing to, cooing to, and talking to your baby—the more time you spend skin to skin and face to face—the more natural it will start feeling, and the closer you'll become. Believe it or not, before you know it, you'll feel like the mother you are (really!), bound to your baby by the kind of love you've dreamed of.

"My new son was premature and was rushed to the NICU right away. The doctors say he'll be there for at least two weeks. Will it be too late for good bonding when he gets out?"

Not at all. Sure, having a chance to bond right after birth—to make contact, skin to skin, eye to eye—is wonderful. It's a first step in the development of a lasting parent-child connection. But it's only the first step. And this step doesn't have to take place at delivery. It can take place hours or days later in a hospital bed, or through the portholes of an incubator, or even weeks later at home.

And luckily, you'll be able to touch, talk to, or possibly hold your baby even while he's in the NICU. Most hospitals not only allow parent-child contact in such situations, they encourage it. Talk to the nurse in charge of the NICU and see how you can best get close to your newborn during this trying time. For more on the care of premature babies, see *What to Expect the First Year*.

Keep in mind, too, that even moms and dads who have a chance to bond in the birthing room don't necessarily feel that instant attachment (see the previous question). Love that lasts a lifetime takes time to develop—time that you and your baby will start having together soon.

Rooming-In

"Having the baby room in with me sounded like a great idea when I was pregnant. But back then I had no idea how tired I was going to be. What kind of mother would I be, though, if I asked the nurse to take her?"

You would be a very human mother. You've just completed one of life's greatest challenges, childbirth, and are about to begin an even greater one, child rearing. Needing a little bit of rest in between is completely normal—and completely understandable.

Full-time rooming-in is a wonderful option in family-centered maternity care, giving new parents the chance to start getting to know their new arrival from minute one. But it's not a requirement, and it's not for everyone. Some women handle it easily, of course—maybe because their deliveries were a breeze or because they came on the job with previous newborn experience. For them, an inconsolable infant at 3 A.M. may not be a joy, but it's not a nightmare, either. However, for a new mom who's been without sleep for more hours than she can count, who's drained from labor and delivery, and who's never been closer to a baby than a diaper ad (sound familiar?), such predawn bouts can leave her feeling overwhelmed and underprepared.

If you're happy having your baby room with you, great. But if you committed to this sleeping arrangement only to realize you'd really rather get some sleep, don't feel you can't opt out. Partial rooming-in (during the day but not at night) may be a good compromise for you. Or you might prefer to get a good night's sleep the first night and start rooming-in on the second. Just make sure that baby is brought to you for feedings—and not given any supplementary bottles—if you're nursing.

Be flexible. Focus on the quality of the time you spend with your baby in the hospital rather than the quantity, and don't feel guilty about factoring your own needs into the equation. Round-the-clock rooming-in will begin soon enough at home. Get the rest you need now and you'll be better equipped to handle it later.

Recovery from a Cesarean Delivery

"What will my recovery from a C-section be like?"

Recovery from a C-section is similar to recovery from any abdominal surgery, with a delightful difference:

Instead of losing an old gallbladder or appendix, you gain a brand-new baby.

Of course, there's another difference, arguably less delightful. In addition to recovering from surgery, you'll also be recovering from childbirth. Except for a neatly intact perineum, you'll experience all the same postpartum discomforts over the next weeks (lucky you!) that you would have had if you'd delivered vaginally: afterpains, lochia, perineal discomfort (if you went through a lengthy labor before the surgery), breast engorgement, fatigue, hormonal changes, and excessive perspiration, to name a few.

As for your surgical recovery, you can expect the following in the recovery room:

Pain around your incision. Once the anesthesia wears off, your wound, like any wound, is going to hurt—though just how much depends on many factors, including your personal pain threshold and how many cesarean deliveries you've had (the first is usually the most uncomfortable). You will probably be given pain relief medication as needed, which may make you feel woozy or drugged. It will also allow you to get some needed sleep. You don't have to be concerned if you're nursing; the medication won't pass into your colostrum, and by the time your milk comes in, you probably won't need any heavy painkillers. If the pain continues for weeks, as it sometimes does, you can safely rely on over-the-counter pain relief. Ask your practitioner for a recommendation and dosing. To encourage healing, also try to avoid heavy lifting for the first few weeks after the surgery.

Possible nausea, with or without vomiting. This isn't always an aftereffect of the surgery, but if it is, you may be given an anti-nausea medication.

Exhaustion. You're likely to feel somewhat weak after surgery, partly due to blood loss, partly due to the anesthetic. If you went through some hours of labor before the surgery, you'll feel even more beat. You might also feel emotionally spent (after all, you did just have a baby—and surgery), especially if the C-section wasn't planned.

Regular evaluations of your condition. A nurse will periodically check your vital signs (temperature, blood pressure, pulse, respiration), your urinary output and vaginal bleeding, the dressing on your incision, and the firmness and level of your uterus (as it shrinks in size and makes its way back into the pelvis). She will also check your IV and urinary catheter.

Once you have been moved to your room, you can expect:

More checking. The nurse will continue to monitor your condition.

Removal of the urinary catheter. This will probably take place shortly after surgery. Urination may be difficult, so try the tips on page 426. If they don't work, the catheter may be reinserted until you can pee by yourself.

Encouragement to exercise. Before you're out of bed, you'll be encouraged to wiggle your toes, flex your feet to stretch your calf muscles, push against the end of the bed with your feet, and turn from side to side. You can also try the exercises on pages 466 and 467. They're intended to improve circulation, especially in your legs, and prevent the development of blood clots. (But be prepared for some of them to be quite uncomfortable, at least for the first 24 hours or so.)

To get up between 8 and 24 hours after surgery. With the help of a nurse, you'll sit up first, supported by the raised head of the bed. Then, using your hands for support, you'll slide your legs over the side of the bed and dangle them for a few minutes. Then, slowly, you'll be helped to step down on the floor, your hands still on the bed. If you feel dizzy (which is normal), sit right back down. Steady yourself for a few more minutes before taking a couple of steps, and then take them slowly; the first few may be extremely painful. Though you may need help the first few times you get up, this difficulty in getting around is temporary. In fact, you may soon find yourself more mobile than the vaginal deliveree next door—and you will probably have the edge when it comes to sitting.

A slow return to a normal diet. While it used to be routine (and still is in some hospitals and with some physicians) to keep women on IV fluids for the first 24 hours after a cesarean delivery and limit them to clear liquids for a day or two after that, starting up on solids much sooner may be a better bet. Research has shown that women who start back on solids earlier (gradually, but beginning as early as four to eight hours post-op) have that first bowel movement earlier and are generally ready to be released from the hospital 24 hours sooner than those kept on fluids only. Procedures may vary from hospital to hospital and from physician to physician; your condition after the surgery may also play a part in deciding when to pull the plug on the IV and when to pull out the silverware. Keep in mind, too, that reintroduction of solids will come in stages. You'll start with fluids by mouth, moving on next to something soft and easily tolerated (like Jell-O), and on (slowly) from there. But your diet will have to stay on the bland and easily digested side for at least a few days; don't even think about having someone smuggle in a burger yet. Once you're back on solids, don't forget to push the fluids, too—especially if you're breastfeeding.

Referred shoulder pain. Irritation of the diaphragm, caused by small amounts of blood in your belly, can cause a few hours of sharp shoulder pain following surgery. A pain reliever may help.

Probably constipation. Since the anesthesia and the surgery (plus your limited diet) may slow your bowels down, it may be a few days until you pass that first movement, and that's normal. You may also experience some painful gassiness because of the constipation. A stool softener, suppository, or other mild laxative may be prescribed to help move things along, especially if you're uncomfortable. The tips on page 427 may help, too.

Abdominal discomfort. As your digestive tract (temporarily put out of commission by surgery) begins to function again, trapped gas can cause considerable pain, especially when it presses against your incision line. The discomfort may be worse when you laugh, cough, or sneeze. Ask the nurse or doctor to suggest some possible remedies. A suppository may help release the gas, as may strolling up and down the hall. Lying on your side or on your back, your knees drawn up, taking deep breaths while holding your incision can also bring some relief.

To spend time with your baby. You'll be encouraged to cuddle and feed your baby as soon as possible (if you're nursing, place the baby on a pillow over your incision or lie on your side while nursing). And yes, you can even lift your baby. Hospital regulations and your condition permitting, you'll probably be able to have modified or full rooming-in; having your spouse bunking with you, too, will be a big help. Don't push the rooming-in agenda, though, if you're not up to it—or just want some rest.

Removal of stitches. If your stitches or staples aren't self-absorbing, they will be removed about four or five days after delivery. The procedure isn't very painful, although you may have some discomfort. When the dressing is off, take a good look at the incision with the nurse or doctor; ask how soon you can expect the area to heal, which changes will be normal, and which might require medical attention.

In most cases, you can expect to go home about two to four days postpartum. But you'll still have to take it easy, and you'll continue to need help both with baby care and self-care. Try to have someone with you at all times during the first couple of weeks.

Coming Home with Baby

"In the hospital, the nurses changed my baby's diaper, gave him a bath, and told me when to nurse him. Now that I'm home with him, I feel underprepared and overwhelmed."

It's true that babies aren't born with how-to's written on their cute, dimply bottoms (wouldn't that be convenient?). Fortunately, they do typically come home from the hospital with instructions from the staff about feeding, bathing, and changing diapers. Already lost those? Or maybe they ended up smeared with mustardy poop the first time you tried to change baby's diaper while simultaneously trying to read the instructions for changing baby's diaper? Not to worry; there's a wealth of information out there to help you tackle your new job as new parent both in books and online. Plus, you've probably already scheduled the first visit to the pediatrician, where you'll be armed with even more information—not to mention answers to the 3,000 questions you've managed to accumulate (that is, if you remember to write them down and bring them along).

Of course, it takes more than know-how to make a parenting expert out of a new parent. It takes patience, perseverance, and practice, practice, practice. Luckily, babies are forgiving as you learn. They don't care if you put the diaper on backward or forgot to wash behind their ears at bath time. They're also not shy about giving you feedback: They'll definitely let you know if they're hungry, tired, or if you've made the bathwater too cold (though at first you may not be able to tell which complaint is which). Best of all, since your baby's never had another mom to compare you with, you definitely stack up really well in his book. In fact, you're the best he's ever had.

Still suffering from a crumbling of confidence? What might help most—besides the passing of time and the accumulation of experience—is to know that you're in good company. Every mom (even those seasoned pros you doubt-less eye with envy) feels in over her head in those early weeks, especially when postpartum exhaustion—teamed with nightly sleep deprivation and the recovery from childbirth—is taking its toll on her, body and soul. So cut yourself plenty of slack (and while you're at it, cut yourself a piece of cheese and maybe a slice of bread, too—low blood sugar can contribute to that overwhelmed feeling), and give yourself plenty of time to adjust and to get with the parenting program. Pretty soon (sooner than you think), the everyday challenges of baby care won't be so challenging anymore. In fact, they'll come so naturally, you'll be able to do them in your sleep (and will often feel as though you are). You'll be diapering, feeding, burping, and soothing with the best of them—with one arm tied behind your back (or at least, one arm folding laundry, catching up on e-mail, reading a book, spooning cereal into your mouth, or otherwise multitasking). You'll be a mother. And mothers, in case you haven't heard, can do anything.

Getting Started Breastfeeding

There's nothing more natural than nursing a baby, right? Well, not always, at least not right away. Babies are born to nurse, but they're not necessarily born knowing how to nurse. Ditto for moms. The breasts are standard issue, they fill with milk automatically, but knowing how to position them effectively in baby's mouth, well, that's a learned art.

Truth is, while breastfeeding is a natural process, it's a natural process that doesn't necessarily come natu-rally—or quickly—to some mothers and babies. Sometimes there are physical factors that foil those first few attempts; at other times it's just a simple lack of experience on the part of both participants. But whatever might be keeping your baby and your breasts apart, it won't be long before they're in perfect sync. Some of the most mutually satisfying breast-baby relationships begin with several days—or even weeks—of fumbling, bungled efforts, and tears on both sides.

Learning as much as you can about breastfeeding ahead of time—including how to deal with those inevitable setbacks—can help speed that mutual adjustment. Doing lots of reading up or even taking a prenatal class in breastfeeding will be invaluable, as will the following:

- Get off to an early start. Right in the birthing room is ideal, if that's possible (see Breastfeeding Basics for a how-to, page 438.) Let your practitioner know that you'd like to begin breastfeeding as soon after delivery as you can (and while you're at it, write down that request in your birth plan, if you're using one). Don't be disappointed if either you or baby (or both of you) isn't up to nursing right away. That doesn't mean you won't be able to start successfully later. And keep in mind that even the earliest of starts won't guarantee a smooth first nursing experience. You both have a lot to learn.

- Keep the nursing team together. Arrange for full or partial rooming-in, if you feel up to it, so you'll be ready to nurse when baby's ready. If you'd rather rest between feedings—you've earned it—ask for a demand-feeding schedule (your baby will be brought to you when he or she is hungry).

- Enlist as much help as you can. Ideally, a lactation specialist will join you during at least a couple of your first baby feedings to provide hands-on instruction, helpful hints, and perhaps some reading materials. If this service isn't offered to you, ask if a lactation consultant or a nurse who is knowledgeable about breastfeeding can observe your technique and redirect you if you and your baby aren't on target. If you leave the hospital or birthing center before getting this help, your technique should be evaluated by some- one with breastfeeding expertise—the baby's doctor, a home nurse, or an outside lactation consultant—within a few days. You can also find empathy, advice, and referrals to lactation consultants by calling your local La Leche League chapter. Or contact the International Lactation Consultant Association (ILCA), (919) 861-5577, ilca.org, for a lactation consultant in your area.

- Don't let well-wishers get in the way. Consider limiting visitors (maybe even to just your spouse) while you and baby are getting the hang of breastfeeding. As anxious as you are to show your new arrival off, you'll need to maintain a relaxed atmosphere—and complete concentration—during those learning-to-nurse sessions.

- Be patient if your baby gets off to a slow start. He or she may be just as tuckered out from delivery as you are, maybe even more so. Newborn babies are sleepy babies, and yours is likely to be especially drowsy and sluggish at the breast if you received anesthesia or had a prolonged, difficult labor. That's no problem because newborns need little nourishment during the first few days of life. By the time your baby starts needing some serious chow, he or she will be ready to do some serious chowing down. What babies do need even early on, though, is nurturing. Cuddling at the breast is just as important as suckling.

- Keep your baby bottle-free. Make sure your baby's appetite and sucking instinct aren't sabotaged between nursings by well-meaning nurses wielding bottles of formula or sugar water. First, because it doesn't take much to satisfy a newborn's tender appetite. If your baby is given even a small supplementary feeding in the nursery, he or she will be too full for your breast when it's time to nurse. If your baby doesn't nurse, your breasts won't be stimulated to produce milk, and a vicious cycle—one that interferes with the establishment of a good demand-and-supply system—can begin. Second, because a rubber nipple requires less effort, your baby's sucking reflex may become lazy when a bottle's offered. Faced with the greater challenge of tackling the breast, baby may just give up. Pacifiers might also interfere with nursing (though not in all cases). So issue orders—through your baby's doctor—that, as recommended by the American Academy of Pediatrics, supplementary feedings and pacifiers should not be given to your baby in the nursery unless medically necessary.

- Nurse on demand. And if the demand isn't there yet, nurse frequently anyway, getting in at least 8 to 12 feedings a day. Not only will this keep your baby happy, it will stimulate milk production and increase your milk supply to meet his or her growing demand. Imposing a four-hour feeding schedule, on the other hand, can worsen breast engorgement early on and result in a baby who's not getting enough to eat later.

- Nurse without limits. It used to be thought that keeping initial feedings short (five minutes on each breast) would prevent sore nipples by toughening them up gradually. Sore nipples, however, result from improper positioning of the baby on the breast and have little to do with the length of the feeding. Most newborns require 10 to 45 minutes to complete a feeding (it's not as easy as it looks). As long as your positioning is correct, there's no need to put time limits on nursing sessions.

Nursing and the NICU Baby

If your baby has to be in the neonatal intensive care unit (NICU) for any reason and can't go home with you, don't give up on breastfeeding. Babies who are premature or have other problems do better on breast milk, even when they're not ready to tackle a breast. Talk to your baby's neonatologist and the nurse in charge to see how you can best feed your baby in this situation. If you can't nurse directly, perhaps you can pump milk to be given to your baby via tube feeding or bottle. If even this isn't possible, see if you can keep pumping milk to keep your supply up until your baby is ready to feed from you directly.

- Go for empty. Ideally, at least one breast should be "emptied" at each feeding—and this is actually more important than being sure that baby feeds from both breasts. When a breast isn't sufficiently drained, baby doesn't get to the hind milk, which comes at the end of a feeding and contains more of the calories baby needs to gain weight than the milk that comes first (foremilk is baby's thirst quencher; hind milk's the body builder). Hind milk is also more satiating, which means it keeps baby's tank fuller longer. So don't pull the plug just because your baby has fed for 15 minutes on breast number one—wait until he or she seems ready to quit. Then offer the second breast, but don't force it. Remember to start the next feeding on the breast that baby nursed from last and didn't empty completely.

Breastfeeding Basics

1. Pick a quiet location. Until you and baby have breastfeeding down pat, set yourselves up in an area that has few distractions and a low noise level.

2. Have a beverage at your side so you can drink as baby drinks. Avoid anything hot (which could scald you or your baby if it spilled); if you're not thirsting for a cold drink, opt instead for something lukewarm. Add a healthy snack, if it's been a while since your last meal.

3. As you become more comfortable with breastfeeding, you can keep a book or magazine handy to keep you busy during marathon feeding sessions. (But don't forget to put your reading matter down periodically so you can interact with your nursing infant.) In the early weeks, turning on the TV could be too distracting. So can talking on the phone; turn down the ringer and let voice mail pick up messages—or have someone else answer.

4. Get comfy. If you're sitting up, a pillow across your lap can help raise your baby to a comfortable height. Make sure, too, that your arms are propped up on a pillow or chair arms. Trying to hold 6 to 8 pounds without support can lead to arm cramps and pain. And put up your legs, if you can.

5. Position your baby on his or her side, facing your nipple. Make sure baby's whole body is facing you—tummy to tummy—with ear, shoulder, and hip in a straight line. You don't want your baby's head turned to the side; rather, it should be straight in line with his or her body. (Imagine how difficult it would be for you to drink and swallow while turning your head to the side. It's the same for your baby.) Proper positioning is essential to prevent nipple soreness and other breastfeeding problems.

Lactation specialists recommend two nursing positions during the first few weeks. The first is called the crossover hold: Hold your baby's head with the opposite hand (if nursing on the right breast, hold your baby with your left hand). Rest your hand between your baby's shoulder blades, your thumb behind one ear, your other fingers behind the other ear. Using your other hand, cup your breast, placing your thumb above your nipple and areola (the dark area) at the spot where your baby's nose will touch your breast. Your index finger should be at the spot where your baby's chin will touch the breast. *Lightly* compress your breast so your nipple points slightly toward your baby's nose. You are now ready to have baby latch on (see step 6).

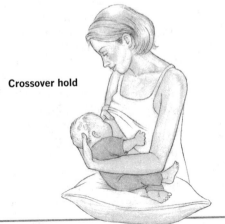

Crossover hold

Football hold

The second position is called the football hold. This position, also called the clutch hold, is especially useful if you've had a C-section and want to avoid placing your baby against your abdomen; or if your breasts are large; or if your baby is small or premature; or if you are nursing twins: Position your baby at your side in a semisitting position facing you, with his or her legs under your arm (your right arm if you're nursing on the right breast). Support your baby's head with your right hand and cup your breast as you would for the crossover hold.

As soon as you're more comfortable with nursing, you can add the cradle hold, in which your baby's head rests in the crook of your arm, and the side-lying hold, in which you and your baby lie on your sides, tummy to tummy. This position is a good choice when you're nursing in the middle of the night.

6. Gently tickle your baby's lips with your nipple until his or her mouth is opened very wide, like a yawn. Some lactation specialists suggest directing your nipple toward your baby's nose and then down to the upper lip to get your baby to open his or her mouth very wide. This prevents the lower lip from getting tucked in during nursing. If your baby turns his or her head away, gently stroke his or her cheek on the side nearest you. The rooting reflex will make baby turn his or her head toward your breast.

7. Once that little mouth is opened wide, move your baby closer. Do not move your breast toward your baby. Many latching-on

problems occur because mom is hunched over baby, trying to shove breast into mouth. Instead, keep your back straight and bring your baby to your breast.

8. Don't stuff your nipple in an unwilling mouth; let your baby take the initiative. It might take a couple of attempts before your baby opens his or her mouth wide enough to latch on properly.

9. Be sure baby latches on to both the nipple and the areola that surrounds it. Sucking on just the nipple won't compress the milk glands and can cause soreness and cracking. Also be sure that it's the nipple and areola that the baby is busily milking. Some infants are so eager to suck that they will latch on to any part of the breast (even if no milk is delivered), causing a painful bruise.

10. If your breast is blocking your baby's nose, *lightly* depress the breast with your finger. Elevating baby slightly may also help provide a little breathing room. But as you maneuver, be sure not to loosen his or her grip on the areola.

11. Check for swallowing. You can be sure that milk is flowing if there is a strong, steady, rhythmic motion visible in your baby's cheek.

12. If your baby has finished suckling but is still holding on to the breast, pulling it out abruptly can cause injury to your nipple. Instead, break the suction first by depressing the breast or by putting your finger into the corner of the baby's mouth to let in some air.

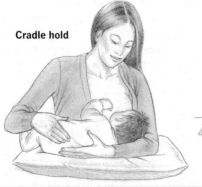

Cradle hold

Side-lying hold

Keeping Track

To be sure each breast gets a chance to be stimulated, use a reminder such as a notation in your breastfeeding journal, a small scrunchie looped around your bra strap, or a bracelet on your wrist to indicate which side you nursed from last. At your next feeding, just start with the other side (and switch the scrunchie or bracelet to the other side, too).

- Don't let sleeping babies lie if it means that they'll sleep through a feeding. Some babies, especially in the first few days of life, may not wake often enough for nourishment. If it's been three hours since your newborn last fed, then it's time for a wake-up call. Here's one way to accomplish this. First, unwrap your baby if he or she is swaddled or heavily dressed; the cool air will help begin the waking process. Then try sitting baby up, one hand supporting the back and the other holding the chin, and rub the back gently. Massaging the arms and legs or dabbing a little cool water on the forehead may help, too. The moment baby stirs, quickly adopt the nursing position. Or lay your sleeping baby on your bare chest. Babies have a keen sense of smell, and the aroma of your breast may awaken him or her.

- Don't try to feed a screaming baby. Ideally, you will feed your baby when he or she first shows signs of hunger or interest in sucking, which might include mouthing his or her hands or rooting around for the nipple, or just being particularly alert. Try not to wait until frantic crying—a late indication of hunger—begins. But if the

frenzy has started, do some rocking and soothing before you put baby to breast. Or offer your finger to suck on until baby calms down. After all, it's hard enough for an inexperienced suckler to find the nipple when calm; when your newborn has worked up to a full-fledged frenzy, it may be impossible.

- Stay calm. Start out as relaxed as you can, and try to stay that way no matter how frustrating the nursing episode becomes. If you've allowed visitors, send them packing 15 minutes before a feeding, and use that time to chill out a little. Do some relaxation exercises before you begin (see page 142) or tune in to some soft music. As you nurse, try to keep your cool. Tension not only hampers milk letdown (your breasts' way of making your milk available for suckling), it can generate stress in your baby (infants are extremely sensitive to mom's moods). An anxious baby can't nurse effectively.

- Keep track. Once your milk comes in and until breastfeeding is well established, keep a running written record of baby's feedings (when they begin and end) as well as of wet and soiled diapers produced each day. While that may sound obsessive, it'll really help give you a good sense of how breastfeeding is going—and also makes it possible for you to report progress to your baby's doctor more accurately (you will be asked). Continue to strive for at least 8 to 12 feedings in each 24-hour period, but never force your baby to suckle. Though the length of feedings may vary considerably, once engorgement and nipple soreness have leveled off, they'll average about half an hour each, usually divided between both breasts (though sometimes a baby will turn away or fall asleep before latching on to breast number two, which is fine as long as number one has been drained well). Your baby's weight gain and diaper record will give you an even clearer picture of baby's intake. There should be at least six wet diapers (the urine should appear clear and not dark yellow) and at least three bowel movements over a 24-hour period. No matter how long baby is suckling, if weight gain and output are satisfactory, you can assume the intake is, too.

Engorgement: When the Milk Comes In

Just when you and your baby seem to be getting the hang of this whole nursing thing, milk gets in the way. Up until now, your baby has been easily extracting tiny amounts of colostrum (premilk), and your breasts have been easily handling the workload. Then it happens, suddenly and without warning: Your milk comes in. Within a few hours, your breasts become swollen, hard, and painful. Nursing from them can become frustrating for baby and seriously uncomfortable for you.

Fortunately, this miserable chapter in breastfeeding history is usually pretty brief, often lasting no more than 24 to 48 hours (though it can occasionally linger as long as a week). While it lasts, here are a variety of ways of relieving engorgement and the discomfort that comes with it:

- Heat it. Use heat briefly to help soften the areola and encourage letdown at the beginning of a nursing session. To do this, place a washcloth dipped in warm, not hot, water on just the areola, or lean it into a bowl of warm water.

- Massage it. You can also encourage milk flow by gently massaging the breast your baby is suckling.

- Cool it. Use ice packs after nursing to reduce engorgement. And although it may sound a little strange and look even stranger, chilled cabbage leaves may also prove soothing (use large outer leaves and make an opening in the center of each for your nipple; rinse and pat dry before applying).

- Dress for it. Wear a well-fitting nursing bra (with wide straps and no plastic lining) around the clock. Pressure against your sore and engorged breasts can hurt, however, so make sure the bra is not too tight. And wear loose clothing that doesn't rub against your sensitive breasts.

- Keep at it. Don't be tempted to skip or skimp on a feeding because of pain. The less your baby sucks, the more engorged your breasts will become— and the more you'll hurt.

Next Stop: Easy Street

Hit a breastfeeding bump or two? Stick with nursing and you'll soon be cruising down Easy Street (as you'll find out, once you get the hang of it, there's no easier way to feed a baby). In the meantime, get the help you need to fix any rough spots you've been facing—either from the tips here or from a lactation consultant. Also, don't let the bumps with a first baby discourage you from nursing your next. Thanks to mom's previous experience (and that of her breasts), nursing is typically second nature with second (and subsequent) babies, making engorgement, nipple soreness, and other problems a lot less common.

The Breastfeeding Diet

It's the couch potato's dream—burning up the calories of a 5-mile run without leaving your lounge chair. And guess what? That dream is your reality now that you're breastfeeding your little Tater Tot. It's true. Milk production burns 500 calories a day, which means that you'll get to eat an extra 500 calories a day (up from your prepregnancy numbers—not your pregnancy allotment) to meet that need.

Hello, potato chips? Not exactly. Quality matters as much as quantity (remember, you're still—sort of—eating for two). The good news is that you're probably an old pro at eating well, what with all the practice you've had for the past nine months. The even better news is that eating well while breastfeeding is very much like eating well while expecting, but with (best news of all) more relaxed recommendations. Plus, while calories definitely count, you still won't need to count them. Just follow the Breastfeeding Diet as best you can:

What to eat. As always, eating well is about getting the right balance of good—and good for you—food. Try to include the following each day while you're breastfeeding:

- Protein: 3 servings

- Calcium: 5 servings (that's up 1 serving from your pregnancy requirement of 4)

- Iron-rich foods: 1 or more servings

- Vitamin C: 2 servings

- Green leafy and yellow vegetables, yellow fruits: 3 to 4 servings

- Other fruits and veggies: 1 or more servings

- Whole-grain and other complex carbohydrates: 3 or more servings

- High-fat foods: moderate amounts —you don't need as much as you did during pregnancy

- At least 8 glasses of water, juice, or other noncaffeinated, nonalcoholic beverages

- DHA-rich foods to promote baby's brain growth (look for this fabulous fat in wild salmon, sardines, walnuts, flaxseed oil, as well as DHA-enriched eggs)

- Prenatal vitamin daily

- Take matters into your own hands. Hand-express a bit of milk from each breast before nursing to lessen the engorgement. This will get your milk flowing, and soften the nipple so your baby can get a better hold on it.

- Switch it. Change nursing positions from one feeding to the next (try the football hold at one feeding, the cradle hold at the next; see page 438). This will ensure that all the milk ducts are being emptied and may help ease the ouch of engorgement.

- Get some relief. For severe pain, take acetaminophen (Tylenol) or another mild pain reliever prescribed by your practitioner.

Leaking Milk

The first few weeks of nursing can be very wet ones. Milk may leak, drip,

You may need to increase your caloric intake as your baby grows bigger and hungrier, or decrease it if you supplement nursing with formula and/or solids, or if you have considerable fat reserves you'd like to begin burning.

What not to eat. When you're breastfeeding, you have a lot more menu options than you did while you were expecting—served up with some caveats. It's fine to pop open the cork on that pinot noir you've been pining for (or flip the top on that ale you've been aching for). But drink within limits (a couple of glasses a week, preferably taken right after you nurse, rather than before, to allow a few hours for the alcohol to metabolize). You can use Milkscreen—simple test strips that detect the volume of alcohol in your breast milk, available at any drugstore—to know if it's safe for your baby. Time to pick up your coffee habit where you left off? Depends on how hefty your habit was. More than a cup or two of joe can make junior jittery and keep you both from getting any sleep. And though it's safe to reel in the sushi again, continue to avoid high-mercury fish, such as shark, tilefish, and mackerel, and to limit those that may contain moderate amounts of that heavy metal.

What to watch out for. If you have a family history of allergies, check with the doctor to see if you should avoid peanuts and foods that contain them (and possibly other highly allergic foods). Also watch out for herbs, even some seemingly innocuous herbal teas. Stick to reliable brands and choose flavors that are considered safe during lactation, including orange spice, peppermint, raspberry, red bush, chamomile, and rosehip. Read labels carefully to make sure other herbs haven't been added to the brew, and drink them only in moderation. And when it comes to sugar substitutes, sucralose (Splenda) or aspartame are considered better bets than saccharine.

What to watch for in your baby. A few moms find that their own diet affects their babies' tummies and temperaments. While what you eat does indeed change the taste and smell of your milk (that happens for all mothers), this is actually a good thing since it exposes your baby to many different flavors. But some babies can occasionally be sensitive to certain foods that end up in mom's milk. If you suspect that something in your diet is turning baby off his or her feed (or turning his or her tummy), try eliminating the food for a few days to gauge the response. Some of the more common troublemakers are cow's milk, eggs, fish, citrus fruits, nuts, and wheat.

For more information on eating while breastfeeding, see *What to Expect: Eating Well When You're Expecting.*

---

or even spray from your breasts, and it can happen at any time, anywhere, without warning. All of a sudden, you'll feel the tingle of letdown—and before you can grab a nursing pad or a sweater to cover up with, you'll look down to see the telltale circle of dampness that gives new meaning to the term "wet T-shirt."

Besides those inopportune and public moments ("So that's why the delivery guy was looking at me funny . . ."), you might find yourself springing spontaneous leaks when you're sleeping or taking a warm shower, when you hear your baby cry, when you think about or talk about your baby. Milk may drip from one breast while you nurse from the other, and if your baby has settled into a somewhat regular feeding schedule, your breasts may be dripping with anticipation before baby latches on.

Though it may be uncomfortable, unpleasant, and endlessly embarrassing, this side effect of breastfeeding is

Medication and Lactation

Many medications are known to be safe for use while you're breastfeeding; others are known not to be; and the scientific jury's still out on the rest. But just as you did while you were expecting, check all medications (prescription or over-the-counter) with your practitioner and your baby's pediatrician before taking them, and be sure any physician who prescribes a new medication knows that you're nursing. Keep in mind that it's usually best to take medication just after a feeding, so that levels in your milk will be lowest when you nurse next time.

completely normal and very common, particularly in the early weeks. (Not leaking at all or leaking only a little can be just as normal, and in fact, many second-time mothers might notice that their breasts leak less than they did the first time around.) In most cases, as breastfeeding becomes established, the system eventually settles down and leaking lessens considerably. In the meantime, while you may not be able to turn off that leaky faucet, you may be able to make living with it a little less messy:

- Stock up on nursing pads. If you're a leaker, you'll find that in the first postpartum weeks, you'll be changing your nursing pads as often as you nurse—sometimes even more frequently. Keep in mind that, like a diaper, they should be changed whenever they become wet. Make sure you use pads that don't have a plastic or waterproof liner; they'll just trap moisture and lead to irritated nipples. Some women prefer the disposable variety,

while others like the feel of the reusable cotton ones.

- Protect your bed. If you find you're leaking a lot at night, use extra nursing pads, or place a large towel under you while you sleep. The last thing you'll want to be doing now is changing your sheets every day or, worse, shopping for a new mattress.

- Don't pump to prevent leaking. Extra pumping won't control the leak; on the contrary, the more you stimulate your breasts, the more milk they'll produce, and the more leaking you'll have to contend with.

- Try to stop the overflow. Once nursing is well established and your milk production has leveled off, you can try to stop the leaking by pressing your nipples (though probably not in public) or holding your arms against your breasts when you feel a leak coming on. Don't, however, do this in the first few weeks because it may inhibit milk letdown and can lead to a clogged milk duct.

Sore Nipples

Tender nipples can make nursing a miserable—and frustrating—experience. Fortunately, most women don't stay sore long; their nipples toughen up quickly and breastfeeding soon becomes a completely painless pleasure. But some women, especially those who have "barracuda babies" (babies with a vigorous suck) or who have been positioning their newborns incorrectly at their breasts, continue to experience soreness and cracking. To ease the discomfort so you can start enjoying breastfeeding:

- Position the right way. Be sure your baby is correctly positioned, facing your breast (see box, page 438). Vary your nursing position so a different part of the areola is compressed at each feeding, but always keep baby facing your breasts.

- Let your nipples breathe (try this at home). Expose sore or cracked nipples to the air briefly after each feeding. Protect them from clothing that rubs and other irritations, and if you're really sore, you might want to consider surrounding them with a cushion of air by wearing breast shells (not shields).

- Keep them dry. Change nursing pads as soon as they become damp. Also, make sure the nursing pads don't have a plastic liner, which will only trap moisture. If you live in a humid climate, wave a blow dryer, set on warm, across each breast (about 6 to 8 inches away) for two or three minutes (no more) after feedings. This is very comforting, if slightly difficult to explain should someone walk in while you're doing it.

- Heal with milk. Breast milk can actually help heal sore nipples. So let whatever milk is left on the breast after a feeding dry there, instead of wiping it away. Or express a few drops of milk at the end of a feeding and rub it on your nipples, letting your nipples dry before you put your bra back on.

- Rub it on. Nipples are naturally protected and lubricated by sweat glands and skin oils. But using a commercial preparation of modified lanolin can prevent and/or heal nipple cracking. After nursing, apply ultrapurified medical-grade lanolin, such as Lansinoh, but avoid petroleum-based products and petroleum jelly itself (Vaseline), as well as other oily products. Wash nipples only with water—never with soap, alcohol, or wipes—whether your nipples are sore or not. Your baby is already protected from your germs, and the milk itself is clean.

- Try tea for two. Wet regular tea bags with cool water and place them on your sore nipples. The properties in the tea may help soothe and heal them.

- Treat them equally. Don't favor one breast because it is less sore or because the nipple isn't cracked; the only way to toughen up nipples is to use them. Plus, for both breasts to become good producers, they both have to get equal stimulation time.

  If one nipple is a lot more sore than the other, nurse from the less tender one first because the baby will suck more vigorously when he or she is hungry. Try to do this only as long as you absolutely have to—and for no more than a few days—because it could keep the sore breast from getting the stimulation it needs and ultimately affect your milk supply. Fortunately, the worst of the soreness shouldn't continue longer than this (if it does, contact a lactation consultant; improper positioning may be the problem).

- Chill out before feeding. Relaxation will enhance the letdown of milk (which will mean that baby won't have to suck as hard), while tension will inhibit it.

- Seek relief. Take acetaminophen (Tylenol) before you nurse to ease soreness.

- Keep a watch. If your nipples are cracked, be especially alert to signs of breast infection (see next page), which can occur when germs enter a milk duct through a crack in the nipple.

When Breastfeeding Gets Bumpy

Once nursing is established, it's usually a smooth ride until baby's weaned. But once in a while, there's a bump or two along the way, among them:

Clogged milk ducts. Sometimes a milk duct clogs, causing milk to back up. This condition—characterized by a small, red, and tender lump on the breast—can lead to infection, so it's important to resolve it quickly. The best way to do this is to offer the affected breast first and let your baby empty it as completely as possible. If baby doesn't finish the job, express any remaining milk by hand or with a breast pump. Keep pressure off the duct by making sure your bra is not too tight (avoiding underwires for now may help) and by varying nursing positions to put pressure on different ducts. Applying hot packs or warm compresses before nursing and gentle massage may also be helpful (baby's chin, if correctly positioned, can provide a clogged duct with an excellent massage). Do not use this time to wean the baby because discontinuing nursing now will only compound the clog.

Breast infection. A more serious and less common complication of breastfeeding is mastitis, or breast infection, which can develop in one or both breasts, most often during the early postpartum period (though it can occur anytime during breastfeeding). The factors that can combine to cause mastitis are failure to drain breasts of milk at each nursing, germs (usually from baby's mouth) gaining entrance into the milk ducts through a crack in the nipple, and lowered resistance in mom due to stress and fatigue.

The most common symptoms of mastitis are severe soreness or pain, hardness, redness, heat, and swelling of the breast, with flulike symptoms—generalized chills and a fever of about 101°F to 102°F. If you develop such symptoms, contact your doctor right away. Prompt medical treatment is necessary and may include bed rest, antibiotics, pain relievers, increased fluid intake, and moist heat applications. You should begin to feel drastically better within 36 to 48 hours after beginning the antibiotics. If you don't, let your practitioner know; he or she may need to prescribe a different type of antibiotic.

Continue to nurse during treatment. Since the baby's germs probably caused the infection in the first place, they won't be harmful. The antibiotics prescribed for the infection will be safe, too. And draining the breast will help prevent clogged milk ducts. Nurse (if you can; it may be quite painful) on the infected breast, and express whatever baby doesn't finish with a pump. If the pain is so bad that you can't nurse, try hand pumping or using a manual breast pump on your breasts (whichever hurts less) while lying in a tub of warm water with your breasts floating comfortably; you can let the milk drip into the water. (Don't use an electric pump in the tub.)

Delay in treating mastitis or discontinuing treatment too soon could lead to the development of a breast abscess, the symptoms of which include excruciating, throbbing pain; localized swelling, tenderness, and heat in the area of the abscess; and temperature swings between 100°F and 103°F. Treatment includes antibiotics and, generally, surgical drainage. The drain may stay in place after surgery. Breastfeeding on that breast usually can't continue in most cases, but you can keep nursing with the other breast until you wean your baby.

Breastfeeding After a Cesarean Delivery

How soon you can breastfeed your newborn after a surgical delivery will depend on how you feel and how your baby is doing. If you're both in good shape, you can probably introduce baby to breast in the recovery room shortly after the surgery is completed. If you're groggy from general anesthesia or your baby needs immediate care in the nursery, this first nursing session may have to wait. If after 12 hours you still haven't been able to get together with your baby, ask about using a pump to express your premilk (colostrum) and get lactation started.

You'll probably find breastfeeding after a C-section uncomfortable at first. It will be less so if you try to avoid putting pressure on the incision with one of these techniques: Place a pillow on your lap under the baby; lie on your side; or use the football hold (page 438), again supported by a pillow, to nurse. Both the afterpains you experience as you nurse and the soreness at the site of the incision are normal and will lessen in the days ahead.

Breastfeeding Multiples

Breastfeeding, like just about every aspect of caring for newborn multiples, seems as though it will be at least twice as challenging. However, once you've fallen into the rhythm of nursing your multiples (and you will!), you'll find that it's not only possible but doubly (or even triply) rewarding. To successfully nurse twins and more, you should:

Eat well—and eat up. Fulfill all the dietary recommendations for lactating mothers (see the Breastfeeding Diet, page 442),

Bottle Baby

Chose the bottle, or the combo? Getting started bottle-feeding is usually a lot easier than getting started breastfeeding (especially because formula comes with instructions, but breasts don't). But there's still plenty to learn, and you can read all about it in *What to Expect the First Year*.

with these additions: 400 to 500 calories above your prepregnancy needs for each baby you are nursing (you may need to increase your caloric intake as the babies grow bigger and hungrier or decrease it if you supplement nursing with formula and/or solids, or if you have considerable fat reserves you would like to burn); an additional serving of protein (for a total of four) and an additional serving of calcium (six total) or the equivalent in calcium supplements.

Pump it up. If your babies are in the NICU and are still too small to breastfeed, or if you need some extra help getting your supply stimulated in the early going, consider using an electric double pump. Later, pumping will allow you to get a few precious extra hours of sleep while someone else feeds the babies. Don't get discouraged if the pump doesn't get you going—no pump can empty a breast as well as a baby can. But regular stimulation from a pump (and your babies) will pump up your milk supply eventually.

Nurse two at a time (or not). You've got two breasts and two (or more) mouths to feed. Are you up to feeding two babies at once? You just might be, especially with a little help (like from oversize nursing

Tandem Nursing

Some mothers of multiples prefer to nurse one baby at a time, finding it easier and more satisfying. Others would rather not spend all day breastfeeding and find that nursing two babies simultaneously saves time and works well. Here are two positions you can use while nursing two at the same time: (1) Position both babies in the football (or clutch) hold. Use pillows to support your babies' heads. (2) Combine the cradle hold and the football hold, again using pillows for support and experimenting until both you and your babies are comfortable.

pillows for twins). An obvious—and big—advantage of tandem nursing two babies is that you don't spend all day and night nursing (first Baby A, now Baby B, and back to Baby A, and so on). To nurse two at the same time, position both babies on the pillow first, and then latch them on (or you can ask someone to hand the babies to you one at a time, especially while you're still getting used to the juggling act).

If tandem nursing doesn't appeal to you, don't do it. You can bottle-feed one (using either pumped milk or formula, if you're supplementing) while nursing the other (and then switch off), or nurse one baby after the other. Some babies are very efficient, taking a full feed in only 10 or 15 minutes. If this is the case with yours, count your little blessings—you won't spend any more time nursing than the average tandem feeder.

Got three (or more) babies to feed? Breastfeeding triplets (and even quads) is possible, too. Nurse two at a time, and then nurse the third one afterward, remembering to switch off which baby gets solo suckling time. For more information on breastfeeding higher-order multiples, check out mostonline.org or tripletconnection.org.

Enlist twice as much help. Get as much help as you can with housework, meal prep, and infant care, to conserve the energy you need to fuel milk production.

Treat each diner differently. Even identical twins have different personalities, appetites, and nursing patterns. So try to tune into the needs of each. And keep extra-careful records to make sure each baby is well fed at each feeding.

Give both breasts a workout. Switch breasts for each baby at each feeding so both breasts are stimulated equally.

Give It Time

So you've been a mom for a week (with the stretch marks, postpartum pains, and bags under your eyes to prove it), and by now you may be wondering: When am I going to feel like one? When will I be able to accomplish latch-on without 20 minutes of fumbling? Or finally get the hang of burping? Or stop worrying about breaking the baby every time I pick her up? When will I be able to coo without feeling like an awkward idiot? When will I figure out which cries mean what—and how to respond to any of them? How do I put on a diaper so it doesn't leak? Get the onesie over baby's head without a struggle? Shampoo that little patch of hair without dripping soap into those tender eyes? When will the job that nature just signed me up for start coming naturally?

The truth is, giving birth makes you a mother, but it doesn't necessarily make you feel like a mother. Only time spent on this sometimes bewildering, sometimes overwhelming, always amazing job will do that. The day-to-day (and night-to-night) of parenting is never easy, but it absolutely, positively gets easier.

So cut yourself some slack, pat yourself on the back, and give yourself time, Mom. Which, by the way, you are.

Postpartum: The First 6 Weeks

B Y NOW YOU'RE PROBABLY EITHER settling into your new life as a fledgling mom or figuring out how to juggle new baby care with the demands of older children. Almost certainly, much of your daily—and nightly—attention is focused on that recently arrived little bundle. Babies, after all, don't take care of themselves. But that doesn't mean you should neglect your own care (yes, moms have needs, too!).

Though most of your questions and concerns are likely to be baby-related right now, you're sure to have some that are a little more mommy-centric, too, from the state of your emotions ("Will I ever stop crying during insurance commercials?"), to the state of your sexual union ("Will I ever want to do 'it' again?"), to the state of your waist ("Will I ever be able to wear jeans that zip?"). The answers: yes, yes, and yes—just give it time.

What You May Be Feeling

The first six weeks postpartum are considered a "recovery" period. Even if you sailed through your pregnancy and had the easiest labor and delivery on record (and especially if you didn't), your body has still been stretched and stressed to the max—and it needs a chance to regroup. Every new mom, like every expectant one, is different—so all will make that recovery at a different rate, with a different collection of postpartum symptoms. Depending on the type of delivery you had, how much help you have at home, and a variety of other individual factors, you may experience all, or only some, of the following:

Physically

- Continued period-like vaginal discharge (lochia), first dark red, then pink, turning brownish, then yellowish white

- Fatigue

- Some continuing pain, discomfort, and numbness in the perineum, if you had a vaginal delivery (especially if you had stitches) or labored before having a cesarean delivery

- Diminishing incision pain, continuing numbness, if you had a C-section (especially if it was your first)

- Gradual easing of constipation and, hopefully, hemorrhoids

- Gradual slimming of your belly as your uterus recedes into the pelvis

- Gradual weight loss

- Gradual decrease in swelling

- Breast discomfort and nipple soreness until breastfeeding is well established

- Backache (from weak abdominal muscles and from carrying baby)

- Joint pain (from joints loosened during pregnancy in preparation for delivery)

- Achiness in arms and neck (from carrying and feeding baby)

- Hair loss

Emotionally

- Elation, moodiness, or swings between the two

- A sense of being overwhelmed, a growing feeling of confidence, or swings between the two

- Little interest in sex or, less commonly, stepped-up desire

What You Can Expect at Your Postpartum Checkup

Your practitioner will probably schedule you for a checkup four to six weeks postpartum. (If you had a cesarean delivery, you may be asked to come in at about three weeks postpartum to have your incision looked at.) During your postpartum visit, you can expect the following to be checked, though the exact rundown of the visit will vary depending on what your particular needs are and your practitioner's style of practice. Don't forget to write down all the questions that are sure to come up (and that you're sure to forget if you don't write them down).

- Blood pressure

- Weight, which may possibly be down by about 17 to 20 pounds

- Your uterus, to see if it has returned to prepregnant shape, size, and location

- Your cervix, which will be on its way back to its prepregnant state but will still be somewhat engorged

- Your vagina, which will have contracted and regained much of its muscle tone

- The episiotomy or laceration repair site, if any; or, if you had a cesarean delivery, the site of your incision

- Your breasts

- Hemorrhoids or varicose veins, if you have either

- Questions or problems you want to discuss—have a list ready

At this visit, your practitioner will also discuss with you the method of birth control that you're planning to use (if you're planning not to get pregnant again immediately, that is). If you plan on using a diaphragm and your cervix has recovered, you will be fitted for one (toss your old one, because it won't fit properly anymore); if you're not fully healed, you may have to use condoms until you can be refitted. Birth control pills may be prescribed now, too, though if you're breastfeeding, your oral contraceptive options will be limited to those that are safe during lactation, such as the progesterone-only mini pill. For more on birth control options, see *What to Expect the First Year.*

What You May Be Wondering About

Exhaustion

"I knew I'd be tired after giving birth, but I haven't gotten any sleep in more than four weeks, and I'm so exhausted, it's not funny."

No one's laughing—especially none of the other sleep-deprived new parents out there. And no one's really wondering why you're so exhausted, either. After all, you're juggling endless feeding, burping, changing, rocking, and pacing. You're trying to tackle the mountain of laundry that seems to grow larger and more daunting each day and the pile of thank-you notes that never seem to get written. You're shopping (out of diapers—again?), and you're schlepping (who knew how much baby stuff you'd need to lug just to pick up milk at the supermarket?). And you're doing it all on an average of about three hours' sleep (if you're lucky) a night, with a body that's still recovering from childbirth. In other words, you have multiple good reasons to be calling yourself Our Lady of Perpetual Exhaustion.

Is there a cure for this maternal fatigue syndrome? Not really—at least not until your baby starts sleeping through the night. But in the meantime, there are many ways of regaining some of your get-up-and-go—or at least enough so you can keep getting up and going:

Get some help. Hire help if you can afford to. If you can't, rely on volunteers. Now's a good time to let your mom, your mother-in-law, or your best friends lend their helping hands. Suggest they take baby out for a stroll while you grab a power nap or they pick up your groceries, dry cleaning, or that bag of diapers you desperately need.

Share the load. Parenting—when there are two parents—is a two-person job. Even if your partner-in-parenting is holding down a 9 to 5, he should be sharing the baby load when he's home. Ditto the cleaning, laundry, cooking, and shopping. Together, divide and conquer the responsibilities, then write down who's on for what and when so there's no confusion. (If you're a single parent, enlist a close friend to help out as much as possible.)

Don't sweat the small stuff. The only small stuff that matters right now is your baby. Everything else should take a distant backseat until you're feeling more energetic. So let the dust bunnies breed where they may (even if it's on top of those thank-you notes you don't have time to get to). And while you're ignoring those thank-you notes, buy some time by sending out a bulk e-mail with baby's picture attached.

Find deliverance. Now that you've delivered, it's time to find stores and restaurants that will deliver, too—whether it's the hot meal you'd never have time to cook, or the rectal thermometer you forgot to buy. Even groceries can find their way to your home via the Internet. Ditto all those baby essentials. Order in bulk so you don't run out of diapers so quickly (but don't buy so far in advance that baby outgrows the diapers before you get a chance to use them).

Sleep when the baby sleeps. Yes, you've heard it before, and probably snorted at the thought. After all, baby's nap time is the only time you can tackle the 300 other things that never seem to get done. But stop snorting and start snoring. Lie down for even 15 minutes during one of the baby's daytime naps, and you'll feel better able to handle the crying when it starts again (in 15 minutes).

Feed your baby, feed yourself. Yes, you're busy feeding baby—but don't forget to feed yourself, too. Fight fatigue by grazing on snacks and mini meals that combine protein and complex carbs to serve up long-term energy instead of the momentary rush: string cheese and crackers; trail mix; precut veggies with bean dip; a smoothie; a yogurt, banana, and a granola bar. Keep your fridge, your glove compartment, and your diaper bag stocked with such grab-and-go snacks so you're never running on empty. While sugar and caffeine (that king-size candy bar and that five-shot latte, taken in

quick succession) may seem the obvious solution for the energy-challenged, remember this: Though they may give you the boost you crave in the short term, they'll quickly lead to an energy crash and burn. And don't just eat; drink plenty of water, too—not only because you've lost a lot of fluid during delivery, but because dehydration can lead to exhaustion. All of these tips apply to all new moms, but are especially important for nursing moms who are still eating for two.

If you're really beat, check with your practitioner to rule out any other physical cause responsible for your exhaustion (such as postpartum thyroiditis; see page 460). If you're feeling a little blue or depressed (see page 456), take steps to get that under control, too, because baby blues are tied to fatigue as well (and also to thyroiditis). If you get a clean bill of health, rest assured—that is, when you can rest at all—your zombie days are numbered. You will live to sleep again.

Hair Loss

"My hair seems to be falling out suddenly. Am I going bald?"

You're not going bald—you're just going back to normal. Ordinarily, the average head sheds 100 hairs a day (just not all at once, so you don't usually notice them), and those hairs are being continually replaced. During pregnancy, however, the hormonal changes keep those hairs from falling out, which means your head hangs on to them (remember how thick your hair felt back in the pregnant days?). But all good things must come to an end, including your reprieve on hair fall. All those hairs that were slated to go during pregnancy will be shed sometime after delivery, usually in the first six months postpartum—and often in unsettling clumps. Some women who are breastfeeding exclusively report that hair fall doesn't begin until they wean their baby or supplement the nursing with formula or solids. You'll take comfort knowing that by the time your baby is ready to blow out the candles on that first birthday cake (and has a full head of hair of his or her own), your hair should be back to normal—and business as usual—too.

To keep your hair healthy, continue taking a vitamin supplement, eat well, and treat your mane humanely. That means shampooing only when necessary (as if you had time for any shampoos now), using a conditioner and/or a detangling leave-on spray to reduce the need to tug at tangles, using a wide-toothed comb if you do have to untangle wet, and avoiding frying your hair with curling or flat irons (as if you have the time to style it, anyway).

Talk to your practitioner if your hair loss seems really excessive.

Postpartum Urinary Incontinence

"I thought I'd have more control over my bladder once my baby was born, but I gave birth nearly two months ago and I'm still peeing when I cough or laugh. Is it going to be like this forever?"

So your new-mom bladder is letting you—and your panties—down? It's completely normal to occasionally leak some urine involuntarily in the months (yes, months) following delivery, usually while laughing, sneezing, coughing, or performing any strenuous activity—and it's pretty common (more than a third of moms spring this particular leak postpartum). That's because pregnancy, labor, and delivery weakened the muscles

around your bladder and pelvis, making it harder for you to control the flow of urine (it took a licking and therefore keeps on dripping). Plus, as your uterus shrinks in the weeks following delivery, it sits directly on the bladder, compressing it and making it more difficult to stem the tide. Hormonal changes after pregnancy can also batter your bladder.

It can take between three and six months, or even longer, to regain complete bladder control. Until then, use panty liners or pads to absorb leaking urine (no tampons, please—they don't block the flow of urine, because it's a different outlet, and they're off-limits postpartum period anyway), and take these steps to help regain control faster:

Keep your Kegels up. Thought you were done with your Kegels now that your baby's delivered? Not so fast. Continuing those pelvic floor–strengthening exercises will help you recover bladder control now and preserve it later on in life.

Keep your weight down. Start shedding those pregnancy pounds sensibly, because all those extra pounds are still applying pressure on your bladder.

Train your bladder to behave. Urinate every 30 minutes—before you have the urge—and then try to extend the time between pees, going (without going) a few more minutes each day.

Stay regular. Try to avoid constipation, so full bowels don't put added pressure on your bladder.

Drink up. Keep drinking at least eight glasses of fluid every day. It might seem that cutting back on water might cut down on the leak, but dehydration makes you vulnerable to UTIs. An infected bladder is more likely to leak, and a leaking bladder is more likely to become infected.

Fecal Incontinence

"I'm so embarrassed because I've been passing gas involuntarily lately and even leaking a little feces. What can I do about it?"

As a new mother, you definitely expected to be cleaning up after your baby—but you probably didn't count on cleaning up after yourself. Yet some newly delivered moms do add fecal incontinence and the involuntary passing of gas to that long list of unpleasant postpartum symptoms. That's because during labor and childbirth, the muscles and nerves in the pelvic area are stretched and sometimes damaged, which can make it difficult for you to control how and when waste (and wind) leaves your body. In most cases, the problem takes care of itself as the muscles and nerves recover, usually within a few weeks.

Until then, skip hard-to-digest foods (nothing fried, no beans, no cabbage), and avoid overeating or eating on the run (the more air you gulp, the more you

---

Help for Leaks That Won't Let Up

Tried every do-it-yourself trick for dealing with postpartum urinary or fecal incontinence—including Kegel-ing until you're blue in the face—but you're still left with a leak? Don't let embarrassment keep you from talking to your practitioner. He or she might suggest biofeedback (a mind-body technique that can be surprisingly effective in relieving incontinence), other treatments, or in a particularly tough case, surgery. Fortunately, the situation most often resolves itself without that kind of intervention.

---

are likely to pass it as gas). Keeping up with your Kegels can also help tighten up those slack muscles as well as the ones that control urine (which also may be leaking these days).

Postpartum Backache

"I thought all my back pain would go away after delivery, but It hasn't. Why?"

Welcome back, backache. If you're like nearly half of all newly delivered moms, your old pal from pregnancy has returned for an unwelcome visit. Some of the pain still has the same cause—hormonally loosened ligaments that haven't yet tightened up. It may take time, and several weeks of soreness, before these ligaments regain their strength. Ditto for the stretched-out and weakened abdominal muscles that altered your posture during pregnancy, putting strain on your back. And of course, now that you've got a baby around, there's another reason for that pain in your back: all that lifting, bending, rocking, feeding, and toting you're doing. Especially as that cute little load you're carrying around gets bigger and heavier, your back will be up against growing stress and strain.

While time heals most things, including those postpartum aches and pains, there are other ways to get your back back on track:

- Tone that tummy. Ease into some undemanding exercises, like pelvic tilts, that will strengthen the muscles that support your back.

- Mend when you bend. And lift. Give your back a break by bending from your knees to pick up that dropped diaper or lift that baby.

- Don't be a slouch on the couch. When feeding your baby, don't slump over (as tempting as that might be, given your state of exhaustion). Your back will thank you if it's well supported (using pillows, armrests, or whatever else lets you sit pretty).

- Get off your feet. Sure, you're running (and rocking) all the time, but whenever you don't have to, take a seat. When you have to stand, placing one foot on a low stool will take some pressure off your lower back.

- Watch your posture. Listen to your mom, Mom—and stand up straight, even when you're swaying from side to side. Slouched shoulders result in an aching back. As your baby gets bigger, avoid resting that growing weight on one hip, which will throw your back off further, plus lead to hip pain.

- Put your feet up. Who deserves to put their feet up more than you? Plus, elevating your feet slightly when sitting—and baby feeding—will ease the strain on your back.

- Wear your baby. Instead of always holding your baby, wear him or her in a baby carrier or a sling. Not only will it be soothing to baby, it'll be soothing to your achy back and arms.

- Pull a switch. Many moms play favorites with their arms, always carrying (or bottle feeding) their baby in one arm or the other. Instead, alternate arms so they each get a workout (and your body doesn't get a lopsided ache).

- Rub it. A professional massage, if you can spare the time and the change, is definitely what your muscles are aching for. But in a pinch, ask your spouse to step in and rub.

- Turn up the heat. A heating pad can spell relief from back pain and muscle aches. Apply it often, especially during those marathon feeding sessions.

As your body adjusts to pumping baby, you'll probably find that pain in your back (and arms, and hips, and neck) diminishing, and you may even find yourself sporting some brand-new triceps. In the meantime, here's something else that might help ease your aches by easing your load: Empty that diaper bag. Lug around only what you absolutely need, which is plenty heavy anyway.

Baby Blues

"I was sure I'd be thrilled once my baby was born. But I'm feeling down instead. What's going on?"

It's the best of times; it's the worst of times. And it's how an estimated 60 to 80 percent of new moms feel after childbirth. So-called baby blues appear (appropriately) out of the blue—usually three to five days after delivery, but sometimes a little earlier or a little later—bringing on unexpected sadness and irritability, bouts of crying, restlessness, and anxiety. Unexpected because—well, for one thing, isn't having a baby supposed to make you happy, not miserable?

It's actually easy to understand why you're feeling this way if you step back for a moment and take an objective look at what's been going on in your life, your body, and your psyche: rapid changes in hormone levels (which drop precipitously after childbirth); a draining delivery, followed by an exhausting homecoming, and all compounded by the round-the-clock demands of newborn care; sleep deprivation; possible feelings of letdown (you were expecting motherhood to come naturally—it hasn't; you were expecting cute and round—you got puffy and cone-headed); breastfeeding stumbling blocks (sore nipples, painful engorgement); unhappiness over your looks (the bags under your eyes, the pooch around your belly, the fact that there are more dimples on your thighs than on your baby's); and stress in your relationship with your partner (what relationship?). With such an overwhelming laundry list of challenges to confront (and don't even get you started on the laundry that's on that list), it's no wonder you're feeling down.

The baby blues will likely fade over the next couple of weeks as you adjust to your new life and start getting a little more rest—or, more realistically, begin functioning more effectively on less rest. In the meantime, try the following tips to help lift yourself out of that postpartum slump:

Lower the bar. Feeling overwhelmed and inadequate in your role as a newbie mom? It may help to remember that you won't be for long. After just a few weeks on the job, you're likely to feel much more comfortable in those maternal shoes. In the meantime, lower your expectations for yourself—and for your baby. Then lower them some more. Make this your mantra, even after you've become a parenting pro: There's no such thing as a perfect parent, or a perfect baby. Expecting too much means you'll be letting yourself down—and bringing your mood down, too. Instead, just do the best you can (which at this point may not be as well as you'd like, but that's okay).

Don't go it alone. Nothing is more depressing than being left alone with a crying newborn, that mountain of spit-up-stained laundry, a leaning tower of dirty dishes, and the promise (make that guarantee) of another sleep-deprived night ahead. So ask for help—from your spouse, your mother, your sister, your friends, a doula, or a cleaning service.

Get dressed. Sounds trite, but it's surprisingly true. Spending a little time making yourself look good will actually help you feel good. So hit the shower and maybe even the blow-dryer before your spouse hits the commuter train, trade in the stained sweats for a clean pair, and consider applying a little makeup (and a lot of concealer).

Get out of the house. It's amazing what a change of scenery can do for your state of mind—especially when the scenery suddenly doesn't include that pile of unopened mail (and unpaid bills). Try to get out of the house at least once a day: Take your baby for a walk in the park, visit with friends (and, if your friends are also moms, you can swap sob stories—and then laugh about them), stroll the mall. Anything that will keep you from hosting another self-pity party.

Treat yourself. Try a movie, a dinner date with your spouse, a 30-minute manicure (someone's bound to agree to watch the baby for that long), or even a long shower. Occasionally, make yourself a priority. You deserve it.

Get moving. Exercise boosts those feel-good endorphins, giving you an all-natural (and surprisingly lasting) high. So join a postpartum exercise class (preferably one that includes babies in the fun or at a club that offers child care), work out to an exercise DVD, step out for some stroller exercise (exercises that tone with the help of a stroller full of baby), or just simply step out for a walk.

Be a happy snacker. Too often, new moms are too busy filling their babies' tummies to worry about filling their own. A mistake—low blood sugar sends not only energy levels plummeting but moods, too. To keep yourself on a more even keel, physically and emotionally, stash sustaining, easy-to-munch snacks within quick reach. Tempted to reach for a chocolate bar instead? Reach away—

especially if chocolate really makes you happy—just not too often, because sugar-induced blood sugar highs have a way of crashing quickly.

Cry—and laugh. If you need a good cry, go for it. But when you're done, turn on a silly sitcom and laugh. Laugh, too, at all the mishaps you're likely having (instead of crying over them)—you know, the diaper blowout, the breasts that leaked in line at the market, the spit-up that spewed only after you realized you left home without wipes. You know what they say: Laughter is the best medicine. Plus, a good sense of humor is a parent's best friend.

Still blue, no matter what you do? Keep on reminding yourself that you'll outgrow the baby blues within a week or two—most moms do—and you'll be enjoying the best of times, most of the time, in no time.

If feelings of depression persist (lasting more than two weeks) or worsen, and start interfering with your functioning, call your practitioner right away and see the next column.

"I feel amazing and have since the moment I delivered three weeks ago. Is all this good feeling building up to one amazing case of letdown?"

Baby blues are common, but they're by no means on every newly delivered mom's to-do list. In fact, there's no reason to believe you're in for an emotional crash just because you've been feeling upbeat. Since baby blues usually occur within the first or second postpartum week, it's pretty safe to assume you've escaped them.

The fact that you're not feeling down, however, doesn't necessarily mean that everybody in your house has escaped the blues. Studies show that while new fathers (who, believe it or not, also go through hormonal changes postpartum) are unlikely to be depressed when their wives are, their risk of falling into a postpartum slump increases dramatically when the new mother is feeling great. So be sure your spouse isn't down with the baby blues; some new dads try to hide such feelings to avoid dumping on their spouses.

Postpartum Depression

"My baby is over a month old, and I still can't stop feeling depressed. Shouldn't I be feeling better by now?"

When the blues just won't fade, chances are postpartum depression is the reason why. Though "baby blues" and "postpartum depression" are often used interchangeably, they're actually two very different conditions. True postpartum depression (PPD) is less common (affecting about 15 percent of women) and much more enduring (lasting anywhere from a few weeks to a year or more). It may begin at delivery, but more often not until a month or two later. Sometimes PPD is late onset; it doesn't start until a woman gets her first postpartum period or until she weans her nursing baby (possibly because of fluctuating hormones). More susceptible to PPD are women who have had it before, have a personal or family history of depression or severe PMS, spent a lot of time feeling down during pregnancy, had a complicated pregnancy or delivery, or have a sick baby.

The symptoms of PPD are similar to those of baby blues, though much more pronounced. They include crying and irritability; sleep problems (not being able to sleep or wanting to sleep the day away); eating problems (having no appetite or an excessive one); persistent feelings of sadness, hopelessness,

Getting Help for Postpartum Depression

No new mother should have to suffer from postpartum depression (PPD). Sadly, too many do, either because they believe it's normal and inevitable after delivery (it isn't) or because they're ashamed to ask for help (they shouldn't be).

Public education campaigns are under way to spread the word about PPD, to make sure that a woman who needs help gets it as quickly as she can—so she can start enjoying her new baby as soon as possible. Hospitals are, or will be, required to send new mothers home with educational materials about PPD, so that they (and their spouses) will be more likely to spot the symptoms early and seek treatment. Practitioners are becoming better educated, too—learning how to look for risk factors during pregnancy that might predispose a woman to PPD, to screen routinely for the illness postpartum, and to treat it quickly, safely, and successfully. Several standardized tests (Edinburgh Postnatal Depression Scale and Cheryl Beck's Postpartum Depression Screening Scale) are effective in screening for PPD.

PPD is one of the most treatable forms of depression. So if it strikes you, don't suffer with it any longer than you have to. Speak up—and get the help you need now. For more help, contact Postpartum Support International, (800) 944-4PPD (4773); postpartum. net.

and helplessness; an inability (or lack of desire) to take care of yourself or your newborn; social withdrawal; excessive worry; aversion to your newborn; feeling all alone; and memory loss.

If you haven't already tried the tips for fading the baby blues (see page 456), do try them now. Some of them may be helpful in easing postpartum depression, too. But if your symptoms have persisted for more than two weeks without any noticeable improvement or if you're having more serious symptoms for more than a few days, chances are your PPD won't go away without professional attention. Don't wait to see if it does. First, call your practitioner and be up-front about how you're feeling. He or she may run a thyroid test; because irregularities in thyroid hormone levels can lead to emotional instability, this is often one of the first steps taken when evaluating postpartum depression (see next page). If your thyroid levels check out normally, ask for a referral to a therapist who has a clinical background in the treatment of postpartum depression and make an appointment promptly. Antidepressants (several are safe even if you're breastfeeding), combined with counseling, can help you feel better fast. Some physicians prescribe low doses of antidepressants during the last trimester of pregnancy to women with a history of depression; others recommend that women who are at high risk take antidepressants right after delivery to prevent postpartum depression. Bright light therapy may also bring relief from the symptoms of PPD. (In light therapy, you sit with your eyes open in front of a box that emits a type of light that mimics daylight, causing a positive biochemical change in your brain that can cheer you up.) Whichever treatment (or combination of treatments) you and your therapist decide is right for you, keep in mind that swift intervention is

Thyroiditis Got You Down?

Nearly all new mothers feel rundown and tired. Most have trouble losing weight. Many suffer from some degree of depression and a certain amount of hair loss. It may not be a pretty picture, but for the majority of moms, it's a completely normal one in the postpartum period—and one that gradually begins to look better as the weeks pass. For the estimated 5 to 9 percent of women who suffer from postpartum thyroiditis (PPT), however, this picture may not improve with time. And, because the symptoms of PPT are so similar to those weathered by all new mothers, the condition may go undiagnosed and untreated.

PPT may start anywhere from one to three months after delivery with a brief episode of hyperthyroidism (too much thyroid hormone). This period of excess thyroid hormone circulating in the bloodstream may last a few weeks or longer. During this hyperthyroid period, a woman may be tired, irritable, and nervous; feel very warm; and experience increased sweating and insomnia—all of which are common in the immediate postpartum period anyway, making an easy diagnosis more elusive. Treatment isn't usually needed for this phase.

This period will typically (but not always) be followed by one of hypothyroidism (too little thyroid hormone). With hypothyroidism, fatigue continues, along with depression (longer lasting and often more severe than typical baby blues), muscle aches, excessive hair loss, dry skin, cold intolerance, poor memory, and an inability to lose weight.

If your postpartum symptoms seem to be more pronounced and persistent than you would have expected, and especially if they are preventing you from eating, sleeping, and enjoying your new baby, check with your practitioner. Tests can determine whether PPT is the cause of your troubles. Be sure to mention any history of thyroid problems in your family, since there is a very strong genetic link.

Most women recover from PPT within a year after delivery. In the meantime, treatment with supplementary thyroid hormone can help them feel much better much faster. About 25 percent of women who have the condition, however, remain hypothyroid, requiring lifetime treatment (which is as easy as taking a pill every day and having a yearly blood test). Even in those who recover spontaneously, thyroiditis is likely to recur during or after subsequent pregnancies. Some may develop hypothyroidism or Graves disease (hyperthyroidism) later in life. For this reason, it makes sense for women who have had PPT to have a yearly thyroid screening and, if they are planning another pregnancy, to be screened in the preconception period and during pregnancy (because an untreated thyroid condition can interfere with conception and cause problems during pregnancy).

critical. Without it, depression can prevent you from bonding with, caring for, and enjoying your baby. It can also have a devastating effect on the other relationships in your life (with your spouse, with other children), as well as on your own health and well-being.

Some women, instead of (or in addition to) feeling depressed postpartum, feel extremely anxious or fearful, sometimes experiencing panic attacks that include rapid heartbeat and breathing, hot or cold flashes, chest pain, dizziness, and shaking. These symptoms also require prompt treatment by a qualified therapist, which may include medication.

About 30 percent of women suffering from PPD also exhibit signs of postpartum obsessive-compulsive disorder (PPOCD), though PPOCD can also occur by itself. Symptoms of PPOCD include obsessive-compulsive behaviors, such as waking up every 15 minutes to make sure the baby is still breathing, furious housecleaning, or having obsessive thoughts about harming the newborn (such as throwing the baby out the window or dropping him or her down the stairs). Women suffering from PPOCD are appalled by their gruesome and violent thoughts, though they won't act on them (only those suffering from postpartum psychosis might; see below). Still, they can be so afraid of losing control and following through with these impulses that they may end up neglecting their babies. Like PPD, treatment for PPOCD includes a combination of antidepressants and therapy. If you're having obsessive thoughts and/or behaviors, be sure to get help by telling your practitioner about your symptoms.

Much more rare and much more serious than PPD is postpartum psychosis. Its symptoms include loss of reality, hallucinations, and/or delusions. If you're experiencing suicidal, violent, or aggressive feelings, are hearing voices or seeing things, or have other signs of psychosis, call your doctor and go to the emergency room immediately. Don't underplay what you're feeling, and don't be put off by reassurances that such feelings are normal during the postpartum period—they're not. To be sure you don't act out any dangerous feelings while you're waiting for help, try to get a neighbor, relative, or friend to stay with you or put your baby in a safe place (such as the crib).

Losing Weight Postpartum

"I knew I wouldn't be ready for a bikini right after delivery, but I still look six months pregnant two weeks later."

Though childbirth produces more rapid weight loss than any diet you'll find on the bestseller lists (an average of 12 pounds overnight), most women don't find it quite rapid enough. Particularly after they catch a glimpse of their paunchy postpartum profiles in the mirror.

The fact is, no one comes out of the delivery room looking much slimmer than when they went in. Part of the reason for that protruding postpartum abdomen is your still-enlarged uterus, which will be reduced to prepregnancy size by the end of six weeks, reducing your girth in the process. Another reason for your belly bloat might be leftover fluids, which should be flushing out soon. But the rest of the problem lies in those stretched-out abdominal muscles and skin, which will likely take some effort to tone up. (See Getting Back into Shape, page 465.)

As hard as it might be to put it out of your mind, don't even think about the shape your body's in during the first six weeks postpartum, especially if you're breastfeeding. This is a recovery period, during which ample nutrition (and rest) is important for both energy and resistance to infection. Sticking to a healthy postpartum diet should start you on the way to slow, steady weight loss. If, after six weeks, you aren't losing any weight, you can start cutting back somewhat on calories. If you're nursing, don't go overboard. Eating too few calories can reduce milk production, and burning fat too quickly can release toxins into the blood, which can end up in your breast milk. If you're not nursing, you can go on a sensible, well-balanced weight-loss diet six weeks postpartum.

Some women find that the extra pounds melt off while they're breastfeeding; others are dismayed to find the scale doesn't budge. If the latter turns out to be the case with you, don't despair; you'll be able to shed any remaining excess poundage once you've weaned your baby.

How quickly you return to your prepregnant weight will also depend on how many pounds you put on during pregnancy. If you didn't gain much more than 25 to 35 pounds, you'll likely be able to pack away those pregnancy jeans in a few months, without strenuous dieting. If you gained 35 or more pounds, you may find it takes more effort and more time—anywhere from 10 months to 2 years—to return to prepregnancy weight and your skinny jeans.

Either way, give yourself a break—and give yourself some time. Remember, it took you nine months to gain that pregnancy weight, and it may take at least that long to take it off.

Long-Term C-Section Recovery

"It's been a week since my C-section. What can I expect now?"

While you've definitely come a long way since you were wheeled into recovery, like every new mom you still have some recuperation ahead of you in the next few weeks. Keep in mind that the more conscientious you are about getting the rest you need now—as well as about following your practitioner's instructions—the shorter that recuperation time will ultimately be. In the meantime, you can expect:

Little or no pain. Most of it should have dissipated by now. But if you do hurt,

some acetaminophen (Tylenol) should do the trick.

Progressive improvement. Your scar will be sore and sensitive for a few weeks, but it will improve steadily. A light dressing may protect it from irritation, and you will probably be more comfortable wearing loose clothing that doesn't rub. Occasional sensations of pulling or twitching and other brief pains around the incision site are a normal part of healing and eventually subside. Itchiness may follow—ask your practitioner to recommend an anti-itch ointment that you can apply. The numbness surrounding the scar will last longer, possibly several months. Lumpiness in the scar tissue will probably diminish, and the scar may turn pink or purple before it finally fades.

If pain becomes persistent, if the area around the incision turns an angry red, or if a brown, gray, green, or yellow discharge oozes from the wound, call your doctor. The incision may have become infected. (A small amount of clear fluid discharge is usually normal, but report it to your physician anyway.)

A four-week wait (at least) for sex. The guidelines are pretty much the same as they are for those who've delivered vaginally, though how well your incision is healing may also be factored into how long you'll need to wait. See the next question for more.

To get moving. Once you're free of pain, you'll be able to begin exercising. Kegel exercises are still important even if you delivered with your perineum intact, because pregnancy took its toll on those pelvic floor muscles. Concentrate, too, on exercises that tighten the abdominal muscles. (See Getting Back into Shape, page 465.) Make "slow and steady" your motto; get into a program gradually and continue it daily. Expect it to take several months before you're back to your old self.

Resuming Sex

"When can we start having sex again?"

That's at least partly up to you, though you'll also want to include your practitioner in the decision (probably not in the heat of the moment). Couples are typically advised to pick up where they left off whenever the woman feels physically ready—usually around four weeks postpartum, though some practitioners give the green light to sex as early as two weeks postpartum, and others still follow the old six-week rule routinely. In certain circumstances (for instance, if healing has been slow or you had an infection), your practitioner may recommend waiting longer. If your practitioner still has you in a holding pattern, but you think you're ready to move forward, ask if there's a reason why you shouldn't. If there isn't, ask your practitioner if you can get busy earlier. If it turns out there is a reason why sex might not be safe yet, hit the cold shower—though maybe together—and wait for clearance. Keep in mind that time will fly when you're caring for a newborn. In the meantime, satisfy each other with lovemaking that doesn't involve penetration.

"My midwife told me I can start having sex, but I'm afraid it's going to hurt. Plus, to be honest, I'm really not in the mood."

Doing "it" isn't topping your to-do list these days—or, more likely, isn't even making the top 20? No surprise there (or down there). Most women lose that loving feeling during the postpartum period—and beyond—for a variety of reasons. First, as you already suspect, postpartum sex can be more pain than pleasure—especially if you delivered vaginally, but, surprisingly, even if you labored and then had a C-section. After all, your vagina has just been stretched to its earthly limits, and possibly torn or surgically cut and sutured to boot—leaving you too sore to sit, never mind contemplate sex. Your natural lubrications haven't turned on yet, making you feel uncomfortably dry where you'd rather be moist—especially if you're breastfeeding. Adding to the pain potential: Low levels of estrogen cause the vaginal tissue to remain thin, and thin is not in as far as vaginas are concerned.

But your libido has other problems to contend with postpartum besides the physical ones: Your understandable preoccupation with a very little and very needy person, who is given to waking up with a full diaper and an empty tummy at the least opportune times. Not to mention a number of other very effective mood killers (the pungent smell of day-old spit-up on your sheets, the pile of dirty baby clothes at the foot of your bed, the baby oil on your nightstand where there used to be massage oil, the fact that you can't remember when you had your last shower). It's no wonder sex isn't on the schedule.

Will you ever live to make love again? Absolutely. Like everything else in your new and often overwhelming life, it'll just take time and patience (especially from your partner, who's almost certainly ready for this dry spell to end). So wait until you're feeling ready, or help yourself get ready with the following tips:

Lubricate. Using K-Y jelly, Astroglide, or another lubricant until your own natural secretions return can reduce pain and, ideally, increase pleasure. Buy them in economy sizes, so you'll be more likely to use them liberally—on both of you.

Loosen up. Speaking of lubrication, drinking a small glass of wine can also help you unwind—and keep you from

Craving More?

For much more information on easing back into sex, birth control, and enjoying the first year, see *What to Expect the First Year.*

tensing up and experiencing pain during intercourse (just make sure you drink it right after a feeding if you're nursing). Another great way to loosen up is massage, so request one prior to closing the deal.

Warm up. Of course, your partner's probably as eager as he's ever been to get down to business. But though he may not need much—if any—foreplay, you definitely do. So ask for it. And then ask for some more. The greater the effort he puts into warming you up (time permitting before baby wakes up again, of course), the better the main event will be for both of you.

Tell it like it is. You know what hurts and what feels good, but your partner doesn't unless you provide him a clearly marked map ("Turn left . . . no, right . . . no, down . . . up just a smidge—there, perfect!"). So speak up when you'd like things to heat up.

Position properly. Experiment and find a position that puts less pressure on any tender areas and gives you control over the depth of penetration (this is one time when deeper will definitely not be better). Woman-on-top (if you have the energy) or side-to-side positions are both great postpartum picks for those reasons. Whoever's in charge of the strides, make sure they're performed at a comfortably slow speed.

Pump it up. No, not that kind of pumping. Pump blood and restore muscle tone to your vagina by doing the exercise you're probably sick of hearing about (but should keep doing anyway): Kegels. Do them day and night (and don't forget to do them when you're doing "it," too, since that squeeze will please you both).

Find alternative means of gratification. If you're not having fun yet through intercourse, seek sexual satisfaction through mutual masturbation or oral sex. Or if you're both too pooped to pop, find pleasure in just being together. There's absolutely nothing wrong (and everything right) about lying in bed together, cuddling, kissing, and swapping baby stories.

Bottom line on your bottom line: Even if sex does hurt a bit the first time (and second and third time), don't write it off—or give it up. It won't be long (though it may seem that way) before the pleasure will be all yours—and your partner's—again.

Becoming Pregnant Again

"I thought that breastfeeding was a form of birth control. Now I hear you can get pregnant while nursing, even before you get your period."

Unless you don't mind becoming pregnant again soon, don't even think about relying on breastfeeding for contraception.

It's true that, on average, women who nurse resume normal cycles later than those who don't. In mothers who aren't nursing, periods usually kick in again somewhere between 6 and 12 weeks after delivery, whereas in nursing mothers the average is somewhere between 4 and 6 months. As usual, however, averages are deceptive. Nursing moms have been known to begin their periods as early as 6 weeks and later than 18 months postpartum. The problem is, there's no sure way to predict when you will get your first postbaby period, though several variables can influence the timing: for example, frequency of nursing (more than three times a day seems to suppress ovulation better), duration of nursing (the longer you nurse, the greater the delay in ovulation), and whether or not feedings are being supplemented (your baby's taking formula, solids, even water can interfere with the ovulation-suppressing effect of nursing).

Why worry about birth control before that first postpartum visit from Aunt Flo? Because the point at which you ovulate for the first time after delivery is as unpredictable as when you menstruate. Some women have a sterile first period; that is, they don't ovulate during that initial cycle. Others ovulate before the period, and therefore they can go from pregnancy to pregnancy without ever having had a period. Since you don't know which will come first, the period or the egg, contraceptive caution is highly advisable.

Of course, accidents can happen. So even if you've been using contraception—and especially if you haven't been—pregnancy is still a possibility. If you do have any suspicion that you might be expecting again, the best thing to do is take a pregnancy test. See page 42 for information on back-to-back pregnancies.

Getting Back into Shape

It's one thing to look six months pregnant when, in fact, you are six months pregnant, and quite another to look it when you've already delivered. Yet most women can expect to come out of the birthing room not much trimmer than when they went in—with a little bundle in their arms and a sizable one still around their middles. As for the zip-up jeans optimistically packed for the going-home trip, they're likely to stay packed, with baggy sweats the comfortable substitute.

How soon after you become a new mother will you stop looking like a mother-to-be? The answer will depend primarily on four factors: how much weight you gained during pregnancy, how well you control your intake of calories, how much exercise you get, and your metabolism and your genes.

"Who needs exercise?" you may wonder. "I haven't stopped moving since I got home from the hospital. Doesn't that count?" Unfortunately, not much. Exhausting as it is caring for a newborn, that kind of activity won't tighten up the perineal and abdominal muscles that have been stretched and left saggy by pregnancy and childbirth—only an exercise program will. And the right kind of postpartum exercise will do more than tone you up. It will help keep baby-toting backaches at bay, promote healing and hasten recovery from labor and delivery, help pregnancy-loosened joints tighten up, improve circulation, and reduce the risk of a variety of other unpleasant postpartum symptoms, from varicose veins to leg cramps. Kegel exercises, which target the perineal

Basic Position

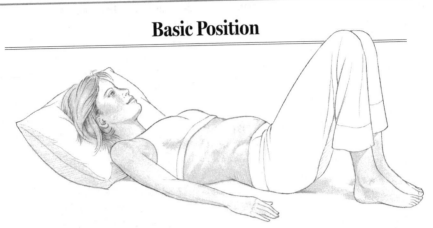

Lie on your back, knees bent, soles flat on the floor. Support your head and shoulders with cushions, and rest your arms flat at your sides.

Pelvic Tilt

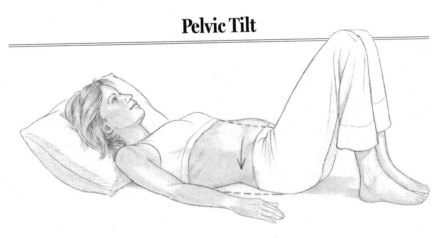

Lie on your back in the basic position. Take a breath. Then exhale as you press the small of your back against the floor for 10 seconds. Then relax. Repeat three or four times to start, increasing gradually to 12, and then 24.

muscles, will help you avoid stress and urinary incontinence and postpartum sexual problems. Finally, exercise can make you happier. As exercise-released endorphins circulate in your system, boosting your mood and your ability to cope, you'll find yourself much better equipped to handle the stresses of new parenthood. In fact, research shows that moms who resume exercising within six weeks of delivery feel better about themselves—and just plain feel better.

And you can probably start sooner than you think. If your delivery was vaginal and uncomplicated and you don't have any other major health issue that

Leg Slides

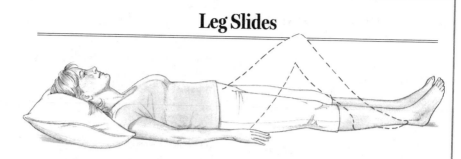

Assume the Basic Position. Slowly extend both legs until they are flat on the floor. Slide your right foot, flat on the floor, back toward your buttocks, inhaling as you go. Keep the small of your back against the floor. Exhale as you slide your leg back down. Repeat with your left foot. Start with three or four slides per side, and increase gradually until you can do a dozen or more comfortably. After three weeks, move to a modified leg lift (lifting one leg at a time slightly off the floor and lowering it again very slowly), if it is comfortable.

Head/Shoulder Lift

Assume the Basic Position. Take a deep relaxing breath; then raise your head very slightly and stretch your arms out, exhaling as you do. Lower your head slowly and inhale. Raise your head a little more each day, gradually working up to lifting your shoulders slightly off the floor. Don't try full sit-ups during the first six weeks—and then only if you have always had very good abdominal muscle tone. Check first, too, for an abdominal separation (see page 469).

might slow you down, you can begin your postpartum exercise program as early as 24 hours after delivery. (If you've had a surgical or a traumatic delivery, check with your doctor first.)

Don't even think about starting off with a bang, however; your recovering body needs to take it slowly and care-fully. The following three-phase program will help guide you. You can supplement it by using a postpartum exercise book or DVD, joining a class for new mothers (the camaraderie helps with motivation, and many include infants in the routines), and making daily strolls with baby a part of your routine.

Workout Rules for the First Six Weeks

- Wear a supportive bra and comfortable clothing.

- Try to divide your exercise schedule into two or three brief sessions rather than doing one long session a day (this tones muscles better and will be easier on your recovering body—plus you're more likely to be able to fit it in).

- Start each session with the exercise you find least strenuous.

- Do exercises slowly, and don't do a rapid series of repetitions. Instead, rest briefly between movements (the muscle buildup occurs then, not while you are in motion).

- As during pregnancy, avoid jerky, bouncy, erratic motions during the first six weeks postpartum, while your ligaments are still loose. Also avoid knee-to-chest exercises, full sit-ups, and double leg lifts during this period.

- Be sure to replenish fluids lost during exercise. Keep a water bottle next to you during your workouts and sip often. Aim for an extra cup or two of fluids for short bouts of exercise (more if your workouts are longer or more strenuous).

- Take it slowly and sensibly. "No pain, no gain" wasn't a motto created with new moms in mind. Don't do more than recommended, even if you feel you can, and stop before you feel tired. If you overdo it, you probably won't feel it until the next day, by which time you may be so exhausted and achy that you won't be able to exercise at all.

- Don't let taking care of your baby stop you from taking care of yourself. Your baby will love lying on your chest as you go through your exercise routine.

Phase 1: Twenty-Four Hours After Delivery

Can't wait to get back on the workout wagon? Easy does it, starting with:

Kegels. You can really start your Kegels as soon as you've delivered (see page 295 for directions if you haven't done them before), though you probably won't be able to feel yourself doing them at first, thanks to perineal numbness. Kegels can be done in any comfortable position, and comfort is key when you've just delivered a baby. Any time is a good time for Kegels, but try to get in the habit of doing them while you're feeding your baby—which you'll be doing a lot in the months to come. Work up to 25 repetitions four to six times a day, and continue for the rest of your life for good pelvic health (and increased sexual pleasure).

Deep diaphragmatic breathing. In the Basic Position (see box, page 466), place your hands on your abdomen so you can feel it rise as you inhale slowly through your nose; tighten the abdominal muscles as you exhale slowly through your mouth. Start with just two or three deep breaths at a time, to prevent hyperventilating, and work up gradually. (Signs that you've overdone it are dizziness or faintness, tingling, or blurred vision.)

Phase 2: Three Days After Delivery

Anxious to get that pre-baby body back? Then you'll be happy to hear that it's time to move up another rung on the exercise ladder. But before you take that step, make sure the pair of vertical muscles that form your abdominal wall have not separated during pregnancy. If they have, you'll have to close them up before the workouts start heating up (see box below). Once the separation has closed, or if you've never had one, move on to Head/Shoulder Lifts, Leg Slides, and Pelvic Tilts (see illustrations on pages 466 and 467).

All these exercises should be done in the Basic Position. At first, do them in bed, then move on to a well-cushioned floor. (An exercise mat is a good investment, not only because it makes these exercises easier and more comfortable to do now, but because your baby can practice rolling over and try his or her first tentative crawls on it later on in the year.)

Close the Gap

Don't look now, but there's probably a hole in the middle of your belly (and it's not your navel). A very common pregnancy condition known in obstetrical circles as diastasis, it's a gap in your abdominal muscles that can develop as the abdomen expands. It can take a month or two after delivery for this gap to close, and you'll have to wait until it does before you start those crunches and other abdominal exercises or you'll risk an injury. To determine if you have a separation, examine yourself this way: As you lie in the Basic Position, raise your head slightly with your arms extended forward; then feel for a soft lump above your navel. Such a lump indicates a separation.

If you do have a separation, you may be able to help correct it more quickly with this exercise: Assume the Basic Position and inhale. Now cross your hands over your abdomen, using your fingers to draw the sides of your abdominal muscles together as you breathe out, pulling your belly button inward toward the spine while raising your head slowly. Exhale as you lower your head slowly. Repeat three or four times, twice a day.

Phase 3: After Your Postpartum Checkup

Now, with your practitioner's go-ahead, you can gradually graduate to a more active workout program that includes walking, running, bicycling, swimming, water workouts, aerobics, yoga, Pilates, weight training, or similar routines. Or sign up for a postpartum exercise class. But don't try to do too much too soon. As always, let your body be your guide.

Milk It

Good news for nursing moms who want to exercise their right to work out. Exercise—even the high-intensity type—doesn't turn your breast milk sour, as you might have heard. Salty, maybe, from the sweat on your nipples—but your baby might actually enjoy that added tang. So go ahead (when your practitioner's given the go-ahead) and exercise to your body's content. Feeding your baby before a workout (or pumping) might make you more comfortable (since your breasts won't be as full), but it isn't necessary. And don't forget to wear a bra that offers you plenty of support—you need it more than ever.

PART 5

For Dads

CHAPTER 19

Fathers Are Expectant, Too

THOUGH IT'S CERTAINLY TRUE—future medical breakthroughs and Hollywood movies notwithstanding—that only women can become pregnant, it's just as true that fathers are expectant, too. As a dad, you're not only an essential member of your baby-making team, but an invaluable nurturer of both your pregnant spouse and your unborn offspring. In the months to come, you'll participate fully in the amazing process of pregnancy—in the excitement, in the responsibility, and, of course, in the worry. Some of your concerns will overlap those of mom-to-be; others will be uniquely yours. And just like your mate, you're entitled to your share of reassurance, not just during the pregnancy and the birth, but during the postpartum period as well.

And so this chapter is dedicated to the equal, but sometimes neglected, partner-in-reproduction. Keep in mind,

however, that the pages that follow aren't intended for your eyes only, any more than the rest of the book is intended only for the mother-to-be. Your spouse can gain some valuable insights into what you're feeling, won-

Get Ready, Get Set . . . Then Go

Giving your baby the best start in life can start even before sperm meets egg. If your partner isn't yet pregnant, you both have time to get yourselves into tip-top baby-making shape first. Read Chapter 1, and follow the suggestions for the preconception period. If you're already expecting, no problem. Just start taking good care of yourselves and each other now.

dering about, and hoping by reading this chapter; you can better understand the physical and emotional challenges she'll be facing during pregnancy, childbirth, and postpartum—and at the same time better prepare yourself for your own role in this adventure—by reading the rest of this book.

What You May Be Wondering About

Dealing with Her Symptoms

"My wife is having every symptom in the book, literally: nausea and cravings and peeing all the time. I'm not sure what to do—I feel so helpless."

Seem like the woman in your life has been taken over by aliens? Close—she's been taken over by pregnancy hormones (which can sometimes make an alien invasion seem like a walk in the park). These hormones, vital to baby production, can also produce a wide variety of uncomfortable (and sometimes bewildering) symptoms: hard for her to cope with and hard for you to stand by helplessly and watch.

Fortunately, you don't have to just stand there—you can actually do something. To help your pregnant partner feel better while helping yourself feel less helpless, read about the symptoms individually in this book, plus try some of the following father-focused symptom-fighting strategies:

Morning sickness. Morning sickness is one pregnancy symptom that definitely doesn't live up to its name. It's a 24/7 experience that can send your spouse running to the bathroom morning, noon, and night—and hugging the toilet far more than she'll be hugging you. So take steps to help her feel better—or at least not worse. Lose the aftershave that she suddenly finds repulsive and get your onion ring fix out of her sniffing range (her sense of smell is in overdrive). Fill her gas tank so she doesn't have to come nose-to-nozzle with the fumes at the pump. Fetch her foods that quell her queasies and don't provoke another run to the toilet—ginger ale, soothing smoothies, crackers (but ask first—what spells r-e-l-i-e-f for one queasy woman spells v-o-m-i-t to another). Be there for support when she's throwing up—hold back her hair, bring her some ice water, rub her back. Encourage her to eat small meals throughout the day instead of three large ones (spreading out the load and keeping her tummy filled may ease her nausea). And remember, no jokes. If you'd been throwing up for 10 straight weeks, you wouldn't find it amusing. Neither does she.

Cravings and aversions. Have you noticed that she's gagging over foods she used to love—or going gaga over foods she's never eaten before (or eaten in such peculiar combinations)? Don't tease her about these cravings and aversions—she's as powerless to control them as you are to understand them. Instead, indulge her by keeping the offending foods out of smelling distance. (Love chicken wings? Love them somewhere else.) Surprise her with the pickle-melon-and-Swiss sandwich she suddenly can't live without. Go the extra mile—or two miles—to the all-night mart for that midnight pint of triple fudge brownie, and you'll both feel better.

A Partner in Parenting by Any Name

Most of the tips in this chapter also apply to the partner in a nontraditional family. Pick and choose questions and answers that fit your situation or can be applied to it.

Exhaustion. If you think *you're* tired at the end of the day, think about this: Your spouse expends more energy lying down on the sofa building a baby than you do bodybuilding at the gym. Which makes her a lot more tired than you've ever known her to be—and a lot more tired than you can even imagine. So pick up the slack. And your slacks. And the trail of socks and sneakers in the hallway. Beat her to the vacuuming and the dusting and the laundry and the toilet cleaning. (The fumes from the cleaning products will make her feel sicker anyway.) Encourage her to watch your cleanup routine from a fully reclining position on the sofa (even if that's always been your favorite position).

Trouble sleeping. She's making a baby, but chances are she isn't sleeping like one. So instead of snoring up a storm next time her pregnancy insomnia strikes, keep your spouse company while she waits for the sandman to show up. Buy her a body pillow to help get her comfy or build her a cozy fort of support with your extra pillows. Relax her with a backrub, run her a bath, bring her a warm cup of milk and a muffin. Do a little pillow talking. Cuddle as needed and as wanted. And if one thing leads to another, you might both sleep better. (Don't expect a sexual nightcap for your efforts, though—there are plenty of reasons why she might not be in the mood these days.)

Frequent urination. There she goes—again. Urinary frequency will be your spouse's constant companion in her first trimester, and it'll come back with a vengeance in the last trimester, too. So try not to hog the bathroom, and always leave it ready for her use. Remember to put the seat down after every use (especially at night), and keep the hallway free of obstacles (your briefcase, your sneakers, that magazine) and lit by a nightlight so she won't trip on her way to the toilet. And be as understanding as you can when she has to get up three times during the movie or stop six times on the way to your parents' house.

Sympathy Symptoms

"It's my wife who's pregnant, so why am I having morning sickness?"

Feeling curiously . . . pregnant? Women may have a corner on the pregnancy market but not on pregnancy symptoms. As many as half, or even more (depending on the study), of expectant fathers suffer from some degree of couvade syndrome, or "sympathetic pregnancy," during their wives' gestation. The symptoms of couvade can mimic virtually all the normal symptoms of pregnancy, including nausea and vomiting, abdominal pain, appetite changes, weight gain, food cravings, constipation, leg cramps, dizziness, fatigue, and mood swings.

Any number of emotions that have settled down in your psyche these days could trigger these symptoms, from sympathy (you wish you could feel her pain, and so you do), to anxiety (you're stressed about the pregnancy or about becoming a father), to jealousy (she's getting center stage; you'd like to share it). But there's more to sympathy symptoms than just sympathy (and other normal father-to-be feelings). In fact, there are actually physical factors in play. Believe it or not, your wife's female hormones aren't the only ones surging these days. Research shows that pregnancy and the postpartum period step up dad's supply, too. Though you (and your fellow fathers-to-be) won't be churning out enough female hormones to grow breasts, you might produce enough to grow a little belly, or send you heaving at the sight of your favorite burger, or running to the fridge for a midnight pickle fest (or all three). And these hormonal fluctuations aren't random or a sign of Mother Nature's twisted sense of humor. They're designed to get you in touch with your nurturing side—nature's way of bringing out the parent in you. Which doesn't only prepare you for the diaper-changing ahead, but helps you cope with the changes you're both facing now. These hormone shifts also make it easier for you to channel those sometimes uncomfortable feelings into productive pursuits. Apply your sympathy to cooking dinner and scrubbing the toilet; work through those anxieties by talking them out with your spouse and with friends who are already dads; feel less left out by becoming more involved in the pregnancy and baby prep.

Rest assured, all symptoms that don't go away during pregnancy will disappear soon after delivery, though you may find that others crop up postpartum. And don't stress out if you don't have a single sick—or queasy or achy—day during your wife's pregnancy. Not suffering from morning sickness or putting on weight doesn't mean you don't empathize and identify with your spouse or that you're not destined for nurturing—just that you've found other ways to express your feelings. Every expectant father, like every expectant mother, is different.

Feeling Left Out

"I hardly feel I have anything to do with the pregnancy, now that conception's out of the way."

Many fathers-to-be feel like they're on the outside looking in, and that's not surprising. After all, mom's the one getting all the attention (from friends, from family, from the practitioner). She's the one with the physical connection to the baby (and the belly to back it up). You know you're about to become a father, but you don't have much to show for it now.

Not to worry. Just because the pregnancy's not taking place in your body doesn't mean you can't share it. Don't wait for an invitation to get you off the bench. Your spouse has a lot on her mind (and a lot to get off her chest), and it's up to you to get into the game. Open up to her about feeling shut out, and ask her to let you in. She might not even realize she's excluding you from the pregnancy, or she may think you're not particularly interested in it.

But also remember, the best way to keep from feeling left out is to step up to the plate and get involved. Here's how:

- Be a prenatal regular. Whenever you can (and if you're not already), join her at her practitioner checkups. She'll appreciate the moral support, but you'll appreciate the chance to hear the practitioner's instructions for yourself (so you can help her follow them better—and help her remember them if pregnancy forgetfulness leaves her in a fog). Plus you'll get to ask all those questions you have. The visits will also give you much-needed insight into the miraculous changes going on in your spouse's body. Best of all, you'll get to experience those momentous milestones with her

Resources for Dads

Expectant fathers are just as hungry for reassurance, support, information, and empathy as expectant mothers. Here are some places you can turn to, both during pregnancy and once you're a full-fledged dad: whattoexpect.com; fathermag.com; fathersforum.com; fatherville.com; bcnd.org.

(hearing the heartbeat, seeing those tiny limbs on ultrasound).

- Act pregnant. You don't have to show up for work in a baby-on-board T-shirt or start sporting a milk mustache. But you can be a true partner in pregnancy: Exercise with her (it'll tone you up, too); take a pass on the alcohol (it's much easier for her to toe the teetotaling line when she has a comrade-in-club-soda); eat well (at least when you're around her); and if you smoke, quit (permanently, since secondhand smoke isn't good for anyone—especially your baby).

- Get an education. Even dads with advanced degrees (including those with MDs) have a lot to learn when it comes to pregnancy, childbirth, and baby care, just as moms do the first time. Read books and magazines; visit websites. Attend childbirth classes together; attend classes for fathers, if they're available locally. Chat up friends and colleagues who've become new fathers recently or chat with other pregnant dads online.

- Make contact with your baby. A pregnant woman may have the edge in bonding with the unborn baby because it's comfortably ensconced in her uterus, but that doesn't mean you can't start getting to know the new family member, too.

  Talk, read, sing to your baby frequently; a fetus can hear from about the end of the sixth month on, and hearing your voice often now will help your newborn recognize it after delivery. Enjoy baby's kicks and squirms by resting your hand or your cheek on your wife's bare belly for a few minutes each night. It's a nice way to get close to her, too.

- Shop for a layette, and a crib, and a stroller with your partner. Decorate the nursery together. Pore over baby-name books. Attend consultations with prospective baby doctors. In general, become active in every aspect of planning and preparing for the baby's arrival.

- Consider taking off. Start looking into your company's paternity-leave policy. This way, you'll be sure not to be left out of all the fun after the baby is born.

Sex

"Ever since my wife's became pregnant, she's been really oversexed. Is that normal (not that I'm complaining)? Is it safe to have sex so often?"

The rumors are true: Some women really can't get enough when they're expecting. And for good reason. Your wife's genitals are swollen with hormones and blood now that she's pregnant, leaving the nerves down below set on tingle mode. Other parts are swollen, too (you might have noticed), including places (such as those breasts and hips) that can make a woman feel more womanly than ever—and more sensually charged. All of which is normal (as is feeling less in the mood, which many women feel,

Expectant Sex Explained

Sure, you've done it before. But have you done it pregnancy-style? Though the basic rules of the game apply when you're expecting, you'll find that pregnant sex requires a few adjustments, a little finessing, and a lot of flexibility—literally. Here are some suggestions to get you going in the right direction:

- Wait for the green light. She was hot to trot yesterday, but today she's cold as ice to your advances? As a pregnant woman's moods swing, so does her sex drive. You'll have to learn to swing along (and to hold on tight).

- Warm her up before you start your own engine. This may go without saying (always), but it's a must when she's expecting. Go as slowly as she needs you to, making sure she's fully charged on foreplay before you hit the road.

- Stop for directions. The road map of what feels good and what doesn't may have changed (even since last week), so don't rely on possibly outdated directions. Always ask before going in. You may need to tread especially lightly when it comes to those super-size breasts. Though they may have swelled to heart-quickening proportions, they can be tender to even the gentlest touch, especially in the first trimester. Which means you may have to look but not touch for a while.

- Put her in the driver's seat. Choose positions with her comfort in mind. A top pregnancy favorite is her on top, since she can control penetration best this way. Another is her facing away on her side (spooning each other). And when her belly starts getting between you, get around it creatively: Try it from behind with her on her knees or sitting on your lap while you lie down.

- Be prepared for rerouting. All roads aren't leading to intercourse? Find alternate paths to pleasure that you both can enjoy—masturbation, oral sex, two-way massage.

too)—safe, also, as long as the practitioner has given the sex go-ahead.

So be there for the taking whenever she's in the mood to grab you. Feel lucky that you're getting lucky so often. But always take your cues from her, especially now. Proceed with seduction if she's up for it and into it, but don't go without the green light.

Though some women are in the mood throughout their nine months, others find that the party doesn't get started until the second trimester; still others find desire spikes in the second, only to dip in the third. So be ready to roll with her changing sexual agenda when she goes from turned on to turned off in 60 seconds (frustrating, possibly, but completely normal). Keep in mind, too, that there will be some logistical challenges in mid- to late pregnancy as her body goes from two-seater to semi.

"I find my wife incredibly sexy now. But she hasn't been in the mood since the day we found out we were pregnant."

Even couples who have always been in sexual sync can find themselves suddenly out of step in the sack once they're expecting. That's because so many factors, both physical and emotional, can affect sexual desire, pleasure, and performance during pregnancy.

Your libido may be getting a lift just from liking what you see; many men find the roundness, fullness, and ripeness of the pregnant form surprisingly sensual, even extra erotic. Or your lust may be fueled by affection; the fact that you're expecting a baby together may have deepened your already strong feelings for your wife, arousing even greater passions.

But just as your sexual overdrive is both understandable and normal, so is her decreased drive. It could be that pregnancy symptoms have leveled her libido (it's not so easy to lose yourself in the moment when you're busy losing your lunch, or to get hot when you're bothered by backache and swollen ankles, or to get it on when you barely have the energy to get up), particularly in those uncomfortable first and third trimesters. Or that she's as turned off by her new roundness as you are turned on by it (what you see as a sexy round bottom, she may see as a big fat ass). Or that she's preoccupied with all things baby and/or having a hard time blending the roles of mother and lover.

When she's not in the mood (even if she's *never* in the mood), don't take it personally. Try, try, again another time, but always be a good sport while you're waiting for your ship to come in. Accept those "not now's" and those "don't touch there's" with an understanding smile and a hug that lets her know you love her even when you can't show it the way you'd like to. Remember, she's got a lot going on in her mind (and in her body) right now, and it's a safe bet that your sexual needs aren't front and center on her plate.

There's definitely a possibility that your patience will pay off, most likely in the second trimester, when some women get their sexual groove back. Even if your sex life doesn't perk up then or if it drops off again in the third trimester

(because of an increase in her fatigue or back pain or because of that growing basketball belly) or in the postpartum period (when neither one of you is likely to be much in the mood), don't worry. Nurturing the other aspects of your relationship (making that love connection without actually making love) will ensure that you'll eventually be able to pick up where you left off sexually.

In the meantime, don't push your sexual agenda, but do step up the romance, communication, and cuddling. Not only will these bring you closer together, but because they're powerful aphrodisiacs for many women, they may just bring you what you're craving. When one thing does lead to another, make sure you proceed with care and caution (see box, page 477)

And don't forget to tell your partner—often—how sexy and attractive you find the pregnant her. Women may be intuitive, but they're not mind readers.

"Now that we're expecting, I just don't seem very interested in sex. Is this normal?"

Expectant fathers, like expectant mothers, can experience a wide range of reactions when it comes to their pregnancy libidos—some of them bewildering, and all of them normal. And there are plenty of good reasons why your sex drive may be in a slump now. Perhaps you and your spouse worked so conscientiously at conception that sex suddenly feels too much like hard work. Maybe you're so focused on the baby and on becoming a dad that your sexual side is taking a backseat. Or the changes in your spouse's body are taking some getting used to (especially because they're an in-your-face reminder of how your life and relationship are also changing). Or fear that you'll hurt her or your baby during sex (you won't) has sent your mojo into hiding. Or it could be a hang-up thing—the hang-up being that you've never made love to a mother before (even though that mother happens to be a woman you've always enjoyed making love to). Or it could be the weirdness factor that's keeping you down: Getting close to your pregnant spouse might mean getting too close for comfort to your baby during a decidedly adult activity (even though baby's completely oblivious). The normal hormonal changes that expectant fathers experience can also slow them sexually.

Confusing these conflicted feelings even more could be miscommunication: You think she's not interested, so you subconsciously put your urges on ice. She thinks you're not interested, so she gives desire a cold shower.

Try to focus less on the quantity of sex in your relationship and more on the quality of the intimacy you're sharing. Less may not be more, but it can still be fulfilling. You might even find that stepping up the other kinds of intimacy—the hand-holding, the unexpected hugs, the confiding of your feelings—might put you both more in the mood for lovemaking. Don't be surprised, too, if your libido gets a boost once both of you have adjusted to the emotional and physical changes of pregnancy.

It's also possible that your sexual slowdown will continue throughout the nine months—and beyond, too. After all, even couples who can't get enough while they're expecting find that their sex lives can come to a screeching halt once there's a baby in the house, at least for the first couple of months. All of this is fine—and all of it is temporary. Meanwhile, make sure the nurturing of your baby doesn't interfere with the care and feeding of your relationship. Put romance on the table regularly (and while you're at it, put some candles there, too, plus a dinner you cooked up while she was napping). Surprise her with flowers or a sexy negligee (they make them for expectant moms, too). Suggest a moonlit stroll or hot cocoa and cuddles on the couch. Share your feelings and fears, and encourage her to share hers. Keep the hugs and kisses coming (and coming . . . and coming). You'll both stay warm while you're waiting for things to heat up again.

Also be sure that your wife knows that your lack of libido has nothing to do with her physically or emotionally. Expectant moms can suffer a crumbling of confidence when it comes to their pregnant body image, particularly as those pounds start piling on. Letting her know (often, through words and touch) that she's more attractive to you than ever will help keep her from taking your drop in sexual interest personally.

For more tips on enjoying sex more when you're doing it less, see page 260.

"Even though the doctor told us that sex is safe during pregnancy, I have trouble following through because I'm afraid of hurting my wife or the baby."

Plenty of fathers-to-be confront that very same fear factor when it comes to expectant lovemaking. And that's not surprising. It's only natural to put your expectant wife and baby-to-be first and to try to protect them at all costs (including at the cost of your pleasure).

But fear not, and take it from the practitioner. If he or she has greenlighted sexual intercourse during pregnancy (and most of the time, that's exactly what'll happen), sex is completely safe up to delivery. Your baby is way out of your reach (even for the particularly gifted), well secured and sealed off in its uterine home, impervious to harm, unable to view or be aware of the proceedings, and perfectly oblivious to what's going on when you're getting it on. Even those mild contractions your spouse might feel after orgasm are nothing to worry about, since they're not the kind that triggers premature labor in a normal pregnancy. In fact, research shows that low-risk women who stay sexually active during pregnancy are actually less likely to deliver early. And not only will making love to your wife do her no harm, but it can do her a world of good by filling her increased needs for physical and emotional closeness, and by letting her know that she's desired at a time when she may be feeling her least desirable. Though you should proceed with care (take your cues from her and keep her needs top priority), you can certainly proceed—and feel good about it.

Still concerned? Let her know. Remember, open and honest communication about everything, including sex, is the best policy.

Pregnancy Dreams

"I've been having the strangest dreams lately—and I'm not sure what to make of them."

So your dream life has been more interesting than your real life these days? You've got lots of company. For just about all expectant mothers and fathers, pregnancy is a time of intense feelings, feelings that run the roller coaster from joyful anticipation to panic-stricken anxiety and back again. It's not surprising that many of these feelings find their way into dreams, where the subconscious can act them out and work them through safely. Dreams about sex, for instance, might be your subconscious telling you what you probably already know: You're worried about how pregnancy and having a baby is affecting and will con-

tinue to affect your sex life. Not only are such fears normal, they're valid. Acknowledging that your relationship is in for some changes now that baby's making three is the first step in making sure your twosome stays cozy.

R-rated dreams are most common in early pregnancy. Later on, you may notice a family theme in your dreams. You may dream about your parents or grandparents as your subconscious attempts to link past generations to the future one. You may dream about being a child again, which may express an understandable fear of the responsibilities to come and a longing for the carefree years of the past. You may even dream about being pregnant yourself, which may express sympathy for the load your spouse is carrying, jealousy of the attention she's getting, or just a desire to connect with your unborn baby. Dreams about dropping the baby or forgetting to strap your newborn into the car seat can express your insecurities about becoming a father (the same insecurities every expectant parent shares). Uncharacteristically macho dreams—scoring a touchdown or driving a race car—can communicate the subconscious fear that becoming a nurturer will chip away at your manliness. The flip side of your subconscious may also get equal time (sometimes even in the same night); dreaming about taking care of your baby helps prepare you for your new role as doting dad. Dreams about loneliness and being left out are extremely common; these speak to those feelings of exclusion that so many expectant fathers experience.

Not all of your dreams will express anxiety, of course. Some dreams—of being handed or finding a baby, of baby showers or family strolls through the park—show how excited you are about the imminent arrival. (You'll find more dream themes on page 291.)

It's Your Hormones (Really)

Think just because you're a guy you're immune to the hormonal swings usually reserved for females? Think again. Research has revealed that expectant and new dads experience a drop in their testosterone levels and an increase in the hormone estradiol—a female sex hormone. It's speculated that this shift in hormones, which is actually common across the animal kingdom, turns up the tenderness in males. It may also contribute to some pretty strange and surprising pregnancy-like symptoms in fathers-to-be, including food cravings, queasiness, weight gain, and mood swings. What's more, it may keep dad's libido in check (often a good thing, since a raging sex drive can sometimes be inconvenient during pregnancy—and definitely when there's a new baby in the house). Hormone levels typically return to normal within three to six months, bringing with them an end to those pseudo pregnancy symptoms—and a return to libido business as usual (though not necessarily to sex life as usual until baby's sleeping through the night).

One thing is for sure: You're not dreaming alone. Expectant mothers (for the same reasons) are subject to strange dreams, too—plus the hormones make them even more vivid. Sharing dreams with each other in the morning can be an intimate, enlightening, and therapeutic ritual, as long as you don't take them too seriously. After all, they're just dreams.

Surviving Her Mood Swings

"I've heard about mood swings during pregnancy, but I wasn't prepared for this. One day she's up, the next day she's down, and I can't seem to do anything right."

Welcome to the wonderful—and sometimes wacky—world of pregnancy hormones. Wonderful because they're working hard to nurture the tiny life that's taken up residence inside your spouse's belly (and that you'll soon be cuddling in your arms). Wacky because, in addition to taking control of her body (and often making her miserable), they're also taking control of her mind—making her weepy, over-the-top excited, disproportionately pissed, deliriously happy, and stressed out . . . and that's all before lunch.

Not surprisingly, an expectant mom's mood swings are usually the most pronounced during the first trimester when those pregnancy hormones are in their greatest state of flux (and when she's just getting used to them). But even once the hormones have settled down in the second and third trimesters, you can still expect to be riding the emotional roller coaster with your spouse, which will continue to take her to emotional highs and lows (and fuel those occasional outbursts) right up until delivery, and beyond.

So what's an expectant dad to do? Here are some suggestions:

Be patient. Pregnancy won't last forever (though there will be times in the ninth month where you both may wonder if it will). This, too, shall pass, and it'll pass a lot more pleasantly if you're patient. In the meantime, try to keep your perspective—and do whatever you can to channel your inner saint.

Don't take her outbursts personally. And don't hold them against her. They are, after all, completely out of her control. Remember, it's the hormones talking—and crying for no apparent reason. Avoid pointing out her moods, too. Though she's powerless to control them, she's also probably all too aware of them. And chances are, she's no happier about them than you are. It's no picnic being pregnant.

Help slow down the swings. Since low blood sugar can send her mood swinging, offer her snacks when she's starting to droop (a plate of crackers and cheese, a fruit-and-yogurt smoothie). Exercise can release those feel-good endorphins she's in need of now, so suggest a before- or after-dinner walk (also a good time to let her vent fears and anxieties that might be dragging her down).

Go the extra yard. That is, go to the laundry room, to her favorite takeout on the way home from work, to the supermarket on Saturday, to the dishwasher to unload . . . you get the picture. Not only will she appreciate the efforts you make—without being asked—but you'll appreciate her happier mood.

Your Pregnancy Mood Swings

"Ever since we got the positive pregnancy test, I seem to be feeling really down. I didn't think fathers were supposed to get depressed during pregnancy."

Fathers share a lot more than the expected bundle of joy with their partners. Long before that bundle arrives, they can share in many of the symptoms, including pregnancy mood slumps—which are surprisingly common in expectant dads. While you can't be as quick to blame your hormones as your spouse can (though men's hormones do fluctuate somewhat during pregnancy, too), it's likely that your emotional low can be linked to the host of normal but conflicted feelings—from anxiety to fear to ambivalence—that most dads-to-be (and moms-to-be) find themselves trying to work out in the months leading up to this major life change.

But you can help boost your pregnancy mood—and perhaps prevent the postpartum blues, which about 10 percent of new fathers suffer from—by:

- Talking. Let your feelings out so they don't bring you down. Share them with your wife (and don't forget to let her share hers, too), making communication a daily ritual. Talk them over with a friend who recently became a father (no one will get it like he will) or even with your own father. Or find an outlet online—a message board for new or expectant dads.

- Moving. Nothing gets your mood up like getting your pulse up. Not only will a workout help you work out your feelings—or pound them out, or pump them out—but it can give your feel-good endorphins a long-lasting boost.

- Getting baby-busy. Gear up for the anticipated arrival by pitching in with all the baby prep that's likely going on. You may find that getting in the baby spirit helps give your spirits a boost.

- Cutting out (or cutting down). Drinking a lot can swing your moods even lower. Though alcohol has a reputation for being a mood booster, it's technically a depressant, so there's a reason why the morning after is never as happy as the night before. Plus, it's a coping mechanism that covers up the feelings you're trying to cope with. Ditto with other drugs.

If these suggestions don't help lift your mood, or if your depression deepens or begins to interfere with your relationship with your spouse, your work, and other aspects of your life, don't wait it out. Seek professional help (from your physician or a therapist) so you can start enjoying what should be a happy and exciting life change.

Labor and Delivery Worries

"I'm excited about our baby's birth, but I'm stressed out about handling it all. What if I can't keep it together?"

Few fathers enter the birthing room without a little trepidation—or a lot. Even obstetricians who've assisted at the births of thousands of other people's babies can experience a sudden loss of self-confidence when confronted with their own baby's delivery.

Yet very few of those father-to-be fears—of freezing, falling apart, fainting, getting sick, and otherwise humiliating themselves or their spouses or falling short of their expectations—are ever realized. In fact, most dads handle childbirth with surprising ease, keeping their composure, their cool, and their lunch. And though being prepared for the birth—by taking childbirth education classes, for instance—generally makes the experience more satisfying for all involved, even most unprepared fathers come through labor and delivery better than they ever would have imagined.

But, like anything new and unknown, childbirth becomes less scary and intimidating if you know what to expect. So become an expert on the subject. Read the section on labor and delivery, beginning on page 380. Check out the Internet. Attend childbirth education classes, watching the labor and delivery

DVDs with your eyes wide open. Visit the hospital or birthing center ahead of time so it'll be familiar ground on labor day. Talk to friends who've attended the births of their children—you'll probably find that they were stressed out about the birth beforehand, too, but that they came through it like pros.

Though it's important to get an education, remember that childbirth isn't the final exam. Don't feel you're under any pressure to perform. Midwives and doctors won't be evaluating your every move or comparing you to the coach next door. More important, neither will your spouse. She won't care if you forget every coaching technique you learned in class. Your being beside her, holding her hand, urging her on, and providing the comfort of a familiar face and touch is what she'll need—and appreciate—most of all.

Still having performance anxiety? Some couples find that having a doula present during birth helps them both to get through labor and delivery with less stress and more comfort (see page 298).

"The sight of blood makes me sick, so I'm worried about being at the delivery."

Most expectant fathers—and mothers—worry about how they'll handle seeing blood at delivery. But chances are you won't even notice it, never mind be bothered by it—for a couple of reasons. First of all, there typically isn't very much blood to see. Second, the excitement and wonder of watching your baby arrive is likely to keep you both pretty preoccupied (that, and the efforts of birthing, of course).

If at first glance the blood does bother you (and it's really likely it won't), keep your eyes focused on your spouse's face as you coach her through those last pushes. You'll probably want to turn back to the main event for that momentous moment; at that point, blood is going to be the last thing you'll notice.

"My wife is having a scheduled C-section. Is there anything I need to know ahead of time?"

The more you learn about C-sections now, the better the experience will be for both of you. Even though you won't be helping out as much as you would if you were coaching your partner through a vaginal birth, your participation will be more valuable than you might think. A dad's reaction at a cesarean delivery can actually affect the level of fear and anxiety his partner experiences—and a less-stressed father contributes greatly to a less-stressed mother. And there's no better way to reduce your stress than knowing what to expect. So sign up together for a childbirth education class that includes C-sections in the curriculum, read up on surgical deliveries and recoveries (see pages 398 and 432), and get as prepped as you can.

Remember that any kind of surgery can seem like a scary proposition, but C-sections are extremely safe for both mom and baby. Plus, most hospitals now strive to make them as family friendly as possible, allowing you to watch (if you want to), sit by your spouse's side, hold her hand, and hold the baby right after birth—just like the couples delivering vaginally down the hall.

Anxiety Over Life Changes

"Ever since I saw him on ultrasound, I've been excited about our son's birth. But I've also been worrying about how different our lives will be once we become parents."

Little babies do bring some large life changes, no doubt about it—and all expectant parents worry about them. Moms-to-be stress about these upcoming changes, too, but being so physically invested in the pregnancy process gives them a head start on working them through (their lives are already different, big time). For dads, the changes can seem less gradual, more jolting. But thinking about them—and even stressing about them—now is actually a really good thing, since it gives you a chance to prepare realistically for the impact parenthood will have on your life. The most common dad-to-be worries include:

Will I be a good father? There isn't a dad-to-be (or mom-to-be) who doesn't have this one on his top-10 worry list. To help you cross it off yours, see page 486.

Will our relationship change? Just about every set of new parents finds that their relationship undergoes some change when baby makes three. Anticipating this change realistically during pregnancy is an important first step in dealing with it effectively postpartum. No longer will being alone together be as simple as closing the blinds and letting voice mail pick up calls; from the moment baby comes home from the hospital, spontaneous intimacy and complete privacy will be precious, and often unattainable, commodities. Romance may have to be planned (a quickie grabbed during baby's nap) rather than spur of the moment, and interruptions may be the rule (you can't let voice mail pick up the baby, after all). But as long as you both make the effort to make time for each other—whether that means catching up with each other over a late dinner once baby's in bed, or giving up a game with the guys so you can play games of an entirely different kind with your spouse, or starting a weekly date night—your relationship will weather

Being There

The very best way to start off your new life as a father is at home with your new family. So if it's possible and financially feasible, consider taking off as much time as you can right after delivery—through the Family and Medical Leave Act (which allows for 12 weeks of unpaid leave for mothers and fathers; see page 187), the policy at your company (ask ahead of time what it is), or by taking a chunk of vacation time (the beach will be there next year, but your baby will be a newborn only once). Or if that's impossible (or not your preference), consider working part-time for a few weeks or doing some work from home.

Should none of these possibilities prove practical, and job responsibilities call, maximize the time you have off from work. Make sure you're home as much as you can be; learn to say no to overtime, early or late meetings, and business trips that can be put off or passed off. Especially in the postpartum period, when your spouse is still recovering from labor and delivery, try to do more than your share of household chores and baby care whenever you're home. Keep in mind that no matter how physically or emotionally stressful your occupation, there is no more demanding job than caring for a newborn.

Make bonding with your new baby a priority, but don't forget to devote some time to nurturing your spouse as well. Pamper her when you're home, and let her know you're thinking of her when you're at work. Call her often to offer support and empathy (and so she can unload as much as she needs to); surprise her with flowers or takeout from a favorite restaurant.

the changes well. Many couples, in fact, find that becoming a threesome deepens, strengthens, and improves their twosome—bringing them closer together than they've ever been before.

How will we divide the child care? Parenting is a two-person job (at least when there are two parents), but that doesn't mean it's clear just how the division of labor will play out once baby makes three. Don't wait until baby needs his first midnight diaper change or his first bath to decide this question. Start divvying up duties now—fairly. Some details of your plan may change once you really start operating as parents (she had signed up for baths, but you turn out to be the better bather), but exploring the options in theory now will make you feel more confident about how baby care is going to work in practice later.

Plus, it'll encourage you to communicate about it openly—something every team needs to do to be effective.

How will work be affected? That depends on your work schedule. If you currently work long hours with little time off, you may need (and want) to make some changes to make fatherhood the priority in your life that you'll want it to be. And don't wait until you officially become a father. Think about taking time off now for doctor's visits, as well as to help your exhausted spouse with baby preparations. Start weaning yourself off those 12-hour days, and resist the temptation to continue your day at the office at home. Avoid trips and a heavy workload during the two months before and after your baby's ETA, if you can. And if it's at all possible, consider taking paternity leave in the early weeks of baby's life.

Will we have to give up our lifestyle? You probably won't have to say good-bye to accustomed activities or your social life as you knew it, but you should expect to make some adjustments, at least up front. A new baby does, and should, take center stage, pushing some old lifestyle habits temporarily aside. Parties, movies, and sports may be tricky to fit in between feedings; cozy dinners for two at your favorite bistro may become noisy meals for three at family restaurants that tolerate squirming infants. Your circle of friends may change somewhat, too; you may suddenly find yourself gravitating toward fellow stroller-pushers for empathetic companionship. Not to say that there won't be a place for old friends—and pastimes from your past—in your new life with baby; just that your priorities will likely do some necessary shifting.

Can I afford a larger family? With child-rearing costs going through the roof, many expectant parents lose sleep over this very legitimate question. But there are plenty of ways to cut those costs, including opting for breastfeeding (no bottles or formula to buy), accepting all the hand-me-downs that are offered (new clothes start to look like hand-me-downs after a few spitting-up episodes anyway), and letting friends and family know which gifts you really need rather than allowing them to fill baby's shelves with stuff you'll never use. If either of you is planning to take extra time off from work (or to put career plans on hold for a while) and this concerns you from a financial standpoint, weigh it against the costs of quality child care and commuting. The income lost may not be so great after all.

Most important: Instead of thinking of what you won't have in your life anymore (or won't have as much opportunity for), try to start thinking of what

you will have in your life: a very special little person to share it with. Will your life be different? Absolutely. Will it be better? Immeasurably.

Fathering Fears

"I want to be a good father, but the thought is terrifying. I've never even seen or held a newborn, much less taken care of one."

Few men are born fathers, any more than women are born mothers. Though parental love may come naturally, parental skills (the stuff you're nervous about) have to be learned. Like every other new dad and mom, you'll grow into parenthood one challenge, one bath, one all-night rocking session, one cuddle and coo at a time. Gradually, with persistence, hard work, and a lot of love (that'll be the easy part, once you gaze into that little face), the role that seems daunting—yes, terrifying—now will become second nature. Though you'll learn plenty on the job—and from your mistakes, which every new parent makes plenty of—you might feel a little more comfortable with some formal preparation.

Fortunately, classes that teach all the baby basics—from diapering to bathing, feeding to playing—are finding their way into communities across the country. There are boot camps for new dads and other preparatory classes in many hospitals and community centers. Ask about those or classes you can take together as a couple at the next prenatal appointment, check into them at the hospital or birthing center you'll be delivering at, or do some research online. Put an infant CPR class on your to-do list, too. You can also learn the ropes by reading *What to Expect the First Year* or online at whattoexpect.com. If you have friends who have recently arrived infants, turn to them for some hands-on instruction. Ask them to let you hold, diaper, and play with their babies.

And remember, too, as you learn, that just as mothers have different parenting techniques, so do dads. Relax, trust your instincts (surprise . . . fathers have them, too), and feel free to find the style that works for both you and your baby. Before you know it, you'll be fathering with the best of them.

Breastfeeding

"My wife is thinking about breastfeeding our new baby, and I know it would be good for him—but I feel a little weird about it."

Up until now, you've thought of your wife's breasts sexually. And that's natural. But here's something that's also natural. Breasts are built the way they are for another good reason and to serve another really important purpose: baby feeding. There is no more perfect food for an infant than breast milk, and no more perfect food delivery system than a breast (make that two breasts). Breastfeeding offers an overwhelming number of health benefits for a baby (from preventing allergies, obesity, and illness to promoting brain development) and for its mother (nursing is linked to a speedier recovery postpartum and possibly a reduced risk of breast cancer later on in life). You can read more about those amazing benefits starting on page 331.

Without a doubt, your wife's decision to choose breast over bottle can make a dramatic difference in your child's life—and in hers. So try to put your feelings aside, and give her your vote of breastfeeding confidence—which counts a lot more than you'd think. Even though you don't know letdown from latch-on, you'll have a tremendous influence on whether your wife sticks with breastfeeding (and the longer she sticks with it, the more health benefits for both her and baby). In fact, research shows that moms are far more likely to try and succeed at nursing when fathers are supportive than if they're ambivalent. So take your influence seriously. Read up on nursing, watch a DVD, talk to other dads whose wives have breastfed, and ask whether a lactation consultant (basically, a nursing coach) will be available at the hospital or birthing center when the baby's ready to chow down for the first time. (Lesson one: It's a natural process, but it doesn't come naturally.) If your wife is too embarrassed to ask for help—or she's just too tired after delivery—be her breastfeeding advocate and make sure she gets it.

Sure, seeing your wife breastfeeding might seem weird at first—almost as weird as breastfeeding might feel to her initially—but before long, it will seem natural, normal, and incredibly special.

"My wife is breastfeeding our son. There's a closeness between them that I can't seem to share, and I feel left out."

Certain biological aspects of parenting naturally exclude you: You can't be pregnant, you can't give birth, and you can't breastfeed. But, as millions of new fathers discover each year, those natural physical limitations don't have to relegate you to spectator status. You can share in nearly all the joys, expectations, trials, and tribulations of your wife's pregnancy, labor, and delivery—from the first kick to the last push—as an active, supportive participant. And though you'll never be able to put your baby to the breast (at least not with the kind of results baby's looking for), you can share in the feeding process:

Be your baby's supplementary feeder. Once breastfeeding is established, there's more than one way to feed a baby. And though you can't nurse, you can be the one to give supplementary bottles

Your Baby Blues

You're overjoyed to be a father, and that's putting it mildly. So why are you also feeling emotionally spent? After all that buildup, all the planning and spending and drama, your child has been born, and you feel not only run-down (that's the sleep deprivation talking) but also a tiny bit let down. Welcome to the Postpartum Club, when you suddenly realize why the word *baby* is so often followed by the word *blues*. Not every new parent experiences the so-called baby blues (about 10 percent of new dads do), but you can expect a profusion of emotions in both of you (fortunately, usually only one of you at a time). Be ready. And be strong. You'll need the patience of a saint, the endurance of a triathlete, a temper with a mile-long fuse, and a sense of humor (big time) to work through this period of adjustment. Adapt the tips for her baby blues (page 456) to your needs during this rough patch. If those don't help, and baby blues progress to depression, ask your doctor for help so you can start enjoying life with your new baby.

(if those will be on the menu for baby). Not only will your being the supplementary feeder give mom a break (whether in the middle of the night or in the middle of dinner), it will give you extra opportunities for closeness with your baby. Make the most of the moment—instead of propping the bottle up to the baby's mouth, strike a nursing position, with the bottle where that breast would be and your baby snuggled close. Opening up your shirt, which allows for skin-to-skin contact, will enhance the experience for both of you.

Don't sleep through the night until your baby does. Sharing in the joys of feeding also means sharing in the sleepless nights. Even if you're not giving supplementary bottles, you can become a part of nighttime feeding rituals. You can be the one to pick baby up, do any necessary diaper changing, deliver him to his mom for his feeding, and return him to bed once he has fallen asleep again.

Participate in all other baby rituals. Nursing is the only baby-care activity limited to mothers. Dads can bathe, diaper, and rock with the best of moms, given the chance.

Bonding

"I'm so excited about our new baby that I'm afraid I'm almost overdoing the attention I'm giving her."

Some things in life you can overdo—but not loving and caring for your baby. Not only do infants thrive on attention from their fathers, there is no better way to cement your relationship with your new offspring. All the time you're spending with the baby will also help your spouse bond better with the baby (a mother who carries the load of baby care alone may find herself too exhausted and resentful to bond well).

And if you're surprised by your enthusiasm for your daughter, don't be. Studies have found that males in both the human and animal kingdoms experience a surge in female hormones when their babies arrive. Nurturing, long thought the province of mothers, apparently comes naturally to dads, too.

As you're busy nurturing your newborn, however, don't forget another relationship that needs looking after: the one with your spouse. Make sure she knows how much you love her, too. And make sure she gets her share of attention.

"I've heard about bonding, and we both got a chance to hold our baby when he arrived. But four days later, I feel love, but I still don't feel all that connected."

Bonding begins with that first cuddle, but it's just the very start of your relationship with your baby. That brand-new connection between you will deepen and strengthen, not just over the next weeks, but over the many years you'll be sharing as father and son.

In other words, don't expect instant results—and don't worry because you feel you haven't had them. Look at every moment with your new son as a new opportunity to build the bond you've started. Every diaper change, every bath, every kiss, every caress, every look into that tiny little face, you'll be bonding.

Keep an Eye on Her Mood

Baby blues are one thing (they're normal and self-limiting), but true postpartum depression is another. It's a serious medical condition that requires prompt, professional treatment. If the mom in your life still seems truly overwhelmed several weeks after the baby comes home or experiences bouts of crying, irritability, or sleep disruptions (other than those caused by the baby), or if she's not eating or otherwise functioning normally—as normally as can be expected given her new responsibilities—encourage her to talk to her practitioner about it. Don't leave it up to her if she says no. She may not recognize the signs of depression. Make sure she gets the treatment she needs to feel better. See page 458 for signs of postpartum depression.

Making eye contact and skin contact (open your shirt and hold him against your chest as you sing him to sleep) can enhance the closeness and tighten the bond. (This kind of contact will also, according to research, speed his brain development, so it's good for both of you.) Keep in mind that the relationship may seem a little one-sided at first (until your newborn is alert enough to be responsive, you'll be doing all the smiling and cooing), but every moment of your attention is contributing to your baby's fledgling sense of well-being and letting him know he's loved. The feedback you'll get once the smiles start coming will confirm your time was well spent—and the connection with your baby was there all along.

If you find your spouse is monopolizing the baby care (she may do this without even being aware of it), let her know you'd like to take on at least your share. Volunteering to spend time alone with the baby whenever possible—while your spouse takes an exercise class, meets a friend for coffee, or just soaks in a tub with a good book—will guarantee that maternal good intentions won't interfere with you and your son getting to know each other. And don't feel you have to spend your quality time with your son at home. Newborns are highly portable, so feel free to pack a diaper bag, strap him into a stroller, car seat, or baby carrier, and take a stroll or run an errand with baby in tow.

Feeling Unsexy After Delivery

"The delivery of our baby was absolutely awesome. But seeing her born seems to have turned me off sexually."

Human sexual response, compared to that of other animals, is

Postpartum Sex?

Are you experiencing the longest sexual dry spell you've had since freshman year? Think you're exhibiting the symptoms of dreaded DSB (deadly sperm backup)? Be patient: Their time will come, and so will yours. Your spouse is still recovering from a significant shock to her system—not just the birthing, but the nine months preceding. She's been through the wringer physically. The doctor or midwife may have already said that sex is technically okay to start up again, but your partner will be the ultimate decision maker on this one. Once she agrees to give it a try, you'll need to proceed very slowly and extremely gently. Ask her what feels good, what hurts, what you can do to help. And don't even consider laying into the entree until you've served up at least a few foreplay appetizers (she'll need lots of massage, and lubrication will help get her juices going because hormonal changes have left her extra dry). Don't be surprised if you get an accidental eyeful of milk right in the middle of the action (milk happens, especially early on). Share a laugh, and get back to business.

extremely delicate. It's at the mercy not only of the body but of the mind as well (dogs don't think about it—they just do it). And the mind can, at times, play plenty of tricks. One of those times, as you probably already know, is during pregnancy. Another, as you're discovering, is during the postpartum period.

It's very possible that the cause of your sudden sexual ambivalence has nothing to do with having seen your baby delivered. Most brand-new fathers find both the spirit and the flesh somewhat less willing after delivery (although there's nothing abnormal about those who don't) for many very understandable reasons: fatigue; fear that your baby will wake up crying at that first kiss (particularly if she is sharing your room); concern that you may hurt your spouse by having sex before her body is completely healed; and, finally, a general physical and mental preoccupation with your newborn, which sensibly concentrates your energies where they are most needed at this stage of your lives. Your feelings may also be influenced by the temporary increase in female hormones and drop in testosterone that many new fathers experience, because it's the male hormones, in both women and men, that fuel libido. That's probably nature's way of helping you nurture—and nature's way of keeping sex off your mind when there's a new baby in the house.

In other words, it's probably just as well that you aren't feeling sexually motivated, particularly if your wife—like most women in the immediate postpartum period—isn't feeling emotionally or physically up to it, either. Just how long it will take for your interest, and hers, to return is impossible to predict. As with all matters sexual, there is a wide range of normal. For some couples, desire precedes even the practitioner's go-ahead—which, depending on the circumstances, may be anywhere from two to six weeks. For others, six months can pass before sex makes a postpartum comeback. Some women find their libidos lacking until they stop breastfeeding, but that doesn't mean they can't enjoy the closeness of lovemaking.

Some fathers, even if they've been prepared for the childbirth experience, do come out of it feeling as if the special place that's always been meant for pleasure has suddenly taken on a practical purpose. But as the weeks pass, that feeling usually does, too. The vagina, after all, has two really important functions: practical and sexual. Neither excludes the other, and, if you think about it, they're very much interconnected. The vagina is used for childbirth only briefly, but it's a source of pleasure for you and your wife for a lifetime.

While you're waiting for your libido to make its inevitable return (and it will!), make sure you're paying your partner plenty of the attention she's undoubtedly in need of. Women who've just delivered typically don't feel their most desirable, and even if she's not in the mood for love—she's definitely in the mood to hear that you love her (and think she's beautiful and sexy). It can't hurt, either, to try some romantic moves to get you both back into the mood— as hard as that might be to accomplish when you've got a newborn in the house. Light some scented candles once baby's finally asleep to mask that pervasive aroma of dirty diapers; offer her a sensuous no-strings-attached massage; bring on the cuddles while you're both collapsed on the coach. Who knows—you might feel that libido return sooner than you'd think.

"Now that my wife's breastfeeding, I can't help feeling differently about her breasts. They seem too functional to be sexy."

Like the vagina, breasts were designed to serve both a practical and a sexual purpose (which, from a procreative perspective, is also practical). And though these purposes aren't mutually exclusive in the long run, they can conflict temporarily during lactation.

Take One for the Team

Are your immunizations up to date? Get your TdaP shot as well as seasonal flu vaccine (and other booster shots you may need) to protect the precious baby who's joined the family. Seventy percent of babies who get whooping cough are infected by immediate family members—including dads.

Some couples find breastfeeding a sexual turn-on, especially if breasts are full for the first time. Others, for aesthetic reasons (leaking milk, for instance) or because they feel uncomfortable about using the baby's source of nourishment for their sexual pleasure, find it a very definite turn-off. They may find this effect wears off, however, as breastfeeding becomes more second nature for all concerned.

Whatever turns you on—or off—is what is normal for you. If you feel your wife's breasts are too functional to be sexy now, focus foreplay elsewhere until you've become more comfortable sharing them with baby (or until baby has been weaned). Be sure, however, to be open and honest with your wife. Taking a sudden, unexplained hands-off approach to her breasts could leave her feeling unappealing. Be careful, also, not to harbor any resentment against the baby for sharing the breasts you love so much; try to think of nursing as a temporary "loan" instead. And enjoy the "interest" that comes with the loan—a healthy, well-fed newborn.

PART 6

Staying Healthy When You're Expecting

If You Get Sick

S O YOU PROBABLY EXPECT TO DEAL with at least a few of the less pleasant pregnancy symptoms during your nine-month stint (a little morning sickness, a few leg cramps, some indigestion and exhaustion), but maybe you weren't planning on coming down with a nasty cold or an ugly (and itchy) infection. The truth is, pregnant women can get sick with the best of them—and even better than the best of them, since suppression of the normal immune system makes expectant moms easier targets for germs of every variety. What's more, being sick for two can make you at least twice as uncomfortable—especially since so many of the remedies you're used to reaching for may need to stay behind medicine cabinet doors for a while.

Fortunately, such pregnancy-unrelated illnesses won't affect your pregnancy (though they may affect the way you feel). Prevention is, of course, the best way to avoid getting sick in the first place and to keep that healthy glow of pregnancy going strong. But when it fails (as when a coworker brings the flu to the office, your nephew's wet kisses are loaded with cold germs, or you pick up some bacteria with those fresh-picked blueberries), quick treatment, in most cases under the supervision of your practitioner, can help you feel better fast.

What You May Be Wondering About

The Common Cold

"I'm sneezing, coughing, and my head is killing me. Can this nasty cold affect my baby?"

Common colds are even more common when you're pregnant because your normal immune system is suppressed. The good news is that you're the only one those nasty bugs will be bugging. Your baby can't catch your cold or be affected by it in any way. The not-so-good news: The medications and supplements that you might be used to reaching for to find relief (or to prevent a cold), including aspirin and ibuprofen, megadoses of vitamins, and most herbs, are usually off limits when you're expecting (see page 509 for information on taking medications during pregnancy). So before you pick the shelves of the drugstore clean, pick up the phone and call your practitioner to ask which remedies are considered safe in pregnancy, as well as those that will work best in your case—there will probably be several you can choose from. (If you've already taken a few doses of a medication that isn't recommended for use during pregnancy, don't worry. But do check with your practitioner for extra reassurance.)

Even if your standard cold medication is shelved for now, you don't have to suffer (or play mother-to-be martyr) when you're laid up in bed with a runny nose and hacking cough—or even if you just feel a cold coming on. Some of the most effective cold remedies don't come in a bottle and are also the safest for both you and your baby. These tips can help nip a cold in the bud, before it blossoms into a nasty case of sinusitis or another secondary infection, while helping you to feel better faster. At the very first sneeze or tickle in the throat:

- Rest, if you feel the need. Taking a cold to bed doesn't necessarily shorten its duration, but if your body is begging for some rest, be sure to listen. On the other hand, if you feel up to it (and you're not running a fever or coughing), light to moderate exercise can actually help you feel better faster.

- Don't starve your cold, fever—or baby. Eat as nutritiously as you can, given how crummy you feel and how little appetite you probably have. Choose foods that appeal to you or at least don't turn you off completely. Try to have some citrus fruit or juice (oranges, tangerines, grapefruit) as

well as plenty of other fruits and vegetables rich in vitamin C every day, but don't take extra vitamin C supplements (beyond what comes in your pregnancy vitamin supplement) without medical approval. The same holds true for zinc and echinacea.

- Flood yourself with fluids. Fever, sneezes, and a runny nose will cause your body to lose fluids that you and your baby need. Warm beverages will be particularly soothing, so keep a thermos of a hot drink or hot soup next to your bed and try to drink at least a cupful an hour. Water and cold juices work fine, too, if that's what you're thirsting for.

- When you're lying down or sleeping, use a couple of pillows to keep your head elevated. This will make it easier for you to breathe through a stuffy nose. Nasal strips (which gently pull your nasal passages open, making breathing easier) may help, too. They're sold over the counter and are completely drug free.

- Keep your nasal passages moist with a humidifier and by squirting the inside of your nose with saline nose drops (which are also drug free and completely safe).

- If your throat is sore or scratchy, or if you're coughing, gargle with salt water (¼ teaspoon of salt to 8 ounces of warm water).

- Try to bring down a fever promptly. For more on fever treatment, see page 497.

- Don't put off calling the doctor or refuse to take a medication he or she prescribes because you think all drugs are harmful in pregnancy. Many are not. But do be sure the prescribing doctor knows you're expecting.

Is It the Flu or a Cold?

Here's how to tell which bug has you down:

The cold. A cold, even a bad one, is milder than the flu. It often starts with a sore or scratchy throat (which typically lasts only a day or two) followed by the gradual appearance of cold symptoms. These include a runny, and later stuffy, nose; lots of sneezing; and possibly slight achiness and mild fatigue. There is little or no fever (usually less than 100°F). Coughing may develop, particularly near the cold's end, and may continue for a week or more after other symptoms have subsided.

The flu. Influenza (or the flu) is more severe and comes on more suddenly. Symptoms include fever (usually 102°F to 104°F), headache, sore throat (which generally worsens by the second or third day), often intense muscle soreness, and general weakness and fatigue (which can last a couple of weeks or longer). There may also be occasional sneezing and often a cough that can become severe. In some cases, nausea or vomiting may occur, but don't confuse this with what is often called the "stomach flu" (see page 501). You can easily avoid coming down with the flu by getting a flu shot.

If your cold is severe enough to interfere with eating or sleeping, if you're coughing up greenish or yellowish mucus, if you have a cough with chest pain or wheezing, if your sinuses are throbbing (see the next question), or if symptoms last more than a week, call your doctor. It's possible that your cold has settled into a secondary infection and prescribed medication may be needed for your safety and your baby's.

Sinusitis

"I've had a cold for about a week. Now my forehead and cheeks are starting to really hurt. What should I do?"

Sounds as though your cold has turned into sinusitis. Signs of sinusitis include pain and often tenderness in the forehead and/or one or both cheeks (beneath the eye), and possibly around the teeth (pain usually worsens when you bend over or shake your head), as well as thickened and darkened (greenish or yellowish) mucus.

Sinusitis following a cold is fairly common, but it is far more common among pregnant women. That's because your hormones tend to swell mucous membranes (including those in and leading to the sinuses), causing blockages that allow germs to build up and multiply in the sinuses. These germs tend to linger longer there, because immune cells, which destroy invading germs, have difficulty reaching the sinuses' deep recesses. As a result, sinus infections that aren't treated can persist for weeks—or even become chronic. Treatment with antibiotics (your practitioner will be able to prescribe one that is safe during pregnancy) can bring relief quickly.

Flu Season

"It's fall, and I'm wondering if I should get a flu shot. Is it safe during pregnancy?"

A flu shot is definitely your best line of defense during flu season. Not only is it safe to receive while you're pregnant, it's considered a good move. In fact, the Centers for Disease Control and Prevention (CDC) recommends that any woman who will be pregnant during flu season (generally October through March) be given the flu shot. And since the CDC puts pregnant women at the top of the priority list for getting vaccinated (along with the elderly and children between the ages of 6 months and 5 years), moms-to-be can waddle to the front of the flu-shot line, even if the vaccine is in short supply. Talk to your ob-gyn or midwife about getting a flu shot. If he or she doesn't offer it, make an appointment with your general practitioner to get one. You can also look for flu-shot clinics that are sometimes set up at local drug and grocery stores during flu season.

The flu vaccine must be taken prior to each flu season—or at least early in the season—for best protection. It's not 100 percent effective because it protects only against the flu viruses that are expected to cause the most problems in a particular year. Still, it greatly increases the chance that you will escape the season flu free. And even when it doesn't prevent infection, it usually reduces the severity of symptoms. Side effects occur infrequently and are generally mild.

When going for your flu shot, ask if you can receive thimerosal-free (or -reduced) vaccine. And stick with the needle, not the nasal spray vaccine (FluMist). That vaccine, unlike the flu shot, is made from live flu virus (which means it could actually give you a mild case of the flu) and is not recommended for pregnant women.

If you suspect you might have the flu (see symptoms in box, facing page), call your doctor so that you can be treated (and so that the flu doesn't progress to pneumonia). Treatment is typically symptomatic—aimed at reducing fever (take steps right away to bring down any fever; see next question), aches and pains, and nasal stuffiness. Most important if you've got the flu (or any virus) when you're expecting: Rest and drink plenty of fluids, essential for preventing dehydration.

Fever

"I'm running a little fever. What should I do?"

During pregnancy, a low-grade fever (one that's under 100.4°F) isn't usually something to be concerned about. But it's also not something to be ignored, which means you should take steps to bring any fever down promptly. Keep a close eye on your temperature, too, to make sure it doesn't start rising.

Any fever over 100.4°F while you're expecting is more of a concern and should be reported to your practitioner right away. That's because the cause (such as an infection that should be treated with antibiotics) can pose a pregnancy problem even when the fever

Flu Shot for Two

Getting a flu shot is good for you when you're expecting, but did you know that its benefits carry over to your newborn as well? Researchers have found that babies born to mothers who were given the flu shot during the last trimester of pregnancy appear to be protected against the virus for the first six months of life. Which means that by getting a flu shot now, you'll be keeping your baby protected until it's time for his or her first flu shot.

doesn't. While you're waiting to speak to your practitioner, take two acetaminophen (Tylenol) to start reducing the fever. Taking a tepid bath or shower, drinking cool beverages, and keeping clothing and covers light will also help bring your temperature down. Aspirin or ibuprofen (Advil or Motrin) should *not* be taken when you're expecting unless they've been specifically recommended by your practitioner.

If you had a high fever earlier in pregnancy and did not report it to your practitioner, mention it now.

Strep Throat

"My three-year-old came down with strep throat. If I catch it, is there a risk to the baby?"

If there's one thing kids are good at sharing, it's their germs. And the more kids you have at home (particularly of the child-care-attending or school-going variety), the greater your chances of coming down with colds and other infections while you're expecting.

So step up preventive measures (don't share drinks, resist the temptation to finish that peanut-butter-and-germ sandwich, wash your hands frequently) and boost your immune system—which is lowered during pregnancy anyway—by eating well and getting enough rest.

If you do suspect that you've succumbed to strep, go to your practitioner for a throat culture right away. The infection will not harm the baby, as long as it is treated promptly with the right type of antibiotic. Your practitioner will prescribe one that is effective against strep and perfectly safe for use during pregnancy. Don't take medication prescribed for your children or someone else in the family.

Urinary Tract Infection

"I'm afraid I have a urinary tract infection."

Your poor battered bladder, which spends months on end being pummeled by your growing uterus and its adorable occupant, is the perfect breeding ground for less welcome visitors: bacteria. These little bugs multiply fast in areas where urine pools or is prevented from moving along, meaning anywhere along a urinary tract that's being squished by the expanding uterus. (It's that same compression that makes you unable to sleep through the night without getting up several times to pee.) That here-and-there compression, added to the muscle-relaxing properties of the hormones flooding your body, makes it much easier for the intestinal bacteria that live quietly on your skin and in your feces to enter your urinary tract and make you miserable. In fact, urinary tract infections (UTIs) are so common in pregnancy that at least 5 percent of pregnant women can expect to develop at least one, and those who have already had one have a 1 in 3 chance of an encore. In some women, a UTI is "silent" (without symptoms) and diagnosed only after a routine urine culture. In others, symptoms can range from mild to quite uncomfortable (an urge to urinate frequently, pain or a burning sensation when urine—sometimes only a drop or two—is passed, pressure or sharp pain in the lower abdominal area). The urine may also be foul smelling and cloudy.

Diagnosing a UTI is as simple as dipping an indicator stick into a urine sample at your practitioner's office; the stick will react to red or white blood cells in the sample. Red blood cells indicate bleeding in the urinary tract; white cells indicate a likely infection. Treating a UTI is as simple as taking a full course of prescribed antibiotics specifically aimed at the type of bacteria found when a lab analyzed that urine sample. (Don't hesitate to take them—your practitioner will prescribe one of the many antibiotics that are safe for use during pregnancy.)

Of course, your best bet is to prevent a UTI in the first place. There are a number of steps you can take to reduce your chances of developing one during your pregnancy (or, in conjunction with medical treatment, help speed recovery when infection occurs):

- Drink plenty of fluids, especially water, which can help flush out any bacteria. Cranberry juice may also be beneficial, possibly because the tannins it contains keep bacteria from sticking to the walls of the urinary tract. Avoid coffee and tea (even decaffeinated varieties) and alcohol, which may increase risk of irritation.

- Wash your vaginal area well and empty your bladder just before and after sex.

- Every time you urinate, take the time to empty your bladder thoroughly. Leaning forward on the toilet will help accomplish this. It sometimes also helps to "double void": After you pee, wait five minutes, then try to pee again. And don't put off the urge when you have it; regularly "holding it in" increases susceptibility to infection.

- To give your perineal area breathing room, wear cotton-crotch underwear and panty hose, avoid wearing tight pants, don't wear panty hose under pants, and sleep without panties or pajama bottoms on if possible (and comfortable).

- Keep your vaginal and perineal areas meticulously clean and irritation free. Wipe front to back after using the toilet to keep fecal bacteria from entering your vagina or urethra (the short tube through which urine is excreted from the bladder). Wash daily (showers are better than baths), and avoid bubble bath and perfumed products— powders, shower gels, soaps, sprays, detergents, and toilet paper. Also, stay out of pools that aren't properly chlorinated.

- Some practitioners recommend eating yogurt that contains active cultures or taking probiotics while you're on antibiotics to help restore the balance of beneficial bacteria. Ask your practitioner; some probiotics are definitely more potent than others.

- Keep your resistance high by eating a nutritious diet, getting enough rest and exercise, and not letting your life get too stressful.

UTIs in the lower part of the urinary tract are no fun, but a more serious potential threat is that bacteria from an untreated UTI will travel up to your kidneys. Kidney infections that aren't treated can be quite dangerous and may lead to premature labor, low-birthweight babies, and more problems. The symptoms are the same as those of UTIs but are frequently accompanied by fever (often as high as 103°F), chills, blood in the urine, backache (in the midback on one or both sides), nausea, and vomiting. Should you experience these symptoms, notify your practitioner immediately so you can be treated promptly.

Yeast Infection

"I think I have a yeast infection. Should I go get some of the medication I usually use, or do I need to see the doctor?"

Pregnancy is never a time for self-diagnosis or treatment—not even when it comes to something as seemingly simple as a yeast infection. Even if you've had yeast infections a hundred

Bacterial Vaginosis

Bacterial vaginosis (BV) is the most common vaginal condition in women of childbearing age, affecting up to 16 percent of pregnant women. A BV condition, which occurs when certain types of bacteria normally found in the vagina begin to multiply in large numbers, is often accompanied by an abnormal gray or white vaginal discharge with a strong fishlike odor, pain, itching, or burning (though some women with BV report no signs or symptoms at all). Doctors are not exactly sure what causes the normal balance of bacteria in the vagina to be disrupted, though some risk factors have been identified, including having multiple sex partners, douching, or using an IUD. BV is not transmitted during sexual contact but is associated with sexual activity (women who have never had sexual intercourse are rarely affected).

During pregnancy, BV is associated with a slight increase in such complications as premature rupture of the membranes and amniotic fluid infection, which may lead to premature labor. It may also be associated with miscarriage and low birthweight. Some doctors test for BV in women who are at high risk for preterm delivery, but no clear evidence indicates that treating such high-risk women reduces the incidence of prematurity. That said, treating symptomatic BV with antibiotics is effective at relieving symptoms. Some research has also suggested that treatment may reduce the complications associated with preterm births triggered by BV and may decrease the number of days these babies spend in the NICU.

times before, even if you know the symptoms backward and forward (a yellowish, greenish, or thick and cheesy discharge that has a foul odor, accompanied by burning, itching, redness, or soreness), even if you've treated yourself successfully with over-the-counter preparations in the past—this time around, call your practitioner.

How you will be treated will depend on what kind of infection you have, something only your practitioner can determine via lab tests. If it does turn out to be a yeast infection, which is very common in pregnancy, your practitioner may prescribe vaginal suppositories, gels, ointments, or creams. The oral anti-yeast agent fluconazole (Diflucan) may also be prescribed during pregnancy, but only in low doses and for no longer than two days.

Unfortunately, medication may banish a yeast infection only temporarily; the infection often returns off and on until after delivery and may require repeated treatment.

You may be able to speed your recovery and prevent reinfection by keeping your genital area clean and dry. Do this by practicing meticulous hygiene, especially after going to the bathroom (always wipe from front to back); rinsing your vaginal area thoroughly after soaping during a bath or shower; skipping irritating or perfumed soaps, and bubble baths; wearing cotton underwear; and avoiding tight pants or leggings (especially those that aren't cotton). In general, let the area breathe whenever you can (sleeping without underwear, if possible).

Eating yogurt containing live probiotic cultures may help keep those yeast bugs at bay. You can also ask your practitioner about using an effective probiotic supplement (many on the market aren't effective). Some chronic yeast infection sufferers find that cutting down on the sugar and baked goods made with refined flour helps, too. Do not douche, because it upsets the normal balance of bacteria in the vagina.

Stomach Bugs

"I've got a stomach bug, and I can't keep anything down. Will this hurt my baby?"

Just when you thought it was safe to come out of the bathroom, you're back with a bug (good-bye morning sickness, hello stomach flu). And if you're still in your first trimester when the bug hits, it could be hard to differentiate the symptoms from those of morning sickness.

Luckily, having a stomach virus won't hurt your fetus, even while it's hurting your stomach. But just because the virus isn't bugging baby doesn't mean it shouldn't be treated. And whether your tummy is turning from hormones, a virus, or from egg salad that sat on the lunch cart too long, the treatment is the same: Get the rest your body's aching for, and focus on fluids, especially if you're losing them through vomiting or diarrhea. They're much more important in the short term than solids.

If you're not urinating frequently enough or your urine is dark (it should be straw-colored), you may be dehydrated. Fluid needs to be your best buddy now: Try taking frequent small sips of water, diluted juice (white grape is easiest on the tummy), clear broth, weak decaffeinated tea, or hot water with lemon. If you can't manage to sip, suck on ice chips or a Popsicle. Follow your stomach's lead when it comes to adding solids—and when you do, keep it bland, simple, and fat-free (white rice or dry toast, low-fiber cereal, applesauce, bananas). And don't

forget that ginger's good for what ails any sick stomach. Take it in tea or in flat ginger ale (best if there's actually ginger in it) or another ginger beverage, or suck or chew on some ginger candies. Remember, too, to supplement when you can. Getting your vitamin insurance is an especially good idea now, so try to take your supplement when it's least likely to come back up. Don't worry, however, if you can't manage to keep it down for a few days or so; no harm done.

If you can't get anything down, talk to your practitioner. Dehydration is a problem for anyone suffering with a stomach bug, but it's especially problematic when you need to stay hydrated for two. You might be advised to take some rehydration fluid (like Pedialyte, which also comes in a soothing freezable form).

Check with your practitioner before you open up your medicine cabinet looking for relief. Antacids like Tums and Rolaids are considered safe to take during pregnancy, and some practitioners may okay gas relievers, but be sure to ask first. Your practitioner may also say you can take certain antidiarrheal medicines, but probably only after your first trimester is safely behind you (see page 511). As always, check with your practitioner before taking anything, just to play it safe.

And sick tummies, take heart: Most stomach bugs clear up by themselves within a day or so.

Listeriosis

"A friend who is pregnant said to stay away from certain dairy products because they can make you sick when you're expecting. Is this true?"

More bad news for adventurous eaters. Unpasteurized milk and cheeses made from unpasteurized milk (including some mozzarella, blue cheese,

Mexican cheeses, Brie, Camembert, and feta) can sometimes make you sick, and that extremely unlikely possibility becomes slightly more likely when you're expecting. These foods, along with unpasteurized juices, raw or undercooked meat, fish and shellfish, poultry, eggs, unwashed raw vegetables, and hot dogs and deli meats, can very occasionally contain Listeria. These bacteria can cause serious illness (listeriosis), especially in high-risk individuals, including young children, the elderly, those with compromised immune systems, and pregnant women, whose immune systems are also somewhat suppressed. Though the overall risk of contracting listeriosis is extremely low—even in pregnancy—the potential of its causing problems in pregnancy is higher. Listeria, unlike many other germs, enters the bloodstream directly and therefore can get to the baby quickly through the placenta (other food contaminants generally stay in the digestive tract and may only pose a threat if they get into the amniotic fluid).

Listeriosis is hard to detect—partly because symptoms can appear anytime between 12 hours and 30 days after contaminated food is eaten, and partly because the symptoms (headache, fever, fatigue, muscle aches, and occasionally nausea and diarrhea) are similar to those of flu, and some can even be mistaken for pregnancy side effects. Antibiotics are needed to treat and cure listeriosis. Untreated, the illness can cause serious complications for mom and baby.

So, clearly, it's important to prevent infection in the first place by staying away from the risky foods that might possibly carry Listeria, especially now, even if it means that your taco salad comes without the fresh queso. See page 116 for more tips on food safety and the prevention of food-borne diseases. Keep in mind, though, that the risk of contracting the infection from day-to-day eating is extremely low, even among expectant diners, so don't stress about the queso you've sprinkled or the smoked turkey you've gobbled up until now.

Toxoplasmosis

"Though I've given all the cat-care chores over to my husband, just the very fact that I live with cats makes me nervous about toxoplasmosis. How would I know if I came down with it?"

Chances are you wouldn't. Most people who are infected show no symptoms at all, though some do notice mild malaise, slight fever, and swollen glands two or three weeks after exposure, followed by a rash a day or two later.

But chances are, too, that you wouldn't come down with the disease in the first place. If you've lived with cats for a long time, it's very likely that you've already become infected and have developed antibodies to the virus that causes toxoplasmosis.

If you turn out not to be immune, and you do experience the symptoms of toxoplasmosis, you'll probably be tested. (Don't try to test yourself, however, since home tests for toxoplasmosis are highly unreliable.) In the unlikely event that the test comes back positive, you'll probably be treated with antibiotics to reduce the risk of transmitting the infection to your baby.

There is little risk to an expectant mother from toxoplasmosis, and the risk of a fetus becoming infected if mom has contracted the infection and is untreated is only about 15 percent. The earlier in pregnancy a mother is infected, the less likely the illness will be transmitted to her baby but the more serious the consequences will be. The later in the pregnancy, the greater the transmission rate but the less severe the potential consequences. Fortunately, the number of pregnant women who contract toxoplasmosis is small to begin with, and only 1 in 10,000 babies is born with severe congenital toxoplasmosis.

Recent advances have made it possible to test fetal blood and/or amniotic fluid and the fetus's liver via ultrasound to learn whether or not the fetus has actually become infected, though not usually before 20 to 22 weeks. If no infection is detected, the fetus is most likely fine.

The best "treatment" of toxoplasmosis, however, is prevention. See page 79 for tips on how to avoid infection.

Cytomegalovirus

"My son came home from preschool with a note saying that there's an outbreak of CMV at his school. Is this something I should worry about catching during pregnancy?"

Luckily, the chances of picking up cytomegalovirus (CMV) from your son and passing it on to your baby are remote. Why's that? A majority of adults were infected in childhood, and if you're among that majority, you can't "catch" CMV now (though it could become "reactivated"). Even if you did come down with a new CMV infection during pregnancy, the risks to your baby are low. Though half of infected moms give birth to infected infants, only a tiny percentage of them ever show any ill effects. The risks are lower still in a baby whose mom had a reactivated infection during pregnancy.

Still, unless you know for sure that you're immune to CMV because you had the infection before, your best defense is a good offense. Take preventative measures such as washing up carefully after changing your son's diapers or helping

him out at the potty, and resist nibbling on your preschooler's leftovers. (And if you work in a child-care or preschool setting, always practice good hygiene protocol.)

Though CMV often comes and goes without any obvious symptoms, it's occasionally marked by fever, fatigue, swollen glands, and sore throat. If you notice any of these symptoms, check with your doctor. Whether these symptoms signal CMV or another illness (such as flu or strep throat), you'll need some sort of treatment.

Fifth Disease

"I was told that a disease I had never even heard of before—fifth disease—could cause problems in pregnancy."

Fifth disease is the fifth of a group of six diseases that cause fever and rash in children. But unlike its sister diseases (such as measles and chicken pox, the ones that get all the attention), fifth disease isn't widely known because its symptoms are mild and can go unnoticed—or may even be totally absent. Fever is present in only 15 to 30 percent of cases. For the first few days, the rash gives the cheeks the appearance of having been slapped, then spreads in a lacy pattern to trunk, buttocks, and thighs, recurring on and off (usually in response to heat from the sun or a warm bath) for one to three weeks. It is often confused with the rash of rubella and other childhood illnesses or even a sun- or windburn.

Concentrated exposure from caring for a child sick with fifth disease or from teaching at a school where it is epidemic somewhat increases that very small risk of contracting the illness. But half of all women of childbearing age had fifth disease during childhood and are already immune, so infection, happily, isn't common among pregnant women. In the unlikely event that a mom catches fifth disease and her fetus does become infected, the virus can disrupt the developing baby's ability to produce red blood cells, leading to a form of anemia or other complications. If you do contract fifth disease, your practitioner will follow you for signs of fetal anemia with weekly ultrasounds for eight to ten weeks. If the baby is infected during the first half of pregnancy, the risk of miscarriage increases.

Again, the odds that fifth disease will affect you, your pregnancy, or your baby are very remote. Still, as always, it makes sense to take the appropriate steps to avoid any infection while you're expecting (see opposite page).

Measles

"I can't remember if I was vaccinated against measles when I was a child. Should I be immunized now?"

No. Measles vaccine (a component of the MMR vaccine) isn't given during pregnancy because of the theoretical risk to the fetus from the vaccine, though there have been no reports of problems among newborns whose mothers were inadvertently vaccinated. Besides, the chances are good that you are already immune to measles, since most women of childbearing age either had the disease or were vaccinated against it as children. If your medical history doesn't include this information and your parents can't recall it, your doctor can run a test to determine whether you are immune. Even if you're not immune, the risk that you might contract measles is extremely remote because the disease has been practically wiped out in the United States (which means it would be highly unlikely that you'd be able to catch it here).

In the exceedingly unlikely event that you are exposed directly to someone with measles and are not immune, your doctor may administer gamma globulin (antibodies) during the incubation period—between exposure and the start of symptoms—to decrease the severity of the illness should you come down with it. Measles, unlike rubella, does not appear to cause birth defects, though it may be linked to an increased risk of miscarriage or premature labor. If you were to contract measles near your due date, there is a risk that your newborn might catch the infection from you. Again, gamma globulin may be administered to reduce the severity of such an infection. Keep in mind that all this is pretty much theoretical, given how rare measles are these days.

Mumps

"A coworker of mine came down with a bad case of the mumps. Should I get immunized so I don't get it myself?"

It's not that easy to get mumps these days—in fact, it's pretty close to impossible. Fewer than 250 Americans contract mumps each year, thanks to routine childhood immunization with MMR (measles, mumps, rubella). And chances are you were vaccinated, too, when you were a child (or, less likely, that you actually had the disease), which means you can't catch it now. If you're not sure whether you were immunized against or had mumps, check with your parents or the doctor who cared for you as a child, if that's possible.

If it turns out you're not immune, you can't be immunized now because the vaccine might be harmful to your fetus. Even without immunity, though, the risk of contracting mumps is very low. It isn't highly contagious through casual contact. However, because the disease appears to

Staying Well

In pregnancy, when you need to stay well for two, the proverbial ounce of prevention is worth far more than a pound of cure. The following suggestions will increase your chances of staying well when you're expecting (and when you're not):

Keep your resistance up. Eat the best diet possible, get enough sleep and exercise, and don't run yourself down by running yourself ragged. Reducing stress in your life as much as you can also helps keep your immune system in tip-top shape.

Avoid sick people like the plague. As best as you can, try to stay away from anyone who has a cold, flu, stomach virus, or anything else noticeably contagious. Keep your distance from coughers on the bus, avoid lunching with a colleague who's complaining of a sore throat, and evade the handshake of a friend with a runny nose (germs as well as greetings can be exchanged in a handshake). Also avoid crowded or cramped indoor spaces when you can.

Wash your hands. Hands are the major spreader of infections, so wash them often and thoroughly with soap and warm water (about 20 seconds does the trick), particularly after exposure to someone you know is sick and after spending time in public places or riding on public transportation. Hand washing is especially important before eating. Keep a hand sanitizer in your glove compartment, in your desk drawer, and in your handbag or briefcase so you can wash up when there's no sink in sight.

Don't share the germs. At home, try to limit germ-spreading contact with sick children or a sick spouse as much as possible. Avoiding finishing up their sandwich scraps and drinking from their cups. And while every sick child needs a dose of kiss-and-hug therapy from mom now and then, be sure to wash your hands and face after those comforting cuddles. Wash your hands, too, after touching their germy sheets, towels, and used tissues, especially before touching your own eyes, nose, and mouth. See that the little patients wash their hands frequently, too, and try to get them to cough and sneeze into their elbows instead of their hands (a good tip for adults, too). Use disinfectant spray or wipes on telephones, computer keyboards, remotes, and other surfaces they handle.

If your own child or a child you regularly spend time with develops a rash of any kind, avoid close contact and call your doctor as soon as you can unless you already know that you are immune to chicken pox, fifth disease, and CMV.

Be pet smart. Keep pets in good health, updating their immunizations as necessary. If you have a cat, take the precautions to avoid toxoplasmosis (page 79).

Look out for Lyme. Avoid outdoor areas where Lyme disease is prevalent, or be sure to protect yourself adequately (see page 507).

To each his or her own. Maintain a no-sharing policy when it comes to toothbrushes and other personal items (and don't let those toothbrushes mingle bristle-to-bristle). Use disposable cups for rinsing in the bathroom.

Eat safe. To avoid food-borne illnesses, practice safe food preparation and storage habits (see page 116).

trigger uterine contractions and is associated with an increased risk of miscarriage in the first trimester or preterm labor later, be alert for the first symptoms of the disease (possibly vague pain, fever, and loss of appetite before the salivary glands become swollen; then ear pain and pain on chewing or on taking acidic or sour food or drink). Notify your practitioner of such symptoms immediately because prompt treatment can reduce the chance of problems developing. You might also want to consider the MMR vaccine before deciding to get pregnant again, just to be on the safe side.

Rubella

"I might have been exposed to rubella on a trip out of the country. Should I be worried?"

Happily, the vast majority of pregnant women in the United States are immune to rubella (German measles), either because they were immunized against it as a child (it's the "R" in the MMR vaccine) or contracted it at some other time in their lives (usually during childhood). In fact, the CDC considers rubella to be eradicated here, so the odds are good that you can't catch it and, consequently, have nothing to worry about. If you're not sure whether or not you are immune (around 25 percent of women may not be immune because they were born outside the United States), you can find out with a simple test—a rubella antibody titer—that measures the level of antibodies to the virus in your blood and is performed routinely at the first prenatal visit by most practitioners. If this test was not performed earlier, it should be now.

In the unlikely event you turn out not to be immune (or if the antibody levels in your blood are low), you still don't have to consider drastic measures imme-

diately. For the virus to do its damage, you have to actually come down with the illness. The symptoms, which show up two or three weeks after exposure, are usually mild (malaise, slight fever, and swollen glands, followed by a slight rash a day or two later) and may sometimes pass unnoticed. If you did come down with rubella during pregnancy (and, again, the odds are extremely remote), whether your baby would be at risk would depend on when you contracted it. During the first month, the chance of a baby developing a serious birth defect from in utero exposure is pretty high. By the third month, the risk is significantly lower. After that, the risk is lower still.

There is no way of absolutely preventing an exposed woman with no immunity from coming down with rubella—but because the chance of being exposed to rubella in the United States is almost nil, that scenario is just about never encountered. Still, if you aren't immune and don't contract the disease this time around, avoid the concern entirely in subsequent pregnancies by being vaccinated after this delivery. As a precaution, you will be advised not to become pregnant for one month following vaccination. But should you conceive accidentally during this time, or if you were vaccinated early in this pregnancy, before you knew you had conceived, don't worry. Apparently, there is no risk when an expectant woman is inadvertently vaccinated early in pregnancy or if she conceives soon after vaccination.

Chicken Pox (Varicella)

"My toddler was exposed to chicken pox at her child-care center—by a child who wasn't immunized. If she comes down with it, could the baby I'm now carrying be hurt?"

Not likely. Well insulated from the rest of the world, a fetus can't catch chicken pox from a third party—only from its mother. Which means you would have to catch it first, something that's unlikely. First of all, your child probably won't catch it and bring it home if she was immunized with the varicella vaccine. Second of all, it's very likely you had the infection as a child (85 to 95 percent of the U.S. adult population has had it) and are already immune. Ask your parents or check your health records to find out whether you have had chicken pox. If you can't find out for sure, ask your practitioner to run a test now to see if you are immune.

Though the chances of your becoming infected are slim if you aren't immune, an injection of varicella-zoster immune globulin (VZIG) within 96 hours of a documented personal exposure (in other words, direct contact with someone who has been diagnosed with chicken pox) may be recommended. It isn't clear whether or not this will protect the baby should you come down with chicken pox anyway, but it should minimize complications for you—a significant plus, since this mild childhood disease can be quite severe in adults. If you should be hit with a severe case, you may be given an antiviral drug to further reduce the risk of complications.

If you become infected during the first half of your pregnancy, the chances are very low (around 2 percent) that your baby could develop a condition called congenital varicella syndrome, which can cause some birth defects. If you come down with chicken pox later in your pregnancy, there's almost zero danger to the baby. The exception is if you get chicken pox just before (within a week of) giving birth or just after delivery. In that extremely unlikely scenario, there's a small chance your newborn will arrive infected and will develop the characteristic rash within a week or so. To prevent neonatal infection, your baby will be given an infusion of chicken pox antibodies immediately after delivery (or as soon as it becomes apparent that you've been infected postpartum).

Incidentally, shingles, or herpes zoster, which is a reactivation of the chicken pox virus in someone who had the disease earlier, does not appear to be harmful to a developing fetus, probably because the mother and thus the baby already have antibodies to the virus.

If you are not immune and escape infection this time, ask your doctor about getting immunized after delivery, to protect any future pregnancies. Immunization should take place at least a month before any new conception.

Lyme Disease

"I live in an area that's high risk for Lyme disease. Is Lyme dangerous when you're pregnant?"

Lyme disease is most common among those who spend time in woods frequented by deer, mice, or other animals carrying deer ticks, but it can also be picked up in forest-free cities via greenery brought from the country or purchased at a farmers' market.

The best way to protect your baby—as well as yourself—is by taking preventive measures. If you are out in woodsy or grassy areas, or if you are handling greenery grown in such areas, wear long pants, tucked into boots or socks, and long sleeves; use an insect repellent effective for deer ticks on your clothing. When you return home, check your skin carefully for ticks. If you find one, remove it right away by pulling straight up on it with tweezers; then drop it into a small bottle and have it tested by your doctor (removing a tick within 24 hours almost entirely eliminates the possibility of infection).

If you've been bitten by a tick, see your doctor immediately; a blood test may be able to determine whether you are infected with Lyme. (Early symptoms may include a blotchy bull's-eye rash at the bite site, fatigue, headache, stiff neck, fever and chills, generalized achiness, swollen glands near the site of the bite; later symptoms may include arthritis-like pain and memory loss.)

Fortunately, studies have shown that prompt treatment with antibiotics completely protects a baby whose mother is infected with Lyme—and keeps mom from becoming seriously ill.

Hepatitis A

"One of the toddlers in the child-care center where I work was just diagnosed as having hepatitis A. If I get it, could it affect my pregnancy?"

Hepatitis A is very common, almost always a mild disease (often with no noticeable symptoms), and rarely passed on to a fetus or newborn. So even if you did catch it, it shouldn't affect your pregnancy. Still, you're better off not contracting an infection of any kind in the first place. So take precautions: Be sure to wash your hands after changing diapers or taking your young charges to the bathroom (hepatitis A is passed by the fecal-oral route), and be sure to wash up well before eating. You might also want to ask your physician about immunization against hepatitis A.

Hepatitis B

"I'm a carrier of hepatitis B and just found out that I'm pregnant. Will my being a carrier hurt my baby?"

Knowing that you're a carrier for hepatitis B is the first step in making sure your condition won't hurt your baby. Because this liver infection can be passed on from mother to baby during delivery, prompt steps will be taken at your baby's birth to make sure that doesn't happen. Your newborn will be treated within 12 hours with both hepatitis B immune globulin (HBIG) and the hepatitis B vaccine (which is routine at birth anyway). This treatment can almost always prevent the infection from developing. Your baby will also be vaccinated at one or two months and then again at six months (this, too, is a routine part of the hepatitis B series), and may be tested at 12 to 15 months to be sure the therapy has been effective.

Hepatitis C

"Should I be worried about hepatitis C during pregnancy?"

Hepatitis C can be transmitted from infected mother to child during delivery, with a transmission rate of about 7 to 8 percent. But because hep C is usually transmitted via blood (for instance, through past transfusions or illegal drug injections), unless you've had a transfusion or are in a high-risk category, it's unlikely you'd be infected. The infection, if diagnosed, can potentially be treated, but not during pregnancy.

Bell's Palsy

"I woke up this morning with pain behind my ear, and my tongue felt numb. When I looked in the mirror, the whole side of my face looked droopy. What's going on?"

It sounds like you've got Bell's palsy, a temporary condition caused by damage to the facial nerve, resulting in weakness or paralysis on one side of the face. Bell's palsy strikes pregnant women three times more often than it does women who are not pregnant (though it's quite uncommon in general) and most often occurs in the third trimester or in the early postpartum period. Its onset is sudden, and most people with the condition—like you—wake up without warning to find their face drooping.

The cause of this temporary facial paralysis is unknown, though experts suspect that certain viral or bacterial infections may cause swelling and inflammation of the facial nerve, triggering the condition. Other symptoms sometimes accompanying the paralysis include pain behind the ear or in the back of the head, dizziness, drooling (because of the weak muscles), dry mouth, inability to blink, impaired sense of taste and tongue numbness, even impaired speaking in some cases.

The good news is that Bell's palsy will not spread beyond your face and won't get worse. More good news: Most cases completely resolve within three weeks to three months without treatment (though for some it can take as long as six months to completely go away). And the best news of all: The condition poses no threat to your pregnancy or your baby. Though you should definitely put a call in to your practitioner, chances are treatment won't be necessary.

ALL ABOUT

Medications During Pregnancy

Open any prescription or over-the-counter drug insert and read the fine print. Virtually all will warn against pregnant women using medications without a doctor's advice. Still, if you're like the average expectant mom, you'll wind up taking at least one prescription drug during your pregnancy and even more over-the-counter medications. How will you know which are safe and which aren't?

No drug—prescription or over-the-counter, traditional or herbal—is 100 percent safe for 100 percent of the people, 100 percent of the time. And when you're pregnant, there's the health and well-being of two people, one very small and vulnerable, to consider every time you take a drug. Happily, only a few drugs are known to be harmful to a developing fetus, and many drugs can be used safely during pregnancy. In fact, in certain situations, using a medication during pregnancy is absolutely necessary.

It's always wise to weigh the potential risks of taking a medication against the potential benefits it will provide, but never more so than during pregnancy. Involving your practitioner in the decision of whether or not to take a drug is a good idea in general, but when you're pregnant, it's essential. So check with your practitioner before taking any medication while you're expecting, even an over-the-counter drug you've used routinely in the past.

One of the tools your practitioner will use to determine the safety of a particular medication is the five-letter rating (A, B, C, D, or X) set up by the Food and Drug Administration to determine whether a drug poses a risk to a fetus. Categories A and B drugs are thought to be generally safe, with those in the A category having undergone controlled studies that showed no risk to the fetus, and those in the B category shown to have no risk to animals or no risk to humans even if animal studies showed an adverse effect. Category C means that the data is inconclusive. The other categories (D and X) are given to drugs that have a demonstrated risk to the fetus (though in some rare life-threatening cases, doctors may prescribe a Category D drug because the risk to the mother—if she doesn't take the drug—is too great). Still, this system is far from perfect since the FDA doesn't require drug manufacturers to conduct long-term studies on pregnant women, for obvious reasons.

Still confused about the ABCs of medications during pregnancy? Here's the bottom line: Never take any drug—prescription, over-the-counter, or herbal—without talking to your doctor or midwife first.

Common Medications

A number of medications are considered safe for pregnant women to take, and these medications can be a welcome relief if you're down and out with a stuffy nose or a pounding headache. Other medications are not recommended in most cases—though in certain cases they may be okayed, such as after the first trimester or for a specific problem. And many medications are completely off-limits when you're expecting. Here's the lowdown on some of the more common medications you may come across during pregnancy:

Tylenol. Acetaminophen is usually given the green light for short-term use during pregnancy, but be sure to ask your practitioner for the proper dosage before taking it for the first time.

Aspirin. Your practitioner will probably advise that you not take aspirin—especially during the third trimester, since it increases the risk for potential problems for the newborn, as well as complications before and during delivery, such as excessive bleeding. Some studies suggest that very low dosages of aspirin may help to prevent preeclampsia in certain circumstances, but only your practitioner will be able to tell you whether it should be prescribed in your case. Other studies suggest that low-dose aspirin, in combination with the blood-thinning medication heparin, may reduce the incidence of recurrent miscarriage in some women with a condition known as antiphospholipid antibody syndrome. Again, only your practitioner can let you know if these medications are safe for you and under what circumstances.

Advil or Motrin. Ibuprofen should be used with caution in pregnancy, especially during the first and third trimesters, when it can have the same negative effects as aspirin. Use it only if it's specifically recommended by a physician who knows you are pregnant.

Aleve. Naproxen, a nonsteroidal anti-inflammatory drug (NSAID), is not recommended for use in pregnancy at all.

Nasal sprays. For short-term relief from a stuffy nose, most nasal sprays are fine to use. Check with your practitioner for his or her preferred brand and dosing suggestions. Saline sprays are always safe to use, as are nasal strips.

Antacids. Heartburn that won't quit (you'll have plenty of that) often responds to Tums or Rolaids (plus you'll get a dose of calcium to boot). But check with your practitioner for the right dosage.

Gas aids. Many practitioners will okay gas aids, such as Gas-X, for the occasional relief of pregnancy bloat, but check with yours first.

Antihistamines. Not all antihistamines are safe during pregnancy, but several will probably get the green light from your practitioner. Benadryl is the most commonly recommended antihistamine during pregnancy. Claritin is also considered safe, but check with your practitioner, because not all will give it the okay, particularly in the first trimester. Many practitioners allow the use of chlorpheniramine (Chlor-Trimeton) and triprolidine on a limited basis.

Sleep aids. Unisom, Tylenol PM, Sominex, Nytol, Ambien, and Lunesta are generally considered safe during pregnancy, and they are okayed by many practitioners for occasional use. Always check with your practitioner before taking these or any sleep aids.

Decongestants. Sudafed is considered the safest oral decongestant if you must use one during pregnancy, as long as it's used in a limited amount. Be sure to check with your practitioner first and to get the right dosage information.

Antidiarrheals. Most antidiarrheals aren't recommended for use during pregnancy. Both Kaopectate and Pepto-Bismol contain salicylates—an active ingredient that is considered off-limits when you're expecting. Ask your practitioner if there is anything you can safely take for diarrhea during pregnancy (staying hydrated will be key, too).

Antibiotics. If your doctor has prescribed antibiotics for you during pregnancy, it's because the bacterial infection you have is more dangerous than taking the antibiotics to fight it off (many are considered completely safe). You'll usually be put on antibiotics that fall into the penicillin or erythromycin families. Certain antibiotics are not recommended (such

Keeping Current

The many lists of safe, possibly safe, possibly unsafe, and definitely unsafe drugs and medication during pregnancy change all the time, especially as new medications are introduced, others change from being prescription-only to over-the-counter, and still others are being studied to determine their safety during pregnancy. To stay current on what is or isn't safe, always ask your practitioner first. You can also turn to the U.S. Food and Drug Administration (contact your regional office, or visit fda.gov) for information. Or try the local office of the March of Dimes, or contact the March of Dimes Resource Center at (888) MODIMES (663-4637); marchofdimes.com. You can also go to safefetus.com to check on the safety of a certain medication during pregnancy.

as tetracyclines), so be sure that any doctor prescribing antibiotics while you're expecting knows that you're pregnant.

Antidepressants. Untreated depression in an expectant mom can have many adverse effects on her baby. Though the research on the effects of antidepressants on pregnancy and on the fetus is ever changing, it does appear that there are several medications that are safe to use, others that should be completely avoided, and still others that can be considered on a case-by-case basis, their use weighed against the risk of untreated (or undertreated) depression. See page 518 for more on antidepressants.

Antinausea. Unisom Sleep Tabs (which contain the antihistamine doxylamine), taken in combination with vitamin B_6, decrease the symptoms of morning sickness but should only be used when recommended by your practitioner. The downside of taking this remedy during the day: sleepiness.

Topical antibiotics. Small amounts of topical antibiotics, such as bacitracin or Neosporin, are safe during pregnancy.

Topical steroids. Small amounts of topical hydrocortisones (such as Cortaid) are safe during pregnancy.

If You Need Medication During Pregnancy

If your practitioner recommends that you take a certain medication while you're expecting, follow these steps for increased benefit and reduced risk:

- Discuss with your practitioner the possibility of taking the medication in the smallest effective doses for the shortest possible time.

Herbal Cures

Herbal supplements and remedies make the most tempting of promises (better memory! sounder sleep! improved immunity!), especially when pregnancy leaves you with fewer self-medicating options open and your medicine cabinet at least partially closed. Would it really hurt to pop a couple of ginkgo biloba pills to give your brain cells a fighting chance of remembering to pay this month's electric bill? Or melatonin to guarantee that you'll sleep like a baby (even when it's a baby-to-be who's keeping you awake)? And what about an echinacea or two to fend off the germs after you were sneezed on (twice) at that afternoon meeting? After all, the bottles say "all-natural," and you did buy them at the health-food store (what could be healthier than that?).

Actually, it could hurt—particularly now that you're sharing those pills with a little someone else. "All-natural" doesn't make herbal preparations "all safe," and neither does a health-food-store pedigree. Herbal preparations are not tested or approved by the FDA and are not required to undergo clini-

cal trials, which means that their safety (or lack of) is unknown. Even herbs that you've heard could be helpful during pregnancy could be dangerous at different points during those nine months. For example, some herbs purported to help bring on labor can cause premature labor if taken before full term. And many herbs are downright dangerous if taken at any time during pregnancy (such as basil oil, black or blue cohosh, clove oil, comfrey, juniper, mistletoe, pennyroyal, sassafras, wild yam, and many others).

It's always smart to proceed with caution when you're self-medicating with herbals, but twice as smart when you're self-medicating for two. To play it safe, don't take any herbal preparation—even ones you used freely preconception—unless it's prescribed by your practitioner for use during pregnancy.

If you'd like to feel like a natural woman during your pregnancy, look into other natural therapies that do not include ingesting anything (such as CAM treatments like acupuncture, massage, and meditation).

- Take the medication when it's going to benefit you the most—a cold medication at night, for instance, so it will help you sleep.

- Follow directions carefully. Some medications must be taken on an empty stomach; some should be taken with food or milk. If your physician hasn't given you any instructions, ask your pharmacist for particulars—most provide handouts with full directions and information (including possible side effects) on each prescription drug they sell. Don't panic if you see that the drug isn't recommended during pregnancy—the vast majority of drugs carry that warning, even if they're considered safe. As long as a practitioner who knows that you're expecting and is familiar with pregnancy drug safety has prescribed or recommended it, it's okay to take it.

- Explore nondrug remedies, and use them, as appropriate, to supplement the drug therapy. For instance, eliminate as many offending allergens from your home as you can, so your physician can reduce the amount of prescribed antihistamines you take. Keep in mind that herbal remedies are still considered drugs and shouldn't be taken without a practitioner's approval.

- Make sure the medication gets where it's supposed to by taking a sip of water before you swallow a capsule or tablet, to make it go down more easily, and by drinking a full glass afterward, to ensure that it is washed speedily down to where it will be absorbed.

- For additional safety, try to get all your prescriptions at the same pharmacy. The pharmacist will have you and all your prescriptions on the computer and should be able to warn you of potential drug interactions. Also, be sure you've gotten the right prescription (or over-the-counter medication). Check the name and dosage on the bottle to be sure it's the one specified by your doctor (many drug names and patient names are similar, and pharmacies do occasionally make mistakes). For additional reassurance, ask the pharmacist what the drug is meant to treat or check out the printed material that comes with the drug. If you know you were supposed to get an antihistamine for your allergies and the drug you are handed is for hypertension, you've obviously got the wrong medication.

- Ask about possible side effects and which ones should be reported to your doctor.

Once you've made certain that a prescribed drug is considered safe for use during pregnancy, don't hesitate to take it because you're still afraid it might somehow harm your baby. It won't, but delaying treatment might.

If You Have a Chronic Condition

A NYONE WHO'S LIVED WITH A chronic condition knows that life can get pretty complicated, what with special diets, medications, and/or monitoring. Add pregnancy into the mix, and you've got your hands even fuller, with the special diet needing to be tweaked, medications modified, and monitoring stepped up. Happily, with some extra precautions and extra effort, most chronic conditions are now completely compatible with pregnancy.

Just how your chronic condition will be affected by pregnancy and how pregnancy will affect your chronic condition will depend on plenty of factors, many of them uniquely yours. This chapter outlines general recommendations for pregnant women with common chronic conditions. Use this alphabetized list as a guide, but be sure to follow your doctor's orders, since they've probably been tailored to your specific needs.

What You May Be Wondering About

Asthma

"I've had asthma since I was a child. I'm concerned that the attacks and the medication I take for them might be harmful now that I'm expecting."

Finding out you're pregnant can take any woman's breath away—but when you're asthmatic, being breathless and pregnant can understandably bring up some extra concerns. While it's true that a severe asthmatic condition does put a pregnancy at somewhat higher risk, fortunately, this risk can be almost completely eliminated. In fact, if you're under close, expert medical supervision—by a team that includes your obstetrician, your internist, and/or your asthma doctor—your chances of having a normal pregnancy and a healthy baby are about as good as a nonasthmatic's (which means you can breathe a little easier now).

Though well-controlled asthma has only a minimal effect on pregnancy, pregnancy can have an effect on asthma, but the effect varies from expectant mom to expectant mom. For about a third of pregnant asthmatics, the effect is positive: Their asthma improves. For another third, their condition stays about the same. For the remaining third (usually those with the most severe disease), the asthma worsens. If you've been pregnant before, you're likely to find that your asthma behaves pretty much the same way in this pregnancy as it did in earlier ones.

It's not surprising that getting your asthma under control before you conceive or as early in pregnancy as possible is the best strategy for you and your baby. The following steps will help you do that, if you haven't yet:

- Identify environmental triggers. Allergies are a major cause of asthma, and you probably already know which ones trigger problems for you. Avoid them, and you'll find the breathing a lot easier during your pregnancy (see page 205 for tips on avoiding allergens). Common offenders are pollen, animal dander, dust, and mold. Such irritants as tobacco smoke, household cleaning products, and perfumes can also provoke a reaction, so it's a good idea to steer clear of them (and, of course, you should quit smoking if you're a smoker—ditto for your spouse). If you were started on allergy shots before pregnancy, you'll be able to continue.

- Exercise with care. If your asthma is exercise-induced, prescribed medication taken before your workout or any other kind of exertion can usually prevent an attack. Talk to your practitioner about other exercise guidelines.

- Stay healthy. Try to avoid colds, flu, and other respiratory infections, which are also asthma triggers (for tips on staying well, see box, page 505). Your doctor may give you medication to ward off an asthma attack at the beginning of a cold, and will probably want to treat any but the most minor bacterial respiratory infections with antibiotics. A flu shot—recommended for every expectant mom—is especially important for you, as is a vaccine for pneumococcal infection, if you're considered high risk (ask your doctor). If you suffer from chronic sinusitis or reflux—both of which are more common in pregnancy anyway—be sure to ask your doctor for a treatment plan, because both conditions can interfere with the management of your asthma.

- Keep a close eye on your peak flow. Follow your doctor's directions to make sure you're getting the oxygen you and your baby need. Monitor your breathing with a peak-flow meter, according to your physician's directions.

- Take a fresh look at your meds. All the medication rules change when you're expecting, so be sure you use only those that your physician has prescribed during your pregnancy. If your symptoms are mild, you may be able to get away without any medication. If they're moderate to severe, you'll be given one of the several medications that are considered safe during pregnancy (in general, inhaled medications appear to be safer than oral medication). Don't hesitate to take medication that you need—remember, you're breathing for two now.

If you do have an asthma attack, treating it promptly with your prescribed medication will help ensure that your baby isn't shortchanged of oxygen. But if the medication doesn't help, call your doctor or head for the nearest emergency room immediately. Asthma attacks may trigger early uterine contractions, but the contractions usually stop when the attack does (which is why it's so important to stop it quickly).

Because of your breathing problems history, you may find the breathlessness that typically comes with late pregnancy especially concerning. But don't worry—it's normal, and it isn't dangerous. Keep in mind, though, that as your growing uterus begins to crowd your lungs, you may notice that your asthmatic flare-ups worsen. Just be sure you treat these attacks quickly.

How will asthma affect your labor and delivery? If you're considering going without medication, you'll be happy to hear that asthma usually doesn't interfere with the breathing techniques of Lamaze and other childbirth education methods. If it's an epidural you have your heart set on, that shouldn't be a problem either (but narcotic analgesics, such as Demerol, will probably be avoided because they may trigger an asthma attack). Though asthma flare-ups during childbirth are rare, your doctor will probably recommend that you continue your regular medications when you're in labor; if

Cancer in Pregnancy

Cancer isn't common during pregnancy, but it happens, just as it can happen during any other time of life. Pregnancy doesn't cause cancer or increase your chances of developing cancer. They're just two life events, one joyous and one challenging, that sometimes take place at the same time.

Treatment for cancer during pregnancy is a delicate balancing act between providing the best treatment for the mother and limiting any possible risk to the fetus. The type of treatment you'll get will depend on many factors: how far the pregnancy has progressed; the type of cancer; the stage of the cancer; and, of course, on your wishes. The decisions you may face in balancing your well-being against your baby's may be emotionally wrenching,

and you'll need plenty of support in making them.

Because some cancer treatments can harm the fetus, especially during the first trimester, doctors usually delay any treatment until the second or third trimesters. When cancer is diagnosed later in pregnancy, doctors may wait until after the baby is born to begin treatment, or they may consider inducing labor early. The reassuring news is that women diagnosed during pregnancy respond just as well to cancer treatment as women who are not pregnant, all other factors being equal.

For more help, contact the National Cancer Institute: cancer.gov, as well as pregnantwithcancer.org or (800) 743-4471, a support system for expectant women with cancer.

your asthma has been serious enough to require oral steroids or cortisone-type medications, you may also require IV steroids to help you handle the stress of labor and delivery. Your oxygenation will be checked when you are admitted to the hospital, and if it is low, preventive medications may be given. Though some babies of moms with asthma experience rapid breathing after delivery, that's usually only temporary.

As for your asthma postpartum, chances are you'll find your symptoms will return to the way they were pre-pregnancy within three months after delivery.

Cystic Fibrosis

"I have cystic fibrosis, and I know that makes pregnancy complicated—but how complicated?"

As someone who's lived with cystic fibrosis (CF) for her whole life, you're already used to the challenges that the condition comes with—but you're also used to working hard at overcoming them. And though the challenges do increase somewhat with pregnancy, there are plenty of things that you and your doctors can do to help make your pregnancy safe and successful.

The first challenge may be gaining enough weight, so working closely with your doctors to ensure that the numbers on the scale keep climbing will be important (a nutritionist may be a helpful addition to your pregnancy team). To keep a closer eye on your weight and your baby's growth—as well as on all aspects of your pregnancy—you'll have more frequent prenatal visits than the average mom-to-be (on the plus side, that means more chances to hear your baby's heartbeat—and more opportunities to ask questions). Your activity

may be limited, and because you'll be at higher risk for premature delivery, additional precautions will be taken to reduce the risk and help ensure that your baby stays safely put until term. It's also possible that periodic hospitalization may be necessary.

Genetic counseling (if you haven't had it already) will be able to determine whether your baby is at risk for being born with CF or not ("not" being the much more likely scenario). If your spouse isn't a carrier for CF, there's very little chance that your baby will be affected by it (though he or she will be a carrier). If your spouse is a carrier, there's a 1 in 2 chance that your baby will be affected; prenatal testing can let you know for sure.

Since you're breathing for two now, your doctors will be keeping a close watch on your pulmonary care—especially as your growing uterus leaves less room for your lungs to expand. You'll also be monitored for pulmonary infection. Some women with severe lung disease may find that their condition can get a little worse while they're pregnant, but only temporarily. In general, pregnancy doesn't seem to have any negative long-term effect on CF at all.

Pregnancy isn't easy no matter what, and it's certainly more challenging for women with CF. But that cuddly reward—the beautiful baby you're working so hard for—can make all those challenges more than worthwhile.

Depression

"I was diagnosed with chronic depression a few years ago, and I've been on low-dose antidepressants ever since. Now that I'm pregnant, should I stop taking the meds?"

More than one out of ten women of childbearing age battles with bouts of depression, so you're far from alone. Luckily for you and all the other expectant moms who share your condition, there's a happy outlook: With the right treatment, women with depression can have perfectly normal pregnancies. Deciding what that treatment should consist of during pregnancy is a delicate balancing act, however, especially when it comes to the use of medications. Together with your psychiatrist and prenatal practitioner, you'll need to weigh the risks and benefits of taking such meds—and not taking them—while you're growing a baby.

Maybe it seems like a simple decision to make, at least at first glance. After all, could there ever be a good reason to put your emotional well-being over your baby's physical well-being? But the decision is actually a lot more complicated than that. For starters, pregnancy hormones can do a number on your emotional state. Even women who've never had an encounter with mood disorders, depression, or any other psychological condition may experience wild emotional swings when they're expecting—but women with a history of depression are at greater risk of having depressive bouts during pregnancy and are more likely to suffer from postpartum depression. And this is especially true for women who stop taking their antidepressants during pregnancy.

What's more, untreated depression isn't likely to affect only you (and those you're close to), it's also likely to affect your baby's health. Depressed mothers-to-be may not eat or sleep as well or pay as much attention to their prenatal care, and they may be more likely to drink and smoke. Any or all of those factors, combined with the debilitating effects of excessive anxiety and stress, have been linked in some studies to an increased risk of preterm birth, low birthweight, and a lower Apgar score for babies. Treating depression effectively, however—and keeping it under control during pregnancy—allows a mother-to-be to nurture her body and her developing baby.

So what does all this mean for you? It means you might want to think twice (and consult with your physician, of course) before you consider tossing your antidepressants. And in doing your thinking—and your consulting—you and your doctor will also want to consider which antidepressant best suits your needs now that you're expecting, which may or may not be the same one (or ones) you were using preconception. Certain meds are safer than others, and some aren't recommended for pregnancy use at all. Your doctor can give you the most up-to-date information, because it's ever-changing. What is known right now is that Wellbutrin is often a good choice during pregnancy. Prozac, Paxil, Zoloft, and other selective serotonin reuptake inhibitors (SSRIs) carry very little risk to the baby and can therefore also be good choices. Studies do show that pregnant women on Prozac might be somewhat more likely to deliver prematurely, and newborns exposed to Prozac and other SSRIs in the womb may experience short-term withdrawal symptoms (lasting no more than 48 hours), including excessive crying, tremors, sleep problems, and gastrointestinal upset immediately after birth. Still, researchers caution that these risks shouldn't keep pregnant women from taking Prozac (or other SSRIs) if their depression can't be treated effectively in other ways, because untreated depression carries its own risks, many with long-term effects.

Your prenatal practitioner—along with your mental health care provider—will be able to steer you toward the best medications for you during pregnancy, so discuss the options with both of them.

Remember, too, that nonmedicinal approaches can also sometimes help manage depression. Psychotherapy may be effective on its own or in conjunction with medication. Other therapies that can sometimes be helpful when used along with medication include bright light therapy and CAM approaches. Exercise (for its release of feel-good endorphins), meditation (which can help you manage stress), and diet (keeping blood sugar up with regular meals and snacks and getting plenty of omega-3 fatty acids may help give your mood a boost) can also be beneficial additions to a treatment program. Talk to your practitioner and mental health care provider to see if these options have a place in yours.

Diabetes

"I'm a diabetic. How will that affect my baby?"

There's lots of good news for pregnant diabetics these days. In fact, with expert medical care and diligent self-care, you have about the same excellent chances of having a successful pregnancy and a healthy baby as any other expectant mom.

Research has proven that the key to managing a diabetic pregnancy successfully—whether the diabetes is type 1 (juvenile-onset diabetes, in which the body doesn't produce insulin) or type 2 (adult-onset diabetes, in which the body doesn't respond as it should to insulin)—is achieving normal blood glucose levels before conception and maintaining them throughout the nine months following it.

Whether you came into pregnancy as a diabetic or you developed gestational diabetes along the way, all of the following will help you have a safe pregnancy and a healthy baby:

The right doctor. The OB who supervises your pregnancy should have plenty of experience caring for diabetic mothers-to-be, and he or she should work together with the doctor who has been in charge of your diabetes. You'll have more prenatal visits than other expectant moms and will probably be given more doctor's orders to follow (but all for a very good cause).

Good food planning. A diet geared to your personal requirements should be carefully planned with your physician, a nutritionist, and/or a nurse-practitioner with expertise in diabetes. The diet will probably be high in complex carbohydrates, moderate in protein, low in cholesterol and fat, and contain few or no sugary sweets. Plenty of dietary fiber will be important, since some studies show that fiber may reduce insulin requirements in diabetic pregnancies.

Carbohydrate regulation is typically not as strict as it used to be because fast-acting insulin can be adjusted if you go over your limit at one meal or another. Still, the extent of your carbohydrate restriction will depend on the way your body reacts to particular foods. Most diabetics do best getting their carbohydrates from vegetable, grain (whole is best), and legume sources rather than from fruits. To maintain normal blood sugar levels, you'll have to be particularly careful to get enough carbohydrates in the morning. Snacks will also be important (even more important than they are for the average mom-to-be), and, ideally, they should include both a complex carbohydrate (such as whole-grain bread) and a protein (such as beans or cheese or chicken). Skipping meals or snacks can dangerously lower blood sugar, so try to eat on schedule, even if morning sickness or indigestion are putting a damper on your appetite. Eating six mini meals a day, regularly spaced, carefully planned, and supplemented as needed by healthy snacks, is your smartest strategy.

Sensible weight gain. It's best to try to reach your ideal weight before conception (something to remember if you plan another pregnancy). But if you start your pregnancy overweight, don't plan on using your nine-month stint for slimming down. Getting enough calories is vital to your baby's wellbeing. Aim to gain weight according to the guidelines set by your physician (slow and steady does it best). Your baby's growth will be monitored using ultrasound, because babies of diabetics sometimes grow very large, even if mom's weight is on target.

Exercise. A moderate exercise program, especially if you have type 2 diabetes, will give you more energy, help to regulate your blood sugar, and help you get in shape for delivery. But it must be planned in conjunction with your medication schedule and diet, with the help of your medical team. If you experience no other medical or pregnancy complications and are physically fit, moderate exercise—such as brisk walking, swimming, and stationary biking (but not jogging)—will likely be on the workout menu. Chances are that only very light exercise (leisurely walking, for instance) will get the green light if you were out of shape prior to pregnancy or if there are any signs of problems with your diabetes, your pregnancy, or your baby's growth.

Precautions you may be asked to take when exercising probably won't differ much from safe exercise tips for any pregnant woman: Have a snack before your workout; don't exercise to the point of exhaustion; and never exercise in a very warm environment (80°F or higher). If you're on insulin, you'll probably be advised to avoid injecting it into the parts of the body being exercised (your legs, for example, if you're walking) and not to reduce your insulin intake before you exercise.

Rest. Getting enough rest is very important, especially in the third trimester. Avoid overdoing it, and try to take some time off during the middle of the day for putting your feet up or napping. If you have a demanding job, your doctor may recommend that you begin your maternity leave early.

Medication regulation. If diet and exercise alone don't control your blood sugar, you'll likely be put on insulin. If you end up needing insulin for the first time, your blood sugar can be stabilized under close medical supervision. If you were taking oral medication before you conceived, you might be switched to injected insulin or an under-the-skin insulin pump during pregnancy. Since levels of the pregnancy hormones that work against insulin increase as pregnancy progresses, your insulin dose may have to be adjusted upward periodically. The dose may also have to be recalculated as you and your baby gain weight, if you get sick or are under emotional strain, or if you overdo your carbs. Studies show that the oral drug glyburide may be an effective alternative to insulin therapy during pregnancy for some mild cases.

In addition to being sure your diabetes medication is on target, you'll need to be extremely careful about any other medications you take. Many over-the-counter drugs can affect your insulin levels—and some may not be safe in pregnancy—so don't take any until you check with both the physician who is overseeing your diabetes and the one taking care of your pregnancy.

Blood sugar regulation. You may have to test your blood sugar (with a simple finger-prick method) at least four or as often as ten times a day (possibly before and after meals) to be sure it's staying at safe levels. If you have type 1 diabetes, your blood may also be tested for glycosylated hemoglobin (hemoglobin A1c), because high levels of this substance may be a sign that sugar levels aren't being well controlled. To maintain normal blood glucose levels, you'll have to eat regularly, adjust your diet and exercise as needed, and, if necessary, take medication. If you were insulin-dependent before pregnancy, you may be more subject to low blood sugar episodes (hypoglycemia) than when you weren't pregnant, especially in the first trimester—so careful monitoring is a must. And don't leave home (or go anywhere) without packing the right snacks.

Urine monitoring. Since your body may produce ketones—acidic substances that can result when the body breaks down fat—during this close regulation of your diabetes, your urine may be checked for these regularly.

Careful monitoring. Don't be concerned if your physician orders a lot of tests for you, especially during the third trimester, or even suggests hospitalization for the final weeks of your pregnancy. This doesn't mean something is wrong, only that he or she wants to be sure everything stays right. The tests will primarily be directed toward regular evaluation of your condition and of your baby to determine the optimal time for delivery and whether any other intervention is needed.

You will probably have regular eye exams to check the condition of your retinas and blood tests and urine collections every 24 hours to evaluate your kidneys (retinal and kidney problems tend to worsen during pregnancy but usually return to prepregnancy status

after delivery if you've been taking care of yourself throughout pregnancy). The condition of your baby and the placenta will likely be evaluated throughout pregnancy with stress and/ or nonstress tests (see page 348), biophysical profiles, and ultrasound (to size up your baby to be sure it's growing as it should be and so that delivery can be accomplished before the baby gets too big for a vaginal delivery). And because there's a slightly higher risk of heart problems in the babies of diabetics, you'll get a detailed ultrasound of the fetal anatomy at 16 weeks and a special ultrasound of the fetal heart (fetal electrocardiogram) at about 22 weeks to make sure everything's going well.

After the 28th week, you may be asked to monitor fetal movements yourself three times a day (see page 289 for one way to do this, or follow your doctor's recommendation).

Because diabetics are at somewhat higher risk for preeclampsia, your doctor will watch you closely for early signs of that condition, too.

Elective early delivery. Women who develop gestational diabetes, as well as women with preexisting mild diabetes that is well controlled, can carry to their due date safely. But when mom's normal blood sugar levels have not been well maintained throughout pregnancy, or if the placenta deteriorates early, or if other problems develop late in pregnancy, her baby may be delivered a week or two before term. The various tests mentioned above help the physician decide when to induce labor or perform a C-section—late enough so the fetal lungs are sufficiently mature to function outside the womb, but not so late that the baby's safety is compromised.

Don't worry if your baby is placed in a neonatal intensive care unit immediately after delivery. This is routine procedure in most hospitals for infants of diabetic mothers. Your baby will be observed for respiratory problems (which are unlikely if the lungs were tested and found to be mature enough for delivery) and for hypoglycemia (which, though more common in babies of diabetics, is easily treated). You should be able to get your baby back soon so you can start nursing, if that's your plan.

Epilepsy

"I have epilepsy, and I desperately want to have a baby. Can I have a safe pregnancy?"

With the right precautions, there could definitely be a healthy baby in your future. Your first step—preferably before you take care of the conception part—is to get your condition under the best possible control, with the help of your neurologist and the doctor you've chosen for your prenatal care. (If you've already conceived, getting that help as soon as possible in your pregnancy is crucial.) For best pregnancy results, close supervision of your condition and possibly frequent adjustment of medication levels will be necessary, as will communication between your doctors.

Most women find that pregnancy does not exacerbate their epilepsy. Half experience no change in their disease, and a smaller percentage find that seizures actually become less frequent and milder. A few discover, however, that their seizures become more frequent and severe.

As for how epilepsy affects pregnancy, expectant moms with epilepsy may be slightly more likely to experience excessive nausea and vomiting (hyperemesis), but they aren't at higher risk for any serious complications.

There seems to be a slight increase in the incidence of certain birth defects in the babies of epileptic mothers, but these appear to be more often caused by the use of certain anticonvulsant medications during pregnancy than by the epilepsy itself.

Discuss with your doctor ahead of time the possibility of being weaned from your medications prior to conception. This may be possible if you've been seizure-free for a period of time. If you have been having seizures, it's important to try to get them under control as soon as possible. You will need medication to do this, but it may be possible to switch to a less risky drug than the one you've been taking. Taking one drug appears to cause fewer problems in pregnancy than multidrug therapy and is the preferred way to go. And it's important not to stop taking a necessary medication for fear of hurting your baby; not taking it—and having frequent seizures—may be more dangerous.

Helping Others with Epilepsy

For more information on epilepsy and pregnancy, check out epilepsyfoundation.org. To help yourself in the future or help other moms with epilepsy, ask your doctor about registering with the Antiepileptic Drug Pregnancy Registry, (888) 233-2334 or aed pregnancyregistry.org. Their goal is to determine which therapies are associated with an increased risk. You will also receive a packet of information about preconception planning and prenatal care.

A detailed structural ultrasound is recommended for anyone on seizure medicine, and certain early pregnancy screening tests may also be ordered. If you've been taking valproic acid (Depakene), the doctor may want to look specifically for neural tube defects, such as spina bifida.

Important for all pregnant women with epilepsy is getting plenty of sleep and the best nutrition, and maintaining adequate fluid levels. Vitamin D supplements may also be recommended, since some epilepsy medications can interfere with metabolism of the vitamin. During the last four weeks of pregnancy, a vitamin K supplement may be prescribed to reduce the risk of hemorrhage, another condition that babies of women taking seizure medications are at slightly greater risk for.

Labor and delivery aren't likely to be more complicated because of your epilepsy, though it is important that anticonvulsant medication continue to be administered during labor to minimize the risk of a seizure during delivery. An epidural anesthesia can be used to manage labor and delivery pain.

Breastfeeding your baby shouldn't be a problem, either. Most epilepsy medications pass into the breast milk in such low doses that they are unlikely to affect a nursing baby.

Fibromyalgia

"I was diagnosed with fibromyalgia a few years ago. How will this impact my pregnancy?"

The fact that you're aware of your condition actually gives you a head start many women don't have. Fibromyalgia, a condition that affects 8 to 10 million Americans each year and is characterized by pain, burning sensations, and achiness in the

Making the Most of Your Meds

If you rely on oral medications to control a chronic condition, you may have to do a little adjusting now that you're expecting. For instance, if morning sickness has you down in the first trimester, taking your meds right before going to bed in the evening—so that they can build up in your system before the morning upchucking begins—may keep you from losing most of your medication through vomiting. (Check with your doctor first, because some medications must be taken at certain times of the day.)

Something else that you'll have to keep in mind—and that your team of doctors will have to keep an eye on: Some medications are metabolized differently during pregnancy. So the dosage you're used to isn't necessarily the right dosage now that you're expecting. If you're not sure whether your dosing is correct now that you're pregnant, or if you have a hunch you're not getting enough medication—or you're getting too much—let your doctors know.

muscles and soft tissues of the body, often goes unrecognized in pregnant women, possibly because the fatigue, weakness, and psychological stress it causes are all considered normal signs of pregnancy.

You're probably already used to being frustrated by fibromyalgia and the lack of available information about it and effective treatment for it. Prepare to become even more frustrated because, unfortunately, there's probably even less known about the effect of pregnancy on fibromyalgia and vice versa. From what is known, there is some substantially good news: Babies born to women with fibromyalgia are not affected in any way by the condition. Beyond that, some recent studies and plenty of anecdotal evidence have suggested that pregnancy can be extra tough on a woman with fibromyalgia. You may feel more tired and stiff and

Chronic Fatigue Syndrome

Fortunately, having chronic fatigue syndrome (CFS) in no way interferes with having a normal pregnancy and a healthy baby. Unfortunately, that's about all scientists know for sure about the effects of CFS on pregnancy. No studies have been done yet, so the little that is known comes from anecdotal evidence, which tends to suggest that CFS affects different women differently during pregnancy. Some moms-to-be note their symptoms actually improve during pregnancy while others say they get worse. It may be hard to tell, since pregnancy is physically exhausting for all women, even those not dealing with CFS.

If you're pregnant with CFS, it's important that the doctor who has been caring for your condition knows about your pregnancy and the practitioner you've chosen for your prenatal care knows about your CFS. Together, incorporating strategies that have helped you in the past, they will be able to help you cope with your CFS while you're nurturing your baby-to-be.

experience aches and pains in more parts of your body than an expectant mom without fibromyalgia (though some lucky women do feel better during pregnancy, so you can definitely hope for that). To keep your symptoms to a minimum, try to reduce the amount of stress in your life as much as possible, eat a well-balanced diet, exercise moderately (but never overdo it), and continue doing safe stretches and conditioning exercises (or yoga, water exercises, and so on) that may have helped you before your pregnancy. Women with fibromyalgia do typically gain 25 to 35 pounds during the first year of having the condition, so that during pregnancy, excessive weight gain can be a problem (not to say that you'll balloon up, but you may have trouble staying within the recommended weight gain guidelines). And since the condition is usually treated with antidepressants and pain suppressants, you'll need to make sure your doctor and prenatal practitioner are in contact with each other and only keep you on medications that are safe for use during pregnancy.

Hypertension

"I've had hypertension for years. How will my high blood pressure affect my pregnancy?"

With more and more older women conceiving, more and more are also conceiving with chronic hypertension, a condition that becomes more common with age. So you've got lots of company (even if you developed your hypertension earlier on in life).

Your pregnancy is considered high risk, which means you'll be putting in more time at the doctor's office and putting more effort into following doctor's orders. But all for a very good cause.

With well-controlled blood pressure, and carefully monitored self-care and medical care, you're likely to have the best payoff of all—a safe pregnancy and a healthy baby.

All of the following can help increase the odds of a successful pregnancy:

The right medical team. The practitioner who supervises your pregnancy should have plenty of experience caring for mothers-to-be with chronic hypertension and should be joined on your pregnancy care team by the doctor who has been in charge of your hypertension.

Close medical monitoring. Your practitioner will probably schedule more frequent visits for you than for other expectant mothers and may order many more tests—but, again, that's time well spent. Having chronic hypertension increases your risk of developing preeclampsia during pregnancy as well as some other pregnancy complications, so your practitioner will pay particular attention to your well-being during your 40 weeks.

Relaxation. Relaxation exercises are soothing for every expectant soul, but particularly for those with hypertension. Research has shown that these exercises can actually lower blood pressure. Check out—and practice—the one on page 142, or consider using a meditation CD or even taking a class.

Other alternative approaches. Try any CAM techniques recommended by your practitioner, such as biofeedback, acupuncture, or massage.

Plenty of rest. Since both emotional and physical stress can send blood pressure up, don't overdo anything. Take frequent rest breaks during your day, preferably with your feet up. If you work at a high-stress job, rest might not do the trick—you may want to consider a leave of absence or cutting down on hours or responsibilities until after the baby arrives. If you have your hands full at home with other children, get as much help as you can handling the load.

Blood pressure monitoring. You may be asked to keep track of your own blood pressure at home. Take it when you're most rested and relaxed.

Good diet. The Pregnancy Diet is a smart place to start, but modify it with the help of your practitioner to fit your needs. Eating plenty of fruits and vegetables, low-fat or nonfat dairy products, and whole grains may be especially helpful in keeping your blood pressure down.

Adequate fluid. Remember to drink at least eight glasses of fluid a day, which should help relieve any mild swelling of your feet and ankles. In most cases, a diuretic (a drug that draws fluid from the body and is sometimes used in the treatment of hypertension) is not recommended during pregnancy.

Prescribed medication. Whether your medications will be changed or not during pregnancy will depend on what you've been taking. Some medications are considered safe for expectant moms; others are not.

Irritable Bowel Syndrome

"I have irritable bowel syndrome and was wondering if being pregnant will make my symptoms worse."

Since pregnancy seems to affect irritable bowel syndrome (IBS) differently in different women, there's no way to predict how it will affect you. Some women report being entirely symptom free while they're expecting; others find their symptoms get somewhat worse during their nine months.

One reason why it's so hard to pinpoint the effect of pregnancy on IBS—and vice versa—is that bowels are almost always impacted (so to speak) by pregnancy. Expectant women are more prone to constipation (a symptom of IBS, too), though some pregnant women find themselves with looser stools more often (also a symptom of IBS). Same for gas and bloating, which typically worsen when you're expecting, whether or not you have IBS. And since the hormones of pregnancy wreak havoc on all parts of the body, even IBS sufferers are left guessing: A woman who is normally diarrhea-predominant might suddenly find herself dealing with constipation, while a woman who is usually stopped up might find it's become easy—too easy—to move her bowels.

To keep your symptoms manageable, stick to the techniques you're used to using to combat IBS during other times in your life: Eat small, more frequent meals (good advice for any pregnant woman); stay well hydrated (ditto); eat a high-fiber diet to improve digestion (double ditto); avoid spicy foods; avoid excess stress; and steer clear of foods or drinks that make your symptoms worse. You might also want to consider adding some probiotics (in the form of yogurt or yogurt drinks with active cultures, or in powder or capsule form) to your diet. They're surprisingly effective in regulating bowel function and they're safe during pregnancy. Check with your practitioner.

Having IBS does put you at a slightly increased risk for premature delivery (so be sure to be alert to any signs of impending preterm contractions; see page 300). There's also a greater chance you might end up delivering via C-section because of your condition.

Lupus

"My lupus has been pretty quiet lately, but I just became pregnant. Is this likely to bring on a flare-up?"

There are still some unknowns about systemic lupus erythematosus (SLE), particularly when it comes to pregnancy. Studies indicate that pregnancy doesn't affect the long-term course of this autoimmune disorder. During pregnancy itself, some women find that their condition improves; other women find it worsens. More confusing still, what happens in one pregnancy doesn't necessarily predict what will happen in subsequent ones. In the postpartum period, there does appear to be an increased risk of flare-ups.

Whether and how SLE affects pregnancy, however, isn't absolutely clear. It does seem that the women who do best are those who, like you, conceive during a quiet period in their disease. Though the risk of pregnancy loss is slightly increased, in general, their chances of having a healthy baby are excellent. Those with the poorest prognosis are women with SLE who have severe kidney impairment (ideally, kidney function should be stable for at least six months before conception). If you have lupus anticoagulant or related antiphospholipid antibody, daily doses of aspirin and heparin may be prescribed.

Because of your lupus, your pregnancy care will include more, and more frequent, tests, medications (such as corticosteroids), and possibly more limitations. But if you, your obstetrician or maternal-fetal medicine specialist, and the physician who treats your lupus all work together, the odds are very much in favor of a happy outcome that will make all that extra effort completely worthwhile.

Multiple Sclerosis

"I was diagnosed several years ago as having multiple sclerosis. I've only had two episodes of MS, and they were relatively mild. Will the MS affect my pregnancy? Will my pregnancy affect my MS?"

There's good news for both you and your baby. Women with MS can definitely have normal pregnancies and healthy babies. Good prenatal care, beginning early (and better yet, modifying therapies even before conception), coupled with regular visits to your neurologist, will help you achieve that most wonderful of outcomes. And the good news carries over to childbirth, too. Labor and delivery aren't usually affected by MS, and neither are pain relief options. Epidurals and other types of anesthesia appear to be completely safe for delivering moms with MS.

As for pregnancy's effect on MS, some women experience relapses when they're expecting, as well as in the postpartum period, but most women are back to their prepregnancy condition within about three to six months of baby's arrival. Some women with ambulatory problems find that as weight gain increases during pregnancy, walking becomes more difficult, not surprisingly. Avoiding excessive weight gain may help minimize this problem. The happy bottom line: Whether or not you experience relapses, pregnancy doesn't seem to affect the overall lifetime relapse rate or the extent of ultimate disability.

To stay as healthy as possible while you're expecting, try to minimize stress and get enough rest. Also try to avoid raising your body temperature too much (stay out of hot tubs and too-warm baths, and don't exercise too hard or outside in hot weather). Do your best to fight off infections, particularly UTIs, which are more common during pregnancy (see page 498 for preventative measures).

Pregnancy can have some impact on MS treatment. Though low to moderate doses of prednisone are considered safe to use during pregnancy, some other medications used for MS may not be. You'll need to work out a medication regimen with your doctors that's safe for your baby and as effective as possible for you.

After delivery, there's a good chance that you'll be able to breastfeed, at least partially. If breastfeeding isn't an option, either because of the meds you need to take or because it's just too physically stressful, don't worry. Not only do babies thrive on good formula, they always do best when mom's feeling well.

Since going back to work early in the postpartum period may increase both exhaustion and stress—which might exacerbate your symptoms—you may want to consider taking that return slowly, finances permitting. If MS does interfere with your functioning while your child is young, see the next page for tips on baby care for parents with disabilities.

One other note: Many women with MS are concerned about passing the disease on to their children. Though there is a genetic component to the disease, placing these children at increased risk of being affected as adults, the risk is really quite small. Between 95 and 98 percent of children of MS mothers end up MS free.

Phenylketonuria

"I was born with PKU. My doctor let me off my low-phenylalanine diet when I was in my teens, and I was fine. But when I talked about getting pregnant, my OB said I should go back on the diet. Is that really necessary?"

A low-phenylalanine diet, which consists of a phenylalanine-free medical formula and precisely measured amounts of fruits, vegetables, bread, and pasta (and which eliminates all high-protein foods, including meat, poultry, fish, dairy products, eggs, beans, and nuts), definitely isn't tasty or easy to follow. But for pregnant women with phenylketonuria (PKU), it's absolutely necessary. Not sticking to the diet while you're pregnant would put your baby at great risk for a variety of problems, including serious mental deficits. Ideally, the low-phenylalanine regimen should be resumed three months before conception, and blood levels of phenylalanine kept low through delivery. (Even starting the diet early in pregnancy may reduce the seriousness of developmental delay in children of mothers with PKU.) And, of course, all foods sweetened with aspartame (Equal or NutraSweet) are absolutely off-limits.

Without a doubt, it'll be tough to return to the diet after so many years of being off of it—but clearly, the benefits to your developing baby will be well worth the sacrifice. If in spite of this incentive you find yourself slipping off the diet, it might help to get some professional help from a therapist who is familiar with your type of condition. A support group of other mothers with PKU may be even more helpful; the misery of such dietary deprivation definitely benefits from the company of those similarly deprived. For more information, check out pkunetwork.org.

Physical Disability

"I'm a paraplegic because of a spinal cord injury, and I use a wheelchair. My husband and I have wanted a baby for a long while, and I've finally become pregnant. Now what?"

Like every pregnant woman, you'll need to deal with first things first: selecting a practitioner. And as with every pregnant woman who falls into a high-risk category, your practitioner should ideally be an obstetrician or maternal-fetal medicine specialist who has experience dealing with women who face the same challenges as you do. That may be easier to find than you'd think because a growing number of hospitals are developing special programs to provide women with physical disabilities better prenatal and obstetrical care. If such a program or practitioner isn't available in your area, you'll need a doctor who is willing to learn "on the job" and who is able to offer you and your husband all the support you'll need.

Just which additional measures will be necessary to make your pregnancy successful will depend on your physical disabilities. In any case, restricting your weight gain to within the recommended range will help minimize the stress on your body. Eating the best possible diet will improve your general physical well-being and decrease the likelihood of pregnancy complications. And keeping up your exercise regimen will help ensure that you have maximum strength and mobility when the baby arrives; water therapy may be particularly helpful and safe.

It should be reassuring to know that, though pregnancy may be more difficult for you than for other pregnant women, it should not be any more stressful for your baby. And no evidence indicates an increase in fetal abnormalities among babies of women with spinal cord injury (or of those with other physical disabilities not related to hereditary or systemic disease). Women with spinal cord injuries, however, are more susceptible to such pregnancy problems as kidney infections and bladder difficulties, palpitations and sweating, anemia, and muscle spasms. Childbirth, too, may pose special problems, though in most cases a vaginal delivery will be possible. Because uterine contractions may be painless, depending on the kind of damage to your spinal cord, you will have to be instructed to note other signs of impending labor—such as bloody show or rupture of the membranes—or you may be asked to feel your uterus periodically to see if contractions have begun.

Long before your due date, devise a fail-safe plan for getting to the hospital, one that takes into account the fact that you may be home alone when labor strikes (you may want to plan to leave for the hospital early in labor to avoid any problems caused by delays en route). You'll also want to be sure the hospital staff is prepared for your additional needs.

Parenting is always a challenge, particularly in the early weeks, and it's not surprising that it will be even more so for you and your husband (who will have to be your more-than-equal parenting partner). Planning ahead will help you meet this challenge more successfully. Make any necessary modifications to your home to accommodate child care; sign on help (paid or otherwise) to at least get you started. Breastfeeding, which is usually possible, will make life simpler (no rushing off to the kitchen to prepare bottles and no shopping for formula). Getting your diapers and other baby needs delivered will also save effort and time. The changing table should be tailored for you to use from your wheelchair, the crib should have a drop side so you can take baby in and out easily, and—if you'll be doing all or some of the baby bathing—the baby tub should be set up somewhere that's accessible (daily tub baths aren't a must, so you can sponge baby on the changing table or on your lap on alternate days). Wearing your baby in a carrier or sling will probably be the most convenient way to tote him or her, since it'll leave your hands free (putting it on first thing in the morning will allow you to slide baby in and out as needed). Joining a support group of parents with disabilities (or checking out online groups) will provide lots of comfort and empathy and also give you a gold mine of ideas and advice.

For more information, contact Through the Looking Glass at (800) 644-2666 or online at lookingglass.org; or the National Spinal Cord Injury Association at (800) 962-9629 or online at spinalcord.org.

Rheumatoid Arthritis

"I have rheumatoid arthritis. How will this affect my pregnancy?"

Your condition isn't likely to affect your pregnancy very much, but pregnancy is likely to affect your condition—and, happily, for the better. Most women with rheumatoid arthritis (RA) notice a significant decrease in the pain and swelling in their joints during pregnancy, though there is also a somewhat greater risk of temporary symptom flare-up in the postpartum period.

The greatest change you may experience while you're pregnant is in the management of your condition. Because some of the medicines used to treat RA (such as ibuprofen and naproxen) are not safe for use later in pregnancy or at all, your physician will need to switch you over to treatments that are safer, such as steroids.

During labor and delivery, it will be important to choose positions that don't put too much stress or strain on affected joints. Discuss with the physician who manages your arthritis, as well as with your prenatal practitioner, which positions might work best.

Scoliosis

"I was diagnosed with mild scoliosis as a teenager. What effects will the curve of my spine have on my pregnancy?"

Thankfully, not much. Women with scoliosis usually go on to have uneventful pregnancies and deliveries, with healthy babies as the happy outcome. In fact, studies have shown that no significant problems occur during pregnancy that could be specifically attributed to scoliosis.

Women with severe curvature of the spine, or those whose scoliosis involves the hips, pelvis, or shoulders, may experience more discomfort, breathing problems, or weight-bearing difficulties during later pregnancy. If you find your back pain increases during pregnancy, stay off your feet as much as possible, take warm baths, enlist your spouse to give you some back rubs, and try the tips on page 237 for combating back pain. You can also ask your practitioner for the name of an obstetric physiotherapist who may be able to help you with some exercises specific to your scoliosis-related pain. Also discuss which CAM approaches (page 85) might be helpful.

If you think you might want an epidural during labor, talk to your practitioner about finding an anesthesiologist who has experience with moms with scoliosis. Though the condition usually does not interfere with the epidural, it may make it a little more difficult to place. An experienced anesthesiologist, however, should have no problem getting the needle where it needs to go.

Sickle Cell Anemia

"I have sickle cell disease, and I just found out that I'm pregnant. Will my baby be okay?"

Not too many years ago, the answer would not have been reassuring. Today, there's much happier news. Thanks to major medical advances, women with sickle cell disease—even those with such related complications as heart or kidney disease—have a good chance of having a safe pregnancy and delivery and a healthy baby.

Pregnancy for the woman with sickle cell anemia, however, is usually classified as high risk. The added physical stress of pregnancy increases her chances of having a sickle cell crisis, and the added stress of sickle cell disease increases the risks of certain complications, such as miscarriage, preterm delivery, and fetal growth restriction. Preeclampsia is also more common in women with sickle cell anemia.

The prognosis for both you and your baby will be best if you receive state-of-the-art medical care. You'll likely have prenatal checkups more frequently than other pregnant patients—possibly every two to three weeks up to the 32nd week, and every week after that. Your care should take a team approach: Your obstetrician should be familiar with sickle cell disease and work closely with a hematologist who's knowledgeable about sickle cell in pregnancy. Though it's not certain whether it's a beneficial therapy or not, it's possible that you'll be given a blood transfusion at least once (usually in early labor or just prior to delivery) or even periodically throughout pregnancy.

As far as childbirth is concerned, you're as likely as any other mother to have a vaginal delivery. Postpartum, you may be given antibiotics to prevent infection.

If both parents carry a gene for sickle cell anemia, the risk that their baby will inherit a form of the disease is increased. For that reason, your spouse should be tested for the trait early in your pregnancy (if he wasn't before conception). If he turns out to be a carrier, you may want to see a genetic counselor and possibly undergo amniocentesis to see if your baby is affected.

Thyroid Disease

"I was diagnosed as being hypothyroid when I was a teenager and am still taking thyroid pills. Is it safe to keep taking them while I'm pregnant?"

It's not only safe to continue taking your medication, it's vital to both your baby's well-being and your own. One reason is that women with untreated hypothyroidism (a condition in which the thyroid gland does not produce adequate amounts of the hormone thyroxine) are more likely to miscarry. Another reason is that maternal thyroid hormones are necessary for early fetal brain development; babies who don't get enough of these hormones in the first trimester can be born with neurological development problems and, possibly, deafness. (After the first trimester, the fetus makes its own thyroid hormones and is protected even if mom's levels are low.) Low thyroid levels are also linked to maternal depression during pregnancy and postpartum—another compelling reason to continue your treatment.

Your dose, however, may need to be adjusted, since the body requires more thyroid hormone when it's in baby-making mode. Check with your endocrinologist and your obstetrician to be sure your dose is appropriate now, but keep in mind that your levels will probably be monitored periodically during pregnancy and postpartum to see if your dose needs further adjustment. Be on the lookout, too, for signs that your thyroid level is too low or too high and report these to your practitioner (though many of those probably familiar symptoms of hypothyroidism, such as fatigue, constipation, and dry skin, are so similar to those of pregnancy that it's often tough to tell which have you down, report them anyway).

Iodine deficiency, which is becoming more common among women of childbearing age in the United States because of reduced iodized salt consumption, can interfere with the production of thyroid hormone, so be sure you are getting adequate amounts of this trace mineral. It's most commonly found in iodized salt and seafood.

"I have Graves disease. Is this a problem for my pregnancy?"

Graves disease is the most common form of hyperthyroidism, a condition in which the thyroid gland produces excessive amounts of thyroid hormones. Mild cases of hyperthyroidism sometimes improve during pregnancy because the pregnant body requires more thyroid hormone than usual. But moderate to severe hyperthyroidism is a different story. Left untreated, these conditions could lead to serious complications for both you and your baby, including miscarriage and preterm birth, so appropriate treatment is necessary. Happily, when the disease is treated properly during pregnancy, the outcome is likely to be good for both mother and baby.

During pregnancy, the treatment of choice is the antithyroid medication propylthiouracil (PTU) in the lowest effective dose. If a woman is allergic to PTU, methimazole (Tapazole) may be used. If neither drug can be used, then surgery to remove the thyroid gland may be needed, but it should be performed early in the second trimester to avoid the risk of miscarriage (in the first trimester) or preterm birth (in the late second and third trimester). Radioactive iodine is not safe to use during pregnancy, so it won't be part of your treatment plan.

If you had surgery or radioactive iodine treatment for Graves before you became pregnant, you'll need to continue your thyroid replacement therapy during pregnancy (which is not only safe but essential for your baby's development).

ALL ABOUT

Getting the Support You Need

Though it's true that every expectant woman needs plenty of support, it's also true that moms-to-be with a chronic condition could use even more. Even if you've had your condition for years, you know everything there is to know about it, and you're an old pro at handling it, you'll probably find that pregnancy changes the rules (including the ones you had memorized).

Enter, that extra support. No pregnant woman should ever have to go it alone, but as a pregnant woman with a chronic condition, you may want and need even more company. Among the kinds of support you'll benefit from:

Medical support. Just like every expectant mom, you'll need to find (if you don't already have one) a prenatal practitioner who can consult with you before you conceive (if possible), care for you during your pregnancy, and make that special delivery when the time comes. Unlike with a lot of other expectant moms, that practitioner won't be the only member of your obstetrical team. You'll also need to bring the doctor or doctors who care for your chronic condition on board. Your team of doctors will work together to ensure that you and baby are both well taken care of—that your baby's best interests are represented in the care of your chronic condition, and your best interests are represented in the care of your baby. Communication will be a vital part of that teamwork—so make sure your doctors are all kept in the loop about tests, medications, and other care components.

All your doctors have lots of other patients, so it's best not to assume that communication's always taking place. If your chronic-care specialist prescribes a new medication, ask if it's been okayed by your prenatal practitioner, and vice versa.

Emotional support. Everyone needs somebody to lean on, but you may find you need plenty of somebodies. Somebody to vent to when you're feeling resentful over your special diet (Easter eggs instead of chocolate bunnies?). To complain to about being stuck in a revolving door of medical procedures (six tests in three days?).

To cry to when you're feeling particularly anxious. To confide in, share with, unload on. To give you the emotional support every expectant mom craves—since you might crave a little more.

Your partner is a perfect source of this support, of course, especially because he sees what you're going through and would do anything to help you. Your friends and relatives may lend a sympathetic ear when you need one, too, even if their own pregnancies were more "normal" and they can't always relate. But you'll probably find that no one quite gets it like another mom in the same situation—and that no one else gives you as much comfort, empathy, and satisfying support.

Depending on your chronic condition and where you live, you may be able to find a support group geared to expectant moms or new moms who are in the same or a similar boat as you. Or with a little help from your medical team, you might even be able to start one (even if it's just a group of two—another mom you can have lunch with or chat with on the phone). Or reach out online, either on pregnancy message boards or chat rooms for those who have the same chronic condition. Not only will you find the emotional hand-holding you're in the market for, but you'll find practical support, too—advice, treatment tips, strategies, diet ideas, and other resources to help you cope with your important dual mission: caring for your chronic condition and nurturing your baby-to-be.

Physical support. Again, there isn't an expectant mom who doesn't need it at some point in her pregnancy (probably at many points): someone to do the shopping when she's too tired to move, to scrub the toilet so she doesn't have to breathe in those fumes, to cook dinner when coming face-to-breast with uncooked chicken makes her heave. But for moms who are juggling the physical demands of pregnancy with the physical challenges of a chronic condition, there's no such thing as too much help. Get it wherever you can, and don't be shy about asking for it. Enlist your partner to pick up the slack (and the dry cleaning and groceries) that you don't have the energy to pick up, but also look to friends, relatives, and, if you can afford it, paid household help.

PART 7

The Complicated Pregnancy

CHAPTER 22

Managing a Complicated Pregnancy

I F YOU'VE BEEN DIAGNOSED WITH A complication or suspect that you're having one, you'll find symptoms and treatments in this chapter. If you've had a problem-free pregnancy so far, though, this need-to-know chapter is not for you (you don't need to know any of it). Most women sail through pregnancy and childbirth without any complications. While information is definitely empowering when you need it, reading about all the things that could go wrong when they're not going wrong is only going to stress you out—and for no good reason. Skip it, and save yourself some unneeded worry.

Pregnancy Complications

The following complications, though more common than some pregnancy complications, are still unlikely to be experienced by the average pregnant woman. So read this section only if you've been diagnosed with a complication or you're experiencing symptoms that might indicate a complication. If you are diagnosed with one, use the discussion of the condition in this section as a general overview—so you have an idea of what you're dealing with—but expect to receive more specific (and possibly different) advice from your practitioner.

Early Miscarriage

What is it? A miscarriage—known in medical speak as a spontaneous abortion—is the spontaneous expulsion of an embryo or fetus from the uterus

Types of Miscarriage

If you've experienced an early pregnancy loss, the sadness you'll feel is the same no matter the cause or the official medical name. Still, it's helpful to know about the different types of miscarriage so you're familiar with the terms your practitioner might be using.

Chemical pregnancy. A chemical pregnancy occurs when an egg is fertilized but fails to develop successfully or implant fully in the uterus. A woman may miss her period and suspect she is pregnant; she may even have a positive pregnancy test because her body has produced some low—but detectable—levels of the pregnancy hormone hCG, but in a chemical pregnancy, there will be no gestational sac or placenta on ultrasound examination.

Blighted ovum. A blighted ovum (or anembryonic pregnancy) refers to a fertilized egg that attaches to the wall of the uterus, begins to develop a placenta (which produces hCG), but then fails to develop into an embryo. What is left behind is an empty gestational sac (which can be visualized on an ultrasound).

Missed miscarriage. A missed miscarriage, which is very rare, is when the embryo or fetus dies but continues to stay in the uterus. Often, the only signs of a missed miscarriage are the loss of all pregnancy symptoms, and less commonly, a brownish discharge. Confirmation of the miscarriage occurs when an ultrasound shows no fetal heartbeat.

Incomplete miscarriage. An incomplete miscarriage is when some of the tissue from the placenta stays inside the uterus and some is passed through the vagina via bleeding. With an incomplete miscarriage, a woman continues to cramp and bleed (sometimes heavily), her cervix remains dilated, pregnancy tests still come back positive (or blood hCG levels are still detectable and don't fall as expected), and parts of the pregnancy are still visible on an ultrasound.

Threatened miscarriage. When there is some vaginal bleeding but the cervix remains closed and the fetal heartbeat (as seen on ultrasound) is still detectable, it is considered a threatened miscarriage. Roughly half of those women with a threatened miscarriage go on to have a perfectly healthy pregnancy.

before the fetus is able to live on the outside (in other words, the unplanned end of a pregnancy). Such a loss in the first trimester is referred to as an early miscarriage. Eighty percent of miscarriages occur in the first trimester. (A miscarriage that occurs between the end of the first trimester and week 20 is considered a late miscarriage; see page 540).

Early miscarriage is usually related to a chromosomal or other genetic defect in the embryo, but it can also be caused by hormonal and other factors. Most often, the cause can't be identified.

How common is it? Miscarriage is one of the most common complications of early pregnancy. It's hard to know for sure, but researchers have estimated that over 40 percent of conceptions end in miscarriages. And well over half of those occur so early that pregnancy is not even suspected yet—meaning these miscarriages often go unnoticed, passing for a normal or sometimes heavier period. See the box above for more on the different types of early miscarriage.

Miscarriage can happen to any woman, and in fact, most women who have one have no known risk factors. Still, some factors somewhat increase the risk of miscarriage. One is age; the older eggs of older mothers (and possibly their older partner's sperm) are more likely to contain a genetic defect (a 40-year-old has a 33 percent chance of miscarrying, while a 20-year-old's odds of losing a pregnancy are 15 percent). Other risk factors include vitamin deficiencies (especially of folic acid); being very overweight or underweight; smoking; possibly hormonal insufficiency or imbalance, including an untreated thyroid condition; certain sexually transmitted diseases (STDs); and certain chronic conditions.

What are the signs and symptoms? The symptoms of a miscarriage can include some or all of the following:

- Cramping or pain (sometimes severe) in the center of the lower abdomen or back

- Heavy vaginal bleeding (possibly with clots and/or tissue) similar to a period

- Light staining continuing for more than three days

- A pronounced decrease in or loss of the usual signs of early pregnancy, such as breast tenderness and nausea

What can you and your practitioner do? Not all bleeding or spotting means you're having a miscarriage. In fact, many situations (other than miscarriage) could account for bleeding (see page 139).

If you do notice some bleeding or spotting, call your practitioner. He or she will assess the bleeding and probably perform an ultrasound. If the pregnancy still appears to be viable (in other words, a heartbeat is detected on the ultrasound), your practitioner may put you on some sort of temporary bed rest, your hormone levels will be monitored if you're still very early in your pregnancy (rising hCG levels are a good sign), and the bleeding will most likely stop on its own.

If your practitioner finds that your cervix is dilated and/or no fetal heartbeat is detected on ultrasound (and your dates are correct), it is assumed a miscarriage has occurred or is in progress. In such a case, unfortunately, nothing can be done to prevent the loss.

If You've Had a Miscarriage

Though it is hard for parents to accept it at the time, when an early miscarriage occurs, it's usually because the condition of the embryo or fetus is incompatible with normal life. Early miscarriage is generally a natural selection process in which a defective embryo or fetus (defective because of genetic abnormality; or damaged by environmental factors, such as radiation or drugs; or because of poor implantation in the uterus, maternal infection, random accident, or other, unknown reasons) is lost because it is incapable of survival.

All that said, losing a baby, even this early, is tragic and traumatic. But don't let guilt compound your misery. A miscarriage is not your fault. Do allow yourself to grieve, a necessary step in the healing process. Expect to be sad, even depressed, for a while. Sharing your feelings with your spouse, your practitioner, a relative, or a friend will help. So will joining or forming a support group for couples or singles who have experienced pregnancy loss or reaching out to others online. This sharing with others who truly know how you feel may be especially important if you've experienced more than one pregnancy loss. For more suggestions on coping with your loss, see Chapter 23.

For some women, the best therapy is getting pregnant again as soon as it is safe. But before you do, discuss possible causes of the miscarriage with your doctor. Most often, miscarriage is simply a random one-time occurrence caused by chromosomal abnormality, infection, chemical or other teratogenic (birth defect–causing) exposure, or chance, and it is not likely to recur.

Whatever the cause of your miscarriage, some practitioners suggest waiting two to three months before trying to conceive again, though intercourse can often be resumed as soon as you feel up to it. Other practitioners let nature take over; they tell their patients that their bodies will know when it's time to conceive again. Some studies have shown that women actually have a higher than normal fertility rate in the first three cycles following a first-trimester loss. If your practitioner does recommend a waiting period, however, use reliable contraception, preferably of the barrier type—condom, diaphragm—until the waiting time is up. Take advantage of this waiting period by getting your body into the best baby-making shape possible (see Chapter 1).

Happily, the chances are excellent that next time around you'll have a normal pregnancy and a healthy baby. Most women who have had one miscarriage do not miscarry again. In fact, a miscarriage is an assurance that you're capable of conceiving, and the great majority of women who lose a pregnancy this way go on to complete a normal one.

If you're in a lot of pain from the cramping, your practitioner may recommend or prescribe a pain reliever. Don't hesitate to ask for relief if you need it.

Can it be prevented? Most miscarriages are a result of a defect in the embryo or fetus and can't be prevented. There are steps you can take, however, to reduce the risk of preventable miscarriage:

- Get chronic conditions under control before conception.

- Be sure to take a daily prenatal supplement that includes folic acid and other B vitamins. New research has shown that some women have trouble

Management of a Miscarriage

Most miscarriages are complete, meaning all the contents of the uterus are expelled via the vagina (that's why there is often so much bleeding). But sometimes—especially the later in the first trimester you are—a miscarriage isn't complete, and parts of the pregnancy remain in the uterus (known as an incomplete miscarriage). Or a heartbeat is no longer detected on ultrasound, which means the embryo or fetus has died, but no bleeding has occurred (this is called a missed miscarriage). In both cases, your uterus will eventually be—or need to be—emptied so your normal menstrual cycle can resume (and you can try to get pregnant again, if you choose to). There are a number of ways this can be accomplished:

Expectant management. You may choose to let nature take its course and wait until the pregnancy is naturally expelled. Waiting out a missed or incomplete miscarriage can take any-where from a few days to, in some cases, three to four weeks.

Medication. Medication—usually a misoprostol pill taken orally, or vaginally as a suppository—can prompt your body to expel the fetal tissue and placenta. Just how long this takes varies from one woman to another, but, typically, it's only a matter of days at the most before the bleeding begins. Side effects of the medication can include nausea, vomiting, cramping, and diarrhea.

Surgery. Another option is to undergo a minor surgical procedure called dilation and curettage (D and C). During this procedure, the doctor dilates your cervix and gently removes (either by suction, scraping, or both) the fetal tissue and placenta from your uterus. Bleeding following the procedure usually lasts no more than a week. Though side effects are rare, there is a slight risk of infection following a D and C.

conceiving and/or sustaining a pregnancy because of a folic acid or vitamin B_{12} deficiency. Once these women begin the appropriate supplementation, they may be able to conceive and carry to term.

- Try to get your weight as close to ideal as possible before conceiving: Being extremely overweight or extremely underweight puts a pregnancy at higher risk.

- Avoid lifestyle practices that increase the risk of miscarriage, such as alcohol use and smoking.

- Use caution when taking medications. Take only those that are okayed by a doctor who knows you are pregnant

and avoid those that are known to be risky during pregnancy.

- Take steps to avoid infections, such as STDs.

If you've had two or more miscarriages, you can have tests to try to determine the possible cause so future pregnancy losses might be prevented (see box, page 542, for more).

Late Miscarriage

What is it? Any spontaneous expulsion of a fetus between the end of the first trimester and the 20th week is termed a late miscarriage. After the 20th week, the loss of the baby in utero is called a stillbirth.

How should you decide which route to take? Some factors you and your practitioner will take into account include:

- How far along the miscarriage is. If bleeding and cramping are already heavy, the miscarriage is probably already well under way. In that case, allowing it to progress naturally may be preferable to a D and C. But if there is no bleeding (as in a missed miscarriage), misoprostol or a D and C might be better alternatives.

- How far along the pregnancy is. The more fetal tissue there is, the more likely a D and C will be necessary to clean the uterus out completely.

- Your emotional and physical state. Waiting for a natural miscarriage to occur after a fetus has died in utero can be psychologically debilitating for a woman, as well as for her spouse. It's likely that you won't be able to begin coming to terms with—and grieving for—your loss while the pregnancy is still inside you. Completing the process faster will also allow you to resume your menstrual cycles soon, and when and if the time is right, to try to conceive again.

- Risks and benefits. Because a D and C is invasive, it carries a slightly higher (though still very low) risk of infection. The benefit of having the miscarriage complete sooner, however, may greatly outweigh that small risk for most women. With a naturally occurring miscarriage, there is also the risk that it won't completely empty the uterus, in which case a D and C may be necessary to finish what nature has started.

- Evaluation of the miscarriage. When a D and C is performed, evaluating the cause of the miscarriage through an examination of the fetal tissue will be easier.

No matter what course is taken, and whether the ordeal is over sooner or later, the loss will likely be difficult for you. See Chapter 23 for help in coping.

The cause of late miscarriage is usually related to the mother's health, the condition of her cervix or uterus, her exposure to certain drugs or other toxic substances, or to problems of the placenta.

How common is it? Late miscarriages occur in about 1 in 1,000 pregnancies.

What are the signs and symptoms? After the first trimester, a pink discharge for several days or a scant brown discharge for several weeks may indicate a threatened late miscarriage. Heavier bleeding, especially when accompanied by cramping, often means a miscarriage is inevitable, especially if the cervix is dilated. (There may be other causes of heavy bleeding, such as placenta previa, page 551; placental abruption, page 553; a tear in the uterine lining; or premature labor, page 556).

What can you and your practitioner do? If you're spotting light pink or brown, call your practitioner. He or she will evaluate the bleeding, possibly do an ultrasound and check your cervix, and probably prescribe bed rest. If the spotting stops, it's likely it wasn't related to miscarriage (sometimes it's triggered by sexual intercourse or an internal exam), which means normal activity can usually be resumed. If your cervix has started to dilate and you have had no bleeding or pain, a diagnosis of incompetent cervix may be made and cerclage (stitching

Repeat Miscarriages

Though having one miscarriage definitely doesn't mean that you're likely to miscarry again, some women do suffer recurring miscarriages (defined as two or three in a row). If you've had several, you may wonder whether you'll ever be able to have a healthy pregnancy. First, know that there's a good chance you will, although you may need to manage future pregnancies differently. The causes of repeated miscarriages are sometimes unknown, but there are tests that may shed light on why the miscarriages took place—even if they each had a different cause.

Trying to determine the cause of a single loss usually isn't worthwhile, but a medical evaluation might be rec-ommended if you have two or more miscarriages in a row. Some factors that might be related to recurrent miscarriage include a thyroid problem, autoimmune problems (in which the mother's immune system attacks the embryo), a vitamin deficiency, or a misshapen uterus. There are now many tests that may pick up risk factors for pregnancy loss and suggest possible ways of preventing it, in some cases very easily. Both parents might also have blood tests to screen for chromosomal problems that can be passed on to a fetus. You may be tested, too, for blood-clotting disorders (some women produce antibodies that attack their own tissues, causing blood clots that can clog the maternal blood vessels

the cervix closed; see page 47) may prevent a late miscarriage.

If you're experiencing the type of heavy bleeding and painful cramping that signal a miscarriage, there's usually nothing, unfortunately, that can be done to stop the inevitable. The further along your pregnancy, the more likely your practitioner might bring you into the hospital. Performing a D and C may be necessary to remove any remnants of the pregnancy.

Can it be prevented? Once a late miscarriage is under way, it isn't preventable. But if the cause of a late miscarriage can be determined, it may be possible to prevent a repeat of the tragedy. If a previously undiagnosed incompetent cervix was responsible, future miscarriages can be prevented by cerclage early in pregnancy, before the cervix begins to dilate. If chronic disease, such as dia-betes, hypertension, or a thyroid condition, is responsible, the condition can be brought under control prior to any future pregnancy. Acute infection can be prevented or treated. And an abnormally shaped uterus or one that is distorted by the growth of fibroids or other benign tumors in some instances can be corrected by surgery. The presence of antibodies that trigger placental inflammation and/or clotting may be treated with low-dose aspirin and heparin injections in a subsequent pregnancy.

Ectopic Pregnancy

What is it? An ectopic pregnancy (also known as a tubal pregnancy) is one that implants outside the uterus, most commonly in a fallopian tube, usually because something (such as scarring in the fallopian tube) obstructs or slows the that feed the placenta). An ultrasound, MRI, or CT scan may be performed on your uterus, your uterine cavity may be assessed with hysteroscopy, and the miscarried fetus itself can be tested for chromosomal abnormalities.

Once you know the cause, or causes, you can talk to your practitioner about treatment options, as well as how best to care for the next pregnancy. Surgery may correct some uterine and cervical issues; thyroid medication can easily treat a thyroid condition, and medically supervised supplementation can just as easily resolve a vitamin deficiency; hormone treatments may also help, as can tests for antibodies and treatment to prevent blood clots (low-dose aspirin and/or heparin). In some instances, patients with a history of early miscarriages who appear to be producing too little progesterone may benefit from taking the hormone, though this treatment is controversial. Or, if excess prolactin is the cause, medication to reduce prolactin levels in the mother's blood may allow a pregnancy to proceed to term.

Even if you've had repeated miscarriages, you still have a good chance of sustaining a successful pregnancy in the future. But that may be hard for you to believe or even to hope for. It will be important to find ways of managing your understandable fear that becoming pregnant again will mean you'll miscarry again. Yoga, visualization techniques, and deep-breathing exercises can help with the anxiety, and support can come from other women who've suffered similar losses. Sharing your feelings openly with your partner may also help. Remember, you're in this together.

movement of the fertilized egg into the uterus. An ectopic pregnancy can also occur in the cervix, on the ovary, or in the abdomen. Unfortunately, there is no way for an ectopic pregnancy to continue normally.

Ultrasound can detect an ectopic pregnancy, often as early as five weeks. But without early diagnosis and treatment of an ectopic pregnancy, the fertilized egg might continue to grow in the fallopian tube, leading to a rupture of the tube. If the tube bursts, its ability in the future to carry a fertilized egg to the uterus is destroyed, and if the rupture is not cared for, it can result in severe, even life-threatening, internal bleeding and shock. Luckily, quick treatment (usually surgery or medication) can help avoid such a rupture and removes most of the risk for the mother while greatly improving the chances of preserving her fertility.

How common is it? About 2 percent of all pregnancies are ectopic. Women at risk of having an ectopic pregnancy include those with a history of endometriosis, pelvic inflammatory disease, a prior ectopic pregnancy, or tubal surgery (conceiving after getting your tubes tied carries a 60 percent chance of an ectopic pregnancy). Also included in the at-risk group are those who became pregnant while using progesterone-only birth control pills; women who became pregnant with an IUD in place (though

You'll Want to Know...

More than half of the women who are treated for ectopic pregnancies conceive and have a normal pregnancy within a year.

Ectopic Pregnancy

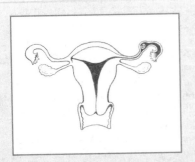

In an ectopic pregnancy, the fertilized egg implants in an area other than the uterus. Here, the egg has implanted in the fallopian tube.

with today's newer IUDs, especially the hormonal kinds, the chance of an ectopic pregnancy is significantly lower); women with STDs; and women who smoke.

What are the signs and symptoms? Early symptoms of an ectopic pregnancy include:

- Sharp, crampy pain with tenderness, usually in the lower abdomen (it often begins as a dull ache that progresses to spasms and cramps); pain may worsen on straining of bowels, coughing, or moving

- Abnormal bleeding (brown spotting or light bleeding that precedes the pain)

If the ectopic pregnancy goes unnoticed and your fallopian tube ruptures, you may experience:

- Nausea and vomiting
- Weakness

- Dizziness and/or fainting
- Severe sharp abdominal pain
- Rectal pressure
- Shoulder pain (due to blood accumulating under the diaphragm)
- Heavier vaginal bleeding

What can you and your practitioner do? Occasional cramping and even slight spotting early in pregnancy is not cause for alarm, but do let your practitioner know if you experience any type of pain, spotting, or bleeding. Call right away if you experience sharp, crampy pain in the lower abdomen, heavy bleeding, or any of the other symptoms of a ruptured ectopic pregnancy just listed. If it is determined that you have an ectopic pregnancy (usually diagnosed through ultrasound and blood tests), there is, unfortunately, no way to save the pregnancy. You'll most likely have to undergo surgery (laparoscopically) to remove the tubal pregnancy or be given drugs (methotrexate), which will end the abnormally occurring pregnancy. In some cases, it can be determined that the ectopic pregnancy is no longer developing and can be expected to disappear over time on its own, which would also eliminate the need for surgery.

You'll Want to Know ...

Occasional cramping in your lower abdomen early in pregnancy is probably the result of implantation, normally increased blood flow, or ligaments stretching as the uterus grows, not a sign of an ectopic pregnancy.

Because residual material from a pregnancy left in the tube could damage it, a follow-up test of hCG levels is performed to be sure the entire tubal pregnancy was removed or has reabsorbed.

Can it be prevented? Getting treated for sexually transmitted diseases (STDs), and the prevention of STDs (through the practice of safe sex) can help reduce the risk of an ectopic pregnancy, as can quitting smoking.

Subchorionic Bleed

What is it? A subchorionic bleed (also called a subchorionic hematoma) is the accumulation of blood between the uterine lining and the chorion (the outer fetal membrane, next to the uterus) or under the placenta itself, often (but not always) causing noticeable spotting or bleeding.

In the vast majority of cases, women who have a subchorionic bleed go on to have perfectly healthy pregnancies. But because (in rare cases) bleeds or clots that occur under the placenta can cause problems if they get too large, all subchorionic bleeds are monitored.

How common is it? Around 1 percent of all pregnancies have a subchorionic bleed. Of those women who experience first-trimester bleeding, 20 percent of them are diagnosed with a subchorionic bleed as the cause of the spotting.

What are the signs and symptoms? Spotting or bleeding may be a sign, often beginning in the first trimester. But many subchorionic bleeds are detected during a routine ultrasound, without there being any noticeable signs or symptoms.

What can you and your practitioner do? If you have spotting or bleeding, call your practitioner; an ultrasound may be ordered to see whether there is indeed a subchorionic bleed, how large it is, and where it's located.

Hyperemesis Gravidarum

What is it? Hyperemesis gravidarum is the medical term for severe pregnancy nausea and vomiting that is continuous and debilitating (not to be confused with typical morning sickness, even a pretty bad case). Hyperemesis usually starts to lift between weeks 12 and 16, but some cases can continue throughout pregnancy.

Hyperemesis gravidarum can lead to weight loss, malnutrition, and dehydration if it's left untreated. Treatment of severe hyperemesis often requires hospitalization—mostly for the administration of IV fluids and antinausea drugs, which can effectively safeguard your well-being and your baby's.

How common is it? Hyperemesis gravidarum occurs in about 1 in 200 pregnancies. This pregnancy complication is more common in first-time mothers, in young mothers, in obese women, in women carrying multiple fetuses, and in women who've had it in a previous pregnancy. Extreme emotional stress can also increase your risk, as can endocrine imbalances and vitamin B deficiencies.

What are the signs and symptoms? The symptoms of hyperemesis gravidarum include:

- Very frequent and severe nausea and vomiting

- The inability to keep any food or even liquid down

- Signs of dehydration, such as infrequent urination or dark yellow urine

- Weight loss of more than 5 percent

- Blood in the vomit

What can you and your practitioner do? If your symptoms are relatively mild, you can first try some of the natural remedies used to fight morning sickness, including ginger, acupuncture, and acupressure wristbands (see page 130). If those don't do the trick, ask your practitioner about medications that can help (a combination of vitamin B_6 and Unisom Sleep Tabs is often prescribed for tough morning sickness cases). But if you're vomiting continually and/or losing significant amounts of weight, your practitioner will assess your need for

---

You'll Want to Know . . .

As miserable as hyperemesis gravidarum makes you feel, it's unlikely to affect your baby. Most studies show no health or developmental differences between infants of women who experience hyperemesis gravidarum and those who don't.

---

intravenous fluids and/or hospitalization, and possibly prescribe some sort of antiemetic (antinausea) drug. Once you're able to keep food down again, it may help to tweak your diet to eliminate fatty and spicy foods, which are more likely to cause nausea, as well as to avoid any smells or tastes that tend to set you off. In addition, try to graze on many small high-carb and high-protein meals throughout the day, and be sure your fluid intake is adequate (keeping an eye on your urinary output is the best way to assess that; dark scant urine is a sign you're not getting, or keeping down, enough fluids).

Gestational Diabetes

What is it? Gestational diabetes (GD)—a form of diabetes that appears only during pregnancy—occurs when the body does not produce adequate amounts of insulin (the hormone that lets the body turn blood sugar into energy) to regulate blood sugar effectively. GD usually begins between weeks 24 and 28 of pregnancy (which explains why a glucose screening test is routine at around 28 weeks). GD almost always goes away after delivery, but if you've had it, you'll be checked postpartum to make sure it's gone.

Diabetes, both the kind that begins in pregnancy and the kind that started before conception, is not harmful to either the fetus or the mother if it is well controlled. But if excessive sugar is allowed to circulate in a mother's blood and thus to enter the fetal circulation through the placenta, the potential problems for both mother and baby are serious. Women who have uncontrolled GD are more likely to have a too-large baby, which can complicate delivery. They are also at risk for developing preeclampsia (pregnancy-induced hypertension). Uncontrolled diabetes could also lead to potential problems for the baby after birth, such as jaundice, breathing difficulties, and low blood sugar levels. Later in life, he or she may be at an increased risk for obesity and type 2 diabetes.

How common is it? GD is fairly common, affecting 4 to 8 percent of expectant women. Because it's more common among obese women, rates of GD are rising along with rising obesity rates in the United States. Older moms-to-be are more likely to develop GD, as are women with a family history of diabetes or GD. Native Americans, Latin Americans, and African Americans are also at somewhat greater risk for GD.

What are the signs and symptoms? Most women with GD have no symptoms, though a few may experience:

- Unusual thirst

- Frequent and very copious urination (as distinguished from the also frequent but usually light urination of early pregnancy)

- Fatigue (which may be difficult to differentiate from pregnancy fatigue)

- Sugar in the urine (detected at a routine practitioner visit)

What can you and your practitioner do? Around your 28th week, you'll be given a glucose screening test (see page 297) and, if necessary, a more elaborate three-hour glucose tolerance test. If these tests show you have GD, your practitioner will likely put you on a special diet (similar to the Pregnancy Diet) and suggest exercises to keep your GD under control. You may also need to check your glucose levels at home using a glucose meter or strips.

If diet and exercise alone aren't enough to control your blood sugar level (they usually are), you may need supplementary insulin. The insulin can be given in shots, but the oral drug glyburide is being used more and more often as an alternative treatment for GD. Fortunately, virtually all of the potential risks associated with diabetes in pregnancy can be eliminated through the careful control of blood sugar levels achieved by good self- and medical care. For more on diabetes control, see page 519.

You'll Want to Know...

There's little reason for concern if your GD is well controlled. Your pregnancy will progress normally and your baby shouldn't be affected.

Can it be prevented? Keeping an eye on your weight gain (both before and during pregnancy) can help prevent GD. So, too, can good diet habits (eating plenty of fruits and vegetables, and whole grains, keeping refined sugar intake down, and making sure you're getting enough folic acid) and regular exercise (research shows that obese women who exercise cut their risk of developing GD by half). Continuing these preventive steps after the baby's born also significantly reduces the risk of diabetes occurring later in life.

Keep in mind, too, that having GD during pregnancy puts you at greater risk of developing type 2 diabetes after pregnancy. Keeping your diet healthy, staying at a normal weight, and, even more important, continuing to exercise after the baby is born (and beyond) significantly cuts that risk.

Preeclampsia

What is it? Preeclampsia (also known as pregnancy-induced hypertension or toxemia) is a disorder that generally develops late in pregnancy (after week 20) and is characterized by a sudden onset of high blood pressure, excessive swelling (edema), and protein in the urine.

If preeclampsia goes untreated, it could progress to eclampsia, a much more serious condition involving seizures (see page 562). Unmanaged preeclampsia can also cause a number of other pregnancy complications, such as premature delivery or intrauterine growth restriction.

How common is it? About 8 percent of pregnant women are diagnosed with preeclampsia. Women carrying multiple fetuses, women over 40, and women with high blood pressure or diabetes are at greater risk of developing preeclampsia. If you're diagnosed with preeclampsia in one of your pregnancies, you have a 1 in 3 chance of developing the condition in future pregnancies. That risk is higher if you are diagnosed with preeclampsia in your first pregnancy or if you develop preeclampsia early in any pregnancy.

What are the signs and symptoms? Symptoms of preeclampsia can include any or all of the following:

The Reasons Behind Preeclampsia

No one knows for sure what causes preeclampsia, though there are a number of theories:

- A genetic link. Researchers hypothesize that the genetic makeup of the fetus could be one of the factors that predisposes a pregnancy to preeclampsia. So, if your mother or your spouse's mother had preeclampsia during their pregnancies with either of you, you are somewhat more likely to have preeclampsia during your pregnancies.

- A blood vessel defect. It has been suggested that this defect causes the blood vessels in some women to constrict during pregnancy instead of widen (as usually happens). As a result of this vessel defect, theorize researchers, there is a drop in the blood supply to organs like the kidney and liver, leading to preeclampsia. The fact that women who experience preeclampsia during pregnancy are at an increased risk later in life of having some sort of cardiovascular condition also seems to indicate that the condition may be the result of a predisposition in some women to high blood pressure.

- Gum disease. Pregnant women with severe gum disease are more than twice as likely to also have preeclampsia compared to women with healthy gums. Experts theorize that the infection causing the periodontal disease may travel to the placenta or produce chemicals that can cause preeclampsia. Still, it is not known if periodontal disease causes preeclampsia or if it is just associated with it.

- An immune response to a foreign intruder: the baby. This theory implies that the woman's body becomes "allergic" to the baby and placenta. This "allergy" causes a reaction in the mother's body that can damage her blood and blood vessels. The more similar the father's and mother's genetic markers, the more likely this immune response will occur.

- Severe swelling of hands and face
- Swelling of the ankles that doesn't go away after 12 hours of rest
- Sudden excessive weight gain unrelated to eating
- Headaches that don't respond to over-the-counter pain relievers
- Pain in the upper abdomen
- Blurred or double vision
- A rise in blood pressure (to 140/90 or more in a woman who has never before had high blood pressure)
- Protein in the urine
- Rapid heartbeat
- Scant urine output
- Abnormal kidney function
- Exaggerated reflex reactions

What can you and your practitioner do? Regular prenatal care is the best way to catch preeclampsia in its early stages (your practitioner might be tipped off by protein in your urine and a rise in your blood pressure, or the symptoms just listed). Being alert to any such symptoms (and alerting your practitioner if you notice them) also helps, particularly if you had a history of hypertension before pregnancy.

If you're diagnosed with preeclampsia, your treatment will probably include bed rest at home and careful blood pressure and fetal monitoring (though more pronounced cases may require hospital bed rest). With severe preeclampsia, the treatment is usually more aggressive and includes delivery within three days of diagnosis. Intravenous magnesium sulfate is begun promptly because it almost always prevents progression to eclampsia.

Though treatments are available to control preeclampsia for short periods of time, there is no cure except for delivery of your baby, which will likely be recommended as soon as the baby is physically mature enough or after medications are given to speed lung maturity. The good news is that 97 percent of women with preeclampsia recover completely, with a speedy return to normal blood pressure, after delivery.

On the research horizon: Scientists are developing simple blood and urine tests that can predict which moms-to-be are likely to develop this complication. They've found that women who eventually develop preeclampsia show high levels of a substance called soluble FH-1 in the blood and urine. Another substance called endoglin may also prove to predict the condition. Ideally, the research will lead to much earlier detection of preeclampsia.

Can it be prevented? Research has suggested that for women at risk for preeclampsia, aspirin or other anticlotting drugs during pregnancy may reduce the risk, though the benefits of this medically induced therapy need to be weighed against its theoretical risks. Some research has suggested that good nutrition, which ensures adequate intakes of antioxidants, magnesium, vitamins (especially D), and minerals,

You'll Want to Know...

Fortunately, in women who are receiving regular medical care, preeclampsia is almost invariably caught early on and managed successfully. With appropriate and prompt medical care, a woman with preeclampsia near term has virtually the same excellent chance of having a positive pregnancy outcome as a woman with normal blood pressure.

may reduce the risk of preeclampsia, as may proper dental care.

HELLP Syndrome

What is it? HELLP syndrome is a combination of conditions that can affect a pregnant woman, either by itself or in conjunction with preeclampsia, almost always in the last trimester. The acronym stands for hemolysis (H), in which red blood cells are destroyed too soon, causing a low red-cell count; elevated liver enzymes (EL), which indicates that the liver is functioning poorly and is unable to process toxins in the body efficiently; and low platelet count (LP), which makes it difficult for the blood to form clots.

When HELLP develops, it can threaten both a mother's life and that of her baby. Women who aren't diagnosed and treated quickly run about a 1 in 4 chance of suffering serious complications, primarily in the form of extensive liver damage or stroke.

How common is it? HELLP syndrome occurs in fewer than 1 in 10 preeclamptic or eclamptic pregnancies and fewer than 1 in 500 pregnancies.

Women who develop preeclampsia or eclampsia are at risk, as are women who have had HELLP in a previous pregnancy.

What are the signs and symptoms? The symptoms of HELLP are very vague, consisting of (in the third trimester):

- Nausea

- Vomiting

- Headaches

- General malaise

- Pain and tenderness in the upper right side of the abdomen

- Viral-type illness symptoms

Blood tests reveal a low platelet count, elevated liver enzymes, and hemolysis (the breakdown of red blood cells). Liver function rapidly deteriorates in women with HELLP, so treatment is critical.

What can you and your practitioner do? The only effective treatment for HELLP syndrome is delivery of your baby, so the best thing you can do is be aware of the symptoms of the condition (especially if you already have or are at risk for preeclampsia) and call your practitioner immediately if you develop any. If you have HELLP, you might also be given steroids (to treat the condition and help mature the baby's lungs) and magnesium sulfate (to prevent seizures).

Can it be prevented? Because a woman who has had HELLP in a previous pregnancy is likely to have it again, close monitoring is necessary in any subsequent pregnancy. Unfortunately, nothing can be done to prevent the condition.

Intrauterine Growth Restriction

What is it? Intrauterine growth restriction (IUGR) is a term used for a baby who is smaller than normal during pregnancy. A diagnosis of IUGR is given if your baby's weight is below the 10th percentile for his or her gestational age. IUGR can occur if the health of the placenta or its blood supply is impaired or if the mother's nutrition, health, or lifestyle prevents the healthy growth of her fetus.

How common is it? IUGR occurs in about 10 percent of all pregnancies. It's more common in first pregnancies, in fifth and subsequent ones, in women who are under age 17 or over age 35, in those who had a previous low-birth-

You'll Want to Know...

A mom who has already had a low-birthweight baby has only a modestly increased risk of having another one—and, to her advantage, statistics show that each subsequent baby is actually likely to be a bit heavier than the preceding one. If you had an IUGR baby the first time around, paying attention to all the possible contributing factors can reduce the risk this time around.

weight baby, as well as in those who have placental problems or uterine abnormalities. Carrying multiples is also a risk factor, but that's probably due more to the crowded conditions (it's hard to fit more than one 7-pounder in a single womb) than to problems with the placenta. Having been small at birth yourself also puts you at an increased risk of having a small baby, and the risk is also higher if the baby's father was born small.

What are the signs and symptoms? Surprisingly, carrying small is not usually a tip-off to IUGR. In fact, there are rarely any obvious outward signs that the baby isn't growing as he or she should be. Instead, IUGR is usually detected during a routine prenatal exam when the practitioner measures the fundal height—the distance from your pubic bone to the top of your uterus—and finds that it's measuring too small for the baby's gestational age. An ultrasound can also detect a baby whose growth is slower than expected for his or her gestational age.

What can you and your practitioner do? One of the best predictors of a baby's good health is birthweight, so having

IUGR can present some health problems for the newborn, including having difficulty maintaining a normal body temperature or fighting infection. That's why it's so important to diagnose the problem early and try to boost baby's chances of a healthy bottom line at birth. A variety of approaches may be tried, depending on the suspected cause, including bed rest, intravenous feedings if necessary, and medications to improve placental blood flow or to correct a diagnosed problem that may be contributing to the IUGR. If the intrauterine environment is poor and can't be improved, and the fetal lungs are known to be mature, prompt delivery—which allows baby to start living under healthier conditions—is usually the best way to go.

Can it be prevented? Optimum nutrition and the elimination of risk factors can greatly improve the chances for normal fetal growth and a normal birthweight. Controlling certain maternal risk factors (such as chronic high blood pressure, smoking, drinking alcohol, or using recreational drugs) that contribute to poor fetal growth can help prevent IUGR. Good prenatal care can also minimize the risks, as can excellent diet, proper weight gain within recommended guidelines, as well as minimizing physical and excessive psychological stress (including chronic lack of rest). Happily, even

You'll Want to Know...

More than 90 percent of babies who are born small for date do fine, catching up with their bigger birth buddies in the first couple of years of life.

when prevention and treatment are unsuccessful and a baby is born smaller than normal, the chances that he or she will do well are increasingly good, thanks to the many advances in neonatal (newborn) care.

Placenta Previa

What is it? The definition of placenta previa is a placenta that partially or completely covers the opening of the cervix. In early pregnancy, a low-lying placenta is fairly common but as pregnancy progresses and the uterus grows, the placenta usually moves upward and away from the cervix. If it doesn't move up and partially covers or touches the cervix, it's called partial previa. If it completely covers the cervix, it's called total or complete previa. Either can physically block your baby's passage into the birth canal, making a vaginal delivery impossible. It can also trigger bleeding late in pregnancy and at delivery. The closer to the cervix the placenta is situated, the greater the possibility of bleeding.

How common is it? Placenta previa occurs in 1 out of every 200 deliveries. It is more likely to occur in women over the age of 30 than in women under the age of 20, and it is also more common in women who have had at least one other pregnancy or any kind of uterine surgery (such as a previous C-section or a D and C following miscarriage). Smoking or carrying multiple fetuses also increases the risks.

What are the signs and symptoms? Placenta previa is most often discovered not on the basis of symptoms but during a routine second-trimester ultrasound (though there isn't even the potential for problems with a previa until the third trimester). Sometimes the condition announces itself in the third trimester (occasionally earlier) with bright-red bleeding. Typically, bleeding is the only symptom. There's usually no pain involved.

What can you and your practitioner do? Nothing needs to be done (and you don't have to give your low-lying placenta a second thought) until the third trimester, by which point most early cases of placenta previa have corrected themselves. Even later on, there is no treatment necessary if you've been diagnosed with previa but aren't experiencing any bleeding (you'll just need to be alert to any bleeding or to signs of premature labor, which is more common with placenta previa). If you're experiencing bleeding related to a diagnosed previa, your practitioner will likely put you on bed rest, pelvic rest (no sex),

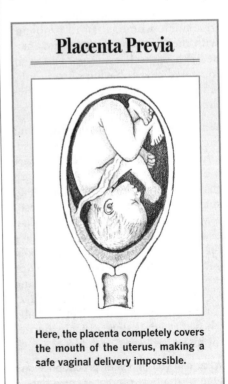

Placenta Previa

Here, the placenta completely covers the mouth of the uterus, making a safe vaginal delivery impossible.

and will monitor you closely. If premature labor seems imminent, you may receive steroid shots to mature your baby's lungs more rapidly. Even if the condition hasn't presented your pregnancy with any problems at all (you haven't had any bleeding and you've carried to term), your baby will still be delivered via C-section.

Placental Abruption

What is it? Placental abruption (also called abruptio placenta) is the early separation of the placenta (the baby's support system) from the uterine wall during pregnancy, rather than after delivery. If the separation is slight, there is usually little danger to the mother or baby as long as treatment is prompt and proper precautions are taken. If the abruption is more severe, however, the risk to the baby is considerably higher. That's because a placenta's complete detachment from the uterine wall means the baby is no longer getting oxygen or nutrition.

How common is it? It occurs in less than 1 percent of pregnancies, almost always in the second half of the pregnancy and most often in the third trimester. Placental abruption can happen to anyone, but it occurs more commonly in women who are carrying multiples, who have had a previous abruption, who smoke or use cocaine, or who have gestational diabetes, a predisposition to clotting, preeclampsia, or other high blood pressure conditions of pregnancy. A short umbilical cord or trauma due to an accident is occasionally the cause of an abruption.

What are the signs and symptoms? The symptoms of placental abruption depend on the severity of the detachment, but will usually include:

- Bleeding (that could be light to heavy, with or without clots)

- Abdominal cramping or achiness

- Uterine tenderness

- Pain in the back or abdomen

What can you and your practitioner do? Let your practitioner know immediately if you have abdominal pain accompanied by bleeding in the second half of your pregnancy. A diagnosis is usually made using patient history, physical exam, and observation of uterine contractions and the fetal response to them. Ultrasound may be helpful, but only about 25 percent of abruptions can actually be seen on ultrasound. If it's been determined that your placenta has separated slightly from the uterine wall but has not completely detached, and if your baby's vital signs stay regular, you'll probably be put on bed rest. If the bleeding continues, you may require intravenous fluids. Your practitioner may also administer steroids to speed up your baby's lung maturation in case you need to deliver early. If the abruption is significant or if it continues to progress, the only way to treat it is to deliver the baby, most often by C-section.

Chorioamnionitis

What is it? Chorioamnionitis is a bacterial infection of the amniotic membranes and fluid that surround and protect your baby. It's caused by common bacteria such as E. coli or by group B strep (which you'll be tested for around week 36 of your pregnancy). The infection is believed to be a major cause of preterm premature rupture of the membranes (PPROM) as well as of premature delivery.

How common is it? Chorioamnionitis occurs in 1 to 2 percent of pregnancies. Women who experience premature rupture of the membranes are at increased risk for chorioamnionitis because bacteria from the vagina can seep into the amniotic sac after it has ruptured. Women who've had the infection during their first pregnancy are more likely to have it again in a subsequent pregnancy.

What are the signs and symptoms? Diagnosis of chorioamnionitis is complicated by the fact that no simple test can confirm the presence of infection. The symptoms of chorioamnionitis can include:

- Fever

- Tender, painful uterus

- Increased heart rate in both you and your baby

- Leaking, foul-smelling amniotic fluid (if membranes have already ruptured)

- Unpleasant-smelling vaginal discharge (if membranes are intact)

- Increased white blood count (a sign the body is fighting an infection)

What can you and your practitioner do? Be sure to call your practitioner if you

---

You'll Want to Know . . .

Rapid diagnosis and treatment of chorioamnionitis greatly reduces the risks to both mother and baby.

---

notice any leaking of amniotic fluid, no matter how small, or if you notice a foul-smelling discharge or any other of the symptoms listed above. If you are diagnosed with chorioamnionitis, you will likely be prescribed antibiotics to wipe out the bacteria, and be delivered immediately. You and your baby will also be given antibiotics after delivery to make sure no further infections develop.

Oligohydramnios

What is it? Oligohydramnios is a condition in which there is not enough amniotic fluid surrounding and cushioning the baby. It usually develops in the latter part of the third trimester, though it could show up earlier in pregnancy. Though the majority of women diagnosed with oligohydramnios will have a completely normal pregnancy, there is a slight risk of umbilical cord constriction if there's too little fluid for your baby to float around in. Often, the condition is simply the result of a fluid leak or puncture in the amniotic sac (one you wouldn't necessarily notice). Less commonly, a low level of amniotic fluid can suggest a problem in the baby, such as poor fetal growth or a kidney or urinary tract condition.

How common is it? Four to 8 percent of pregnant women are diagnosed with oligohydramnios during their pregnancy, but among overdue women (those two weeks past their due dates), the number rises to 12 percent. Women with a post-term pregnancy are most likely to have oligohydramnios, as are those who have premature rupture of membranes.

What are the signs and symptoms? There are no symptoms in the mother, but signs that would point to the condition are a uterus that measures smaller than it should and a decreased amount of amniotic fluid, detected via ultrasound. There might also be a noticeable decrease of fetal activity and sudden drops in the fetal heart rate in some cases.

What can you and your practitioner do? If you're diagnosed with oligohydramnios, you'll need to get a lot of rest and drink plenty of water. The amount of amniotic fluid will be closely monitored. If at any point oligohydramnios endangers the well-being of your baby, your practitioner may suggest amnioinfusion (in which fluid levels are augmented with sterile saline) or may opt for an early delivery.

Hydramnios

What is it? Too much amniotic fluid surrounding the fetus causes the condition known as hydramnios (also called polyhydramnios). Most cases of hydramnios are mild and transient, simply the result of a temporary change in the normal balance of the amniotic fluid production, with any extra fluid likely to be reabsorbed without any treatment.

But when fluid accumulation is severe (which is rare), it may signal a problem with the baby, such as a central nervous system or gastrointestinal defect, or an inability to swallow (babies typically swallow amniotic fluid). Too much amniotic fluid can put your pregnancy at risk for premature rupture of membranes, preterm labor, placental abruption, breech presentation, or umbilical cord prolapse.

How common is it? Hydramnios occurs in 3 to 4 percent of all pregnancies. It is more likely to occur when there are multiple fetuses and can be related to untreated diabetes in the mother.

What are the signs and symptoms? More often than not, there are no symptoms at all with hydramnios, though some women may notice:

- Difficulty feeling fetal movements (because there's too much of a cushion)
- Unusually rapid growth of the uterus
- Discomfort in the abdomen
- Indigestion
- Swelling in the legs
- Breathlessness
- Possibly, uterine contractions

Hydramnios is usually detected during a prenatal exam, when your fundal height—the distance from your pubic bone to the top of your uterus—measures larger than normal, or during an ultrasound that measures the amount of fluid in the amniotic sac.

What can you and your practitioner do? Unless the fluid accumulation is fairly severe, there's absolutely nothing you need to do except to keep your appointments with your practitioner, who will continue to monitor your condition. If the accumulation is more severe, your practitioner may suggest you undergo a procedure called therapeutic amniocentesis, during which fluid is withdrawn from the amniotic sac to reduce the amount. Since hydramnios puts you at increased risk for cord prolapse, call your practitioner right away if your water breaks on its own before labor.

Preterm Premature Rupture of the Membranes (PPROM)

What is it? PPROM refers to the rupture of the membranes (or "bag of waters") that cradle the fetus in the uterus, before 37 weeks (in other words, before term, when the baby is still premature). The major risk of PPROM is a premature birth; other risks include infection of the amniotic fluid and prolapse or compression of the umbilical cord. (Premature rupture of the membranes, or PROM, that isn't preterm—that is, it takes place after 37 weeks, but before labor begins—is discussed on page 363.)

How common is it? Preterm premature rupture of membranes occurs in fewer than 3 percent of pregnancies. Women most at risk are those who smoke during pregnancy, have certain STDs, have chronic vaginal bleeding or placental abruption, have had a previous early membrane rupture, have bacterial vaginosis (BV), or who are carrying multiples.

What are the signs and symptoms? The symptoms are leaking or gushing of fluid from the vagina. The way to tell whether you're leaking amniotic fluid and not urine is by taking the sniff test: If it smells like ammonia, it's probably urine. If it has a somewhat sweet smell, it's probably amniotic fluid (unless it's infected; then the fluid will be more foul smelling). If you have any doubts about what you're leaking, call your practitioner to be on the safe side.

What can you and your practitioner do? If your membranes have ruptured after 34 weeks, you'll likely be induced and your baby delivered. If it's too soon for your baby to be delivered safely, chances are you'll be put on in-hospital bed rest

> ## You'll Want to Know . . .
>
> With prompt and appropriate diagnosis and management of PPROM, both mother and baby should be fine, though if the birth is premature, there may be a long stay in the neonatal intensive care unit for baby.

and be given antibiotics to ward off infection, as well as steroids to mature your baby's lungs as quickly as possible for a safer early delivery. If contractions begin and the baby is believed to be too immature for delivery, medication may be given to try to stop them.

Rarely, the break in the membranes heals and the leakage of amniotic fluid stops on its own. If that happens, you'll be allowed to go home and resume your normal routine while remaining on the alert for signs of further leakage.

Can it be prevented? Vaginal infections, particularly BV, can lead to PPROM; therefore, watching out for and treating these infections may be effective in preventing some cases of PPROM.

Preterm or Premature Labor

What is it? Labor that kicks in after week 20 but before the end of week 37 of pregnancy is considered to be preterm labor.

How common is it? Preterm labor is a fairly common problem; about 12 percent of babies are born premature in the United States.

Risk factors leading to premature labor include smoking, alcohol use, drug abuse, too little weight gain, too much weight gain, inadequate nutrition, gum infection, other infections (such as STDs, bacterial vaginosis, urinary tract infections, amniotic fluid infection), incompetent cervix, uterine irritability, chronic maternal illness, placental abruption, and placenta previa. Women who are younger than 17 or older than 35 years old, those who are carrying multiples, and those with a history of premature delivery are also at increased risk. Preterm births are also more common among African American and disadvantaged women. In addition, a fairly large number of premature labors are induced by practitioners in an appropriate response to a medical condition that requires an early birth, such as pre-eclampsia or PPROM.

Still, much more needs to be learned about what causes labor to begin early; at least half of the women who go into preterm labor have no known risk factors.

What are the signs and symptoms? Signs of premature labor can include all or some of the following:

- Menstrual-like cramps

- Regular contractions that intensify and become more frequent even if you change positions

- Back pressure

- Unusual pressure in your pelvis

- Bloody discharge from your vagina

- Rupture of membranes

- Changes in the cervix (thinning, opening, or shortening) as measured by ultrasound

What can you and your practitioner do? Because each day a baby remains in the womb improves the chances of both survival and good health, holding off labor as long as possible will be the primary goal. Unfortunately, however, there isn't

> ## You'll Want to Know...
>
> A baby born prematurely will likely need to spend time in a neonatal intensive care unit (NICU) for the first few days, weeks, or, in some cases, months of his or her life. Though prematurity has been linked to slow growth and developmental delays, most babies who arrive too early catch up and have no lasting problems at all. Thanks to advances in medical care, your chances of bringing home a normal, healthy infant after a premature birth are very good.

much that can be done to stop early labor. The measures that were once routinely recommended (bed rest, hydration, home uterine activity monitoring) don't seem to work to stop or prevent contractions, though many doctors still prescribe them. Other steps your practitioner may advise if you're experiencing early contractions include progesterone supplementation to decrease uterine activity (usually reserved only for women with a prior preterm delivery or with a short cervix who are not carrying multiples or receiving tocolytics); antibiotics (if a GBS culture—see page 326—is positive); or tocolytics (that can temporarily halt contractions, and give your practitioner time to administer steroids to help your baby's lungs mature more quickly, so that he or she will fare better should a preterm birth become inevitable or necessary). If at any point your practitioner determines that the risk to you or your baby from continuing the pregnancy outweighs the risk of preterm birth, no attempt will be made to postpone delivery.

Can it be prevented? Not all preterm births can be avoided, since not all are due to preventable risk factors.

Predicting Preterm Labor

Even among women who are at high risk for preterm labor, most will carry to term. One way to predict preterm labor is to examine cervical or vaginal secretions for a substance known as fetal fibronectin (fFN). Studies show that some women who test positive for fFN stand a good chance of going into preterm labor within one to two weeks of the test. The test, however, is better at diagnosing women who are *not* at risk for going into preterm labor (by detecting no fFN) than as an accurate predictor of women who are at risk. When fFN is detected, steps should be taken to reduce the chances of preterm labor. The test is now widely available, but is usually reserved for high-risk women only. If you aren't considered high risk for preterm birth, you don't need to be tested.

Another screening test is one for cervical length. Via ultrasound before 30 weeks, the length of your cervix is measured to see if there are any signs that the cervix is shortening or opening. A short cervix puts you at an increased risk of going into early labor, especially if it began shortening early in pregnancy.

However, all the following measures may reduce the risk of preterm delivery (while boosting your chances of having the healthiest pregnancy possible): taking folic acid before pregnancy; getting early prenatal care; eating well (and getting enough vitamins, especially vitamin D); getting good dental care; avoiding smoking, cocaine, alcohol, and other drugs not prescribed by your doctor; getting tested for and, if necessary, treated for any infections such as BV and UTIs; and following your practitioner's recommendations as to limitations on strenuous activity, including sexual intercourse and hours spent standing or walking on the job, especially if you have had previous preterm deliveries. The good news is that 80 percent of women who go into preterm labor will deliver at term without any interventions at all.

Symphysis Pubis Dysfunction (SPD)

What is it? Symphysis pubis dysfunction, or SPD, means the ligaments that normally keep your pelvic bone aligned become too relaxed and stretchy too soon before birth (as delivery nears, things are supposed to start loosening up). This, in turn, can make the pelvic joint—aka the symphysis pubis—unstable, causing mild to severe pain.

How common is it? The incidence of diagnosed SPD is about 1 in 300 pregnancies, though some experts think that more than 2 percent of all pregnant women will experience SPD (but not all will have it diagnosed).

What are the signs and symptoms? The most common symptom is a wrenching pain (as though your pelvis is coming apart) and difficulty when walking. Typically, the pain is focused on the pubic area, but in some women it radiates to the upper thighs and perineum. The pain can worsen when you're walking and doing any weight-bearing activity, particularly one that involves lifting one leg, such as when you're climbing up stairs, getting dressed, getting in and out of a car, even turning over in bed. In very rare cases, the joint may gape apart, a condition called diastasis symphysis pubis or symphyseal separation, which can cause more serious pain in your pelvis, groin, hips, and buttocks.

What can you and your practitioner do? Avoid aggravating the condition by limiting weight-bearing positions and minimizing as best you can any activity that involves lifting or separating your legs—even walking, if it's very uncomfortable. Try stabilizing those floppy ligaments by wearing a pelvic support belt, which "corsets" the bones back into place. Kegels and pelvic tilts can help to strengthen the muscles of the pelvis. If the pain is severe, ask your practitioner about pain relievers or turn to CAM techniques, such as acupuncture or chiropractic.

Very rarely, SPD can make a vaginal delivery impossible and your practitioner may opt for a C-section instead. And in even rarer cases, SPD can worsen after delivery, requiring medical intervention. But for most moms, once your baby is born and production of relaxin (that ligament-relaxing hormone) stops, your ligaments will return to normal.

Cord Knots and Tangles

What is it? Once in a while, the umbilical cord becomes knotted, tangled, or wrapped around a fetus, often at the neck (when it is known as a nuchal cord). Some knots form during delivery; others form during pregnancy when the baby moves around. As long as the knot remains loose, it's not likely to cause any problems at all. But if the knot becomes tight, it could interfere with the circulation of blood from the placenta to the baby and cause oxygen deprivation. Such an event happens only rarely, but when it does, it is most likely to occur during your baby's descent through the birth canal.

How common is it? True umbilical cord knots occur in about 1 in every 100 pregnancies, but only in 1 in 2,000 deliveries will a knot be tight enough to present problems for the baby. The more common nuchal cords occur in as many as a quarter of all pregnancies but very rarely pose risks to the baby. Babies with long cords and those who are large-for-gestational age are at greater risk for developing true knots. Researchers speculate that nutritional deficiencies that affect the structure and protective barrier of the cord, or other risk factors, such as smoking or drug use, carrying multiples, or having hydramnios, may make a woman more prone to having a pregnancy with a cord knot.

What are the signs and symptoms? The most common sign of a cord knot is decreased fetal activity after week 37. If the knot occurs during labor, a fetal monitor will detect an abnormal heart rate.

What can you and your practitioner do? You can keep a general eye on how your baby is doing, especially later in your pregnancy, by doing regular kick counts and calling your practitioner if you notice any change in fetal activity. If a loose knot tightens during delivery, your practitioner will be able to detect the drop in your baby's heart rate, and will make the appropriate decisions to ensure your baby's safe entry into the world. Immediate delivery, usually via C-section, is often the best approach.

Two-Vessel Cord

What is it? In a normal umbilical cord, there are three blood vessels—one vein (which brings nutrients and oxygen to the baby) and two arteries (which transport waste from the baby back to the placenta and the mother's blood). But in some cases, the umbilical cord contains only two blood vessels—one vein and one artery.

How common is it? About 1 percent of singletons and 5 percent of multiple pregnancies will have a two-vessel cord. Those at greater risk include Caucasian women, women over age 40, those carrying a multiple pregnancy, and those with diabetes. Female fetuses are more likely to be affected by a two-vessel cord than males.

What are the signs and symptoms? There are no signs or symptoms with this condition; it's detected on ultrasound examination.

What can you and your practitioner do? In the absence of any other abnormalities, a two-vessel cord in no way harms the pregnancy. The baby is most likely to be born completely healthy. So the first thing you can do is not worry.

If you've been found to have a two-vessel cord, your pregnancy will be monitored more closely, since the condition comes with a small increased risk of poor fetal growth.

Uncommon Pregnancy Complications

The following complications of pregnancy are, for the most part, rare. The average pregnant woman is extremely unlikely to encounter any of them. So, again (and this deserves repeating), read this section *only* if you need to—and even then, read just what applies to you. If you are diagnosed with any of these complications during your pregnancy, use the information here to learn about the condition and its typical treatment (as well as how to prevent it in future pregnancies), but realize that your practitioner's protocol for treating you may be different.

Molar Pregnancy

What is it? In a molar pregnancy, the placenta grows improperly, becoming a mass of cysts (also called a hydatidiform mole), but there is no accompanying fetus. In some cases, identifiable—but not viable—embryonic or fetal tissue

is present; this is called a partial molar pregnancy.

The cause of a molar pregnancy is an abnormality during fertilization, in which two sets of chromosomes from the father become mixed in with either one set of chromosomes from the mother (partial mole)—or none of her chromosomes at all (complete mole). Most molar pregnancies are discovered within weeks of conception. All molar pregnancies end in miscarriage.

You'll Want to Know . . .

Having had one molar pregnancy doesn't put you at much higher risk for having another one. In fact, only 1 to 2 percent of women who have had one molar pregnancy go on to experience a second.

How common is it? Luckily, molar pregnancies are relatively rare, occurring only in 1 out of 1,000 pregnancies. Women under the age of 15 or over the age of 45, as well as women who have had multiple miscarriages are at a slightly increased risk for a molar pregnancy.

What are the signs and symptoms? The symptoms of a molar pregnancy can include:

- A continuous or intermittent brownish discharge

- Severe nausea and vomiting

- Uncomfortable cramping

- High blood pressure

- Larger than expected uterus

- Doughy uterus (rather than firm)

- Absence of embryonic or fetal tissue (as seen on ultrasound)

- Excessive levels of thyroid hormone in the mother's system

What can you and your practitioner do? Call your practitioner if you experience any of the symptoms listed above. Some of these symptoms can be difficult to differentiate from normal early pregnancy signs and symptoms (many completely normal pregnancies include some spotting and cramping, and most include nausea), but trust your instincts. If you think something's wrong, talk to your practitioner—if only to get some much-needed reassurance.

If an ultrasound shows you do have a molar pregnancy, the abnormal tissue must be removed via a dilation and curettage (D and C). Follow-up is crucial to make sure it doesn't progress to choriocarcinoma (see next column), though luckily, the chances of a treated molar pregnancy turning malignant are very low. Your practitioner will probably suggest that you not get pregnant for a year following a molar pregnancy.

Choriocarcinoma

What is it? Choriocarcinoma, an extremely rare form of cancer related to pregnancy, grows from the cells of the placenta. This malignancy most often occurs after a molar pregnancy, miscarriage, abortion, or ectopic pregnancy, when any left-behind placental tissues continue to grow despite the absence of a fetus. Only 15 percent of choriocarcinomas occur after a normal pregnancy.

How common is it? Choriocarcinoma is extremely rare, occurring in only 1 out of every 40,000 pregnancies.

What are the signs and symptoms? The signs of the disease include:

- Intermittent bleeding following a miscarriage, a pregnancy, or the removal of a molar pregnancy

- Abnormal tissue discharge

- Elevated hCG levels that do not return to normal after a pregnancy has ended

- A tumor in the vagina, uterus, or lungs

- Abdominal pain

What can you and your practitioner do? Call your practitioner if you experience any of the above symptoms, but keep in mind that it's extremely

---

You'll Want to Know . . .

With early diagnosis and treatment of choriocarcinoma, fertility is unaffected, though it's usually recommended that pregnancy be deferred for one year after treatment for choriocarcinoma is complete and there is no evidence of residual disease.

unlikely that they indicate a choriocarcinoma. If you are diagnosed, the news is very reassuring. While any type of cancer carries with it some risk, choriocarcinoma responds extremely well to chemotherapy and radiation treatments and has a cure rate of more than 90 percent. Hysterectomy is almost never necessary because of this type of tumor's excellent response to chemotherapy drugs.

Eclampsia

What is it? Eclampsia is the result of uncontrolled or unresolved preeclampsia (see page 548). Depending on what stage of pregnancy a woman is in when she becomes eclamptic, her baby may be at risk of being born prematurely since immediate delivery is often the only treatment. Although eclampsia is life-threatening for the mother, maternal deaths from it are quite rare in the United States. With optimum treatment and careful follow-up, the majority of women with eclampsia return to normal health after delivery.

How common is it? Eclampsia is much less common than preeclampsia and occurs in only 1 out of every 2,000 to 3,000 pregnancies, typically among women who have not been receiving regular prenatal care.

What are the signs and symptoms? Seizures—usually close to or during delivery—are the most characteristic symptom of eclampsia. Postpartum seizures can also occur, usually within the first 48 hours after delivery.

What can you and your practitioner do? If you already have preeclampsia and start to seize, you'll be given oxygen and drugs to arrest the seizures and your labor will be induced or a C-section performed when you're stable. The majority of women rapidly return to normal after delivery, though careful follow-up is necessary to be certain blood pressure doesn't stay up and seizures don't continue.

Can it be prevented? Regular checkups with your practitioner will allow him or her to pick up on any of the symptoms of preeclampsia. If you are diagnosed with preeclampsia, your practitioner will keep a close eye on you (and your blood pressure) to make sure your condition doesn't progress to eclampsia. Taking steps to try to prevent preeclampsia can also help avoid eclampsia.

You'll Want to Know . . .

Very few women receiving regular prenatal care ever progress from the manageable preeclampsia to the more serious eclampsia.

Cholestasis

What is it? Cholestasis of pregnancy is a condition in which the normal flow of bile in the gallbladder is slowed (as a result of pregnancy hormones), causing the buildup of bile acids in the liver, which in turn can spill into the bloodstream. Cholestasis is most likely to occur in the last trimester, when hormones are at their peak. It usually goes away after delivery.

Cholestasis may increase the risks for fetal distress, preterm birth, or stillbirth, which is why early diagnosis and treatment are crucial.

How common is it? Cholestasis affects 1 to 2 pregnancies in 1,000. It's more common in women carrying multiples, women who have previous liver damage, and in women whose mother or sisters had cholestasis.

What are the signs and symptoms? Most often, the only symptom noticed is severe itching, particularly on the hands and feet, usually late in pregnancy.

What can you and your practitioner do? The goals of treating cholestasis of pregnancy are to relieve the itching and prevent pregnancy complications. Itching can be treated with topical anti-itch medications, lotions, or corticosteroids. Medication is sometimes used to help decrease the concentration of bile acids. If cholestasis is endangering the well-being of the mother or fetus, an early delivery may be necessary.

Deep Venous Thrombosis

What is it? Deep venous thrombosis, or DVT, is the development of a blood clot in a deep vein. These clots show up most commonly in the lower extremities, particularly the thigh. Women are more susceptible to clots during pregnancy and delivery, and particularly in the postpartum period. This happens because nature, wisely worried about too much bleeding at childbirth, tends to increase the blood's clotting ability—occasionally too much. Another factor that can contribute is the enlarged uterus, which makes it difficult for blood in the lower body to return to the heart. If untreated, a DVT can result in the clot moving to the lungs and becoming life threatening.

How common is it? Deep venous thrombosis occurs once in every 1,000 to 2,000 pregnancies (it can also occur postpartum). DVT is more common if you are older, a smoker, have a family or personal history of clots, or have hypertension, diabetes, or a variety of other conditions, including vascular diseases.

What are the signs and symptoms? The most common symptoms of a deep vein thrombosis include:

- A heavy or painful feeling in the leg
- Tenderness in the calf or thigh
- Slight to severe swelling
- Distention of the superficial veins
- Calf pain on flexing the foot (turning the toes up toward the chin)

If the blood clot has moved to the lungs (a pulmonary embolus), there may be:

- Chest pain
- Shortness of breath
- Coughing with frothy, bloodstained sputum
- Rapid heartbeat and breathing rate
- Blueness of lips and fingertips
- Fever

What can you and your practitioner do? If you've been diagnosed with DVT or any kind of blood clot in previous pregnancies, let your practitioner know. In addition, if you notice swelling and pain in just one leg at any time during your pregnancy, call your practitioner right away.

Ultrasound or MRI may be used to diagnose the blood clot. If it turns out that you do have a clot, you might be treated with heparin to thin your blood and prevent further clotting (though the heparin may need to be discontinued as you near labor to prevent you from bleeding excessively during childbirth). Your clotting ability will be monitored along the way.

With a clot that reaches the lungs, clot-dissolving drugs (and, rarely, surgery) may be needed, as well as treatment for any accompanying side effects.

Can it be prevented? You can prevent clots by keeping your blood flowing—getting enough exercise and avoiding long periods of sitting will help you do this. If you're at high risk, you can also wear support hose to prevent clots from developing in your legs.

Placenta Accreta

What is it? Placenta accreta is an abnormally firm attachment of the placenta to the uterine wall. Depending on how deeply the placental cells invade, the condition may be called placenta percreta or placenta increta. Placenta accreta increases the risk of heavy bleeding or hemorrhaging during delivery of the placenta.

How common is it? One out of 2,500 pregnancies will have this attachment abnormality. Placenta accreta is by far the most common of these attachment problems, accounting for 75 percent of cases. In placenta accreta, the placenta digs deeply into the uterine wall, but does not pierce the uterine muscles. In placenta increta, which accounts for 15 percent of cases, the placenta pierces the uterine muscles. In placenta percreta, which accounts for the final 10 percent, the placenta not only burrows into the uterine wall and its muscles, but also pierces the outer part of the wall and may even attach itself to other nearby organs.

Your risk of placenta accreta increases if you have placenta previa and have had one or more cesarean deliveries in the past.

What are the signs and symptoms? There are usually no apparent symptoms. The condition is usually diagnosed via color Doppler ultrasound or may only be noticed during delivery when the placenta doesn't detach (as it normally would) from the uterine wall after the baby is born.

What can you and your practitioner do? Unfortunately, there is little you can do. In most cases, the placenta must be removed surgically after delivery to stop the bleeding. Very rarely, when the bleeding cannot be controlled by tying off the exposed blood vessels, removal of the entire uterus may be necessary.

Vasa Previa

What is it? Vasa previa is a condition in which some of the fetal blood vessels that connect the baby to the mother run outside the umbilical cord and along the membrane over the cervix. When labor begins, the contractions and opening of the cervix can cause the vessels to rupture, possibly causing harm to the baby. If the condition is diagnosed before labor, a C-section will be scheduled and the baby will be born healthy nearly 100 percent of the time.

How common is it? Vasa previa is rare, affecting 1 in 5,200 pregnancies. Women who also have placenta previa, a history of uterine surgery, or a multiple pregnancy are at greater risk.

What are the signs and symptoms? There are usually no signs of this condition, though there may be some bleeding in the second or third trimester.

What can you and your practitioner do? Diagnostic testing, such as with ultrasound or, better yet, a color Doppler ultrasound, can detect vasa previa. Women who are diagnosed with the condition will deliver their babies via C-section, usually before 37 weeks, to make sure labor doesn't begin on its own. Researchers are studying whether vasa previa can be treated using laser therapy to seal off the abnormally positioned vessels.

Childbirth and Postpartum Complications

Many of the following conditions can't be anticipated prior to labor and delivery—and there's no need to read up on them (and start worrying) ahead of time, since they're very unlikely to occur during or after your childbirth. They are included here so that in the unlikely event you experience one, you can learn about it after the fact, or in some cases, learn how you can prevent it from happening in your next labor and delivery.

Fetal Distress

What is it? Fetal distress is a term used to describe what occurs when a baby's oxygen supply is compromised in the uterus, either before or during labor. The distress may be caused by a number of factors, such as preeclampsia, uncontrolled diabetes, placental abruption, too little or too much amniotic fluid, umbilical cord compression or entanglement, intrauterine growth restriction, or simply because the mother is in a position that puts pressure on major blood vessels, depriving the baby of oxygen. Sustained oxygen deprivation and/or decreased heart rate can be serious for the baby and must be corrected as quickly as possible—usually with immediate delivery (most often by C-section, unless a vaginal birth is imminent).

How common is it? The exact incidence of fetal distress is uncertain, but estimates range from 1 in every 25 births to 1 in every 100 births.

What are the signs and symptoms? Babies who are doing well in utero have strong, stable heartbeats and respond to stimuli with appropriate movements. Babies in distress experience a decrease in their heart rate, a change in their pattern of movement (or even no movement altogether), and/or pass their first stool, called meconium, while still in the uterus.

What can you and your practitioner do? If you think your baby might be in distress because you've noticed a change in fetal activity (it seems to have slowed down significantly, stopped, become very jerky and frantic, or otherwise has you concerned), call your practitioner immediately. Once you are in your practitioner's office or in the hospital (or in labor), you'll be put on a fetal monitor to see whether your baby is indeed showing signs of distress. You may be given oxygen and extra fluids via an IV to help better oxygenate your blood and return your baby's heart rate to normal. Turning onto your left side to take pressure off your major blood vessels may also do the trick. If these techniques don't work, the best treatment is a quick delivery.

Cord Prolapse

What is it? A cord prolapse occurs during labor when the umbilical cord slips through the cervix and into the birth canal before the baby does. If the cord becomes compressed during delivery (such as when your baby's head is pushing against a prolapsed cord), the baby's oxygen supply is compromised.

How common is it? Fortunately, cord prolapse is not common, occurring in 1 out of every 300 births. Certain pregnancy complications increase the risk of prolapse. These include hydramnios, breech delivery or any position in which the baby's head does not cover the cervix, and premature delivery. It can also occur during delivery of a second twin. Prolapse is also a potential risk if your water breaks before your baby's head has begun to "engage," or settle into the birth canal.

What are the signs and symptoms? If the cord slips down into the vagina, you may actually be able to feel it or even see it. If the cord is compressed by the baby's head, the baby will show signs of fetal distress on a fetal monitor.

What can you and your practitioner do? There's really no way to know in advance if your baby's cord is going to prolapse. In fact, without fetal monitoring, you may not know until after the fact. If you suspect that your baby's umbilical cord has prolapsed and you are not in the hospital yet, get on your hands and knees with your head down and pelvis up to take pressure off the cord. If you notice the cord protruding from your vagina, gently support it with a clean towel. Call 911 or have someone rush you to the hospital (on the way to the hospital, lie down on the back seat, with your bottom elevated). If you are already in the hospital when the cord prolapses, your practitioner may ask you to move quickly into a different position, one in which it will be easier to disengage the baby's head and take pressure off the umbilical cord. Delivery of your baby will need to be very quick, most likely by C-section.

Shoulder Dystocia

What is it? Shoulder dystocia is a complication of labor and delivery in which one or both of the baby's shoulders become stuck behind the mother's pelvic bone as the baby descends into the birth canal.

How common is it? Size definitely matters when it comes to shoulder dystocia, which occurs most frequently in larger babies. Fewer than 1 percent of babies weighing 6 pounds have shoulder dystocia, but the rate is considerably higher in babies weighing more than 9 pounds. For that reason, mothers who have uncontrolled diabetes or gestational diabetes—and therefore may give birth to very large babies—are more likely to encounter this complication during delivery. The chances also rise if you go past your due date before delivering (since your baby will probably be larger) or if you've previously delivered a baby with shoulder dystocia. Still, many cases of shoulder dystocia occur during labors without any of these risk factors.

What are the signs and symptoms? Delivery stalls after the head emerges and before the shoulders are out. This can occur unexpectedly in a labor that has progressed normally up to that point.

What can you and your practitioner do? A variety of approaches may be used to deliver the baby whose shoulder is lodged in the pelvis, such as changing the mother's position by sharply flexing her legs onto her abdomen or applying pressure on her abdomen, right above the pubic bone.

Can it be prevented? Keeping your weight gain within the recommended range can help ensure that your baby doesn't get too big to maneuver through the birth canal, as can carefully controlling diabetes or gestational diabetes. Picking a labor position that allows your pelvis to open as widely as possible might also help you avoid dystocia.

Serious Perineal Tears

What is it? The pressure of your baby's large head pushing through the delicate tissues of your cervix and vagina can cause tears and lacerations in your perineum, the area between your vagina and your anus.

First-degree tears (when only the skin is torn) and second-degree tears (when skin and vaginal muscle are torn) are common. But severe tears—those that get close to the rectum and involve the vaginal skin, tissues, and perineal muscles (third degree) or those that actually cut into the muscles of the anal sphincter (fourth degree)—cause pain and increase not only your postpartum recovery time, but your risk of incontinence, as well as other pelvic floor problems. Tears can also occur in the cervix.

How common is it? Anyone having a vaginal delivery is at risk for a tear, and as many as half of all women will have at least a small tear after childbirth. Third- and fourth-degree tears are much less common.

What are the signs and symptoms? Bleeding is the immediate symptom; after the tear is repaired, you may also experience pain and tenderness at the site as it heals.

What can you and your practitioner do? Generally, all lacerations that are longer than 2 cm (about 1 inch) or that continue to bleed are stitched. A local anesthetic may be given first, if one wasn't administered during delivery.

If you end up tearing or having an episiotomy, sitz baths, ice packs, witch hazel, anesthetic sprays, and simply exposing the area to air can help it heal more quickly and with less pain (see page 423).

Can it be prevented? Perineal massage and Kegel exercises (see pages 352 and 295), done during the month or so before your due date, may help make the perineal area more supple and better able to stretch over your baby's head as he or she emerges. Warm compresses on the perineum and perineal massage during labor may help avoid tearing.

Uterine Rupture

What is it? A uterine rupture occurs when a weakened spot on your uterine wall—almost always the site of a previous uterine surgery such as a C-section or fibroid removal—tears due to the strain put on it during labor and delivery. A uterine rupture can result in uncontrolled bleeding into your abdomen or, rarely, lead to part of the placenta or baby entering your abdomen.

How common is it? Fortunately, ruptures are rare in women who've never had a previous C-section or uterine surgery. Even women who labor after a previous C-section have only a 1 in 100 chance of rupture (and the risk is far lower when a woman undergoes a repeat C-section without labor). Women at greatest risk of uterine rupture are those who are attempting a vaginal birth after cesarean (VBAC) and have been induced with prostaglandins and/or Pitocin (oxytocin). Abnormalities related to the placenta (such as placental abruption, a placenta that separates prematurely; or placenta accreta, a placenta that is attached deeply in the uterine wall) or to the fetus's position (such as a fetus lying crosswise) can also increase the risk of uterine rupture. Uterine rupture is more common in women who have already had six or more children or have a very distended uterus (because of multiple fetuses or excess amniotic fluid).

What are the signs and symptoms?
Searing abdominal pain (a sensation that something is "ripping") followed by diffuse pain and tenderness in the abdomen during labor are the most common signs of uterine rupture. Most typically, the fetal monitor will show a significant drop in the baby's heart rate. The mother may develop signs of low blood volume, such as an increased heart rate, low blood pressure, dizziness, shortness of breath, or loss of consciousness.

What can you and your practitioner do?
If you have had a previous C-section or abdominal surgery in which the uterine wall was cut through completely, you'll need to weigh your risks when considering your labor options, especially if you want to attempt a vaginal birth. Discuss with your practitioner the data that show that prostaglandins should not be used to induce labor in a woman who's had previous uterine surgery.

If you do have a uterine rupture, an immediate C-section is necessary, followed by repair of the uterus. You may also be given antibiotics to prevent infection.

Can it be prevented? For women with increased risk factors, fetal monitoring during labor can alert your practitioner to an impending or occurring rupture. Women who are trying for a VBAC delivery should not be induced.

Uterine Inversion

What is it? Uterine inversion is a rare complication of childbirth that occurs when part of the uterine wall collapses and turns inside out (in effect, very much like a sock being pulled inside out), sometimes even protruding through the cervix and into the vagina. The full range of problems that can cause uterine inversion is not fully understood, but in many cases it includes the incomplete separation of the placenta from the uterine wall; the placenta then pulls the uterus with it when it emerges from the birth canal. Uterine inversion, when unnoticed and/or untreated, can result in hemorrhage and shock. But that's a remote possibility; the condition occurs rarely and is unlikely to go unnoticed and untreated.

How common is it? Uterine inversion is very rare; reported rates vary from 1 in 2,000 births to 1 in several hundred thousand. You are at greatest risk for a uterine inversion if you've had an inversion during a previous delivery. Other factors that slightly increase the very remote risk of an inversion include an extended labor (lasting more than 24 hours), several previous vaginal deliveries, or use of drugs like magnesium sulfate or terbutaline (given to halt preterm labor). The uterus also may be more likely to invert if it is overly relaxed or if the cord is pulled too hard in the third stage of childbirth.

What are the signs and symptoms?
Symptoms of uterine inversion include:

- Abdominal pain

- Excessive bleeding

- Signs of shock in the mother

- In a complete inversion, the uterus will be visible in the vagina

What can you and your practitioner do? Know your risk factors and inform your practitioner if you've had a uterine inversion in the past. If you do have one, your physician will try to push your uterus back up where it belongs, and then give you drugs like Pitocin (oxytocin) to encourage any floppy muscles to contract. In rare cases, where this does not work, surgery is an option. In either case, you might need a blood transfusion to make up for blood lost during the inversion. Antibiotics may be given to prevent infection.

Can it be prevented? Because a woman who has had one uterine inversion is at an increased risk for another, let your practitioner know if you've had one in the past.

Postpartum Hemorrhage

What is it? Bleeding after delivery, called lochia, is normal. But sometimes the uterus doesn't contract as it should after birth, leading to postpartum hemorrhage—excessive or uncontrolled bleeding from the site where the placenta was attached. Postpartum hemorrhage can also be caused by unrepaired vaginal or cervical lacerations.

Hemorrhage can also occur up to a week or two after delivery when fragments of the placenta are retained in, or adhere to, the uterus. Infection can also cause postpartum hemorrhage, right after delivery or weeks later.

How common is it? Postpartum hemorrhage occurs in somewhere between 2 and 4 percent of deliveries. Excessive bleeding may be more likely to occur if the uterus is too relaxed and doesn't contract due to a long, exhausting labor; a traumatic delivery; a uterus that was overdistended because of multiple births, a large baby, or excess amniotic fluid; an oddly shaped placenta, or one that separated prematurely; fibroids that prevent symmetrical contraction of the uterus; or a generally weakened condition of the mother at the time of delivery (due to, for example, anemia, preeclampsia, or extreme fatigue). Women taking drugs or herbs that interfere with blood clotting (such as aspirin, ibuprofen, ginkgo biloba, or large doses of vitamin E) are also at greater risk for postpartum hemorrhage. Rarely, the cause of the hemorrhage is a previously undiagnosed bleeding disorder in the mother that is genetic.

What are the signs and symptoms? The symptoms of postpartum hemorrhage include:

- Bleeding that soaks through more than one pad an hour for several hours in a row

- Heavy, bright-red bleeding for more than just a few days

- Passing very large clots (lemon size or larger)

- Pain or swelling in the lower abdominal area beyond the first few days after delivery

The loss of large amounts of blood can make a woman feel faint, breathless, dizzy, or cause her heart to speed up.

What can you and your practitioner do? After the placenta is delivered, your practitioner will examine it to make certain that it's complete—that no part of it is remaining in your uterus. He or she will probably give you Pitocin (oxytocin) and may also massage your uterus to encourage it to contract, in order to minimize bleeding. Breastfeeding (if you will be nursing) as soon as possible will also help your uterus to contract.

You should expect bleeding following delivery, but alert your practitioner immediately if you notice abnormally heavy bleeding or any of the other symptoms listed above during the first postpartum week. If the bleeding is severe enough to be categorized as hemorrhage, you may need intravenous fluids or possibly even a blood transfusion.

Can it be prevented? Avoiding any supplement or medication that may interfere with blood clotting (such as the ones listed on the previous page), especially in the last trimester and the immediate postpartum period, will reduce the possibility of abnormal postpartum bleeding.

Postpartum Infection

What is it? The vast majority of women recover from delivery without any problems at all, but childbirth can occasionally leave you open to infection. That's because it can leave you with a variety of open wounds—in your uterus (where the placenta was attached), in your cervix, vagina, or perineum (especially if you tore or had an episiotomy, even if it was repaired), or at the site of a C-section incision. Postpartum infections can also occur in your bladder or kidney if you were catheterized. A fragment of the placenta inadvertently left behind in the uterus can lead to infection, too. But the most common postpartum infection is endometritis, an infection of the lining of the uterus (the endometrium).

While some infections can be dangerous, especially if they go undetected or untreated, most often infections simply make your postpartum recovery slower and more difficult, and they take time and energy away from your most important priority: getting to know your baby. For that reason alone, it's important to get help for any suspected infection as quickly as possible.

How common is it? As many as 8 percent of deliveries result in an infection. Women who had a cesarean delivery or those who had premature rupture of the membranes are at greater risk of infection.

What are the signs and symptoms? Symptoms of postpartum infection vary, depending on where the infection is, but there's almost always:

- Fever

- Pain or tenderness in the infected area

- Foul-smelling discharge (from the vagina in the case of a uterine infection, or from a wound)

- Chills

What can you and your practitioner do? Call your practitioner if you're running a postpartum fever of around 100°F for more than a day; call sooner if the fever is higher or if you notice any of the other symptoms above. If you have an infection, you'll probably receive a prescription for antibiotics, which you should take as prescribed for the entire course, even if you begin to feel better quickly. You should also get plenty of rest (a near impossibility with a newborn in the house, but do the best you can) and drink lots of fluids. If you're breastfeeding, check with your physician and your pharmacist to be sure that any medication you're given is breastfeeding-friendly (most antibiotics are).

Can it be prevented? Meticulous wound care and cleanliness after delivery (wash your hands before touching the perineal area, wipe from front to back after going to the bathroom, and only use maxi pads—not tampons—for postpartum bleeding) can definitely help prevent infections.

If You're Put on Bed Rest

The thought of lying in bed with a stack of magazines and the TV remote may sound pretty appealing—until it's prescribed in the form of bed rest. Bed rest, unfortunately, is no pajama party. Once reality sets in and you realize that you can't even run out for milk or meet some friends for a latte, the appeal of lounging around all day is quickly lost. That's why it's important not to lose sight of the big picture (healthy pregnancy, healthy baby) and to remind yourself that your practitioner probably has good reason for keeping you off your feet.

If you've been put on bed rest, you're in good company. A million pregnancies a year (that's one quarter of pregnancies) are classified as "high-risk" or "at-risk." And 70 percent of these moms will be put on bed rest at some point during their 40 weeks. Even though there is much controversy surrounding the benefits of bed rest, it continues to be prescribed because many practitioners believe, based on their experience with their patients, that it works in preventing preterm labor or slowing the progress of pre-eclampsia and keeps an otherwise high-risk pregnancy from becoming more complicated. Among the rationales suggested for a prescription of bed rest: Staying off your feet takes pressure off the cervix; it reduces the strain on your heart and improves blood flow to your kidneys, which helps eliminate excess fluids; it increases circulation to your uterus, providing additional oxygen and nutrients to your baby; and it minimizes the level of stress hormones in your bloodstream that can trigger contractions.

Certain moms-to-be are more likely to wind up on bed rest, including those who are over 35, who are carrying multiples, who have a history of miscarriage due to incompetent cervix, who have particular pregnancy complications, or who have certain chronic conditions.

Whether bed rest truly helps prevent preterm labor or minimizes the risks of other complications, it is clear that being off your feet for a long period of time comes with its share of drawbacks. Women on prolonged bed rest can suffer hip and muscle pain, headaches, muscle loss (which can make it much harder to bounce back after delivery), skin irritations, and depression, and may be more prone to blood clots. Not being able to get moving may also aggravate many of the normal symptoms of pregnancy, such as heartburn, constipation, leg swelling, and backaches. Finally, bed rest may decrease your appetite, which might be good for your waistline (what waistline?) but not so good for your growing baby (or babies), who counts on those extra calories and nutrients.

The good—and reassuring—news is that many of the side effects of bed rest can be minimized with these tips:

- Keep things circulating. Maximize blood flow to your uterus by lying on your side, not your back. To feel cradled and comfortable, put a pillow under your head, a body pillow under your belly and between your knees (or two pillows), and perhaps a pillow behind you as well, if that helps you balance. Change sides every hour or so to lessen body aches and prevent skin irritations.

Types of Bed Rest

"**B**ed rest" is the general term used when your practitioner wants you to limit your activities. But it's likely your marching (or in this case, nonmarching) orders came with a list of very specific can-dos and definitely don't-dos. That's because bed rest comes in a variety of packages, from just getting off your feet every couple hours, to resting in bed but being allowed to get up periodically, to staying in bed with bathroom privileges, to staying in bed 24/7 (sometimes in the hospital). What kind of bed rest you're prescribed depends a lot on why you've been put on bed rest to begin with. Here's the lowdown on each type of bed rest:

Scheduled resting. In the hopes of preventing full bed rest later, some practitioners ask moms-to-be with certain risk factors (such as multiples or advanced maternal age) to rest for a prescribed amount of time every day. The recommendation may be to sit with your feet up or lie down (better yet, nap) for two hours at the end of every workday or rest for an hour, lying down on your side, for every four hours that you're awake. Some practitioners may ask you to simply shorten your workday in your third trimester and restrict activities such as exercise, stair-climbing, and walking or standing for extended lengths of time.

Modified bed rest. With modified bed rest, you're generally prohibited from working, driving, and doing household chores (now that's something to celebrate!). Sitting up at your desk to surf the web is okay, as is standing just long enough to make yourself a sandwich or take a shower. You may even be granted one night a week to go out, as long as your outing doesn't involve a long walk or any stairs. Women on modified bed rest may split their day between the couch and the bed, but going up or down stairs should be kept to a minimum.

Strict bed rest. This usually means you need to be horizontal all day except for bathroom trips and a brief shower (a tepid bath is preferred). If there are stairs in your house, you're going to have to pick a floor and stay there. (Some women will be allowed to make a roundtrip once a day; for others it might be once a week.) And your spouse (or your mom or a friend or the person you hire to help you) is going to have to make sure that the chores are getting done and that you have all you need to get by for the day. This may mean keeping a cooler or a mini fridge with breakfast, lunch, dinner, and lots of healthy snacks by the side of your bed.

Hospital bed rest. If you need constant monitoring as well as IV drugs because preterm labor has already begun, you will be admitted to the hospital. And if your labor is successfully stalled, you may need to extend your hospital stay to ensure total bed rest. Your bed may even be positioned at a slight angle (feet higher than head) so that gravity can help keep your babies growing in your womb for as long as possible.

▪ Move what you can. Talk to your practitioner about doing arm exercises each day (using light weights) to keep your upper-body muscles from weakening—usually allowed if you're on modified bed rest. If you get the go-ahead, you can perform bicep curls, tricep curls, and overhead presses, all in a sitting position. Follow with stretching and shoulder rolls.

- Stretch what you can, as much as you can. Also check with your practitioner about whether gentle leg stretches—flexing your feet and circling your ankles (without lifting them above hip level)—can be on the bed rest agenda. This can prevent blood clotting in the legs and may keep your muscles a little stronger.

- Watch what you eat, and how much you eat. A significant dip in a mom's appetite can lead to weight loss for her and a lower birthweight for her baby—so if you find yours slacking, fight back by grazing on nutritious, easy-to-digest snacks (high-fiber ones, like dried fruit, will also combat constipation). Of course, if you find yourself eating too much (out of boredom or depression), excessive weight gain might also become an issue—so keep an eye on nonstop nibbling, too, especially high-calorie nibbling.

- Keep the fluids flowing. Staying hydrated is always important when you're expecting, but especially on bed rest (getting enough fluids will minimize swelling and constipation, and possibly prevent contractions). So make sure your bedstand is stocked with water and other beverages.

- Beat heartburn with gravity. More lying can spell more heartburn. Sitting up slightly in bed (if you're allowed), especially after eating, will keep the burn at bay.

- Keep your expectations realistic after delivery. Cut yourself some postpartum slack, factoring in all that your body has been through. You just won't have the same aerobic capacity or muscular strength that you had before you took to bed, even if you were off your feet for just weeks. So give yourself a chance to recover, and plan on building back up to your former fitness level slowly. Walking, postpartum yoga, and swimming are good beginning activities when your practitioner green-lights exercise again.

Bed rest doesn't just impact your physical well-being. It could also affect your sanity. To stay sane while you're staying horizontal:

Reach out. Keep the phone by your side, and let family and friends know they need to be on call for venting (or whining, or worrying, or giggling). Stay connected through e-mail as well (this is one of the many reasons why you'll also want a computer by your side—or a laptop on your lap, or where your lap used to be). And don't forget to visit websites and message boards, where you'll meet other moms-to-be in the exact same shoes (or slippers).

Be prepared. Anticipate what you're going to need each day, and ask your spouse to gather it together for you before he leaves in the morning. Stock a bedside mini fridge or cooler with lots of water, fruit, yogurt, cheese, and sandwiches. Be sure the phone, magazines, books, and TV remote are all within arm's reach.

Structure the day. Try to establish a routine—even if the highlight is a soak in a tepid tub followed by a nap, or a morning on the couch followed by an afternoon in bed. You'll feel a little better if you give the day some sort of structure.

Work from home. If you're on modified bed rest and work in a fully wired field, it may be possible to work from home for all or part of the time you are on

Moms Helping Moms

Every pregnancy comes with some challenges, but a pregnancy that's high risk (or one that's been complicated) can come with a whole lot more. Facing those challenges is always easier when you've got company—other moms who know exactly what you're going through because they're going through it, too (or have already gone through it) themselves. There may be support groups in your area for the specific pregnancy challenge you're facing (ask your practitioner), but you're also likely to find that support online.

bed rest. Between conference calls and e-mails, you can actually be very productive as a gestating telecommuter. Speak to both your practitioner and your boss to be sure everyone is on the same page about what your capabilities and your limits are (and if your job is emotionally stressful, you may not get the go-ahead from the obstetric powers that be).

Get your baby shopping done. Pretty much anything you can do in a store, you can do online. So use this bed-rest time to get baby-ready on the web. Register for your layette, order your crib, or find your future doula, lactation consultant, and babysitter online. And while you're at it, order your groceries, too (you're out of milk again, aren't you?).

Deliver dinner. While you're waiting for your special delivery, tap into your neighborhood network of restaurants that deliver. Keep those menus within arm's reach, or look for them online.

Try some movie magic. Sign up with a DVD-by-mail service and catch all those films you didn't have a chance to see in the theater—and won't have time to see once you have a baby in the house.

Entertain in bed. Get your friends together for a bedroom potluck or pizza and a movie. (Best part of this plan: They'll have to clean up the crumbs, not you.)

Get crafty. Teach yourself to knit, crochet, or quilt. Better yet, have a talented pal come over and teach you. You'll be creating sweet treasures for your little one and getting some much-needed companionship, too. Or take up scrapbooking (you'll soon have more mementos to save than ever before).

Get organized. Put all those old photos into an album (finally), or enter your address book into a computer database. You'll be glad you did when you're able to print out those address labels (for your baby announcements, thank-you notes, party invites, holiday cards . . .) instead of hand-writing them.

Sit pretty. Do the things that make you feel good each day, even when it sometimes seems pointless. Brush your hair, put on makeup, slather your tummy in yummy-smelling lotion (your skin will be itchy and dry anyway). If you can afford it, consider having a hairstylist or manicurist make a house call. (Drop the hint to your friends that this would make a great shower gift.) Don't fall into that "nobody's going to see me anyway" trap—looking good makes you feel good, whether anyone else sees you or not.

Freshen up. Charge your spouse with changing the sheets on your well-used bed once a week. Keep baby wipes and hand sanitizers nearby to keep yourself clean and relatively fresh between showers and baths.

Start a journal. Think of the bright side: Now's the perfect time to begin recording your thoughts or feelings about pregnancy or bed rest, or writing a few letters to your baby that you can share with him or her in years to come. Check out *The What to Expect Pregnancy Journal and Organizer,* which can help you preserve pregnancy moments. Writing your feelings down is also a great way to vent.

Keep your eyes on the prize. Frame one of your ultrasound pictures, and keep it by your side—so when the going gets tough, you can remind yourself that you have the best reason in the world not to go anywhere at all.

Coping with Pregnancy Loss

PREGNANCY IS SUPPOSED TO BE a joyous time, filled with excitement, anticipation, and pink-and-blue daydreams about life with your baby-to-be (mixed in with a little normal trepidation and anxiety). And usually, it is all of those things, but it isn't always. If you've experienced the loss of a pregnancy or a newborn, you know firsthand that the depth of your pain can be beyond words. This chapter is dedicated to helping you handle that pain and cope with one of life's most difficult losses.

Miscarriage

Just because it often takes place very early in pregnancy doesn't mean that miscarriage isn't painful for expectant parents. The grief that can come with a miscarriage is real, no matter how early in pregnancy you lost your baby. Even though you never saw your baby, except perhaps on ultrasound, you knew that he or she was growing inside of you, and you may have already formed a bond, however abstract. From the moment you found out you were pregnant, you may have daydreamed about your baby and imagined yourself a mother. And then, all the excitement of months (and years, and decades) to come abruptly came to a stop. Understandably, you may feel a range of emotions: sad and disheartened over the loss; angry and resentful that it happened to you; possibly withdrawn from friends and family (especially those who are pregnant or just had babies). You may have trouble sleeping and eating at first and accepting the finality of it all. You may cry a lot, or you may not cry at all. These are among the many natural, healthy responses to a pregnancy loss. (Remember that your reaction is what's normal for you.)

In fact, for some couples, coping with early pregnancy loss may be, at least in certain ways, just as difficult as coping with a loss later on. Why? First of all, because so many couples hold off on spreading the word about their pregnancy until the third month has passed, even close friends and family may not have been told yet, which can mean that support may be hard to come by. Even those who knew about the pregnancy and/or are told about the miscarriage may offer less support than they would have if the pregnancy had been further along. They may try to minimize the significance of the loss with a "Don't worry, you can try again," not realizing that the loss of a baby, no matter how early in pregnancy it occurs, can be devastating. Second, the fact that there is no possibility of holding the baby, taking a photo, having a funeral and burial—rituals of grieving that can all help offer some closure for parents of stillborn infants—may complicate the recovery process.

Still, if you've suffered a miscarriage (or an ectopic or molar pregnancy), it's important to remember that you have the right to grieve as much—or as little—as you need to. Do this in any way that helps you heal and eventually move on.

Perhaps you'll find closure in a private ceremony with close family members or just you and your spouse. Or by sharing your feelings—individually, through a support group, or online—with others who experienced early miscarriage. Since so many women suffer a miscarriage at least once during their

A Personal Process

When it comes to dealing with a miscarriage or other pregnancy loss, no one emotional formula must be followed. Different couples confront, cope with, and process their feelings in completely different ways. You may find yourself deeply saddened, even devastated by the loss—and discover that healing comes surprisingly slowly. Or you may handle the loss more matter-of-factly, seeing it as a bump in the road to having a baby. You may find that after some momentary sadness, you're able to put the experience behind you more quickly than you might have expected—instead of lingering over the loss, you may choose to look ahead to trying again. Just remember: The normal reaction to a pregnancy loss is the reaction that's normal for you. Feel whatever you need to feel in order to heal and move ahead.

reproductive years, you may be surprised to find how many others you know have had the same experience as you but never talked about it with you, or maybe even talked about it at all. (If you don't feel like sharing your feelings—or don't feel you need to—don't. Do only what's right for you.) Some of the tips for those who have later pregnancy losses may be helpful for you, too. You may also want to read about the Stages of Grief (see box on page 585), which may or may not apply to you.

Accept that you may always have a place in your heart for the pregnancy you lost, and you may feel sad or down on the anniversary of the due date of your lost baby or on the anniversary of the miscarriage itself, even years later. If you

Coping with Repeat Miscarriages

Suffering one pregnancy loss can be hard enough to cope with. But if you've suffered more than one, you may find it infinitely harder—with each loss hitting you a little harder than the last. You may be discouraged, depressed, angry, irritable, unable to focus on the rest of your life (or on anything beyond your losses). The healing of your psyche may not only take a lot longer than the healing of your body, but the sadness can be literally debilitating. What's more, the emotional pain may lead to physical symptoms, including headaches, appetite loss or overeating, insomnia, and overwhelming fatigue. (Some couples handle even repeat losses more matter-of-factly, and that's completely normal, too.)

Time may not heal all, but it will definitely help eventually. In the meantime, patience, knowledge, and support may be your best remedies. Pregnancy loss support groups may be available in your area, so ask your practitioner, or find a support group online, if you think that might help you (some couples prefer to turn to each other for support). Sharing with others who have suffered through pregnancy losses, especially multiple losses, can help you feel less alone, as well as more hopeful. Most of all, don't let guilt add to your burden. Miscarriage is not your fault. Instead, try to focus on how strong you've been (even if you haven't always felt that strong) and how determined you are to have a baby.

find it helps, plan on doing something special at that time—at least for the first year or so—that will be cheering yet allows you to remember: planting some new flowers or a tree, having a quiet picnic in the park, sharing a commemorative dinner with your spouse.

While it's normal to mourn your loss—and important to come to terms with it your way—you should also start to feel gradually better as time passes. If you don't, or if you have continued trouble coping with everyday life—you're not eating or sleeping, you're not able to focus at work, you're becoming isolated from family and friends—or if you continue to feel very anxious (anxiety is an even more common symptom following miscarriage than depression is), professional counseling can help you recover.

Try to remind yourself that you can—and most likely will—become pregnant again and give birth to a healthy baby. For the vast majority of women,

a miscarriage is a onetime event—and actually, an indication of future fertility.

Loss in the Uterus

When you don't hear from (or feel) your baby for several hours or more, it's natural to fear the worst. And the worst is that your unborn baby has died.

You are likely to be in a fog of disbelief and grief after being told your baby's heartbeat can't be located and that he or she has died in your uterus. It may be difficult or even impossible for you to carry on with any semblance of your usual life while carrying around a fetus that is no longer living, and studies show that a woman is much more likely to suffer severe depression after the delivery of a stillborn if the delivery is delayed more than three days after the death is diagnosed. For this reason, your emotional state will be taken into account while your practitioner decides what to do next. If labor is imminent, or has already started, your stillborn baby will probably be delivered. If labor isn't clearly about to start, the decision of whether or not to induce labor immediately, or to allow you to return home until it begins spontaneously, will depend on how far you are from your due date, on your physical condition, and on how you're doing emotionally.

The grieving process you will go through if your fetus has died in utero will probably be very similar to that of parents whose baby has died during or after birth. The same steps will help you begin the long healing process, including, when possible and practical, holding your baby in your arms and having a funeral or memorial service. See below for more.

Loss During or After Birth

Sometimes the loss of a baby occurs during labor or delivery, sometimes just after delivery. Either way, your world comes crashing down. You've waited for this baby for months—and now you're going home empty-handed.

There's probably no greater pain than that inflicted by the loss of a child. And though nothing can completely heal the hurt you're feeling, there are steps you can take now to lessen the inevitable sadness that follows such a tragedy:

- See your baby, hold your baby, name your baby. Grieving is a vital step in accepting and recovering from your loss, and it's difficult to grieve for a nameless child you've never seen. Even if your child has malformations, experts advise that it is better to see him or her than not to because what is imagined is usually worse than the

reality. Holding and naming your baby will make the death more real to you and ultimately easier to recover from. So will arranging for a funeral and burial or a memorial service, which will give you another opportunity to say good-bye. If there is a burial, the grave will provide a permanent site where you can visit your baby in future years.

- Save a photo or other mementos (a lock of hair, a footprint), so you'll have some tangible reminders to cherish when you think about your lost baby in the future. Try to focus on the details you'll want to remember later—big

Postpartum Depression and Pregnancy Loss

Every parent who loses a baby has reason to feel sad. But for some, the sadness can be deepened by postpartum depression and/or anxiety. Untreated, postpartum depression can prevent you from experiencing the stages of grief that are essential to healing. Though it might be hard to distinguish postpartum depression from the depression brought on by the tragic loss of a baby, any kind of depression requires help. If you're exhibiting signs of depression (loss of interest in everyday activities, inability to sleep, loss of appetite, extreme sadness that interferes with your ability to function), don't hesitate to get the help you need. Speak to your prenatal practitioner or your regular doctor, and ask to be referred to a mental health professional. Therapy—and, if necessary, medication—can help you feel better.

Lactation Suppression When a Baby Dies

If you've suffered the devastating loss of your baby, the last thing you need is another reminder of what would have been. Sadly, nature can deliver that reminder when the end of pregnancy (even when it has ended tragically) automatically signals the beginning of lactation, and your breasts fill with the milk that was intended to feed your baby. This can be incredibly painful to cope with, both physically and emotionally—as can handling milk production that has already been fully initiated (because your baby died after you started nursing or pumping in the NICU).

If your baby died in utero or at birth, and you never had a chance to nurse, you'll have to deal with breast engorgement. Ice packs, mild pain relievers, and a supportive bra can help minimize the physical discomfort you'll feel. Avoiding hot showers, nipple stimulation, and expressing milk from your breasts will help avoid further milk production. The engorgement will pass within a few days.

If your baby died after you already began nursing or pumping (as might happen with a baby in the NICU), ask the nurses in the hospital or a lactation consultant for help. You'll likely be advised to remove enough milk (using a pump, or manually if you prefer) to reduce the pressure in your breasts but not enough to empty them and encourage more production. The frequency and duration of pumping varies from one woman to another, depending on the amount of milk you've been producing, the frequency of feedings, and the length of time since the birth of your baby, but, in general, you should gradually go longer between expressions and pump for a shorter period of time. Be aware that it's normal for drops of milk to be present in your breasts for weeks or even months after breastfeeding and/or pumping is discontinued.

If you have a large amount of milk, either in storage or in production (if you're producing a lot of milk or if you were pumping for twins, for instance), you might want to consider donating your breast milk to a milk bank. Donation of the milk may help you find some meaning in the death of your baby. But, as always, do what helps you most.

---

eyes and long lashes, beautiful hands and delicate fingers, a headful of hair.

- Discuss autopsy findings and other medical reports with your practitioner to help you accept the reality of what happened and to help you in the grieving process. You may have been given a lot of details in the delivery room, but medications, your hormonal status, and the shock you were feeling probably prevented you from fully understanding them.

- Ask friends or relatives to leave the preparations you made for baby at home. Coming home to a house that looks as though a baby was never expected will only make it more difficult to accept what has happened.

- Keep in mind that the grieving process usually has many steps, including denial and isolation, anger, depression, and acceptance. Don't be surprised if you feel these emotions, though not necessarily in this order. And don't be surprised if you don't feel all of them or if you experience other emotions instead or in addition. Everyone is different and everyone reacts differently, even in a similar situation—especially such a personal one.

- Expect a difficult time. For a while, you may be depressed, very anxious, or just deeply sad and have trouble sleeping, eating, or focusing at work. You may be short-tempered with your spouse and with your other children, if you have any. You may feel lonely— even if you're surrounded with people who love you—and empty, and you may even imagine you hear your baby crying in the middle of the night. You will probably feel the need to be a child yourself, to be loved, coddled, and cared for. All this is normal.

- Cry—for as long and as often as you feel you need to.

- Recognize that fathers grieve, too. His grief may seem less intense or more short-lived—partly because, unlike you, he didn't carry the baby inside him for so many months. But that doesn't make the pain he's feeling any less real or the process of mourning any less vital to healing. Sometimes, fathers may have a harder time expressing their grief, or they may bottle up their emotions in an effort to be strong for their partners. If you sense that's the case with your spouse, you may both find comforting release in talking the pain out. Encourage him to share with you, with a counselor, or with another father who's been through such a loss.

- Take care of each other. Grief can be very self-absorbing. You and your spouse may find yourselves so consumed by your own pain that you don't have the emotional reserves left to comfort each other. Unfortunately, relationship problems can sometimes result when partners shut each other out that way, making recovering even more difficult. Although there will

almost certainly be times when you'll want to be alone with your thoughts, also make time for sharing them with your spouse. Consider seeking grief counseling together, too, or joining a couples support group. It may not only help you both find comfort but also help preserve—and even deepen—your relationship.

- Don't face the world alone. If you're dreading the friendly faces asking, "So, did you have your baby?" take a friend who can field the questions for you on the first several trips to the supermarket, dry cleaners, and so on. Be sure that those at work, at your place of worship, at other organizations in which you're active, are informed before you return, so you don't have to do any more difficult explaining than is absolutely necessary.

- Realize that some friends and family may not know what to do or say. Some may be so uncomfortable that they withdraw during the mourning period. Others may say things that hurt more than help: "I know just how you feel," or "Oh, you can have another baby," or "It's a good thing the baby died before you became attached to it." Though they certainly mean well, they may not understand that no one who hasn't lost a baby can know how it feels, that another baby can never take the place of the one you lost, or that parents can become attached to a baby long before birth. If you're hearing such comments frequently, ask a close friend or relative to explain your feelings and to let others know that you would rather they just say they are sorry about your loss.

- Look for support from those who've been there. Like many other parents, you may derive strength from joining a support group for parents who have lost infants. There are support groups online, too, that may offer some solace. (Try compassionatefriends.org or missingangel.org.) But try not to let such a group become a way of holding on to—rather than letting go of—your grief. If after a year you're still having problems coming to terms with your loss (sooner, if you're having trouble functioning), seek individual therapy.

- Take care of yourself. In the face of so much emotional pain, your physical needs may be the last thing on your mind. They shouldn't be. Eating right, getting enough sleep, and exercising are vital not just in maintaining your health but also in aiding your recovery. Make a conscious effort to sit down for meals, even if you're not feeling very much like eating. Take a warm bath or do some relaxation exercises to help you unwind before bed, so you'll sleep better at night. Try to build some physical activity into your day, even if it's just a walk before dinner. And let yourself take a break from grieving once in a while. See a movie, accept an invitation to visit friends, take a weekend in the country—and enjoy yourself without feeling guilty. For life to go on, after all, you need to go on living.

- Remember your baby as privately or publicly as you need to. When it comes to a memorial service, do whatever feels right to you. That might be a completely private ceremony—which allows you and your spouse to share your feelings alone—or one that surrounds you with the love and support of family, friends, and community.

- Honor your child's memory in a way that has meaning to you, if that helps. Buy books for a child care center that serves kids in need, or donate to an organization that helps disadvantaged expectant and new moms; plant a tree or a new flower bed in your backyard or in a local park.

- Turn to religion, if you find it comforting. For some grieving parents, faith is a great solace.

- Do become pregnant again, if that's what you want—but not in an effort to feel better or to replace the child you've lost. It's best to wait until the period of deepest sorrow has passed before contemplating conceiving again. See page 586 for more.

- Expect your pain to lessen over time. At first, there will be only bad days, then a few good days mixed in; eventually, there will be more good days than bad. But be prepared for the possibility that remnants of the pain may last a lot longer. The grieving process, which may include nightmares and fleeting but painful flashbacks, is often not fully completed for as long as two years, but the worst is usually over three to six months after the loss. If after six to nine months your grief remains the center of your life, if you're having trouble functioning or focusing, or have little interest in anything else, seek help. Also seek help if, from the beginning, you haven't been able to grieve at all. And remember that postpartum depression can cloud the healing process, too; see page 579.

- Recognize that guilt can unnecessarily compound grief and make adjusting to a loss more difficult. If you feel that the loss of your baby was your punishment for having been ambivalent about your pregnancy, or for lacking the nurturing or other qualities necessary for motherhood, or for any other reason, seek professional support to help you understand that you are in no way responsible for your loss.

Seek help, too, if you've suffered self-doubts in the past and now believe your doubts have been confirmed (you couldn't produce a live baby). If you feel guilty even thinking about getting your life back to normal because you sense it would be disloyal to the child you've lost, it may help to ask your baby, in spirit, for forgiveness or for permission to enjoy life again. You might try doing it in a "letter," in which you express all your feelings, hopes, and dreams.

- Sometimes, organ donation may be possible when a baby is born alive and with some functioning organs but has a hopeless prognosis. The possibility of helping another baby live may bring some comfort in that case.

Loss of One Twin

The parent who loses one twin (or more babies, in the case of triplets or quads) faces celebrating a birth (or births) and mourning a death (or deaths) at the same time. If this happens, you may feel too conflicted to either mourn your lost child or enjoy your living one—both vitally important processes. Understanding why you feel the way you do may help you better cope with your feelings, which may include all or just some of these:

- You may feel heartbroken. You've lost a baby, and the fact that you have another doesn't minimize your loss. Realize that you're entitled to mourn the baby you've lost, even as you're celebrating your other baby's birth. In fact, mourning that loss is an important part of the healing process. Taking the steps for grieving parents described in the previous section can help you more easily accept your baby's death as a reality.

Why?

The painful question "Why?" may never be answered. But it may be helpful to attach some reality to the tragedy by learning about the physical causes of the death of a fetus or newborn. Often, the baby looks perfectly normal, and the only way to uncover the cause of death is to carefully examine the history of the pregnancy and do a complete examination of the fetus or baby. If the fetus died in utero or was stillborn, pathological examination of the placenta by an expert pathologist is also important. Knowing what happened (and this isn't always possible to determine) doesn't really tell you why it happened to you and your baby, but it helps bring closure to the event, and it will help you prepare for a future pregnancy.

- You may be happy, too, but ambivalent about showing it. It may seem somehow inappropriate to be excited about the arrival of your surviving baby or even disloyal to the one who didn't live. That's a natural feeling but one you'll need to try to let go of. Loving and nurturing the sibling is a wonderful way of honoring your lost baby—besides, it's essential to your living baby's well-being.

- You may want to celebrate, but don't know if it's okay to. A new baby is always something to celebrate, even when the happy news comes with sadness. If you're uncomfortable holding a baby-welcoming event without acknowledging your loss, consider first holding a memorial ceremony or farewell for the baby who has passed away.

Pregnancy Reduction

Sometimes an ultrasound reveals that one (or more) of the fetuses in a multiple pregnancy can't survive or is so severely malformed that the chances of survival outside the womb are minimal—and worse yet, that the ailing fetus may be endangering your other healthy one(s). Or there are so many fetuses that there is a significant risk to the mother and all her babies. In such cases, your practitioner may recommend a pregnancy reduction. Contemplating this procedure can be agonizing—it may seem like sacrificing one child to protect another—and may leave you plagued with guilt, confusion, and conflicted feelings. You may come to your decision of whether to proceed (or not proceed) easily, or it may be an excruciating decision-making process.

There may be no easy answers, and there are definitely no perfect options, but you'll want to do whatever you can to make peace with the decision you end up making. Review the situation with your practitioner, and seek a second opinion, or third, or fourth, until you're as confident as you can be about your choice. You can also ask your practitioner to put you in touch with someone from the bioethics staff of the hospital (if that's available). You may want to share your feelings with close friends, or you may want to keep this personal decision private. If religion plays an important role in your life, you'll probably want to look to spiritual guidance. Once you make your decision, try not to second-guess: Accept that it's the best decision you can make under the difficult circumstances. Also try not to burden yourself with guilt, no matter what you choose. Because none of this is your fault, there's no reason to feel guilty about it.

If you end up undergoing pregnancy reduction, you may expect to experience the same grief as any parent who has lost one or more babies.

■ You may view your baby's death as punishment, perhaps because you really weren't sure you wanted or could handle being the parent of multiples or because you wanted a girl more than you wanted a boy (or vice versa). Though this kind of guilt is common among parents who experience a pregnancy loss of any kind, it's completely unwarranted. Nothing you did—or thought or imagined or wished for—could have caused the loss.

■ You may feel disappointed that you won't be a parent of multiples. It's normal to be sad over the loss of this excitement, especially if you've been imagining and planning for the arrival of multiples for months. You may even feel twinges of regret when seeing sets of multiples. Don't feel guilty about feeling that way; it's completely understandable.

■ You may be afraid that explaining your situation to family and friends will be awkward and difficult, especially if they've been eagerly awaiting the twins. To make facing the world a little easier, enlist a friend or close relative to spread the word so you won't have to. In the first few weeks, try to take someone with you when you go out with your baby, so they can anticipate and answer the inevitable—and possibly painful—questions.

- You may have trouble handling the reactions and comments of family and friends. In trying to help, friends and family may overdo the excitement when welcoming your living child, without acknowledging the one you've lost. Or they may urge you to forget your lost baby and appreciate your living one. As well intentioned as their actions and words may be, they can hurt and upset you. So don't hesitate to tell people—especially the ones who are closest to you—how you feel. Let them know that you need to grieve for what you have lost as well as celebrate the new arrival.

- You may feel too depressed over your loss to care for your new baby—or, if you're still pregnant, to care for your baby by taking the best possible care of yourself. Don't beat yourself up over your unhappy or conflicted feelings. They're normal, and completely understandable. But do make sure that you get the help you need so you can start meeting your baby's needs—both physical and emotional. Support groups may help, and so can counseling.

- You may feel that you're alone in your pain. Getting support from others who know what you're going through can help more than you can imagine. Find that support in a local support group or online. You can contact Centers for Loss in Multiple Births (CLIMB), at climb-support.org.

Stages of Grief

Whether the loss of a baby comes early in pregnancy, near term, or at delivery, you'll likely experience many feelings and reactions. Though you can't wish them away, understanding them will eventually help you come to terms with your loss. Many people who suffer a loss go through a number of steps on their road to emotional healing. These steps are common, though the order in which the first three occur may vary; so, too, may the feelings you experience.

- Shock and denial. There may be numbness and disbelief, the feeling that "this couldn't have happened to me." This is a mental mechanism designed to protect your psyche from the trauma of the loss.

- Guilt and anger. Desperate to pin the blame for such a senseless tragedy on something, you may blame it on yourself ("I must have done something wrong to cause the miscarriage" or "If I'd been happier about the pregnancy, the baby would still be alive"). Or you may blame others—God, for letting this happen, or your practitioner (even if there is no reason to). You may feel resentful and envious of those around you who are pregnant or who are parents, and even have fleeting feelings of hatred for them.

- Depression and despair. You may find yourself feeling sad most or all of the time, crying constantly, unable to eat, sleep, be interested in anything, or otherwise function. You may also wonder if you'll never be able to have a healthy baby.

- Acceptance. Finally, you'll come to terms with the loss. Keep in mind that this doesn't mean you'll forget the loss—just that you'll be able to accept it and get back to the business of life.

No matter what you're feeling—and given your situation, your feelings may be all over the emotional map—give yourself time. Chances are that you'll feel progressively better—and better about feeling better.

Trying Again

Making the decision to try again for a new pregnancy—and a new baby—after a loss isn't always easy, and definitely is not as easy as those around you might think. It's an intensely personal decision, and it can also be a painful one. Here are some things that you might want to consider when deciding when—and if—you try again:

- Trying again for another baby after losing one (or more) takes courage. Give yourself the credit you deserve—and the pat on the back you need—as you embark on this process.

- The right time is the time that's right for you. It may take just a short time for you to feel emotionally ready to try for another baby—or it may take a much longer time. Don't push yourself (or let others push you) into trying too soon. And don't second-guess yourself (or paralyze yourself) into waiting longer than you have to. Listen to your heart, and you'll know when you're emotionally healed and when you're ready to contemplate a new pregnancy.

- You'll need to be physically ready, too. Check with your practitioner to see whether a waiting period will be necessary in your case. Often, you can try as soon as you feel up to it (and as soon as your cycle begins cooperating). If there's a reason why you have to wait longer than you want to (as may be the case after a molar pregnancy), use the time to get yourself into the best physical condition possible for conception (see Chapter 1), if you're not already.

- A new pregnancy may be less innocent. Now you know that not all pregnancies end happily, which means you probably won't take anything about your new pregnancy for granted. You may feel more nervous than you did the first time, especially until you've passed the anniversary of the week you lost your last pregnancy (and if you lost your baby at or just before or after birth, you may worry more the entire time). You may try to keep your excitement in check, and you may find that your joy is tempered by trepidation—so much so that you may even hesitate to attach yourself to your new baby until that fear of loving and losing again has dissipated. You may be extra-attuned to every pregnancy symptom: the ones that give you hope (swollen breasts, morning sickness, those frequent runs to the bathroom) and those that trigger anxiety (those pelvic twinges, those crampy feelings). All of this is completely understandable and completely normal, as you'll find out if you reach out to others who've carried a new pregnancy to term after experiencing a loss. Just make sure that if these kinds of feelings keep you from nurturing and nourishing your new pregnancy, you quickly get some help working them out.

Looking forward to the ultimate reward—that baby you're so anxious to cuddle—instead of looking back on your loss will help you stay positive. Remember, the vast majority of women who have experienced a pregnancy loss or the loss of a baby go on to have completely normal pregnancies and completely healthy babies.

Index

The Next Steps in
What to Expect®

What to Expect® the First Year

Expecting a baby? Then you'll definitely want to know what to expect the first year. And here it is: the all-in-one, easy-to-use, month-by-month guide that explains everything you'll want to know (and need to know) about that amazing first year with your amazing baby—from first cuddle to first smile to (maybe even) first steps. Packed with the most reassuring answers and the most practical and realistic tips on all things baby, from decoding and comforting crying to finding sleep solutions, getting started breastfeeding to starting solids, basic baby care, safety, first aid, and much more. *Over 10 million copies in print.*

◆ ◆ ◆

What to Expect® the Second Year

It's the complete why, when, and how-to guide to the "wonder year"—twelve jam-packed months of amazing milestones, lightning-speed learning, and endless discoveries. Covering from the first birthday to the second, it's everything you need to know about caring for, nurturing, understanding, and keeping up with your one-year-old, including feeding (tips to tempt picky palates), sleep (your toddler's and yours), talking (decoding those first words), and behavior (defusing those first tantrums).

◆ ◆ ◆

What to Expect® Eating Well When You're Expecting

Everything you need to know to nourish a healthy pregnancy, including 175 delicious recipes.

◆ ◆ ◆

The What to Expect® Pregnancy Journal & Organizer

The all-in-one planner that helps an expectant mom keep track of every detail of pregnancy, from diet to checkups to shopping for baby's layette.

◆ ◆ ◆

The What to Expect® Baby-Sitter's Handbook

Everything a baby-sitter needs to know about caring for a child, from newborn to preschooler.

FOR WHEN YOU'RE READY TO START AGAIN:

What to Expect® Before You're Expecting
A step-by-step guide to making a baby, including prepping for conception, boosting your fertility, adjusting your lifestyle, timing sex for baby success, and more.

FOR SPANISH-SPEAKING PARENTS:

Qué Puedes Esperar Cuando Estás Esperando
The Spanish-language edition of *What to Expect® When You're Expecting*

◆ ◆ ◆

Qué Puedes Esperar en el Primer Año
The Spanish-language edition of *What to Expect® the First Year*

Available at your local retailer or visit workman.com/whattoexpect
Join the community, see videos, "Ask Heidi," and more at whattoexpect.com

FOR MORE INFORMATION, PLEASE CONTACT:

WORKMAN PUBLISHING COMPANY, INC.
225 Varick Street
New York, NY 10014-4381
info@workman.com